THE ELDER JAMES WHATMAN

ENGLAND'S GREATEST PAPER MAKER
(1702–1759)

THE MILL POND, OLD MILL, HOLLINGBOURNE

THE ELDER JAMES WHATMAN

ENGLAND'S GREATEST PAPER MAKER
(1702–1759)

A Study of Eighteenth Century Papermaking Technology
and its effect on a critical phase in
the history of English White Paper manufacture

J.N. BALSTON

State Papers 1747

1992

© J.N. Balston, 1992

Published by J.N. Balston
West Farleigh, Kent

ISBN 0 9519505 0 9 (Volume 1)
ISBN 0 9519505 2 5 (Set of 2 volumes)

Camera-ready copy by M. Notcutt, Oxford

Production consultancy by Laurence Viney, Berkhamsted

Printed in Great Britain by St. Edmundsbury Press,
Bury St. Edmunds, Suffolk

Printed on Acid free paper

Foreword

"'TIS NOW BECOME A HISTORY LITTLE KNOWN". This slender observation has more than a ring of truth about it when we apply it to the history of papermaking in the British Isles before the 19th Century, as distinct from the history of the paper industry, albeit not much better off itself. This book is primarily concerned with the introduction of improved methods of making paper that took place in these islands during the period covering the late 17th C. to the end of the 18th as well as the paper makers responsible for this, together with the effects that these advances in technology had on the economic performance of the industry; and, indeed, so far as the manufacture of White paper was concerned, its survival. What sources are there to draw on ?

The Bibliography of Paper and Papermaking, as Coleman has pointed out,[1] may be extensive, but so far as papermaking in this country is concerned very little of it is of real significance for the period that we shall be dealing with here. This situation is aggravated further by the fact that the present day industry has *changed direction so radically* that few people remain who would still be familiar with the methods used to make paper even, say, a generation or so ago. A proper understanding of the earlier techniques is thus in danger of being lost for ever. For earlier periods, as with many other occupations, there are a number of quaint accounts often cited in the literature but only rarely do these throw any illuminating information on our subject. There are, in fact, only three substantial and perceptive accounts of the process for the period with which we are concerned, one English and two French; these were repeated endlessly almost without alteration in the Encyclopaedias of the 18th C. Although still based substantially on Desmarest's account of papermaking,[2] the 3rd–6th Editions of the *Encyclopaedia Britannica* (1797–1823) show some signs of relating more recent developments, no doubt prompted by John Farey's account of the process (1813) in Rees' *"Cyclopaedia"* though even here it is at heart an engineer's approach to the subject.

As the 19th C. progressed the situation improves for the historian as more and more technical records survived and are available to him; other sources of information, like Patents and Encyclopaedias, became more specific in their accounts; and trade associations and directories more explicit about the nature of the mills and their products. (The sources available for the period covered by this book are outlined in the Preface to the Appendices).

In order to place the advances in papermaking technology in their proper context one must obviously have a sound history of the industry. It was not until 1957 that what are in effect the only authoritative histories that span our period were published, Professor Coleman's economic history and Dr. Shorter's monumental work on English Paper Mills,[3] mainly geographical in character, but at the same time determining as far as this was possible the succession of occupants of the paper mills identified. Neither of these important works professes to cover papermaking and the history of papermaking beyond a point that served their respective needs. Consequently, a considerable vacuum continues to exist in this subject and, as already indicated, it is one of the main objects of this work to fill this void. (As to

---

[1]. Bib. 15
[2] Bib. 21
[3] Bib. 12

why this is so important is a subject that will be referred to in the Introduction to this book which follows).

Technology, however, does not exist in isolation; it has to be developed and applied by people. Another prime objective of this work, therefore, is to link these two together and when this is attempted one runs into difficulties immediately due to the almost total absence of documentary information. In earlier times, that is to say before the application of steam power to the industry (effectively at the beginning of the 19th C.), one has to remember that papermaking was essentially a rural industry; that few, if any, records have survived of its activities and installations; and that, although there were clearly "journeymen", and spasmodic records of "apprenticeships" are to be found, there was no Guild of Paper Makers from which one might obtain information about their status. It is perhaps worth quoting from Dr. Shorter's introductory remarks to articles he wrote on the paper mills in the Maidstone district:

> Identifying early paper mills and tracing their history is not always an easy process, especially in cases where few domestic records of the properties and the paper makers have survived. In such cases small items of information found in various documents have to be pieced together to give what can only be a bare outline of the history of the mills. Sometimes there is difficulty in tracing the separate histories of old paper mills which were close together, because many of the early references merely give the names of the paper makers and their localities without specifying the mills.[4]

Shorter elaborates on these difficulties in his earlier work on English Paper Mills pointing out that "up to about 1800 a great many of the principal sources are of a strictly primary nature".[5] Later, he added the remark that "expert genealogical work would probably be required to establish beyond doubt that many early paper mills in these three counties (Kent, Middlesex and Buckinghamshire), and particularly those at Dartford and about Maidstone in Kent, were nurseries from which paper makers who had been trained there in the arts of making good paper went off to establish or continue the manufacture at other mills".[6] We shall see in this book how right or wrong some of Shorter's conclusions were; but there is no doubt about the correctness of the principle that he proposed. Altering Carlyle's definition very slightly one might say that the history of the paper industry for this early period "is the essence of innumerable genealogies" and no apologies are made for following this course of action here seeing that it is possibly the only method left to us to throw more light on the origins and growth of this industry.

What has been said above provides us with more, and updated, information about the general organisation and distribution of paper mills relevant to our subject, their occupants and relationships. As a result of this we can now, for example, build up a credible picture of the leading protagonist in these developments, the elder James Whatman, his origins and activities during the first 39 years of his life, a subject not covered at all by the biographer of the two Whatman paper makers, Thomas Balston.[7] Despite the fact that even with this new approach we have learnt little more about him personally beyond the date of his baptism and that of his marriage with a few scattered references in between these events, none of which tells us anything specific about the art of papermaking or how he came to learn this, what it does

4   Bib. 7, 1960 (Mar.) 61
5   Bib. 12, (1957) 20ff
6   ibid. 57
7   Bib. 1

to understand the principles on which these changes were based and the difficulties encountered by the paper makers that has led to a situation in which the full significance of the New Technology has not been properly appreciated.

(v) Though some important developments took place during the earliest period of European papermaking, the process remained virtually static in character for the next five centuries after which one can recognize in it a number of radical changes in direction. This book, as intimated in (iv), is concerned with the effect of the first of these on papermaking in the British Isles, namely, during the latter part of the 17th C. and during the 18th; its significance for the whole future of papermaking will be referred to again below.

The next change in direction is often associated with the invention of the papermachine and its introduction at the beginning of the 19th C. This, however, when seen through the eyes of a paper maker, is a major oversimplification of the actual events that marked this change in direction and takes us back to the caveat referred to in (iii) above. Although this is a subject outside the scope of this book it is worth taking a closer look at this situation, if for no other reason than to illustrate the point made there.

Fundamental changes in different parts of the process led to a situation that was entirely different from anything that had gone before and at the same time altered the intrinsic characteristics of the paper produced. The period in which this second change in direction took place embraced the start of what has been termed here the chemical era in papermaking which affected the raw materials used in the process. Chemical bleaching, introduced ca. 1790, not only widened the range of rags that could be used for the manufacture of White paper, but also for the first time provided the paper maker with a means of intensifying the degree of whiteness of his product, a process that had formerly relied on the laundering of textiles (as opposed to the cleaning of the rags) and the addition of blue materials to the pulp. The chemical age, together with the use of steam, enabled him at a later stage to boil dirty rags with alkali to remove other impurities.

This phase also included the invention of the papermachine at the very end of the 18th C. and the mechanization of the sheet-making process, often hailed by historians as the major watershed in the history of the industry. That there is an element of truth in this assertion cannot be denied; it certainly cut the ground from underneath the striking journeymen of the handmade industry, one of the reasons for its invention.[8] Nevertheless, the papermachine could have remained a technical curiosity had it not been possible to extend the capacity of yet another stage of the papermaking process. After the invention of the machine by Nicholas Louis Robert (1796-8) and the development of viable models by Bryan Donkin in 1807, it took another decade before Didot, for one, began to realise that the papermachine was not going to revolutionize this industry unless it could be made to *dry* paper as fast as it was made. From an engineering aspect this problem was capable of solution, as indeed it was. But the paper maker sees these things in a rather different light. If a wet sheet of paper is allowed to dry without restraint it will contract on drying to dimensions in the plane of the sheet that are more or less proportional to those in the wet state; but on a papermachine what starts out as a square of wet paper on the wire is reeled as a rectangle in the dry state. Instead of *contracting,* the paper in the direction of the machine may end up as much as 106% of its original length in contrast to a contraction that takes place in the Cross direction. This distortion becomes built into the paper through inter-cellulose fibre bonds and leads to all the problems that are associated with this anisotropic condition.

The new Master Paper Maker then had to learn to live with the problems created by inadequate control over bleaching and the ensuing chemical degradation of the fibre; distortion arising from drying paper in web form; and overcoming difficulties in yet another stage of the papermaking process, namely, relating the sizing of the paper to his new-found manufacturing capacity. Not all materials lend themselves to rapid drying and gelatine is one such substance where

---

[8] This comment is in no way an attempt to belittle the achievement of this invention. On the contrary, it has been made merely to draw a distinction between the *engineering* and *papermaking* aspects of this innovation. There are many different ways of making a sheet of paper and our concern here is not primarily with the mechanics of this operation. By all accounts the papermachine was not conceived in the first place as a volume production unit although there were other contemporary pressures within the industry, witness the large increase in the number of vats per mill, that would have made this new invention attractive (see Bib.74. 52).

the properties are altered drastically, if this is done.[9] So it was fortunate for the paper maker that at about that time Engine or Rosin sizing came to his rescue, albeit only for the manufacture of inferior papers.

It can be seen from this example that in reality the change in direction that took place during the first decades of the 19th C. was a very much more complex affair, affecting all stages of the process as well as the properties of the paper, than the mere introduction of a mechanical sheet–making process. Because of their interdependence they really have to be seen by the historian as a single package.

Later changes in direction, also outside the scope of this book, included a revolution in the latter half of the 19th C. in the types of raw material used for making paper, bringing with it to the paper mill chemical methods and plant for extracting them. During the 20th C. with the added knowledge of the physical and chemical properties of cellulose it became possible with experience to provide the paper maker with tailor–made pulps from their countries of origin to suit different types of paper. This in turn led to the streamlining of these separate operations and the creation of the integrated pulp and paper mill in one place, thus transforming the geographical distribution of the industry from a domestic to an international locale. From the 1960's onwards these changes were taken a stage further with the automation of the process and this resulted in yet another major change of course requiring quite different skills from the paper maker to cope with the new operating practices. One might say, in fact, that today the term paper engineering had replaced that of papermaking.

Leaving aside for the moment all the other factors that led to these changes, the moral of all this is that in order to have a proper understanding of the history of the industry it is a very necessary requirement to have not only appropriate knowledge of the changes in its technology but to see them also in a contemporary light. This is very much the case when assessing the significance of the British industry's first change in direction, the introduction of the New Technology in the 18th C., a change that tends to be made light of in histories. Had it not followed the course it did, the second change in direction, that at the beginning of the 19th C., might not have taken place at all or would at best have been very seriously impeded. The fact is that an increase in the rate of sheet–making and drying *had to be* accompanied at some time or other by a more productive method of pulp preparation than that offered by the traditional process. As will be seen later in this book the New Technology brought with it even more important benefits to the industry than this.

To grasp the significance of this change the principles on which it was based must be clearly understood. There can be few (or are there still some?) paper makers and historians who believe (as was quite usual in the past) that the formation of a sheet of paper is dependent on an arty–crafty process of fibre entanglement and that the vatman's final shake applied to the mould adds the last kink to this process. That the vatman's art was one of the major European skills in undeniable, but these skills were directed at making sheets of paper that were uniform in weight one to another and where the stuff was evenly distributed within them. The actual sheet–making process, from the preparation of the stuff to the finished sheet, was dependent instead on a complex mixture of physical and chemical forces; and it is this aspect

[9] Statements of this kind usually require qualification of some kind. Paper makers managed to introduce during the 19th C. what was known as on–machine sizing using gelatine, but there was a wide gap between this kind of sizing, often no more than a lick of size, and the gelatine sizing employed for the best qualities of White paper. In the latter case one would probably find gelatine contents ranging from between 8–12% by weight, a very substantial quantity which required drying under very carefully controlled conditions of humidity and temperature, quite unsuited to the conditions one would find on a papermachine. It is not proposed to enter into a discussion here on the behaviour of the protein network in the gelatine molecule when subjected to different drying conditions; it is enough to say that very different kinds of film result from these variations. To try to overcome some of these difficulties in the case of fine papers made on papermachines, recourse was made later in the century to spar drum drying the web.

instead is to put us in a position to deduce the events of the intervening years with some confidence. This in turn enables us to examine more closely his contribution to that little known subject the history and development of papermaking within this industry during a very critical period. This is the real essence of this study and because of the dearth of information its extraction is achieved only through a long and complicated process.

Because of the complexity these deficiencies cause in the treatment of this subject, to keep the main theme of this book as free from side issues as possible, the larger items have been relegated to five Appendices[8] and the smaller items to footnotes. The latter perform four functions: (i) to indicate the source of information; (ii) to clarify a point made in the text; (iii) to take out of the text the smaller side issues, not warranting the use of a separate appendix, that might detract from the continuity of the argument; and, finally, (iv) to provide possible leads to other investigators.

The Introduction to this book covers several different aspects of paper and papermaking as it is to-day contrasted with the same in the past, stressing the need for an understanding of the principles inherent in the changes in direction that took place. It sets the scene for this work. The Bibliography at the end of it is mainly limited to works referred to frequently in the text; many other literary sources were used but these are recorded individually in footnotes.

Finally, whereas this book through its various indexes can be used as a reference work, its main purpose is to provide an account of new developments in papermaking technology introduced for the main part into the British Isles from Continental sources in the late 17th and early 18th Cs. Because of the very scattered nature of sparse data, the treatment of this subject is of necessity a very closely argued case which *does not lend itself to cursory reading*. At the same time no claim is made that the last word has been said here on this subject. Far from it, much work remains to be done.

---

[8]   These appendices are an integral part of this work. The first four are for the *specialist* reader and contain information supporting the existence, location and history of some of the more important and least documented paper mills of the Maidstone district together with their occupants.
The fifth Appendix covers various aspects of 17th/18th Century papermaking technology and contains technical information that *complements* the technology discussed in the text, and should *not* be overlooked by either non-specialist or specialist reader.

Acknowledgements

The origins of this book are complex stemming from a study started more than nineteen years ago of early watercolour papers, a study that changed direction after a few years to the history of papermaking. Until his death in 1988 I had the unfailing support and encouragement of Edo Loeber in pursuing this work. Among all those kind people who have helped me compile this book I am indebted first and foremost to Edo for his patience and for providing me with invaluable information based on a profound knowledge of the equipment, materials and mills that supplied Europe with its paper in past centuries.

This work could easily have left the rails at an early stage had it not been for timely advice from Professor Coleman whose history of the industry has been an indispensable source of information. Likewise, as will be seen from the numerous references to them, the late Dr. Shorter's publications have provided a corner-stone to my own searches and I am most grateful to Mrs. Doris Shorter for granting me permission to make free use of this work. I am also deeply indebted to Mr. R.J. Spain for his help and his unrivalled knowledge of Kent Water Mills; to Dr. John Gascoigne (Messrs. Cross & Bevan) for his guidance on matters concerning cellulose and the microbiological aspects of rag fermentation; to the indefatigable researches of and some twelve years correspondence with Tom Gravell on countermarks; and to Paul Mary Pollard (formerly Keeper of Early Printed Books, Trinity College Library, Dublin) for many very useful references and for her sustained interest in my work over a period of some 14 years.

Special mention should be made here of the help I have received from Dr. Frederick Hudson (formerly Reader of Music, University of Newcastle upon Tyne) whose discoveries were among several factors that prompted me to take a closer look at the achievements of the elder Whatman; from Henk Voorn (Koninklijke Bibliotheek BE's Gravenhage) with his incomparable knowledge of Dutch papermaking history; from Professor Alan Crocker (University of Surrey) on the history of the papermaking industry of that County; and from Colin White (M.C.W. Technologies Ltd., Maidstone) who kindly acted as agent in obtaining copies of Mr. Jouko Laamanen's highly accomplished stereoscan electron micrographs of cellulose fibres reproduced here by kind permission of the Finnish Pulp & Paper Research Laboratories.

In compiling this book I am particularly grateful for the help and services I have received from Mr. W.N. Yates (Archivist) and Miss K. Topping (Asst. Archivist) and other members of the Staff, the West Kent Archives Office (recently redesignated the Centre for Kentish Studies), Maidstone; Miss A.M. Oakley, Archivist, Cathedral, City and Diocesan Record Office, Canterbury; Mr. D.C.G. Allan, Curator-Librarian, Royal Society of Arts; Mr. T.G. Smith, Librarian & Archivist, H.M. Customs Museum and Library; Miss L. Collins, late Research Dept., Society of Genealogists; Mr. R.A. Stutely, Assistant, Maidstone Museum; The Keeper of MSS. The Guildhall Library, London; Mr. D.J. Johnson, Deputy Clerk of the Records, House of Lords; Mrs. Jill Lever, The British Architectural Library (Drawings Collection); The Huguenot Society of London; The Chairman and Members of the East Kent Mills Group; the late Mr. C.P. Davies (Folkestone); Mr. Douglas Welby (River, nr. Dover); Mr. M.J. Fuller and Mrs. Jean Stirk.

I am also grateful for permission to make use of or reproduce material from Thomas Balston's biography of the two Whatmans (Mr. H.R. Balston); Documents and Wills (The Public Record Office, Chancery Lane); The Archivist, Division of Archives & MSS, Pennsylvania Historical Museum Commission to quote from the Journals (1790–1809 n.d.) Vol.LVII, Joshua and Thomas Gilpin Collection MS 58); the British Library Map Library; the Kent County Library; the Shirley Institute, Manchester; the Textile Institute, Manchester; and Dr. H.F. Rance.

Grateful acknowledgement is also made to many others who have helped in supplying information for this book, reference to which is made in footnotes at the appropriate points in the text.

Lastly, but by no means the least, in getting this work into a presentable printed form I have had help and advice from numerous quarters including Mrs. Jill Eddison and Mr. Anthony Balston in reading the text in its early stages; in photocopying, amending and assembling the typescript by Mrs. Pamela Longhurst of Whatman plc.; the advice and skill of my son–in–law, Martin Notcutt, and others in transcribing the whole work onto disc; and especially the accurate correcting work of Lyn Cullum and Sara Hirtenstein; together with highly proficient proof–reading undertaken by my daughter, Rosemary Brass, Mr. Tom Colverson and Christabel Morgan, contributing the final adjustments to this complicated work, for all of which I am eternally grateful. I would also like to express my gratitude to the Directors of Whatman plc. for consenting to warehouse and distribute the limited edition of this book.

Contents
Volume 1

Contents
Volume 2 – The Appendices

viii

List of Illustrations

PLATES

FIGURES

In Volume 2, The Appendices

TABLES

MAPS

Introduction

PAPER AS A SUBSTANCE has been described in recent times as the fifth element thus superseding the mediaeval concept of the *quinta essentia*. This designation, almost by definition, turns it into a commonplace, not to say a universal, material and as such, like its cousins the air we breathe and the water we drink, tends to rest unnoticed until our attention is drawn to it by some defect or because of its absence when needed. As a consequence very few people have any idea as to how this commodity is made, or was made in the past, though many to–day subscribe to the worthy cause of using recycled paper to preserve another "tree" from destruction. But how realistic is this concept when one views the past ?

In reality this situation applies only to relatively modern times. For one thing no trees would have been involved in making paper during the period covered by this book. Again, working backwards in time, the annual per capita consumption of paper in Great Britain in 1974 was 312 lb. (142 kg.)[1] compared to 1.5 lb. (0.68 kg.) for all types of paper at the beginning of the 18th C. and very approximately 0.25 lb. (110 g.) four centuries ago.[2] It is clear from these figures that in the past paper was a comparatively scarce commodity, most of which would have been confined both in use and distribution to very limited areas. Indeed, in the 15th C. many people may never have seen a sheet of paper.

But it is not just a question of differences in quantities, used past and present, that have changed this concept. One of the first points to recognize is that papers made in the past were quite different from those in use to–day. Much of the paper nowadays *is* commonplace, nondescript and characterless because these are qualities that one expects to find in a blank sheet of paper for everyday use; or, put another way, all that is required is a uniform and unobtrusive background. All the same in spite of this generally unassuming image it is possible to recognize that the quality of some modern paper can be such as to uplift the status of the product, the feel of a printed page, the crispness of a newly minted banknote and so on, although these qualities are a mere shadow of those that were to be found in the finest papers made in the past or similar ones whose manufacture survived into this century.[3]

Yet another difference is that whereas to–day an enormous variety of special papers exist, developed over the past 150 years, which are used for all manner of technical, security, decorative or hygienic purposes, prior to this virtually the only categories that existed would

---

[1] *Pulp and Paper International 1975* (Review Number), p. 15. The 1974 figures for the United States were 614 lb (287 kg.).

[2] Coleman, D.C. Bib. 15, p. 15.

[3] Many examples of the way these qualities have enhanced the appearance (and the durability) of the works for which these papers were used could be cited here (be they for printed books, drawings, watercolours, maps or whatever). However, there is one particular one that exemplifies unsolicited admiration for the quality of the paper itself and nothing else. It was a common experience to observe visitors being shown round Springfield mill (and no doubt the same applied to other mills making similar qualities of paper) that, when they came to the finishing room and saw the carefully matured handmade paper stacked ready for packing, they would stretch out their hands to touch it just as they might have done to touch an ancient marble column or a piece of finely polished wood, simply because the inherent beauty of such materials stimulates an aesthetic response in us. Moreover, unlike many of the synthetic surfaces that we are confronted with today, these materials are attractive to our sense of touch because the moisture they contain, or else adsorb, renders them compatible with our skin.

have been classified as Writing, Printing and Wrapping paper, the first two being embraced within the term "White" paper whose development and manufacture are the principal concern of this book.[4]

To summarise, then, the quantities of paper consumed in the past would have been vastly different from those we are accustomed to handle to–day; the processes and materials used to make them totally different; and the qualities of the final product of an entirely different order.[5] To comprehend the significance of these differences as and when they arise in situations discussed in this book, it will be necessary to adjust one's viewpoint so that one is always standing in the shoes of contemporaries; seen in retrospect it is very easy to underestimate the effects and problems created for early paper makers by restrictive regulations, changes in method or those resulting from a variety of other circumstances unless this practice is observed.

To assist the reader in making this adjustment certain concepts must be instilled into his mind, obvious though some of these may seem at first sight:

(i) The paper makers of the "handmade" era did not appear out of thin air. Their art represented one of the major European skills and to achieve even a modicum of this required a lengthy period of training and the possession of some very specialised equipment. This presupposes the existence of some source where their training and equipment could be obtained. Where the industry was well established this situation would not have created problems. It is only when a new centre was founded remote from other areas that a careful investigation is required to determine the motives and origins of the paper makers concerned in this.

(ii) To avoid misunderstandings it has to be understood that the process and equipment used to make paper in the past undoubtedly varied *in detail* from country to country, and even between districts, but the general principles remained the same within a given period. In order to simplify the description of these, and the changes that took place, the processes and equipment exemplified in the three most important accounts of papermaking[6] have been used for this purpose.

(iii) The traditional process was made up of a number of different stages (to be described later in this book). There is a tendency, which must be resisted, to focus too much attention on the actual sheet–making process at the expense of the other stages, some of which were of equal importance. This can lead to underestimating the effects and problems created by changes in method in one or other of these stages. A general example of this is given under (v) below.

(iv) The 18th C. witnessed the bringing together of its elements and their introduction to the British Paper Industry of what has been called in this book "The New Technology".[7] The most important element in this related to fundamental changes in the treatment of the cellulose fibre; its effects on the contemporary sheet–making process; and, most important of all, the effect of this on the economic performance of the industry itself. It has been a failure

---

[4]   White paper was the term used in the trade, in earlier periods, for the best qualities of paper, distinguishing it from inferior qualities such as Whited–Brown or other coloured papers. This definition is sufficient in the present context; it is, however, an over–simplification and a fuller interpretation will be given later in the book. The wrapping paper class would also have included small quantities of papers used for other purposes such as sugar bakers blue paper, coloured papers used for artists drawings, etc.

[5]   To give but one example many uses to which "White" paper is put today are temporary in character; the information recorded can be converted into micro–film or stored in computers. In the past paper had to be extremely durable to withstand repeated handling over long periods e.g. for use in ledgers, registers and the like.

[6]   See Foreword p. i.

[7]   The New Technology was comprised of several elements, the most important of which was the development of the Hollander Beating Engine (see Chapter VI) and its effect on the performance of the industry; others included improvements to the surface of Writing paper and new methods of constructing the papermaking mould (both covered in Chap. V).

that must be grasped if the changes that took place, not only at this stage in the history of the industry but also in its later stages, are to be understood e.g. when one enters the chemical era or where thermal energy plays an important role.

The New Technology and the underlying principles are discussed in the pages that follow in as straightforward a manner as possible and should present no difficulties to the non−technical reader. They have to be placed, however, in an historical context and this is where one runs into the difficulties described earlier in the Foreword.

The contents of this book are *not* concerned with the history of papermaking in general; but, as the subtitle indicates, it deals with the evolution of and the problems encountered in the manufacture of White paper in Britain up to the end of the 18th C., a class of paper that has played a vital role in the civilizing of our society; and it also deals with the paper makers who made it. Its manufacture was only established in this country, and to start with insecurely at that, after a long struggle against the imported equivalent and by combating various other obstacles in its path in the form of politics, patents, monopolies, economic factors and inefficient methods of collecting its raw materials. The first chapter is designed to bring this situation into focus both in terms of describing the set−up in the industry leading up to its change in direction as well as outlining the nature of the contemporary papermaking process.

In this country the first signs of these changes appeared in the latter part of the 17th C. but only came to fruition in the 18th. A case is made out later in this book showing that the elder James Whatman was the main architect in making these innovations effective in association with his close friend Richard Harris, a paper maker. Both were born and reared in the Maidstone district where a comparatively new centre of papermaking had come into being. Before considering the actual components of the New Technology the origins and nature of the Maidstone paper industry are examined in order to place Whatman and Harris in perspective and determine, as far as this is possible, the sources that helped shape the improvements they perfected. These innovations are discussed in later chapters, followed by an account of their subsequent dissemination in so far as it affected the paper industry in Kent. To guard against criticism that this could be seen as being too limited in its approach *vis−à−vis* improvements in the manufacture of White paper in the rest of the country, a case is made out (a) for Kent having the lion's share of White paper manufacture for this period and thus being seen as a more than representative sample of the industry as a whole; and (b) that the spread of the technology there appears to have been ahead of other counties.

To assist the reader who may be totally unfamiliar with the history of papermaking as a whole, a short resumé of this is given below with a number of references should he or she wish to enlarge their knowledge of this subject. The nature of paper and the papermaking process are discussed progressively in greater detail throughout this book. At this point it is sufficient to know that a sheet of paper is formed by separating specially prepared fibres suspended in water with a sieve−like structure through which the water passes leaving a mat of fibres behind, on the face of it a very simple operation but in reality a very complex one. The sieve−like structure is known as the papermaking mould, whose construction after remaining more or less unaltered for six centuries was revolutionized by the elder James Whatman, another major achievement; but this is a subject, the development of Wove paper, which because of its complexity has been treated separately in a work that is "in preparation".

The Beginnings

All kinds of materials including paper have been used at one time or another by Man for graphic purposes, some of them from very early times indeed. Some, like stone, antlers, pottery, wood etc.,[10] bear no resemblance to paper; those closer to it were textiles, like linen and silk; and prepared skins, like parchment. Paper is made from cellulose extracted from plants[11] and its nearest relatives were, in its earliest days, Papyrus (made from the plant *Cyperus papyrus*), a product whose life–span covered at least four millenia, twice that of the known history of paper;[12] and various bark cloths, which were perhaps the most closely related of these materials and from which true paper may have been developed.[13] Just when this transition occurred is not known but was in all probability some considerable time before the usually accepted discovery attributed to Ts'ai Lun (China) in A.D. 105. Paper was also used at an early date in Korea and Japan,[14] but its progress westwards was slower, only reaching Samarkand and Baghdad during the 8th C.

The acquisition of the art of papermaking by the Arabs has in the past often been attributed to the capture of Chinese prisoners (among whom, presumably, were some paper makers) at the battle of the River Talass (Kazakhstan) in 751 A.D.[15] The Arabs, however, had known of the existence of paper for at least 100 years before this and it seems more than likely that although the capture of the prisoners may have accelerated this process, papermaking had probably spread into Turkestan before this date. In the period that followed, waves of Arab invasions took it even further west through North Africa to reach Spain by the 10th C.,[16] but it was not until the 12th C. that paper made in Spain is first attributed to European paper makers.

Paper, which might be regarded as being even more European in character,[17] was made in Italy in the 13th C., slightly later in France and then Germany in the 14th C. Papermaking was established in both Switzerland and the Netherlands during the early part of the 15th C., but it was not until the very end of this century (1490's) that John Tate set up what is

---

[10] *The Art of Drawing, 11,000 BC – AD 1900* (The Trustees of the British Museum, 1972 Exhibition Catalogue), a document that makes curiously scant references to paper.

[11] Paper can be made from non–cellulosic fibres; but these are exceptional forms of paper and though these are mentioned briefly in Appendix V the term "paper" as used throughout this book refers to paper made from cellulose.

[12] Pattie, T.S. and Turner, E.G., *The written word of Papyrus* (The British Library Board, 1974 Exhibition Catalogue).

[13] Loeber, E.G. Bib. 45, p. 2

[14] *Papermaking, Art and Craft* (Library of Congress, Washington, 1968 Exhibition Catalogue, pp. 8 ff.)

[15] Clapperton, R.H. Bib.33 up to p. 68.

[16] Valls i Subira, O. "Arabian Paper in Catalonia", *The Paper Maker* (Hercules Powder Company, 1963), Vol. 32, No.1, p. 21. For more detail the reader should consult Valls *La Historia del papel en Espana, siglos X–XIV* (Madrid, 1978).

[17] At some point after papermaking had become a European activity the utensils and process underwent several fundamental changes. For instance, the European Mould became a rigid structure with a wire cover as distinct from the Oriental Mould which had a flexible cover made from organic materials such as bamboo, grass and hair (the magnitude of this transition with its technical implications has never been fully recognized. Just when it took place and who was responsible for it is unknown, but a fully developed rigid mould was certainly in use in Italy by 1250). The Europeans also introduced the "Felt" (to be discussed later in this book) onto which a sheet of paper was transferred (couched) from the mould facing; in the Oriental and Arabian Mould the vatman merely rolled up the flexible cover and unrolled it again up–side down onto a board. The Europeans used "rags" (also discussed later in this book) rather than the unwoven fibre; and by the beginning of the 14th C., at least, they had replaced starch, soap or gum sizing with gelatine size, these being additives to the cellulose base to confer on it ink–bearing properties. (This transition is discussed in more detail in Bib.76.)

regarded as the first paper mill to be built in England, Sele Mill on the River Beane near Hertford;[18] and *White* paper was made at this mill.

Before embarking on an the account of its first change in direction it might be as well to defend the reputation of the paper industry from an accusation sometimes made against it that it was slow to modernise its operations when compared to the progress made by other industries during the 18th C. Though possibly true for some parts of Europe this is an unfair comment on the industry in the United Kingdom. That there might have been a certain measure of inertia to overcome could have been due to the fact that it was a rural industry and would not, therefore, have been subject to the effects of abrasive competition met with in urban centres. Moreover, as mentioned, the industry had to surmount many serious obstacles not related to its papermaking operations which in any case did not lend themselves easily to methods capable of improving the rate of production.

Until steam became available as a source of motive power the paper mill was tied to the horsepower of the waterwheel more or less limiting it in size to a maximum of probably no more than three vats when using the traditional and very ancient process. Improvements to the waterwheel, made later in the 18th C. but not widely used until the 19th, certainly increased the scope of these operations. In the account that follows, the introduction of the New Technology, by no means an easy innovation to master, led not only to a great increase in productivity but created a potential for increasing the scale of operations, an essential prerequisite for the next step forward into the chemical and steampowered era.

The advances in chemistry and engineering, the technical achievements of other industries and their products, growth in population and demand, in fact all the pressures of the industrial revolution combined with the effects of liberalizing influences on labour relations and wages affected the paper industry in many other ways so that by the turn of the century it was swept precipitately into an entirely different phase in its history, invention following invention with great rapidity. But from the very nature of its process before it could make this advance it had to wait for other developments to take place, putting new materials and sources of power at its disposal.

---

[18] Shorter, A. Bib. 12, p. 174. It was not until nearly a century after this that papermaking is first mentioned in Scotland and Ireland, both in 1590 (Shorter, A. Bib. 9, p. 192; Pollard, P.M. Bib. 19, p. 223; and "Papermaking in Ireland in 1590" *Irish Booklore* Vol.III 1977 83–86).

Chapter I

PART I

A SUMMARISED HISTORY OF THE BRITISH PAPER INDUSTRY
FROM THE 15TH–17TH CENTURIES : FROM ENTREPRENEUR TO
MASTER PAPER MAKER

Reference has been made in the Introduction to this book to the comparatively late appearance of papermaking in this country (early 1490's) when John Tate built his paper mill in Hertfordshire; Sele mill is the first paper mill of which we have a record.[1] It has been suggested that one of the reasons for this tardiness may have been the abundance of parchment available to those who needed a material for documents. With wool as the principal national product parchment, prepared as a by–product from the flesh side of sheepskin, would have been reasonably cheap as a writing material besides being a more durable support than paper.[2] This may have been an important cause up till the period when Printing was invented (1454); the stimulus to papermaking provided by the latter was no doubt the main reason for Tate's enterprise. After this it is doubtful whether the availability of parchment was anything more than a contributory factor in the continuing failure of the industry to gain a footing in this country.[3]

The last documented reference to Sele mill in an active role is 1499;[4] Tate died in 1507 leaving instructions for his mill to be sold[5] and no further records of its existence have been discovered.[6] Tate's initiative appears to have come to nothing, possibly because the paper makers were foreigners and returned to their native country without imparting their skills to anyone here. On present evidence attempts to revive interest in establishing papermaking facilities in this country, whether for White or Brown paper, were for much of the 16th C. sporadic and short–lived.

Facts are very scarce for this period and accounts of it equally limited. Further details, not really relevant to our purpose here, may be found in works already cited.[7] Coleman produces evidence to support the view that during this period, and indeed long after this, *it was not economical to produce White paper in this country*; it could be imported more easily and cheaply from abroad. Contemporary comment suggested that this situation arose partly from a lack of the necessary skills to make White paper[8] (more will be said about this subject

---

[1] Hills, R.L. Bib.78 Chap.I.

[2] Overend, G.H. Bib.66 178.

[3] For a more extensive discussion of the subject, the replacement of Parchment by Paper, see Coleman, D.C. Bib.15 6–10.

[4] Shorter, A. Bib.12 174.

[5] Coleman, D.C. Bib.15 40–41.

[6] Shorter, A. Bib.12 44 note 1 and p.174. Mention is also made of much later references to this site and to a paper mill active there in 1785. It is only from a 16th C. source that one learns that Tate may have been alone in this field.

[7] Shorter, A. Bib.12 Chap.I: Coleman, D.C. Bib.15 Chap.III.

[8] There were contemporary claims that the French were actively engaged in sabotaging efforts to import these skills.

later) and partly from a shortage of linen rags, whose already inadequate stocks were being depleted even further by the practice of exporting them. There were other reasons for this erratic and unstable state of affairs, reasons which will become apparent. One of these, for instance, stems from the restrictions on Printing imposed by the Tudor and Stuart monarchies;[9] these undoubtedly had a serious adverse effect on the establishment of a domestic White paper industry while they lasted.

It is important for any readers not familiar with the history of the industry that from this point onwards they should be careful to distinguish between facts relating to the emergence of a paper industry which may or may not have been engaged exclusively in the manufacture of Brown paper and those concerned with the formation of a recognizable White paper industry. In this book interest is focused on the development of White paper manufacture and the point to be watched is the distinction between the potential for this and its realisation.

The next important figure in the papermaking scene is John Spilman, active from 1587, and it is during his lifetime that our attention is drawn to this distinction. By this time the small nucleus of a paper industry, perhaps no more than half-a-dozen mills, had established itself in this country.[10] Shorter believed that, although those mills that are known to have been set up at various times during the 16th C. had all disappeared by the 1580's, "there may well have been other mills of which we have no record but which lasted long enough to have been considered as potential rivals to Spilman's White paper manufactory". Indeed, the widely dispersed and seemingly patternless nature of their occurrence alone suggests that there must have been others, a notion that is more or less confirmed by the inferences to be made from Spilman's repeated Petitions to the Crown for the protection of his privileges; the idea also receives support from other indications of papermaking activity which, though perhaps concerned with papers of an inferior quality during Spilman's time (such as Press papers used in the Woollen Industry, for instance), may have been potential sources for White papermaking at a later date; this aspect will be discussed more fully in Chapter II. Contemporary evidence suggests that some of these rival paper makers had the necessary capability to make White paper, if they had the opportunity to do so.[11]

---

[9] "The English Provincial Printer" (British Library Exhibition Notes by Alan Sterenberg, 1983). It is pointed out here that prior to 1695 Parliament controlled what could be printed; the Stationers' Company who could print and where. The Licensing Act of 1662, renewed every 2 years, restricted printing to London, Oxford, Cambridge and York. These restrictions lapsed in 1695. (More will be said about this subject later).

[10] Shorter, A. Bib.12 28/29.

[11] Overend, G.H. Bib.66 188/194 cites (189) an undated Petition to the Privy Council, which refers to divers persons, "not regarding her Majestie's said speciall pleasure and graunt, have.....erected certaine paper milles, and doe daily gather upp, collect, and ingrosse the said commodities (the linen rags etc.), and most specially the best and finest stuff thereof wherewith your suppliant doth use to make white writyng paper.....". This is a reference to 3 Buckinghamshire paper makers, who had lately erected a paper mill and were using the rags in question. Whereas there is no positive evidence that these, or other paper makers also referred to, were engaged in White paper manufacture, the long succession of petitions and complaints made by Spilman strongly suggests that he was on the defensive against such a situation. In fact the City of London pointed out to him (194) that if he thought that "hee was the first that devised that art of making paper within this realm, wee cannot but note the errour of that suggestion, for that divers others before him have perfourmed the same".

JOHN SPILMAN (1552-1626)

John Spilman was a German, who had arrived in this country as an immigrant and a jeweller by profession ca.1582. But to judge from his subsequent record he was clearly an entrepreneur prepared to turn his hand to anything that might increase his wealth and, in due course, he made an investment in the manufacture of White paper. Mainly on account of his subsequent success in this venture his career is well covered in the literature.[12] In spite of having served a short prison sentence in Nuremberg (1573) and having in addition a persistent record as a debtor there, it is somewhat surprising to find that soon after his arrival in this country he obtained Royal favour and patronage as "Goldsmyth to our Jewelles", an office he continued to hold, after Elizabeth's death, under James I. But Spilman seems to have owed his success to something rather more than the acquisition of a minor function in the Royal Establishment. One might assume from the high level assistance that was accorded to him in his other affairs that he was in great favour with the Queen and may thus have had intelligence of other opportunities in the offing. During the 1580's, for instance, an unsuccessful petition (1585) for a monopoly of paper manufacture by a Stationer, Richard Tottyl,[13] may have prompted Spilman to make a similar application. Tottyl had complained about "the dearth of good paper in this realme" and, even if he was not the direct source of Spilman's inspiration, this topic was at least being aired and not a new one.[14]

The story of his obtaining suitable premises for his White paper manufactory (1586-1588) and their conversion to papermaking can be found in the accounts already referred to and need not be covered again here. All the same it is as well to note in this context that a characteristic feature of British Industries in Plantagenet and Tudor times was their relative backwardness compared to their continental counterparts. As early as 1327 English patents had taken the form of protecting foreign workmen introducing new Arts.[15] The Tudors, particularly, imported many foreign craftsmen of all kinds and actively encouraged the settlement of refugees with special skills, including those of papermaking.[16] In the Elizabethan period Lord Burghley, the Queen's Secretary of State, was very active in this form of patent protection and it is worth mentioning here that not only was Spilman on his special list but that both he and Sir Walter Mildmay were instrumental in securing the lease of the Dartford site for Spilman's paper mill.

---

[12] Overend, G.H. Bib.66 180/195 gives one of the most comprehensive accounts of Spilman's papermaking set-up in England. Sporhan-Krempel, L. "Hans Spilman from Lindau" (The Paper Maker, Hercules Powder Company, 1963 Vol.32 No.2 p.16) gives more of a biographical account than one concerned with papermaking, but it throws some interesting sidelights on his character. Precisely when papermaking started at Dartford is not known, probably 1587/8.

[13] Coleman, D.C. Bib.15 42 and Note 3. Over and above Tottyl's unsuccessful petition reference is made here to another one made at about this time. Tottyl's was by no means a lone voice on this subject.

[14] It seems likely that, if Spilman had any previous knowledge of papermaking, it would have been of a casual nature only. Lindau itself had no paper mills at the time of his boyhood there, although there were some in the surrounding district; but, since he appeared as a jeweller in Nuremberg by 1570, he must have spent his time serving his apprenticeship in this trade rather than spending much of it on anything else. The same might be said of his period of residence in Nuremberg, where they had already established a name for papermaking. Even so it is not the kind of business that one could master readily without close contact with it. What he might well have noticed was the difference in quality between the paper known to him in Germany and that which he found in Elizabethan England. It is perhaps of interest to note that Spilman revisited Lindau in 1598, whilst on a political mission to Germany for Queen Elizabeth; and it is reported that he went to see some of the newly built paper mills there during his stay.

[15] Hyde-Price, W. Bib.67.

[16] See also this chapter n.72; and again in Chap.II n.24 pp.65,77.

It is also important to note that, although Spilman's name is indissolubly linked with the papermaking at his Dartford mill in Kent,[17] he himself *was not in any sense a paper maker*. Instead he imported German craftsmen to make his paper for him.[18] Nevertheless Spilman's appearance on the English papermaking scene is of interest to us on at least five counts:

(i)   As an Entrepreneur as distinct from a "Master Paper Maker".

(ii)   The protection of his papermaking interests through letters patent issued to him by the Queen in 1589 giving him a monopoly of the manufacture of White writing paper and control over many other aspects of papermaking, later supplemented by further powers and privileges creating thereby opposition and discontent in other quarters, a pattern that was to become all too familiar about a hundred years later.

(iii)   The employment of foreign craftsmen.

(iv)   The production of good quality countermarked (?) White paper.

(v)   As a legendary figure.

It is not proposed to enlarge on these points beyond noting briefly their significance in relation to the development of the industry in this country.

Taking (i) and (iii) above first, the combination of these two provided a pattern that seems to have been typical in the evolution of our embryonic White paper industry, a combination that was to surface again towards the end of the 17th C. This comprised a promoter of a papermaking enterprise who, not being a paper maker himself, employed the skills of foreigners to make White paper for him. This appears to have been the case at Fen Ditton (1550), at Dartford (1588) and at Dalry in Scotland (1590's), where German skills were used in each case.[19] As we know of nobody who had made paper in this country before Tate, it seems fairly certain that he too must have imported paper makers from abroad, possibly German also. This procedure was to be used again from 1670–1690, except that in this later period French expertise was employed rather than German. This kind of relationship, namely between the owner and those who actually ran the business, was to change completely later on.

In the meantime attempts to establish a domestic industry of any noteworthy size, for the manufacture of white or brown paper, had not been successful in the interval between Tate and Spilman, but it succeeded in gaining a footing in the period immediately after this. Between 1601–1650 no less than 41 paper mills came into operation;[20] Shorter noted that "this was fairly remarkable in view of the time that must have been necessary for the training and acquisition of craftsmen"; the importance of this conclusion cannot be emphasised enough, and it bears out the first of the precepts enunciated in the Introduction to this book.

---

[17]   See Thomas Churchyard's well-known poem on Spilman; and the imposing monument to him and his wife in Dartford Church as a testimony of this.

[18]   Overend, G.H. Bib.66 186. Reference is made to a warrant in 1588 aimed to prevent "such high Germaines that be worckmen with Mr. Spilman" and other foreign journeymen returning to their native country. Foreigners were regarded with suspicion at the time of the Armada and it would appear from this warrant that Spilman had already lost some of his men. Nothing at present is known about them. A German paper maker, Hans Buchshor, is reported to have been buried at Dartford. Other unusual names, later associated with Dartford, like Quelch (Welsh or Welshman) and Stidolph (in Kent from 1300) are not connected with this situation.

[19]   Shorter, A. Bib.9 15 & 192.

[20]   Shorter, A. Bib.9 19, 20 Fig.1.

Taking points (ii) and (v) next, Spilman's privileges and his image, we find that, although Tate's efforts were recognized and rewarded by Henry VII, the first evidence of protection in this country for the manufacture of White paper was that granted to Spilman by Queen Elizabeth. Others had petitioned her for it before, but had not been successful. One feels that Spilman must have been a figure rather larger than life and with a certain charisma that enabled him to obtain privileges and miscellaneous favours where others had failed. Moreover, his venture into papermaking evidently made its mark early and sufficiently forcibly for it to be cited as evidence one hundred years later (1690), that "White papermaking was not a new invention in this country", evidence presented, somewhat ironically, by paper makers who were defending themselves against the very privileges that had permitted Spilman to achieve success. But, so far as we are concerned, the point to note here is that already in Spilman's time the native objection to the privileges of monopoly was finding expression. This applied particularly, if this was done at the expense of those already in the field or of those who had legitimate aspirations to similar objectives, a situation likely to be aggravated even further if these privileges were conferred on a foreigner. It is easy to dismiss all this lightly as an example of the political jockeying of the period, but the evidence points rather to these being deep-rooted national sentiments and, as will become apparent, they undoubtedly helped shape the forces that later overcame a critical phase in the history of English White paper manufacture.

The remaining point, (iv), the production of good quality White paper, will be examined later after consideration has been given to the general progress of the industry following Spilman.

The Growth of the Domestic Paper Industry in the 17th C.

The domestic industry had gained a firm footing by 1650; this consisted almost entirely of mills engaged in the production of Brown paper, a concept strongly supported by contemporary comment and by the consistently high level of imports of White paper from the Continent.[21] On a nationwide scale the industry continued to expand from the 41 mills (identified by Shorter) in 1650 to 63 mills by 1675, 100+ by 1690 and 209 (England and Wales) in 1712.[22] If these results are represented graphically, one obtains a smooth accelerating growth curve with a fairly sharp upturn after 1675. Seen from a global viewpoint there is no obvious sign of any exogenous factor affecting rate of growth; superficially, it all looks quite normal. But it will be demonstrated later that an interpretation of this kind can be very misleading; seen from a regional point of view one obtains a very different picture, a difference that is of considerable importance when one is seeking to piece together the pattern of development of the White paper industry. This difference will be exposed and examined in some detail in Chapter II.

Although imports remained at a high level throughout this period, what this fact and the fact that we had a growing industry do not tell us is whether White paper manufacture petered out with the death of Spilman (as some have suggested) and, if it did, whether the skills followed suit or found other outlets in papermaking at a lower level of quality, or whether White paper production continued throughout this period at a low but slowly increasing volume.

---

[21] Coleman, D.C. Bib.15 13, Table I.
[22] Shorter, A. Bib.9 22, 28 & 75.

To account for the existence of a substantial body of independent makers of White paper in this country in the 1680's, and especially those in Kent, some of whom may have been influenced by the earlier operations at Dartford or may have served their apprenticeship there, one must assume that both the production and skills of English craftsmen had survived, albeit under very unfavourable conditions with economic and statutory restraints and a shortage of the right materials. Under such adverse conditions these paper makers must have been forced for much of the time into making Brown paper; but, when we come to consider the process, such conditions would not have precluded them from making White paper whenever circumstances favoured this.

The Threshold of a New Era

We have a picture then of a paper trade almost entirely dominated for much of the 17th C. by imported White paper, complemented by a rapidly growing domestic source of Brown paper;[23] and within all this a small potential capacity for making White paper, if not the actualization of this itself. When viewed retrospectively it can be seen that soon after 1670 this simple picture is complicated by the effects of a number of external factors, effects which were to create a new era for the nascent White paper industry. During the next thirty years an embargo on French imports (1678–1685),[24] further rises in Customs Duties (after 1690) and War (1690–1697) all played a major role in shifting the sources and reducing the quantities, temporarily, of imports; and superimposed on this state of affairs were the effects on the industry of an influx of Huguenot refugees. Based on Shorter's figures for the number of paper mills for this period it was noted earlier that there was quite a sharp upturn after 1675 of the curve representing the industry's growth and this is reflected in both the quality and the quantity of White paper production. Whereas this change may have been stimulated by the influence and practices of the refugees, this alone cannot account for the acquisition of the necessary skills within such a short period; one is forced into presupposing the existence of a latent native potential (see Chap.II).

The period in question is a turbulent and confusing one to analyse; however, in the context of this book, it is important that this should be done since it is the threshold from which this study of the changes in 18th C. papermaking technology really begins. For the sake of brevity, but at the same time in some danger of oversimplifying the matter, the principal protagonists in this situation may be identified as Eustace Burnaby and certain other figures associated with him, later to be overshadowed by Nicholas Dupin and the COMPANY of White paper makers who, in turn, were confronted by a rising generation of English Master Paper Makers. To present this subject meaningfully is not so much a matter of portraying the

---

[23] Coleman, D.C. Bib.15 Chap.I 15–23 and Tables I & II. Coleman quantifies here the steady rise in White paper imports during most of the 17th C., this falling away temporarily towards the end. Likewise he shows that at the beginning of the 17th C. imports of Brown paper were high and that as the domestic paper industry grew (cf. Shorter's figures for the number of paper mills given earlier), the quantities declined rapidly.
      During the 15th C. White paper imports came mainly from Italy; but during the same century the sources of supply started shifting to France, which became England's principal supplier during the 16th and for the first three–quarters of the 17th C. During the 17th C. Holland supplied this country with White paper whenever embargoes were placed on French goods; and this, ultimately, led them to superseding the French at the end of the century as the principal supplier.

[24] Coleman, D.C. Bib.15 65. lists 3 embargoes; 1666/7, very brief but may have been noticed by some paper makers (see Chap.II); 1678–1685 and 1689–1697, the latter being almost coincidental with the War.

people involved as one of outlining the various forces at work and the strategies adopted by the parties concerned.

1670-1700

Nearly 30 years ago Professor Hazen wrote "I speak in praise of Eustace Burnaby, the first maker of white paper in England after Spilman".[25] Prudently, he qualified this statement immediately by writing, "This means more precisely the first *identifiable* maker of good paper: poorer paper was assuredly made in England throughout the seventeenth century, but difficulties with the supply of rags and difficulties about the supply of trained workmen contributed to the central fact, that English mills could not compete with the established supply of good French paper before 1678". It is not the intention here to argue against the overall validity of this claim; viewed from a distance it is probably as fair a summary of the situation as one is likely to find. All the same it is a challenging statement and it may prove instructive to consider parts of it in more detail in the context of the present study. Accordingly, these assertions will be examined later in their proper context.

In the meantime our attention needs to be focused on the next of the protagonists, Nicholas Dupin and the COMPANY of White paper makers; their technical contribution to the industry will be considered as a separate issue in Chapter V. There are many parallels between Burnaby's intrusion into the papermaking scene and Dupin's and, indeed, Spilman's. Burnaby's appearance is so fleeting that it seems very doubtful whether he had any real influence at all on the *development* of White paper manufacture. This is not to deny the existence of very good White paper bearing his countermark; nor to quarrel with such an experienced and distinguished bibliographer's statement that his paper was better than the general run of "unidentifiable" paper of the preceding period. But, taking a broader view of the changes that were beginning to take place, the real credit must be given to Dupin and the COMPANY for the part they played in this.

Until comparatively recent times the paper industry in this country was run almost without exception, either remotely or directly, by individuals; or, at most, by partnerships of two or three. The one notable exception to this was that of the COMPANY of White paper makers. The joint stock company, as a means of financing various enterprises, had had a long history in England before this period.[26] Between 1670-1700 there was a marked increase in this kind of activity. Coleman has written "One of the notable features of the industrial history of later Stuart England is the flood of patents for various sorts of inventions, devices and projects as well as for many new joint stock companies;"[27] and the developing paper industry was in no way immune to this influence and parts of it, at least, were temporarily caught up in this flood.

An approach to papermaking in this way will clearly produce different results from one carried out in the normal way. For our purpose the joint stock company may be regarded as a combination of entrepreneurs, whose object was to corner the market by means of a

[25]   Hazen, A.T. Bib.5 316.
[26]   Scott, W.R. Bib.43.
[27]   Coleman, D.C. Bib.15 59.

monopoly and with a sufficiency of capital to enable them to outbid potential competitors. To function they obviously had to put forward some sort of proposition to obtain the privileges and the necessary capital. The so-called "Invention" was one way of achieving this goal. One has to understand that many of these inventions, which formed the basis of innumerable petitions, were far from being new ideas or new methods. More often than not they were either old ones served up in a new guise; or, as will be seen, they often represented standard procedure already used in other countries "but never practised before in any of our kingdoms etc.", which was a favourite way of putting it.[28]

Hitherto it had been individual entrepreneurs, like Tate, Gresham, Spilman, Burnaby and many anonymous papermill proprietors, who had provided the capital for papermaking enterprises; and this pattern was to continue into the 18th C. though with a marked shift in control from proprietor to paper maker. So why, it may be asked, was it necessary to introduce the joint stock company into this scene ? Probably the main answer to this question is that papermaking was "temporarily caught up in the flood", the spate of inventions providing endless opportunities for the sharks of the day to form such companies. Moreover the political and economic climate favoured this development. We had been importing the bulk of our White paper requirements from France to whom our attitude had become increasingly hostile; the arrival of the Huguenot refugees, some of whom had been here since 1670 and some of whom were also among France's most skilled craftsmen, was all that was needed to fuel the heightened industrial activity following the Restoration with new ideas and practical know-how for patents. As events showed there was clearly entrenched opposition to such an invasion of the industry. In order to gain a foothold therefore one must assume that Nicholas Dupin and his 34 fellow petitioners (some half of these being French) saw that their only hope of success would be to obtain privileges and capital on a sufficient scale to sweep away this opposition; and the obvious solution to this problem was to form a joint stock company.

They were successful in obtaining a Charter from James II in 1686, giving them the *sole* right to make White paper in England and Wales for a period of 14 years. With the help of energetic management they succeeded in maintaining their position for a time; but since in essence this success was derived from power rather than economic advantage or superior technical skill, it was short-lived. When peace returned in 1697 and paper flooded into the country again from the Continent, they found themselves on the same footing as the rest of the industry and their privileges were of no further use to them; and so, not surprisingly, they disappeared from the scene.

The Governor and Company of White Paper Makers of England produced a situation that in many ways resembled Spilman's, only more so. Where Spilman had had to contend with an almost hypothetical opposition, the COMPANY had to face a now firmly established opposition made up of English paper makers[29] and paper sellers, who were able to voice in

---

[28] Overend, G.H. Bib.66 203. He points out that under the Statute of Monopolies a person who had first imported an invention publicly known abroad into this country was counted as the first inventor in these realms. This subject is discussed more fully in Chapter V where some of these inventions are examined.

[29] Amongst these was a group of 14 paper makers, mostly from Kent and Buckinghamshire and known as the ANCIENT PAPER MAKERS, who signed a Petition in 1690 against the Act before Parliament which would confirm the Monopoly

(continued...)

Parliament their dislike of privilege much more forcibly, and effectively in the long term, than in Spilman's time. In fact the joint stock approach to papermaking did not rear its head again for perhaps well over a century and a half after this and then only under circumstances that demanded very high capital investment in paper machinery and associated plant and buildings. In spite of its short duration and swift demise the COMPANY undoubtedly contributed technically to the progress and improvement of White paper manufacture in this country, unlike Spilman and Burnaby who merely resorted to the adaptation of an existing and well-tried process to a new environment.

Returning to the subject of Burnaby it may be noted that he had anticipated the actions of the COMPANY by some years. He was granted a patent (No.178) in 1675 for "the art and skill of making all sorts of White paper for the use of writing and printing, being a manufacture never practised in any of our kingdoms or dominions", 11 years before the COMPANY'S Charter, granted in 1686. But such a claim was really nothing more than an entrepreneurial smoke-screen put out to protect his intended papermaking operation.

Very little is known about Burnaby and his mill. Hazen believed that he might have had a barley mill somewhere near Windsor, which he may have converted into a paper mill; *or*, since it is known that his paper mill was "within five miles of Windsor", he has also suggested that he might have leased one of the paper mills owned there by the Dean and Canons of St. George's Chapel, Windsor. Burnaby, the son of a Northamptonshire gentleman, does not appear to have had any previous connection with papermaking, so that one immediately queries the source of his patent claims. That he was an entrepreneur there seems to be little doubt; he had many other interests.[30] Quite possibly then he may have been inspired, as seems to have been the case with Spilman, by another's suggestion and to have proceeded thence to exploit the other's expertise in his own name, perhaps as part of a bargain or a means of entrée to the British industrial scene. Hazen provides fairly convincing evidence that, prior to 1678, Burnaby was associated at his mill with another paper maker who is known to us by the countermark "PLG", believed to be initials of a French refugee, Peter le Gaultier.[31] The earliest "EB" (Eustace Burnaby) countermark cited by Hazen is to be found

---

[29](...continued)
    granted to the COMPANY (Hist.MS.Commission 13th Report App.Pt.V. MS.House of Lords 1690–91 [1892 pp.75/6]; and Overend, G.H. Bib.66 210 ff.). The Ancient Paper Makers are mentioned again several times in this book both in the main text and in the Appendices. They disputed the claims that members of the COMPANY were the inventors of the art of making White Writing and Printing paper and claimed that the domestic paper makers not only had served their apprenticeships but were more skilled in the art than the patentees.

[30] Besides his interests in French Barley and Papermaking, Burnaby is known to have petitioned for a Patent in 1687 "for working and weaving superfine white thread and fine linen.... ..not hitherto made in England". Again, this was ahead of Dupin's venture into this same field. He had another Patent of 1678/9 granting him sole use and art of planting safflower for dyers' use.

[31] To account for Hazen's claim that Burnaby was the first (identifiable) maker of White paper in England after Spilman it is important that as much light as possible should be thrown on this rather shadowy figure "PLG" and, in particular, that his origins were in fact French. In addition to the evidence that Hazen gives showing that "PLG" was working at Burnaby's paper mill, it is clear from the style of the countermarks themselves (illustrated in Hazen's article) that they are French rather than English in appearance. Hazen has also attempted to identify "PLG" and having proposed Peter le Gaultier tries to trace his origins, not altogether convincingly, as a French paper maker. Further information which may be added to Hazen's is given below.
    The name Gau(l)tier occurs with some frequency in Huguenot records and a Peter Gaultier occurs in a list of Denizations dated 1688. It should be noted that denization could have been effected years, even decades, after immigration; so that
    (continued...)

in a document dated 1677, indicating that his mill must have become operational for the manufacture of White paper soon after 1675, the date of his Patent; but Burnaby had sold his rights in this by 1682[32] and abandoned his papermaking activity at the same time.[33]

Burnaby's withdrawal may have been due to finding himself increasingly out of his depth in a business with which he was not familiar, depending, it would appear, entirely on the skills of his paper maker, le Gaultier; and, in addition to this, faced with the prospect of growing opposition from more forceful competitors. Although the COMPANY did not obtain their Charter until 1686, there was already a great deal of skirmishing going on before this date within the industry; two other patentees had already appeared on the scene by 1682, George Hagar who had also formed a papermaking company and Nathaniel Bladen, whose Patents will be examined in more detail in Chapter V. Hagar had a very chequered and troubled career, having been bankrupted in 1677 and pursued subsequently by his creditors who tried to force him to give up his patent, but he is of some importance to us in that after being involved with a number of paper mills[34] he occupied Dartford No.2 paper mill in Kent for a year, 1697/8, a matter which will be considered again. His troubles need not concern us here; they are mentioned simply because they illustrate the activities and scheming that were taking place around 1682, when Burnaby retired from the papermaking scene.

[31](...continued)

    denization in 1688 does not necessarily preclude the attribution of countermarks in documents dated 1678 to Gaultier. The Huguenot Society of London also possesses a pedigree of a Henri Gaultier of Angoulesme. There is no "Pierre" in the pedigree, but it indicates (a) that there were Gaultiers in Angoulême, one of the great papermaking centres of France; (b) that Henry's family were settling in England towards the end of the 17th C.; and (c) that Ann, Henry's grand–daughter, married William Janssen, son of Sir Theodore Janssen, who had played a prominent role in a dispute with the COMPANY of White Paper Makers in the 1680's and whose father and uncles had important papermaking interests in Angoulême (see Cameron, W.J. Bib.18 16/17 for an account of the Janssens). Cameron (ibid. 4 note 7) has also commented that "PLG's" (Pierre Gaultier) relationship to the paper maker of the same name at Beauvais paper mill, Angoulême, in 1648 remains to be determined. Although none of this throws any positive light on the origins of Pierre Gaultier, it does suggest strongly that he had connections with Angoulême, papermaking and persons with mutual opposition to the COMPANY. Were there alternatives to Gaultier as a source of inspiration to Burnaby? French refugees had been arriving in this country for a long time before 1678. Nicholas Dupin, for instance, had become a naturalised English subject in 1670. A "Mr. Henry Million" (of whom we shall be hearing more later) seems to have been a sort of common denominator in his relationship with Burnaby on the one hand (in the 1670's) and an active partner of Dupin's in the 1690's (though these were in all probability father and son). The question arises did Dupin and Burnaby ever meet through the agency of Mr. Million before 1675 or in fact ever? The COMPANY certainly knew all about Burnaby, both as a Patent holder and as a manufacturer of White paper. On balance Peter le Gaultier seems to have been a much more likely source of inspiration to Burnaby than anyone else.

[32]   Hazen, A.T. Bib. 5 332.

[33]   There seems to be more than one style of "EB" countermark (see App.V. extension to Figure 13; "Countermarks noted in the V & A Library sample"). Since there are uncertainties about the precise date of these documents, it cannot be assumed that "EB" necessarily represents Eustace Burnaby though it must be added there seems to be no credible alternative. Gravell, T.L. Bib.16 16:May:90 has supplied the author with a wide range of "EB" (d.o.d.'s 1694, 1704, 1705/6, 1706, 1709 and 1715 in American documents) marks that are not only stylistically consistent and entirely different from the marks cited above, but accord with "Elliston and Basket" marks (in full) d.o.d.'s 1697, 1704/5. For an example and a further note on this subject see Ext. Fig.13 n.1.

[34]   The intrigues surrounding Hagar's patent and papermaking activities are too complicated to describe here. For an account see Cameron, W.J. Bib.18 4–6; and Coleman, D.C. Bib.15. 62. Hagar joined forces with a William Sutton of Byfleet mill, Surrey, allegedly to promote the former's patent; these plans were frustrated by a creditor after Hagar had leased Eynsham mill in Oxfordshire which he was forced to leave. Later, in evidence in his appeal for the abatement of his bankruptcy (1689/1690), he claimed to have had interests in several mills in Surrey. Shorter, A. Bib.12 215 cites a reference to him setting up a paper mill at Stanwell in Middlesex and then making a final appearance at Dartford.

By 1682 another figure had appeared on this scene, Lady Theodosia Ivy, to whom Bladen assigned the rights of his papermaking patent (No.220 of 1682), potentially a very important one to do with the preparation of rags for papermaking (Chap.V); and, in addition, Burnaby also sold his patent to her in the same year. Hazen has suggested that after 1682 Lady Theodosia may have continued to lease the mill formerly used by Burnaby and that Peter Gaultier continued to run it for her. To support this contention he cites the occurrence of "PLG" countermarks in a series of pamphlets said to have originated from this mill and which appeared between 1678-1688. Although Burnaby's patent actually expired in 1689, Lady Theodosia still entered a petition to the House of Commons in 1690 claiming that she was the owner of both Burnaby's and Bladen's patents, this petition being part of the opposition being mounted at that time against the COMPANY who were asking Parliament to reaffirm their Charter, originally granted to them by James II but who had since been deposed (1688). Nevertheless she still had Bladen's patent and no doubt sensing the weakness in their position caused by the lapse of Burnaby's patent, le Gaultier petitioned, unsuccessfully, in 1691 for a very similar Patent of his own for making "Fine Paper". When we stand a little way back from this situation, we can see that Hazen's image of Burnaby as a paper maker is little more than a front and that in reality in return for setting him up in his own trade le Gaultier had supplied Burnaby with imported know-how as material for his Patent and then made "EB" countermarked paper for him. These assumptions would certainly account for the known facts of this situation.

Following Burnaby's departure and the granting of their monopoly Burnaby's and Bladen's Patents were clearly obstacles in the COMPANY'S path[35] and in order to strengthen their hand they secured for themselves a much more pretentious and all-embracing patent of John Briscoe's (1685). This may well have contained elements of novelty, a kind of patent of improvement as it were (more in words probably than in fact) outflanking the others and, as Cameron has suggested,[36] it may have embodied elements of Hagar's patent as well, which Briscoe had wheedled out of him. It was not until 1689 that the COMPANY attempted to monopolise the White paper market previously held by the French and in order to raise more capital and re-assert their rights under William III they brought their CASE before Parliament, confident that under the terms of their Charter of 1686 they had brought together all the best letters Patent concerned with White paper manufacture, implying in this claim that they had either acquired the rights of or had superseded the Patents of Burnaby (1675), Bladen (1682), Hagar through the agency of William Sutton who had gone over to their side and leased his Byfleet mill to them (1682), Jackson (1684), Briscoe (1685) and Dupin et alia (1686). In their CASE not only did the COMPANY seek to confirm their right to "the sole Power of making White-Writing and Printing-Paper for Fourteen Years" but they also sought

[35] Jenkins, R. Bib.34 states that in 1685 Burnaby was given permission to introduce a Bill into the House of Commons "for the encouragement of the manufacture of Paper"; but the matter was not proceeded with. Although by this date Burnaby had retired from active participation in papermaking, one might interpret his intention here as one of protecting both his Patent (now Lady Theodosia's) and the industry from the incursions of the embryonic COMPANY.

[36] Cameron, W.J. Bib.18 3-7. It is believed that Briscoe, who was a salter, had managed to extract the secrets of Hagar's patent (Hagar formerly a dyer) and had joined forces with Shales, both original members of the COMPANY, subsequently embodying the information in their own Patent. William Sutton, who had originally joined forces with Hagar, to promote the latter's patent, was the tenant of Byfleet mill in Surrey. Sutton initially organised much of the resistance to the COMPANY'S monopoly, but eventually joined them, leasing his mill to them and agreeing to assign Hagar's patent to them. Hagar, however, contested this; but it has never been discovered whether the COMPANY ever acquired his patent or not. (See also Chap.V p.195).

other privileges such as powers for compulsory purchase of "Paper-Mills, Corn-Mills or Streams the COMPANY shall judge to be proper for the setting up of the manufacture". Not surprisingly this Bill was fiercely contested by Hagar, Lady Theodosia Ivy and the Dean of St. George's Chapel, Windsor, the Paper-Sellers and the Paper-Makers together with a few others who appeared on the scene later. Before considering this opposition it will be necessary to return to a subject connected with both Burnaby and Spilman to appreciate the significance of the claims and counterclaims of the parties concerned.

More space has been devoted in this chapter to Eustace Burnaby than our main concern with the development of White paper manufacture would seem to warrant, particularly after remarking that he does not appear to have had any positive influence on this. But Burnaby, whom we shall not be concerned with again, is of interest to us for other reasons than his unquestionably fine White paper. Though this was not a new invention in this country and though Burnaby's claims were no more than a smoke-screen, it brings us back to Professor Hazen's challenging statement. At the same time it would be an appropriate moment to discuss the fourth point of interest in Spilman's achievement, "the production of good quality countermarked White paper".

It was indicated earlier that as this study proceeds various facets of contemporary papermaking technology will be discussed in progressively greater detail; this is in order to help the reader understand their significance in relation to the development of the industry, a point that has been overlooked in some accounts of its history.[37] For the moment the papermaking process can be summarised by describing five basic stages in it:

(i) Rag Sorting and Fermentation, the collecting together of fibrous raw materials into a state of readiness for use in Stage (ii).
(ii) Rag Breaking and Beating, the dismemberment and dispersion of these materials into an appropriately treated, fine and homogeneous suspension of fibre in water.
(iii) Sheetmaking, Pressing and Drying, the conversion of this fibre into a sheet of paper by the removal of water, first in the process of forming the sheet and followed by further water removal in a press and then hanging the sheet up to dry.
(iv) Sizing the dried sheet with gelatine size and re-drying it to give it ink-bearing properties.
(v) The sorting and finishing of the sized paper.

The formation of a sheet of paper on the papermaking mould by the Vatman at his vat (iii) is the most eye-catching stage of these five, and justifiably so; to be able to do this was one of the major European skills. It follows from this then that it would require just as much skill to make a sheet of Brown paper as a White. There are minor points on which one might dispute this assertion. For example, regularity of surface, basis weight and formation would have been controlled within finer limits in papers required for printing and even more so for writing on than in papers used for more ordinary purposes; the papermaking moulds may have

---

[37] (i) A general account of the papermaking process and the papermaking mould will be found at the end of this chapter. (ii) More specialized aspects of the process will be covered in Chapters V and VI. (iii) Finally, certain fundamental aspects of the sheetmaking and rag preparation processes are dealt with in App.V.

been constructed more finely also. Nevertheless, it requires great skill to make by hand any sort of sheet at all whether it be white or brown.

This is not all. It takes almost as much skill to prepare the materials correctly in stage (ii) as it does to convert them into sheets of paper. Although the higher quality and stronger materials used for White paper would have required proportionately greater skill in their preparation than those used for Brown paper, especially in the later periods of papermaking, this to some extent would have been offset by the relatively crude methods in use then for breaking and beating the rags. It would be true to say, however, that in the lowest grades of materials used for papermaking many of these would have been so rotten that almost any form of grinding or hammering machinery could have dispersed them. All the same one cannot assume that all of the paper made in England during the 17th C. between Spilman and Burnaby's time was necessarily the lowest grade only, requiring inferior skills.

If one is likely to find deficiencies in papermaking skills at this time, one is much more likely to have found them in stage (iv), the gelatine sizing process, than in any of the other stages; though, here again, this would have applied for the most part to the production of Writing paper only; and, further, the difficulties of this process would not have been confined to papers made in this country.[38]

It can be seen from what has been said above that, apart from the very lowest qualities of paper, the differences in the skills required to make White paper and Brown paper are marginal rather than fundamental. Obviously, this margin will be more marked between the finest Writing paper and Brown than, say, between White "ordinary", by far and away the largest category of White paper to be imported,[39] and Brown. One must be careful, then, in making too sweeping assertions that we had not the skills to make White paper in England during the first three-quarters of the 17th C. The important point here is not whether we actually produced White paper, identifiable or not, equal in quality to Burnaby's but whether we had the capability of doing this or not; and, assuredly, we had.

Reverting to Professor Hazen's statement once again the inference that we make from this is that "difficulties with the supply of rags" had meant that English mills were unable to compete with continental paper *during the period between* Spilman's and Burnaby's papermaking. There is little doubt that the shortfall in the supply of rags, that he mentions, proscribed the existence of a healthy domestic White paper industry; but, equally, one must take into account the fact that, to judge from the special powers he had to seek, Spilman was faced with exactly the same difficulty and yet was successful; and the same may be said for Burnaby making paper 80 years later and yet he too managed to make the best quality of

---

[38] There are several contemporary illustrations that may be cited here showing that the ink-bearing properties of paper often left something to be desired. One such instance is quoted by Coleman (Bib.15. 50). Here is another together with the remedy from Gore, W. "The Art of Limning" (1674): "It is necessary I should say somthing (sic) concerning the preparing, or making the paper firm, that it may receive colour without sinking, in regard it often happens......that colours sink; otherwise there are also papers, which are so firm themselves, which nevertheless may be prepared, chusing to be certain rather than uncertain of a good firm ground, that you may not make imperfect and defective work; but upon parchment it is altogether unnecessary" (this, of course, carrying its own in-built size). Gore follows this statement with a do-it-yourself sizing process involving sponging the surface of the paper with a (warm) sol of "the best white glew" boiled in fair rain water "to the consistencie of calfs broth or gelly".

[39] Coleman, D.C. Bib.15. 15.

White paper. The explanation for their respective successes lay not in the fact that they had some new invention, but that either through privilege or good fortune these two paper makers were able to obtain and *sort* sufficient quantities of the whitest rags to enable them to make the best qualities of paper. Though all this may seem only too obvious, the fact is that the industry at this time was small, relatively dispersed and dependent on very casual and inefficient methods for collecting and distributing rags. The result was that paper makers would have used whatever rags they could lay their hands on and would not have been too selective in their sorting; consequently, at best, they would have been forced to make "Ordinary" Printing rather than, say, White Writing paper. There seems to be ample contemporary evidence, both in Spilman's time and a hundred years later, that this was the case and that first quality white rags were being swallowed up indiscriminately in the manufacture of papers which, though possibly White in many cases, were of indifferent quality.[40]

Again, apropos of Hazen's remarks about the dearth of trained workmen at this time, it has been demonstrated earlier that the Brown paper industry, if not White as well, had shown significant growth between 1600–1670. One must assume then from what has been said about the papermaking process that somewhere within the domestic industry there was a fair quota of the skills needed for making White paper.

The truth of the matter is that, though there were obvious deficiencies in the rag collecting and distributing system, one of the main obstacles to the establishment and growth of White paper manufacture lay in the fact "that it was (still) not economical to produce White paper in England", for economic reasons rather than technical; another being the absence of any provincial printing industry to stimulate growth, a severely inhibiting factor due in this case to political rather than technical restraints. Though Spilman's achievement is always given as an example of a successful venture in papermaking, we really know nothing about the profitability of his performance. On the one hand it is clear that his mill survived and continued to operate until 1724 and there seems to be evidence that White paper manufacture continued for much if not all of this period;[41] but, on the other hand, it is also known that Spilman encountered difficulties and as he was so hedged around with privileges it is impossible to assess his financial achievement.

Burnaby and others like him, with no such privileges, might have found White paper manufacture a profitable pursuit only as long as the embargo on French goods lasted, in this case 1678–1685 (an influence considered again in Chapter II). Likewise, it has been observed

---

[40] Though steps were taken in 1666/7 to try and conserve supplies of rags for paper through the Act for Burying in Woollen, this was not made enforceable until an Act of 1678 (Mr. Million, at that time friendly with Burnaby, almost certainly lobbied for this). Evidently ineffective the next stage was to prohibit the export of rags (1686/7). Even this measure had to be re-affirmed in the Act of 1690 confirming the Charter granted to the COMPANY of White Paper Makers, who were still agitating for further powers to conserve rags as late as 1697. This all points to the fact that measures of this kind had not really altered a situation that had lasted ever since Spilman's day and certainly had not proved to be any more effective in Burnaby's time.

[41] THE CASE AND Circumstances of Paper-making IN ENGLAND TRULY STATED (Petition of 1690 BM. Cup.645.b.11) claims "THAT the Art of making White and Brown-Paper was brought to England by Sir John Spelman (sic) a German, to whom King James I.....(in addition to a monopoly)....gave him an Estate of 200 l. per Annum at Dartford in Kent, where he erected a Paper Mill, *which is to this day imployed* in making White and Brown-paper". This is an extract from a Petition submitted by the Paper Makers and Paper Sellers in 1690 in what Cameron (Bib.18) has described as the second round in the campaign opposing the COMPANY'S Bill in the Commons.

how the COMPANY, despite their special position and initial success, also succumbed in the end to the same adverse economic conditions. The cards were still heavily stacked against the domestic industry at that time affecting Burnaby, the COMPANY and others alike.

The facts are that we imported and distributed paper, under the stringent control of the Stationers' Company, from Italy, France and Germany where the paper industry had been firmly established for several centuries. These industries were clearly much more organised and catered for much larger populations than that of England;[42] and, moreover, they could obtain labour more cheaply and, as Professor Hazen has rightly pointed out, materials would have been more abundant also. The English White paper makers were there but conditions, for the most part outside their control, did not allow them to meet this competition.[43] It is difficult in these circumstances to accept Professor Hazen's reasons for the absence of high quality paper production in this country without some reservations, particularly in respect of his reference to the absence of trained workmen. Without special privileges we might never have heard of Spilman and, indeed, if it had not been for the influence of a French refugee coupled with strained relations with France, we might never have seen Burnaby's fine White paper either, let alone have identified it by means of a countermark.[44]

Quite apart from finding it necessary to moderate Hazen's claims, if we examine the papermaking scene of Burnaby's time and that immediately preceding it, there are definite pointers to the existence of a domestic White paper industry. Reference has been made in a footnote to the fact that contemporary claims were made that Spilman's Dartford mill was still "imployed in making White and Brown-Paper". Exactly what followed at Dartford after Spilman's death in 1626 can only be guessed at. Spilman's son, who succeeded him, may have kept the mill going until he too died, in 1641; or he may have leased it to someone else. Certainly, the mill continued to produce noteworthy paper makers and among them may be numbered some of the Ancient Paper Makers of Kent including William Blackwell[45] and George Gill. Gill, who started making paper only a year or two after Burnaby, "made *very*

[42]   Towards the end of the 17th C. the population of France has been reckoned as ca. 19–20 million compared to 5.5 million for England and 2.5 million for Holland.

[43]   Another important influence, to be referred to in greater detail later, was that of the ascendant Dutch paper industry, ascendant both commercially and, more especially, technically during the 17th C.

[44]   The word "countermark" has already been used several times in this chapter and this is perhaps an appropriate place to explain what is meant by it. For our purpose, at this point, a Countermark may be defined as the watermark emblem, initials or name, found in a sheet of paper representing the paper maker or owner of the paper mill. (For a more comprehensive definition and examples of this see Preface to App.I & II. For obvious reasons these marks are usually found only in the better qualities of paper; but their absence does not necessarily mean that the paper is inferior. One can still find good quality White paper without a countermark.
      Countermarks had been used from very early times by European paper makers, but, so far as one can tell, they were rare in English papers before the 18th C. and only becoming common after ca.1760 (see Chapter III n.36 and again Chap.VII n.357). Since we know of no predecessors to Tate, one might reasonably assume that his use of an 8-pointed Star together with the use of "ER" under a Crown, suggested as Spilman's mark, owe their existence to the influence of their continental paper makers. This is supported by the rather more common use of these marks in the British Isles towards the end of the 17th C. by "paper makers" like Dupin, Denis Manes, the COMPANY and Peter le Gaultier, all of whom were either French in origin or strongly influenced by French practices. It would not be surprising, therefore, to find that Burnaby's mark and indeed those of some other contemporary English paper makers, had been prompted from the same source.

[45]   Shorter, A. Bib.12 180 has pointed out that William Blackwell was the occupant of Dartford No.1 mill by 1670, if not before this. The name William Blackwell appears in the Dartford Ratebook in 1651 and, traditionally, it has been held that he was apprenticed to the Spilmans.

good White paper" according to the historian, Dr. John Harris;[46] and, in some cases, this paper may be identifiable.[47] But, in addition to this evident continuity, one also has to account for a more general expansion in the number of Master Paper Makers, some of whom undoubtedly made White paper of a kind from 1670 onwards; some possibly earlier than this (see Chapter II). This new generation of paper makers may be seen as "bridging the gap" between the Entrepreneurs of the earlier periods and the Master Paper Makers of the 18th C. Because they were essentially provincial paper makers one has to assume that to begin with, at least, they had not been caught up in the Post–Restoration "flood", neither had they a French refugee at their elbows to induce them into making their paper identifiable. Nevertheless, there is little doubt that they were aware of the political situation and that, in due course, they were influenced by the immigrant paper makers and their practices. In fact Hazen may not be correct in assuming that around 1678 Burnaby was alone in making his paper identifiable.[48]

In the last few pages the object has been to define more precisely than has been the case so far what sort of differences existed between the manufacture of White and Brown paper. It will have been understood by now that both White and Brown cover a wide spectrum of qualities. White paper could range from the very best quality, Writing paper, down through various grades of Printing paper to the cheaper qualities of printing and Copy paper (what one might use to-day for scribbling pads). At the other end of the scale was Brown paper used for wrapping goods, shop papers etc. and these could rise in quality to Whited–Browns and Littress, often made up from a mixture of brown and white pulps from Vat Bottoms, Broken sheets re–pulped and rags too dirty to use in White paper.[49] A short description of the papermaking process and a discussion of the skills required for the various stages has shown that at that time there were no fundamental differences between the processes used in the manufacture of White and Brown paper; such differences as did exist were ones of degree. The real differences, apart from the different furnishes used for these papers, would have lain more in the care with which these processes were carried out and better judgement of the degree of treatment given to the materials used e.g. in fermentation, beating and sizing. In this respect a paper maker who had had experience of White paper manufacture would clearly have an advantage over one who had made only Brown. However, in these pages it has also been shown, albeit only summarily, that in this country we clearly had a small active White paper section of the industry and, by inference, a potential for expansion whenever an opportunity might arise. All this should not be seen as an attempt to make out a case, in defiance of other evidence, that after Spilman we had a thriving domestic White paper industry in this country. On the contrary, the intention has been to try to correct what might

[46] Harris, John Bib.4 191.

[47] Shorter, A. Bib.9 248 fig.28 (c) illustrates a "GG" countermark found in a document dated ca.1676. The exact date when George Gill began his papermaking is uncertain; it could have been at any time between 1676 and 1680, the latter date being the first documentary evidence of his presence in the Maidstone district has preference (see Chap.IV note 72 and Fig.4).

[48] Although no examples of English countermarks have been discovered (to the author's knowledge) before Thomas Quelch's (d.o.d 1680; Shorter, A. Bib.12 265 No.140; and 1685 No.141) and Rice Watkin's (The Paper Makers and Paper Sellers Petition of 1690 BM. Cup.645.b.11 a cursive "W" and identified in a later "Addition to the case of the Paper-Sellers") other than Burnaby's and George Gill's (?) the inference is that English countermarks in a few cases could have been just as early as Burnaby's. Quelch could have been making White countermarked paper at Wolvercote at any time after 1674; and Rice Watkins could have been active at Sutton Courtenay mill by 1672. There may well have been others because there are a significant number of unidentified countermarks of this period (see Chap.III n.36).

[49] For a more comprehensive definition of White paper see Chapter V.

otherwise easily become an over–simplified picture of White paper manufacture in England *before* the 18th C., such as one might gain from certain sources of contemporary comment.[50]

In the last two decades of the 17th C. this question of White versus Brown paper manufacture, and the claims as to who could or could not make it, came to a head when the COMPANY brought their case for a monopoly in White papermaking before Parliament in 1689. The Bill was eventually passed and they obtained their monopoly, short–lived though this proved to be. For this book the main interest lies in their technical contribution (Chap.V); but it is the opposition that they provoked from the rest of industry that is of particular significance in the present context.

The passage of the Bill through the Commons and the House of Lords has been described in detail by Cameron.[51] The main features of this campaign are (a) the strength of the opposition; and (b) some of the implications that arise from the objections that came from the paper makers. As much of the industry at that time was concentrated around London, the opposition came from the counties immediately to the West of London, Buckinghamshire being the principal source; and Surrey and Kent. Initially, the COMPANY'S case was met with objections from Hagar and the case of many hundred paper makers and owners of paper mills; the Dean of Windsor and Lady Theodosia Ivy. Some of these petitions have been lost, but their case was re–stated in a Petition of the Paper Makers and Paper Sellers, referred to earlier, and the points which emerge from this are:

(i)   The paper makers claimed that they could not make their mills pay, if they were prevented from making (the much more lucrative) White paper. The inference from this statement is that many of them must have already been making White paper, a manufacture which they did not wish to be deprived of.

(ii)   In the past their trouble had been that they were consistently undersold by the French. The inference here is that, even if they had not been able to sell White paper because of this, they had the capability of making it and wished to make the most of the current embargo (1689–1697).

(iii)   In the first paper makers' petition the claim was made that the Ancient Paper Makers had had twenty years experience in making White paper to the COMPANY'S three or four. This theme, in different forms, appears repeatedly in later Petitions e.g. after referring to the fact that prior to the COMPANY'S application for a monopoly "Mr. Burnaby and Mr. Hager (besides Sir John Spelman mentioned in the Paper–Sellers Case) have had Patents at the same time for the making of White,Writing and Printing Paper, and that the same hath been an Antient *English* Manufacture, and the making thereof a settled Trade in this Kingdom and by many now used and exercised...."(Paper Makers). If the original claim of the Ancient Paper Makers bears any resemblance to

[50]   Coleman, D.C. Bib.15 48–59 in covering the post–Spilman period to 1720 provides examples of attempts to establish White paper manufacture before 1680 and cites some of the contemporary comments on this sector of the industry. From these one might get the impression that it was all a total failure and a hopeless task. This was no doubt largely true; but, at the same time, one has to account for the appearance of White paper manufacturers like George Gill (and others) by 1680 and none of these to our knowledge had been trained by the current influx of refugees. One has to seek some explanation for their appearance (see Chap.II).

[51]   Cameron, W.J. Bib.18.

the truth, then they must have been in this business as early as 1669. As will be demonstrated later there may be some truth in this claim.

(iv)   After the Bill had gone to the House of Lords a re-edited version of the Paper Sellers' and Paper Makers' Petitions in *manuscript* form[52] was signed by 14 Ancient Paper Makers, 5 from Buckinghamshire; 6 from Kent;[53] 1 from Berkshire and 1 from an unidentified mill. They all re-affirmed the points made earlier including a claim that if the Bill went through it would ruin a thousand families of paper makers, who had *served their apprenticeships* and were more skilled in the art of making White paper than the Patentees. Though this is clearly an exaggeration of the situation, it is implicit that the English paper makers had at least served their apprenticeships, whereas many, if not most, of the members of the COMPANY were nothing more than speculators.

Many other points were, of course, made in the various petitions, but they are not particularly relevant to the issue under discussion here.

It might be thought by some that the points made above overstate the importance of the claims made by the Paper Makers. Indeed, in various accounts of this affair the limelight usually falls on the COMPANY and, since they were successful in obtaining their monopoly, the case for the Paper Makers, who are for the most part anonymous, receives less attention than it deserves. If it is examined more carefully the opposition will be seen to fall into two distinct phases; first, general opposition which Cameron believes may have been organised by William Sutton of Byfleet mill in Surrey; and, second, opposition from the Ancient Paper Makers. What had happened was that the original case (and a few later additions), put forward by the Paper Makers, the Paper Sellers, and individuals like the Dean of Windsor and Lady Theodosia Ivy, evidently made an impression on Parliament. When the Bill went before the Committee in the House of Commons a compromise was reached allowing the Paper Makers to make White paper up to the value of 4 shillings a Ream, the COMPANY to make it above that price; and certain concessions were made to the Dean of Windsor, and Lady Theodosia's Patents were to be respected. These concessions split the Paper Makers and at about this time Sutton went over to the COMPANY'S side with the result that much of the Paper Makers' opposition melted away. It left behind, however, a hard core in the form of the 14 Ancient Paper Makers; there may have been others but we only have the signatures of fourteen. They objected strongly on a number of grounds, claiming amongst other things that they had time out of mind made paper from 3 shillings to 20 shillings a ream; they also claimed that they controlled far more paper mills than the COMPANY.

What we are probably seeing here is the division of the industry into those mills that made the cheaper sorts of paper regularly and those mills which made the better sorts, if not the best at times, but who were forced to make the lower grades on occasions;[54] both, therefore, could claim the right to make White paper, but only one of these parties had established a reputation in this manufacture. This notion is supported not only by the claims which the

---

[52]   Historical Manuscripts Commission Rep.xiii. App.Pt.V, House of Lords MSS.272 (15:May:1690).

[53]   The 6 from Kent were Edward Quelch (Dartford No.2); George Gill (Turkey Mill); William Blackwell (Dartford No.1); William Harris (Gurney's mill); James West (Millhall mill); and Alexander Russell (Shoreham mill).

[54]   Harris, John Bib.4 191. Albeit at a rather later date when he noted that George Gill made "very good white paper", he also noted "The Brown and White Brown Paper which they make here is chiefly from Old Ropes and Sails etc...." This was at Turkey mill ca.1716.

Ancient Paper Makers made regarding the higher prices at which they sold their papers, but also in their knowledge of the kind of rags needed for White Writing paper and the prices paid for them, which had in fact risen dramatically. In one of the Paper Sellers' Petitions[55] it is stated, for example, "that there is a considerable number of *Antient Paper-makers now working in Mills very proper for making of Writing and Printing Paper, and have Workmen who by their Experience well know the best way of sorting white Rags to make fine Writing and Printing Paper*". This is evidence, if ever any was needed, that the English makers of White paper at that time knew what they were about.[56]

It is not at all certain what the exact status of the Ancient Paper Makers was. In the literature they tend to be regarded rather as a collection of rustic paper makers who were dragged into the political arena to serve the ends of the Paper Sellers and that when the latter had lost their case they could retire to the obscurity from which they had come. The object here has been to try to dispel this impression and convey instead something that was probably much nearer the truth, namely, that these Ancient Paper Makers represented the real backbone of the domestic British White Paper industry for that period, continuing long after the COMPANY had disappeared into the beginnings of the next century as the forerunners of the 18th C. Master Paper Makers.

One is still left with the question, how Ancient were these paper makers ?[57] It will become clearer later on, when some of them are considered in more detail, that there were a few among their number who may have owed their title to the fact that they were descended from papermaking families of some repute rather than to any longstanding merit of their own performance. One of them, for instance, appeared as a Master Paper Maker only one year before he signed the 1690 Petition; another, according to the best information available, did not become a Master Paper Maker until one or two years *after* he had signed the Petition; both of them, however, could have been descended from established papermaking families, though there is no proof of this at present.[58] In other cases it is known that the paper makers in question were active from a very much earlier date, one possibly as far back as the 1650's and another whose family was making paper in the 1630's; these have an obvious claim to the title of "Ancient".

---

[55] From "An ADDITION TO THE CASE of the Paper-Sellers" BM.Cup.645.b.ll.

[56] With possibly extremely rare exceptions, rags are no longer used by the paper industry to-day (see App.V p.225). It is very unlikely then that any modern paper maker would have the least conception of the skills and experience required of a rag sorter sorting rags for high quality White paper, a seemingly humble occupation. During the 20th C. the mill chemist would have provided data on the general physical and chemical quality of this heterogeneous raw material, the paper maker knowing that quality could be improved at a later stage with an alkali boil and bleaching. Although by the third decade of the 19th C. the paper maker would have had these treatments available to him his control over their effectiveness would have been primitive to say the least of it. Consequently, he would have been proportionately more dependent on the skill of his rag-sorters. If, however, one goes back further to the pre-chemical era of papermaking i.e. where the paper maker had no means of improving the quality of his rag furnish other than with a cold water wash, then one begins to realise that *he was even more dependent on the skill of his sorters.* Although these rags would have been derived almost exclusively from linen, they would have been much dirtier than and potentially just as variable as rags comprised of mixed fibres (see App.V pp.191,257/8).

[57] The word "Ancient" cannot mean "old" here since some of the signatories must have been under 30 years of age. The OED gives as a Noun Ancient B(6) "a title of dignity"; as an adjective (7) "having the experience of wisdom and age".

[58] For more information on William Harris and Alexander Russell, the Ancient Paper Makers concerned here, see under App.II and under App.IV respectively.

This brings us to the end of the 17th C. With the peace of Ryswyck (1697) trade with France was resumed; but, although White paper imports rose rapidly again from 1697 to a record level in 1702 when we were at war again with France, the bulk of the imported paper now came from Holland, Italy and to a lesser extent from Germany;[59] France never regained her former position. The imported White paper, however, put paid to the COMPANY'S activities very rapidly. Since the COMPANY was prevented by the terms of its Charter from making the cheaper sorts of paper, this factor may well have contributed to its decline when faced with foreign competition.[60]

In this condensed account of the early history of the paper industry in England, a stage has now been reached, across the threshold as it were, where one can begin to consider the factors that may have influenced the contribution to English papermaking by the two James Whatman in the 18th C., more especially that of the elder Whatman, the subject of this book. It has not been an easy task, however, to summarise this early history in the space of a few pages and at the same time steer the findings in a direction that will help us understand the more detailed and specialized aspects of the work that follows. Before embarking on this subject it may be helpful to recapitulate, first emphasising those features which have a special bearing on the next phase of this investigation.

The need for an historical setting

Paper made to–day may not be a very inspiring commodity, but this concept must not obscure the quality of the papers made and used universally before the 19th C. Though these have been replaced by an entirely new kind of paper, the one kind is descended from the other and even that kind made before the 19th C. underwent marked changes, particularly among the better qualities known as White paper, paper used for writing and printing. To understand how this evolution came about, what the principal factors were in bringing about change and who the principal protagonists were, how they stood in relation to one another, some sort of historical background is needed.

The establishment of a domestic paper industry in the 17th C. and a capability for White paper manufacture by the end of it; an early history dominated by Entrepreneurs

Modern histories of the industry give the impression that apart from certain well documented entrepreneurs the domestic manufacture of White paper did not gain a footing in the United Kingdom until very late in the 17th C. and even then only a precarious one; and, indeed, some go further than this and claim that it was not until after 1740 that this manufacture became firmly established. Such conclusions are supported by contemporary comment originating most probably from views held by the Stationers who not only controlled distribution but also had a vested interest in importing paper because they could buy it cheaper from abroad than at home, particularly the better qualities. In the main the facts bear this out and as a consequence the origins of domestic White paper manufacture have been neglected, any emphasis being placed on the contribution to this made by the Huguenot refugees towards the end of the century. There is no doubt that important advances were

[59] Coleman, D.C. Bib.15 21, Table II.
[60] Scott, W.R. Bib.43 Vol.III. 63.

made by them (Chap.V), but a closer examination of this incursion lifts the curtain a little and exposes underlying domestic competition; and the fact that it existed at all demands an explanation of its origins. Part I of this chapter then has been written not to deny the general truth of the conclusions reached concerning the early history of this manufacture, but to correct the detail of it, manifested particularly in Chapter II.

Despite an unfavourable environment for the founding of one, the facts are that a rapidly growing and settled domestic industry came into being at the beginning of the 17th C. and with a corresponding decline in the imports of Brown paper this must have been devoted mainly to making this product. This was a significant achievement; and as a by-product it provided a reservoir of skills from which White paper manufacture could have developed where and when circumstances allowed this. Although there is contemporary evidence that Spilman's mill continued to produce White and Brown paper during this period, initially European production, which enjoyed the advantages of greater experience, abundant raw materials, cheaper labour and a larger market, would have militated against the pursuit of the uneconomical operation that faced the domestic paper maker; in any case the absence of a provincial printing trade denied the local paper maker a ready market for such paper.

The early history of the industry is studded with names like Tate, Bishop Thirlby, Sir Thomas Gresham, Spilman and Burnaby who came and went contributing no noteworthy technical innovations to the industry; as entrepreneurs they merely financed an operation that had altered little over four centuries, some surviving only under stringent monopolistic conditions. It was not until late in the 17th C. that potentially significant advances in technology made their appearance, advances that in the right hands could improve the quality of White paper and the economics of its manufacture; but the realization of this lay in the future.

Meanwhile the other side of the coin displayed the steady growth of a domestic industry and accompanying skills, be it for making Brown or White paper (it matters little), which rendered this country progressively less dependent on continental sources supplying either of these classes, particularly in the second half of the century when international tensions and trade embargoes created increasing opportunities for the manufacture of White. It was clearly from this reservoir that a corpus of paper makers which included the Ancient Paper Makers must have been enlisted who made the better, if not the best, qualities at times; in short the domestic competition that confronted the immigrants.

In response to this threat the immigrants formed a joint stock company, petitioned successfully for a monopoly to make White paper and secured for themselves, by fair means or foul (Chap.V), a wide range of Patents to support their claims. Undoubtedly the Huguenot refugees brought with them better ways of doing some things and managing scarce resources, both of which must have stimulated in due course an equivalent response from our native paper makers. Although temporarily vanquished by the COMPANY it was the Ancient Paper Makers and others of like mind who were to survive into the next century as a formative influence on the future of British papermaking. But, as will become apparent in Chapter II, this is not the whole story; the omission lies in a failure to account for the origin and training of this "reservoir of skills", especially in those places where they were to prove most effective. Unlike the Brown the development of a White industry, other than technical considerations, had to cope with numerous obstacles in its path. Nevertheless the potential, if not the actualization, for this existed and grew in parallel in the latter half of the century.[61]

Raising the potential for change

By the turn of the century the technical potential for achieving this goal was there and in retrospect one can see that the industry was on the threshold of a new era albeit at that point in a position of stalemate. For the most part the basic process remained unchanged,[62] but a new element was emerging that increasingly characterises the new era. The entrepreneurs were to be superseded in the 18th C. by a generation of Master Paper Makers in direct control of their mills, a trend dating well back into the 17th C.[63] One might describe this development in terms of two separate curves, one representing the Entrepreneurs in decline with the other ascendant curve of the Master Paper Makers. But even these new paper makers would have failed to overcome the difficulties of this critical phase in the successful development of *a viable* English White paper industry had it not been for important changes that were to take place in the decades that followed.

---

[61] Coleman, D.C. Bib.15 fig.2 facing p.90 shows that although White paper imports continued at a high level and did not decline significantly until ca.1740, the increasing demand for this paper was clearly being met by increased domestic production. In fact, by 1721 it was estimated that we were producing about two–thirds of our total needs in Brown and White. (Chap.III).

[62] Minor modifications here and different practices there might have led to paper mills in one region showing more progress than in another. But the basic process remained unaltered until about the mid–17th C.; even then, it showed that fundamental changes were taking place, slowly, only in Holland.
It has been suggested that perhaps English paper mills may have been slow in replacing the undershot with the overshot waterwheel as a source of power. It is possible that this might have accounted for the failure of mills in some areas; but certainly in Kent, where the White paper industry became established at an early date, most waterwheels were overshot by the end of the 16th C., if not at an earlier date (see Chap.VI).

[63] The 17th C. mills had clearly been managed by Master Paper Makers, but these had been subservient figures to the promoter of the enterprise, not a free agent and few, if any, emerge as positive figures until late in the century. The new Masters would either have served an apprenticeship or had a good working knowledge of papermaking, directing their mills without any external interference.

PART II

THE EARLY 18TH CENTURY

The Changing Situation

By the end of the 17th C. the seeds of change had all been sown and the first few decades of the 18th C. may be regarded as a period of gestation rather than one of effective implementation towards any definite goal. Imports of White paper during this period continued to overshadow the trade and the domestic industry was still in an emergent stage. One of the most important factors in bringing about a change in this state of affairs was the introduction of the New Duties in 1712. Unquestionably over the next 30 years these more stringent tariff measures helped the industry get on its feet so that by the 1740's one finds imports falling dramatically.[64] The picture is not quite as simple as this and there were many other factors that entered into this equation, such as the potential already existing within the White paper industry to exploit this situation; as also a corresponding change in the relationship between the industry and the Stationers; and, later, an increase in productivity that would save materials and improve the competitiveness of the domestic product; then there would be the effects of war and so on. But in all this one eventually comes back to the paper maker, the person who could make it effective.

As one studies the growth of the size of the industry[65] one becomes more and more aware of the names of real paper makers, although their papers are rarely identifiable. For instance, during this period one sees the emergence of paper makers like the French refugees, Henri de Portal and Daniel Roussillon (both with mills in Hampshire), the name of the former becoming one of the most famous in English papermaking and whose family held perhaps the longest contract ever made in the paper industry, namely, one with the Bank of England; Robert Slade (Berkshire); John Bates and Edward Spicer (Buckinghamshire); Thomas Meale and John Beckford (Oxfordshire); John Durham (Gloucestershire); and, slightly later, Edward Band (Somerset) and William Jubb (Surrey). In Kent, to be treated in more detail in later chapters, we have names like George and William Gill; Peter and Richard Archer; the Quelch and Harris families; Andrew Johannot (the patronymic of a famous French papermaking family of the Auvergne); the Russells; and, finally, James Whatman, the elder (1702–1759). No doubt, if more records had survived, or more paper been identifiable, one could add to this list. The important point is that one is now confronted with an ever-growing number of paper

---

[64] Tariffs were raised as early as 1660 and again in 1690, but it was the New Duties of 1712 and the amendments that followed that in the end proved to be the more effective. For further information on this very complicated subject see Coleman, D.C. Bib.15 Chapter V "Taxation and Protection" 122–129 and fig.2 opp. p.90. (The subject is also discussed again briefly in Chapter V of this book; and its ultimate impact in Chapter VII Part II).

[65] In terms of the number of vats, the paper industry in England and Wales virtually trebled in size during the 18th C. The figures given below are based on Shorter, A. Bib.9 75–78, 104, but are no more than estimates:–

(Date)	(No. of Mills)	(No. of Vats)
1711	200	250
1738	278	338
1785	380	–
1800	425	750

makers who can be associated with certain mills and districts; who can be identified at this time, or later through their successors, with the production of the better qualities of White paper; and who, in some cases, can be shown to have had an influence in advancing the technology of this industry.

To complete the picture of this background we need to know something about the general location of the White paper industry of this period; in addition we need to know the reason for choosing Kent as an area for a study of its manufacture and development; and, also, to discover something about the Whatman family in order that we can place the elder of the two papermaking James Whatmans, the principal subject of this book, in a papermaking perspective.

The Location of the White Paper Industry

The most important uses for White paper were Writing and Printing and the largest markets for this class of paper would have been found in the principal cities and centres of learning. Consequently, in this country one would expect to find that the main concentrations of White paper manufacture at this time (ca.1700–1740) were in the vicinity of London with lower concentrations near Dublin, Edinburgh with others establishing themselves near important cities like Norwich and Bristol.

The earlier statutory restrictions on printing lapsed in 1695. Whereas prior to this date printing in England had been limited to London, Oxford, Cambridge and York, by 1750 more than 50 towns had a newspaper of their own; and, having a local facility for printing, this led in turn to a great expansion in the printing of miscellaneous items such as notices, billheads, catalogues etc.[66] Undoubtedly this encouraged, where this was feasible, the growth of a White paper industry in the locality.

White mills for this period are not easy to identify and, in any case, many of them were almost certainly mixed brown and white mills making small quantities of White paper, if an opportunity for this arose.[67] What can be said is that since the main concentrations of paper mills (brown and white) were located in the vicinity of London, the biggest market, it is in this area that one would expect to find White paper manufacture established and expanding.[68] To judge from the very scarce evidence, this seems largely to have been the case; but this is said with some reservations. Other "white" mills had been established near Dublin and Edinburgh, with even more scattered about England (only three identifiable mills of any kind before 1750 in Wales) but these are difficult to associate with any particular market.[69]

---

[66] "The English Provincial Printer" (British Library Exhibition Notes by Alan Sterenberg, 1983).

[67] A good example of this type of mill was Barton Mill, Canterbury, Kent, which ground oats as well as making both Brown and White paper (Further references to this mill and its occupants will be found in Chapter II).

[68] Maps showing the distribution of paper mills (all types) in England from 1495 onwards (and from 1651 onwards in periods covering 25 years) may be found in Shorter, A. Bib.12 92–115; and one specifically for 1690 in Bib.9 30).

[69] The two most prominent mills in Oxfordshire for this period (Wolvercote and Eynsham) are known to have supplied paper to the University. (Coleman, D.C. Bib.15 93 states that "in the printing of certain books by the Universities of Oxford and Cambridge, and of Scotland, English paper was being used along with foreign in the early years of the century". Cambridge probably obtained such supplies from mills to the West or Northwest of London). In the case of Norwich,

(continued...)

Market considerations aside there were many other important factors that determined the location of paper mills, not least of which would have been the question of adequate and reliable sources of water power, that is not those subject to seasonal effects. In the case of White paper sources of pure water were essential for the process. Obviously there were many other details to take into account, a subject that will be examined more closely in Chapter III, such as the availability of white rags, skilled labour and convenient access to markets etc.; these need not concern us at this juncture.

To meet the demands of London by far and away the largest concentrations of paper mills of all types, active between 1700–1740, were to be found in Kent and Buckinghamshire, with smaller concentrations in Surrey, Middlesex, Hampshire and Berkshire.[70] Based on very diffuse information, e.g. from what we know about the Ancient Paper Makers together with certain other paper makers and their mills, it seems probable that the numbers of White paper makers within these concentrations may have followed the same pattern. A *very rough guesstimate*, based on Shorter's "English Paper Mills" produces the following result:

[69](...continued)

which up to the end of the 17th C. was the second city in the country, there were also 2 mills capable of supplying at least printing quality early in the 18th C.; but due to the generally low profile of the river system, possibly the quality of the water and the general decline of the city itself, Norfolk never became an important papermaking county (and the same really applies to the whole of East Anglia). In the West country there were important mills such as Wookey Hole (Somerset), Postlip (Gloucestershire), possibly one or more of four 17th C. and three early 18th C. mills in Worcestershire and similar numbers in Shropshire that may have kept Bristol supplied with White paper as well as other cathedral cities in the Midlands. The situation is complicated by the fact that in some of these outlying areas paper made there was often shipped to markets elsewhere e.g. London, so that one cannot necessarily identify small groups of mills in these districts with a local market. Coleman (ibid. 58) mentions several ports like Southampton, Rochester and other south coast ports from Exeter to Falmouth handling quantities of English made paper. There were quite considerable concentrations of paper mills in Lancashire and Yorkshire, with others scattered in neighbouring counties. A lot of these undoubtedly made Press papers for the wool industry, but there must have been some amongst them capable of supplying the White paper needs of York (e.g. Thornton–le–Dale, White from late 17th C. paper maker, William Warren), Durham and other cities in the North. Paper had been made in both the Dublin and Edinburgh areas since 1590 and during the first quarter of the 18th C. many new mills were established in the vicinity of Edinburgh (see Shorter, A. Bib.9 Chap.8); and a similar picture for the Dublin area (see Shorter, A. ibid. Chap.9).

[70] Shorter, A. Bib.12 has a series of maps showing the location of paper mills (all types) in England and Wales for various periods. From these it can be seen that very roughly just under 40% of the paper mills lie within a radius of ca.70 miles of London for the period 1700–1750. These maps do not appear to show all the mills that excise figures indicate (see this chapter note 65). The number and distribution of the mills in the London catchment area, shown below, are taken instead from Shorter's App.B. They must be regarded as *very approximate* and show only those mills (all types) active between 1700–1740.

County	Number of Mills
Kent	24 (+ 3 ?)
Buckinghamshire	21 (+ 3/4)
Surrey	10 (majority in the West of the county)
Middlesex	6
Hampshire	12
Berkshire	7

It is very difficult to be precise about these numbers. Those for Kent are reasonably certain, but in other areas one finds some mills with 17th C. origins difficult to trace with any certainty in the 18th; and others mentioned, say, for the first time in 1745 but which may have existed earlier.

MAIDSTONE AREA

No.	Mill	River/Stream	Type
1.	Forstal mill	Cossington Stream	White
2.	Cobtree mill	Sandling Stream	White ?
3.	Millhall mill	East Malling Stream	White
4.	Turkey mill	River Len	White
5.	Poll mill	River Len	White
6.	Otham mill	River Len	
7.	Lower Tovil mill	River Loose	
8.	Upper Tovil mill	River Loose	
9.	Ivy mill	River Loose	
10.	Gurney's mill	River Loose	White
11.	Upper mill	River Loose	
12.	East Malling	East Malling Stream	
13.	Snodland	Leybourne Stream	
14.	Old mill, Hollingbourne	River Len	White

WEST KENT

No.	Mill	River	Type
15.	Dartford No.1 mill	River Darent	White
16.	Dartford No.2 mill	River Darent	White
17.	Eynsford mill	River Darent	White
18.	Shoreham mill	River Darent	White
19.	Basted mill, Wrotham	River Shode	White

NORTH KENT

No.	Mill	River	Type
20.	Sittingbourne mill		White ?

EAST KENT

No.	Mill	River	Type
21.	Buckland mill, Dover	River Dour	
22.	Barton mill, Canterbury	River Stour	White
23.	River mill, Dover	River Dour	
24.	Chartham mill	River Stour	White

SOUTH KENT

No.	Mill	River	Type
25.	Goudhurst mill	River Teise	

(May have been closed down by 1700.)

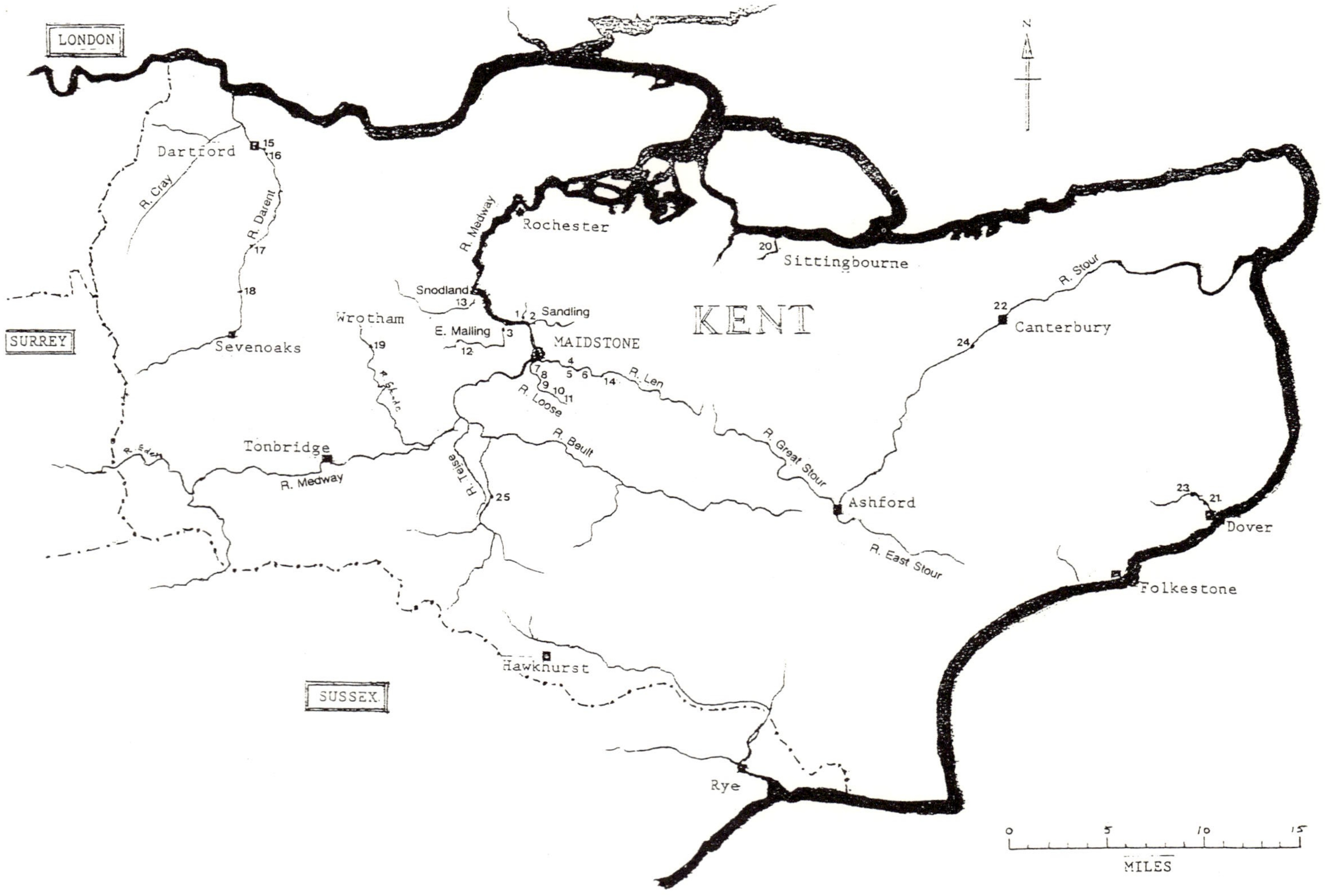

Map 1 – THE PAPER MILLS OF KENT DURING THE PERIOD 1700-1740

County	*Approx. No. of White Mills act.1700–1740*		
Kent	13	+	2 ?
Buckinghamshire	7	+	3 ?
Surrey	2	+	3 ?
Middlesex	3		
Hampshire	3	+	3 ?
Berkshire	3	+	1 ?

These figures must be regarded *only* as a very conjectural indication of White papermaking capacity in the counties round London. A great deal depends on what sort of definition of White paper one applies to this kind of estimate; how much might have been made at a given mill;[71] and as to whether more or fewer mills should have been included in this list, either because of their past record or possibly because they may have been making White paper a few years after 1740, the limit set for this. The information is probably good enough for us to come to the conclusion that *Kent was close to being, if not actually, the most important White papermaking county in England by 1740.* If it were not for the fact that in this book our main concern is with the elder Whatman, this conclusion alone would justify the choice of this county for an initial study of domestic White paper manufacture in the 18th C., influencing proportionately any conclusions that might be drawn from an extension of this work. In the event it was not the numbers of mills that wrought change, but the work of individual paper makers.

The Location of Paper Mills in Kent during the period 1700–1740

Map No.1 opposite shows the location of the paper mills and the key to the numbers is given below. The mills have been grouped into 5 areas and these same areas will be referred to again in the chapters that follow. The right hand column indicates the probable potential of a given mill for making White, even though it may have been the "cheaper sorts"; but this assessment must be qualified by saying that even the most famous of these mills, Turkey Mill, was forced on occasions in the very early decades of the century to make Brown paper as well as White; and although we know that Barton Mill, Canterbury, sometimes made White paper, one's guess is that more often it was making Brown.

---

[71] Ignoring county boundaries, the chain of mills in Buckinghamshire, Berkshire and Middlesex, together with a few in western Hampshire, may have produced more White paper than Kent. But one has to take into account in this equation the number of vats per mill. Some like Turkey Mill (Kent) probably had 3 vats during this period and possibly 5 by the end of it. Several other Kent mills had 2 vats.

THE WHATMANS

It will be noticed from the list of paper mills in Kent given above that by 1740 the Maidstone area had the largest concentration of paper mills (all types) in a county that may have had more than any other county in England at that time. In other words it can be seen as one of the most important papermaking centres in the country in terms of the number of mills and even perhaps one of the oldest.[72] It was into this papermaking district, in 1702 in Loose village, that James Whatman, the elder of the two papermaking Whatmans, was born. We shall be looking more closely at his ancestry, his background and circumstances in Chapter III. Only a brief résumé is given below of his ancestry and life up to 1740 merely to place him as a figure in this summarised history of the industry.

The Whatmans were a Kent family that can be traced back to a Laurence Whatman, who died at Hawkhurst in 1469.[73] Over the centuries the family, which had no known connection with the paper industry, gradually migrated northwards and by the 17th C. had become widely dispersed among the principal parishes of the High Weald of Kent; the branch that we are particularly interested in had moved to Brenchley (a village about 10 miles South West of Maidstone) ca. 1550 and thence to Loose, just outside Maidstone, in 1688, where the father of the first papermaking Whatman, also a "James", settled as a tanner. His son and heir was born there in 1702 and inherited his father's trade and tan yards in 1726; and, it seems, until the time of his marriage in 1740 he was described as a "Tanner of Loose". And then, quite inexplicably, the histories and biographies transform him into a famous paper maker, another landmark in the history of English papermaking.

From what has been said already about the earlier history of English papermaking, one might well ask if James Whatman, the tanner of Loose, was any different from John Tate, the mercer; John Spilman, the jeweller; and Eustace Burnaby, the gentleman barley miller, all of whom contributed nothing more to their papermaking enterprises than money ? But the events of his later years prove that he was someone very different from these. "James Whatman" has been dubbed "England's greatest Paper Maker". Whether one would agree to such a title or not, the problem with this accolade is that it has usually been associated with his better known son, many people formerly believing that there had been only one James Whatman. Thomas Balston in his biography of the two papermaking Whatmans[74] has since put the record straight. Nevertheless, the fact remains that beyond knowing something of the father's remarkable achievement in the 1750's (and even the significance of this has not been fully appreciated),[75] virtually nothing has been forthcoming in the existing accounts of his early years, which could explain his sudden transformation into a paper maker of some standing.

---

[72] In 1567, more than 20 years before Spilman's venture into papermaking, reference is made to the "Makers of White and Browne paper" in both the Petition made by and the Patent granted to the Mayor, Juratts and Cominaltie of Maidstone concerning the settlement of Protestant refugees from the Netherlands. (State Papers Domestic 9 Eliz. Vol.43 No.19 June 1567 and Patent Rolls Eliz. Part 4 No.1033 Nov.1567). It is not known, however, whether paper makers were in fact among those who ultimately found refuge in Maidstone. This subject is discussed in more detail in Chapter II, where a case, albeit purely speculative, can be made out for this.

[73] For a pedigree of the Whatman family (to 1766 only) and Notes on this see App.II.

[74] Balston, T. Bib.1.

[75] This failing is clearly exposed in work completed, but as yet unpublished, by the author, covering the invention and development of wove paper by the elder Whatman and the implications of this in terms of White paper manufacture; and, indeed, in its effects on the future course of the paper industry itself (Bib.76).

Any experienced paper maker will know that there must have been more to this than is usually implied in the histories of the industry, particularly if the authors were not conversant with the technology of the period or the skills of the trade.

One of the main objectives of this work then will be to discover, if possible, more about his early history and especially those reasons which may have persuaded him to change from his inherited occupation as a tanner and to become a paper maker instead. But this is not all; anyone is free to change his business, but it is not in everyone's power to re-shape, uplift, expand and steer his exchanged occupation in an entirely new direction. In order to try to find an explanation for this one must clearly go beyond personal considerations and search for any influence there may have been within the industry that might help us understand how this came about.

These questions are examined in the Chapters that follow. Chapter II, for example, is devoted to an investigation of the origins and development of papermaking in the Maidstone district as a prelude to exploring the environment in which the elder Whatman was born and grew up; and Chapter III concentrates on "testing the evidence", evidence which consists of certain isolated facts about Whatman that have come to light in the last twenty years or so and which have not so far received the attention they merit. They are examined there in some detail and from varying viewpoints to see if anything can be deduced beyond the bald evidence they present to us. Up till now so little has been discovered about this important paper maker that it is vital that as much information as possible is extracted from the few facts we have in order to reconstruct a plausible picture of the man and the situation that existed then.

In spite of this it will become obvious that there are still many unfilled gaps in this history and resort has to be made to *assumptions*, made on the best evidence available, to bridge these. To support these assumptions and the conclusions reached in this work the text is followed by 5 Appendices containing detailed back-up information. Appendices I–III contain information on the paper mills in the Hollingbourne area and in the Sandling Ward of Boxley parish, both villages in the vicinity of Maidstone, together with what is known about their occupants and others indirectly associated with them; it will be seen from this that one obtains a revealing picture of the local environment. Appendix IV gives similar information on the origins of the early Maidstone paper makers as well as an account of two other early Kent paper mills. Finally, Appendix V is made up of sections covering various aspects of the contemporary papermaking process and allied subjects. For a proper understanding of the text these appendices should be consulted; in addition they may also serve as a source of information for those who might wish to extend this work in another direction.

PART III

THE PAPERMAKING PROCESS IN GENERAL USE IN BRITAIN AT THE BEGINNING OF THE 18TH CENTURY

A. An outline of the process.
B. The papermaking mould.

The nature of White paper is discussed later in this work;[76] the process in general use in this country is described below, the emphasis being on the phrase "in general use" because the 18th C. saw the process in a state of transition. Whichever state the process was in, it is a common error, often manifesting itself in the literature dealing with the history of papermaking, to interpret the older processes in terms of the hand–making process known to us to–day. There are, of course, many similarities; but, at the same time, there are major differences. If one takes the White paper of to–day, there are many differences between this paper and the White paper made during the first half of this century; going back into the 19th C. one finds a great number of technical changes taking place during that century and these produced papers that were fundamentally different from those made towards the end of the 18th C. as indeed the latter were fundamentally different from earlier papers. In other words one has at least five or even six generations of paper between the paper we know to–day and that made for the period under review. If we are to understand the developments that took place in the manufacture of White paper during the 18th C. (and, equally, for those that took place later), it is important that we should be able to recognize what these differences are and how they may have affected the physical and chemical properties of the paper itself.

The description given below is an *outline* of the process that was in general use at the beginning of the 18th C. Contemporary accounts are *very scarce* indeed and those that have survived have to be read with a certain degree of insight. Probably the best one for this period is Mr. Henry Million's given to John Houghton F.R.S. in 1699.[77] The object of this outline is to give readers who may not be familiar with the handmade papermaking process an idea of the various stages and the terms used so that they will be able to appreciate the significance of the changes in papermaking practices that were taking place.

A. *AN OUTLINE OF THE PROCESS*

1. *The Raw Material : Rags*
In the period (1700–1740) White paper in this country was manufactured from Linen rags.[78] The rags received at the paper mill would have been a mixture of all kinds and qualities. The first step was to *sort* them into grades ranging from the best and whitest quality down to lower qualities, dirtier and weaker rags mixed perhaps with coloured rags and woollens etc., the trash sometimes described as "offal".

---

[76] For further discussion see Chapter V.
[77] Houghton, John Bib.20 Vol.II May–June 1699.
[78] For a more detailed discussion of Rags see App.V.

Plate 2 – Making a Sheet at the Vat

(1)

(2)

(3)

Based on a wood–engraving by H. Brooke (1931)

(1)   Dipping the mould, inclined at an angle, into the stuff.

(2)   The Vatman drawing the mould towards himself to collect up
       the stuff. The back edge of the mould must always be kept
       above the level of the stuff in the vat.

(3)   Levelling out and forming the sheet before all the water has
       drained away.

Plate 3   33

Above: Forming the Sheet.   *Below:* The Formed Sheet

2. *Washing*
The rags were then *washed* with cold water in vessels fitted with false bottoms and gratings at the sides to remove superficial dirt.

3. *Fermenting*
After this the rags were subjected to a *fermenting process*, in which the method and its duration varied considerably from place to place and according to the type of rag. Typically, the rags were placed in heaps or in vessels, wetted and left to sweat and rot for a period that depended on the paper maker's judgement.[79] The period varied from 4 to 5 days up to weeks sometimes. Mr. Million warns "If they be not taken in their time, they'll mildew, discolour and never make good paper; nay, they'll take fire as wet hay will" (May 26th 1699).

4. *Stock Preparation*
This process was divided into 3 stages.[80]

(i) *Breaking* the rags and *Washing* them
The rags were placed in very solid wooden troughs together with water and pounded with hammers armed with pointed nails and raised and lowered by a rotating shaft worked off the mill's waterwheel. The object was to tease out or dismember the woven textiles, converting them back again into their original threads. At the same time water was passed through the trough, escaping with the dirt from the disintegrating rags through a hair sieve and down the drain.

The pulp produced at this stage was known as *First Stuff* or (later) as *Half–Stuff*. The half-stuff was placed in boxes with a sloping bottom to allow the water to drain away, the level of the half–stuff falling as this took place. When drained the level in the box would be made up with additional half–stuff sufficient to meet the needs of the next stage. Sometimes it was left in the box, which must have "no iron work", to mellow for a week "more or less according to the weather".

(ii) *Beating the half–stuff*
The half–stuff, taken from the boxes, was then placed in another set of wooden troughs and pounded with hammers fitted with blunter nails, which had the object of breaking the threads down into their basic fibres. The beaten material, now being in a very finely divided state, was not washed again since this would have resulted in a considerable loss of fibre down the drain.

The pulp produced at this stage was known either as the second–stuff or simply as the *stuff*.

(iii) *Refining and Dilution*
Depending on the effectiveness of the beating operation, the stuff in some mills might have been subjected to further treatment using hammers without any nails. The object of this was

---

[79] The nature of and the reasons for using the fermentation process are given in App. V. The subject is also examined in Chapter VIII pp.359/360.
[80] See Plate 11 & 12, Chapter VI.

to remove any "knots" and "strings" etc. that might have escaped dispersion in the beating process.

Before the stuff could be used in the next stage, the vat, it had to be diluted considerably by the addition of further water. This operation and the thorough mixing of the stuff with the added water could have been done in the same trough as the refining. The *Consistency* of the stuff, as it is known, would thus have been reduced from a porridge–like material to something like thin milk. The diluted stuff was then transferred to the vat, where further dilution would have taken place to suit the kind of paper required.

There were, obviously, variations to this procedure. Mr. Million, for instance, says that after "beating" to produce the "second stuff", the pulp is removed to boxes once again and the beating may be repeated until the stuff "appears as if it were flower and water". Thereafter, "'tis fit for the pit mortar, which has flat hammers without nails".

5. *Making the Sheet of paper : and Sheet Consolidation*
This would have been accomplished in five distinct stages:–

(i) *The Vat*
The vat or the vessel holding the Stuff from which the sheet was to be made may have been of various shapes and sizes. It is frequently illustrated as a large round, cask–like, vessel with a rectangular frame superimposed on it to meet the vatman's requirements. Plate 3 shows a modern vat.[81]

The vatman, standing facing his vat, would pick up a rectangular wooden frame (the *Mould*) faced with a sieve–like wire structure (the *Cover* or facing) and at the same time attach to it another light, closefitting, rectangular wooden structure like a slightly raised picture frame (the *Deckle*) and dip this assemblage into the diluted stuff in the vat. (A contemporary mould and deckle are illustrated in the section that follows this one. See Plate 5).

When the vatman withdrew his mould again, it was done in such a way that a shallow pond of stuff was retained on the face of the mould (held horizontally now) by the raised edge of the deckle (See Plate 2). Then, in a matter of seconds, the water drained away through the wire cover leaving a newly formed *sheet of paper* on the wire face of the mould. In the very short period while the water was draining away the vatman would cause a slight *wave* to ripple across the face of the mould (away from his body) to get rid of the surplus stuff by flipping it over the back edge of the deckle before "closing" or "shutting" the sheet with a slight shaking movement.[82]

---

[81] The specific gravity of cellulose is ~1.53 (crystalline 1.59–1.6 : amorphous 1.47). Whereas rags and paper will float on water for a short time due to the presence of entrapped air, thoroughly wetted and beaten cellulose will sink quite rapidly in water. In order to avoid uneven consistency of stuff in the vat (and as a consequence variable sheet weights) the stuff in the vat has to be stirred frequently either with a paddle or a deckle; modern vats were fitted with a rotating paddle or "hog".

[82] In the very short period between the vatman dipping his mould into the vat and separating the deckle from the mould (very approximately somewhere between 5–20 seconds, varying according to the size and weight of the sheet and the nature of the stuff) the skill of the vatman may be seen (a) in assessing the quantity of stuff that he collects as a pond

(continued...)

The vatman then separated the deckle from the mould, which had the wet sheet still on it, and passed the latter to another member of the vat crew, the *Coucher*. "Passing" is an over-simplification; the vatman actually slides the mould along the "stay", a platform running along the left side of the vat, to a position where the coucher can reach it.

The moulds are always made *in pairs* so that there are two moulds to one deckle. The vatman, having passed the first mould to the coucher, picks up the pair to it, which the coucher has pushed along the *Bridge* (the opposite side of the vat to the vatman) to a position from which he can retrieve it, attaches the deckle and repeats the sheetmaking process while the coucher is dealing with the first mould.

(ii)   *Couching* (pronounced "cooching")
The object of the couching operation is to transfer the newly-formed sheet of paper, in its wet and fragile state, from the wire face of the mould to a *Felt*, which is a piece of fairly coarse woven woollen fabric (rather similar to a blanket and *not* to be confused with "FELT", the material used for hats etc.) slightly larger than the sheet of paper.

The coucher faced in the opposite direction to the vatman and was positioned close to the side of the vat at a point where he could draw the mould that the vatman had pushed along the stay towards himself, raising one edge of it at the same time so that it rested on a vertical strut known as the *Ass*; this allowed more water to drain from the wet sheet on the mould while the coucher pitched a felt in front of him on to a block of wood below so that it would lie flat. He was then ready to couch or transfer the sheet of paper from the face of the mould onto the felt that lay below and before him. (See Plate 4a for the position of the coucher [2] in relation to the vat and the ass).

He then took the mould with the wet sheet on it from the ass, swung it above and across the felt below in such a way that it was suspended in a vertical position with the lower edge resting on the right edge of the felt below him. Then by means of a combined rotary and pressing action he transferred the sheet onto the felt ending with the empty mould once more in a vertical position on the other (left) side and ready to be returned to the vatman along the bridge. Having done this he repeated the cycle, drawing the pair to the other mould towards himself along the stay and raising the edge onto the ass. He then pitched another felt so that it rested exactly on top of the sheet that he had just couched. By repeating this process he built up before him a pile of wet sheets of paper interleaved with felts.[83] This pile, when it reaches a pre-arranged size, is known as a *Post*.

---

[82](...continued)
   on the face of his mould; (b) in forming a sheet that is uniform in thickness and appearance as near as makes no difference in all parts; the back side of the sheet, as we shall see later, known as *la bonne rive* tends to be slightly thicker than the front; and (c) when he gets rid of the surplus stuff, he ends with a sheet that is as near as possible to the weight of the previous sheet and conforms to the basis weight of the kind of paper that he is making, whether it be a tissue on the one hand or an extra-weight, similar to a board, on the other.
   A beginner is quite likely to fall into the vat in trying to lift out the mould incorrectly; and, if he escapes this, he will probably produce a wedge-shaped, badly formed sheet far from any desired basis weight required. A vatman's apprenticeship lasted 7 years and even this training did not necessarily produce a good vatman. A good vatman's skill was a skill of a very high order.
[83]   The Papermaking Felt and the Couching operation are discussed in greater detail in Chapter V.

THE ILLUSTRATION BELOW IS BASED ON AN EARLY 20TH C. WATERCOLOUR
OF ONE OF THE VATHOUSES AT SPRINGFIELD MILL, MAIDSTONE, KENT

This picture illustrates the position of the Coucher (2) in relation to the Vat and Vatman.

On the left of the picture the Coucher has just removed a mould from the Ass (1). On his right is the Felt Board (3) covered with a pile of Felts placed there by the Layer, who is not shown in this picture. The Layer would be away to the right.

The boy shown opposite the Coucher may have been either an apprentice or the Upper End Boy, helping the Coucher arrange his felts.

To prevent a wet edge to the Post the Coucher periodically ran his hand along the right edge of the Post to remove excess water. This excess water was caused by water tending to run down the mould when still in the vertical position and accumulating in the lower edge of the sheet making that side of the Post wetter than the other.

Hemming was another term used by some Vatmen. In order to keep the ends of the Post level and prevent them from sagging, making it difficult for the Coucher to transfer the sheet from the Mould to the Felt, a longer felt was inserted every now and then and the ends tucked in or "hemmed" to counteract any sagging.

It should be understood that historically, and even during this century, there were undoubtedly many variations of the procedures illustrated above. The object here has been to give a general picture of Vathouse operations.

(iii) *Pressing*

The post, resting on its block of wood, was dragged away to a press; a screw–press would have been used at that time. Mr. Million wrote "The coucher whistles and 4 or 5 men come immediately. The post is drawn under the press with two little hooks. The pressing is quickly done with 2 or 3 pulls". This is probably an underestimate of the effort actually required. During this process further dewatering takes place and the sheet is consolidated.

(iv) *Laying*

After Pressing, the post was dismantled by another member of the vat crew, the *Layer*, who separated the now consolidated, but still moist, sheets of paper from the felts, returning the latter to the coucher for use again in another post. He laid the sheets, as he came to them, in a neat pile known as a *Pack*.[84]

It might be said at this point that these first four stages of the sheet–making and consolidating process were carried out by a vat crew working together with a rhythm that ensured that each operation matched the others so that the cycle of circulating the pair of moulds, couching and returning the felts for re–use was not interrupted, causing delays. This means that each member of the crew had to be very adept in the use of both hands carrying out separate operations simultaneously.

(v) *Pack–Pressing*

This was the final stage in the consolidation of the wet sheet. The packs were taken away and placed in the same or another press depending on circumstances and pressed again, but this time with wet sheet against wet sheet. The pressure was applied gradually to prevent the sheets from bonding together. The object was to remove further water. Mr. Million has described this operation very concisely. The pack "'tis set by till towards the end of their day's work (which is about 3 or 4 o'clock in the afternoon; for they begin their day by 3 or 4 in the morning) and then the whole day's work is press'd as before, and set exactly one on another that it looks like one solid Paste Board", that is all the packs (collectively) pressed together.

6. *Drying the Waterleaf Paper* (See Plate 4b)

Mr. Million described this as follows: "The paper is carried up into the *Loft* and hung 6 or 7 Sheets together upon lines fastened to a thing they call a *Tribble*, each containing 30 lines ten or twelve feet long". (The 6 or 7 sheets were known as *Spurs*; and the lines were probably cow–hair ropes).

In the better equipped paper mills the Lofts were carefully sited and fitted with *Louvers* (overlapping boards to admit air but exclude rain) to maximize and control the flow of air through the building.

---

[84] The skill of the layer may easily be overlooked since it appears to be so easily performed. After flipping the top felt back on to the stand (or felt board) beside the coucher, he then has to detach the still wet sheet from the next felt and raise it *without damaging it* and lay it *without wrinkling it* or "breaking its back" exactly on top of the sheet below it; and all this has to be done rapidly and in time with the rhythm of the rest of the vat operations.

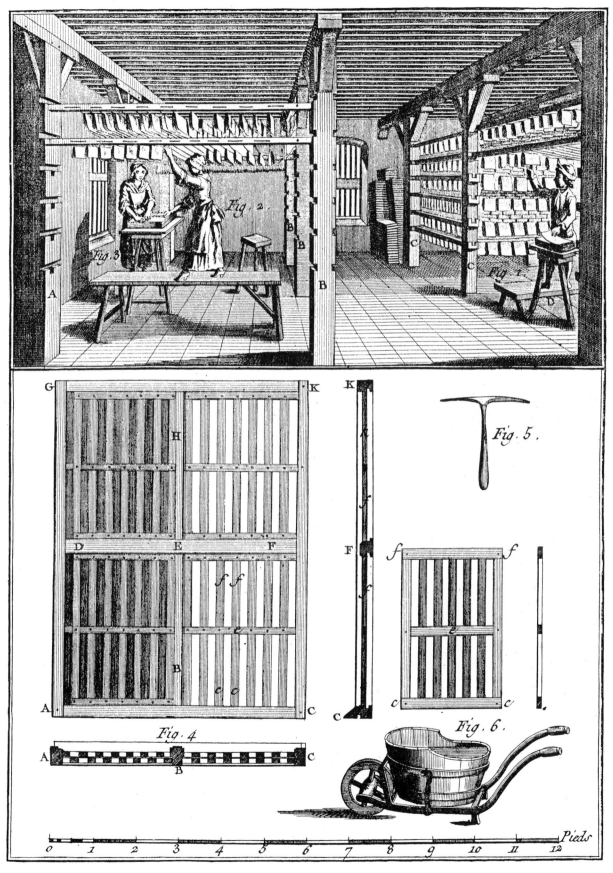

Fig.2   The girls are folding moist (pack–pressed) sheets of paper over a Peel (Fig.5) prior to lifting them onto the tribble ropes (usually made of cow–hair). The Dribbles (Treble) can be seen above the two girls. These consist of a framework for holding the tribble ropes and are slotted into post B at intervals.

Fig.4   This illustrates the Louvers shown here in an open and closed state. These are for controlling the flow of air into the drying loft.

When dried the paper was *taken down*, smoothed and (Mr. Million) "laid in heaps 6 or 7 feet high in a very dry place where it stands till sizing". The paper in this state is known as *Waterleaf paper* i.e. unsized and absorbent.

7. *Sizing*

In the waterleaf state the paper will not bear ink. The paper has to be *sized* and the *Size* used in those days was gelatine extracted from Parchment, Scrowls (scrolls) and Pieces (trimmings from limed and de-haired hides when shaping prior to tanning)[85] etc. to which *"alum"* was added (this was potash alum and not the pure aluminium sulphate used in modern times). Mr. Million's description is worth quoting here:-

"Chusing a fine, dry, temperate day, they put into a copper two barrels of water; and into this, when just warm, sixty pounds weight of clean parchment or vellum shavings; which they boil till it be reduced to a perfect size; then streined through a fine cloth, on which is strewed a due proportion of white vitriol (zinc sulphate)[86] and roch-allom finely powdered, into a tub a foot deep."

"Near to this tub are brought 4 or 5 reams of Paper; and a full gage, or so much as can be taken up with the hands at a time, is dipped into the size, being so hot as the hands can well bear it; and by a certain gentle quick management, it is so ordered, that every sheet shall be sized: after which, it is put regularly (i.e. in a neat pile) into the press, pressed, moved thence into the drying loft, and hung *usually* sheet by sheet (this process is known as *"parting"*) till dry. But note, the direct rays of the sun must not come nigh it till it is dry, for otherwise the size would become drawn out."[87]

The sizing process, it might be added, was one of the trickiest operations in the papermaking process.

---

[85] The object of the tanning process is to render the gelatine in the de-haired hides insoluble with tannic acid obtained from an infusion of gall-nuts or oak bark, probably, in this case. The gelatine-like substances contained in the skin combine with the tannin to form an insoluble compound which, with the modified tissues of the skin, constitute leather. In other words if the gelatine is required as a by-product, it must be obtained from the trimmings of skins to be used for parchment rather than for leather. Likewise, it can be extracted from unwanted parchment as was the case during the First World War when there was a shortage of gelatine.

[86] Zinc sulphate was not added to size normally in modern times. It was added in the past to clarify turbid gelatines and "whiten" discoloured ones (see App.V p.260; it may also have acted as an antiseptic. Its use was frowned on in some quarters.

[87] To obtain satisfactory sizing the gelatine size must be dried from the "gel" state. So after the paper has been immersed in the size bath it has to be cooled to convert the gelatine from the sol to the gel state. In past times this was probably achieved unconsciously as the paper was transported from the size house to the drying loft *and during subsequent parting*. It was important, therefore, that once there, the temperature, whether it was that of the drying loft or exposure to the sun, was never raised to a point where the gelatine film melted and reverted to the sol state. This could lead to patchy sizing or a total failure. Hence Mr. Million's cautionary advice not to allow the paper to be exposed to the heat of the sun while still wet. Equally, the "cooling" had to be achieved moderately i.e. not chilled as might have been the case on a frosty morning. Hence the choice of a "temperate day".

8. *Finishing*

When the sized paper was dry, and in most cases this would have meant *air-dried*, it was taken down, as before, straightened out carefully,[88] smoothed and rubbed to remove felt-hairs, placed in heaps and pressed (in a dry screw press), standing in the press overnight.

After pressing, the paper would have been taken into the *Salle* and *sorted* for various defects.[89] Printing papers were *not* finished as the paper would have been moistened again before printing and any "finish" would have been nullified. For the finer sorts of paper a glazing process may have been used. This may have taken the form of hammering or the use of a glazing wheel to buff the surface.[90] Probably in most cases the paper would have merely received another dry pressing. The paper was then counted into *quires* and *reams* and (Mr. Million) *bales* consisting of 10 reams. Unlike to-day the quires were folded, *broken* sheets put between them; and the worst quires were placed on the *outsides* of the ream when being packed and tied up in *Wrappers* "made of the settlings of the fat" (or vat bottoms as they would have been known to-day).

9. *Yield*

Figures are sometimes given in papermaking histories for quantities of rags, for example, imported for papermaking. We can only guess to-day what sort of quantities of acceptable paper these may have yielded. Even in the best managed hand-making process of to-day, with multiple operations to carry out particularly those involving the handling of paper in the wet state, a considerable amount of damage is bound to occur, resulting in undesirable levels of rejects judged by modern process standards. With the aid of steam and modern machinery some of this waste is recoverable for re-use in papers of a rather lower quality. Although the scalding of damaged sized paper was practised in the past, it is unlikely that it was very effective. To this waste then may be added the losses occurring in the preparative stages, which must have been considerable in the fermenting, rag-breaking and beating operations, as well as in the initial sorting of the rags, which were often covered in filth. If, in addition, one takes into account the possibility of short weight and high moisture contents (particularly in rags brought in by sea), in the author's view (and it is purely a personal view) the 18th C. paper maker would have been lucky to have got a 60% yield from the rags he had purchased. (With high quality rags and good management, yields might have improved later in the 18th C. to, say, 70%; still a low figure).[91] [For an illustrated account of Papermaking by Hand, albeit a description of the process as it is to-day, see Green, J. Barcham Bib.40].

---

[88] Sheets containing gelatine size and dried hanging over ropes would have set stiffly in a folded shape, particularly in warm dry weather. To avoid breaking the back of the sheet, the paper had to be flattened carefully and then pressed. In large sheets of paper creasing may sometimes be observed running down the spine of the sheet from front to back. This could also have been caused during the sizing process where large sheets had to be sized folded over a stick; or, again, it may have resulted from drying over a rope clogged with size or from size draining away from the point of suspension. Paper mills with any sort of reputation to maintain would have sorted these defects out. However, one sometimes finds examples of this creasing in large watercolours where artists (like Girtin, for instance) used cheap wrappers for some of their paintings.

[89] For further notes on defects and sorting standards see Chap.V.

[90] See Chap. V p.191

[91] See Chap III n.78 (If one assumes a 70% yield later in the century, the percentages are not altered significantly e.g. 80% for 1750 and 71% for 1800). At what date paper makers attempted to quantify yields is not known, but J.A. Dusatoy (formerly Hampshire, later Lyng mill, Norfolk) published "The Paper-Makers Ready Reckoner; or calculations to show the prime cost of any ream of paper" (Romsey, Hants 1805). According to the quality of the rags he reckoned yields ranging from 75-87.5%, figures which, if modern methods of measurement had been used, look decidedly optimistic.

Plate 5 – A Single Faced Laid Mould
(1698)

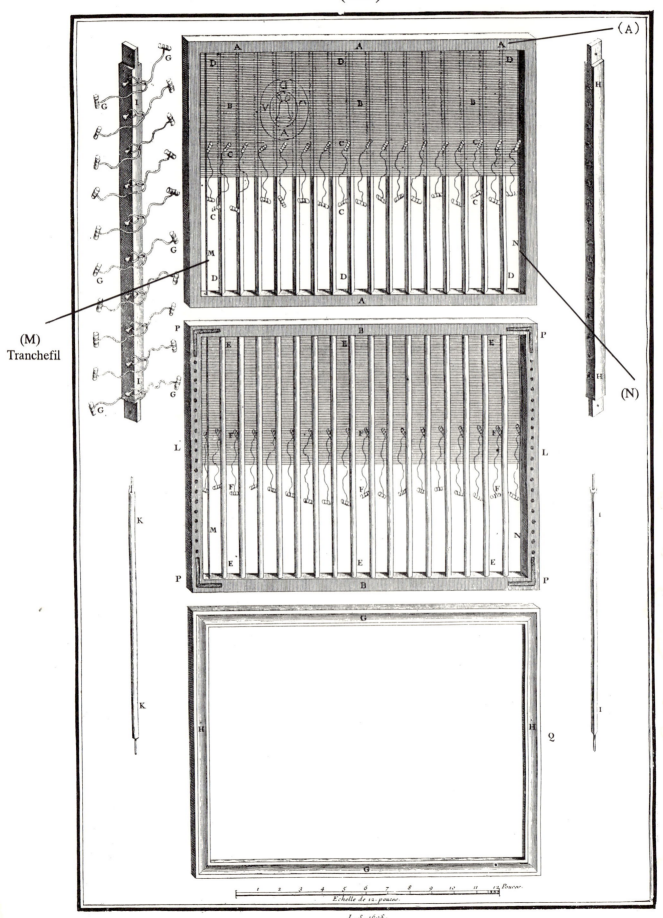

(M)
Tranchefil

B. *THE PAPERMAKING MOULD*

Although the elder Whatman, later in his life, was responsible for revolutionizing the construction of the paper maker's mould, we are not concerned with the details of this in this present work.[92] Certain aspects of mould construction are, however, discussed later (see Chapter V), necessary in order for the reader to appreciate an important innovation introduced towards the end of the 17th C. But there is another point that arises in Chapter III concerning a special kind of wiremark found in early sheets of paper, the cause of the mark being more conveniently discussed here rather than later. This wiremark, known as the Tranchefil mark, is of special interest to bibliographers for a number of reasons, perhaps the most important of these being that the wiremark indicates the position of the edge of the mould in relation to the folding of the paper in a printed work. The occurrence of this wiremark is common in early sheets of paper, though it is not known how universal this was. Certainly, Whatman was using the wires that caused these marks in his moulds in use in the year 1740 and even in those for the year 1757; thereafter he dispensed with them.[93]

Plate 5 shows (top) the upper side and (centre) the underside of a late 17th C. French papermaking mould. The Deckle is shown at the bottom of this illustration and, as mentioned earlier, this is clipped over the upper side of the mould during the sheet–making process.

As can be seen from this illustration, the mould frame (A) is rectangular, made of wood and braced by a series of *Ribs* or *Bars* (D) slotted into the two longer sides of this framework (the Front and the Back of the mould). The ribs support the Wire Cover or facing and ensure that it is rigid and that it does not sag or distort in use. It has to stand up to a good deal of wear and tear.

The cover, in this "single–faced Laid Mould", is made up of *Laid* wires that run transversely and which are relatively rigid and set close together; and *Chainwires,* which are very fine and grouped in pairs, are twisted together during the construction of the facing; they *usually* lie just above each rib (i.e. shown running vertically in Plate 5). Their function is to hold the laid wires in position and, as will be described in Chapter V, determine the spacing between the latter. Both kinds of wire cause wiremarks in the sheet of paper, which may be seen by holding the sheet up to the light and looking through it. (There are no such wiremarks in Wove paper).

In the early moulds there were a pair of chainwires set between the outermost ribs and the mould frame itself (about half–way between) and, therefore, *not* placed above a rib. These wires were known as *Tranchefils*. Their function may have been to act as a kind of selvedge to prevent the laid wires becoming displaced at the edges of the cover. In a sheet of paper made on this kind of mould, the single–faced or "Antique" mould (as it is known to–day), it will be observed that the ordinary chainwire marks are flanked on either side by *Shadows*, caused by the ribs underneath them; the tranchefil wiremarks, having no ribs under them, are shadowless. In Plate 5 these wires are marked as (M) and (N).

---

[92] The construction of the mould is described in detail in the author's work (as yet unpublished) "The Development of Early Wove Papers" (Bib. 76).

[93] The disappearance of these wires is also discussed in the work referred to in the note above. It is quite possible that Tranchefil wiremarks continued to appear in some papers made by the Whatmans after this date, that is as long as moulds of the older type of construction survived.

Chapter II

THE EMERGENCE OF MAIDSTONE
AS A PAPERMAKING CENTRE IN THE 17TH CENTURY

It was demonstrated in Chapter I how the manufacture of White paper had obtained a significant foothold in this country by the end of the 17th C. even if this was at times a somewhat insecure one. This situation changed dramatically during the 18th C. and in order to study more closely the critical phase through which this industry passed it was suggested that, because of the noteworthy concentration of White mills that had come into being there by 1740, Kent should be used as a sample area for this purpose. The details of the evolution of the Kent paper industry have not, however, been examined yet. In the context of the above it is most important that the status of the environment in which the county's paper makers, including the elder Whatman, grew up and its relevance to their achievements should be seen to have a realistic basis, especially that of Maidstone, the main component of this region.

Elucidating the details of this has proved to be *a very difficult* task attributable to an acute shortage of informative documents, a situation inevitably leading to many speculative conclusions which, at first sight, may appear to be too conjectural for the weight they have to carry. However, it will be seen in this chapter that the majority of the early occupants of the Maidstone paper mills can be identified with some certainty. But to determine how these mills came to be there, where their occupants came from and why, is a very different matter, remembering especially in this connection the precept enunciated earlier[1] that paper makers of that era did not appear out of thin air. The evidence used to arrive at solutions to these questions is too complicated to present in full in the text, but the enquiring reader who has doubts and wishes to follow the details supporting the proposals set out below is strongly recommended to consult Appendices III & IV for this information.

With paper mills springing up all over the country at this time[2] and a consequent increase in the number of paper makers it might be asked is there any good reason why the elder Whatman should be singled out and why attention should be focused on his predecessors and his locality. Whatman's case will be considered in later chapters where the reasons for examining these and the associated questions will become apparent. Existing accounts tend to omit these subjects and Whatman is treated as just another, albeit distinguished, member of this growing population. No particular questions are asked; he is regarded as a paper maker who happened to appear on the scene, which might have been anywhere in the country, fortuitously. All this comes about if we view the progress of the industry globally; but it was stressed in Chapter I that if one examines this situation in regional terms, a very different picture emerges. The difference between the two approaches centres on two main features:

(i)   The growth of the industry in Kent; and, in particular, the spectacular growth in the Maidstone district.

---

[1]   See Introduction.
[2]   See Chap. I, n.65.

TABLE I

This Table gives the dates of the first references to paper mills in England and Wales between 1495–1683 based mainly on Shorter Bib.12. The list is divided into three columns:
(i) Mills in Kent; (ii) Mills in other Counties within a radius of ca. 70 miles of London; (iii) Mills in the rest of England

Date	Kent	Surrey, Cambs., Hants., Herts., Mddsx., Bucks., Berks., Oxon., Beds.		Rest of England	
1495		Sele	Herts.		
1550		Fen Ditton	Cambs.		
1554/69				Bemerton	Wilts.
1574		Osterley Park	Mddsx.		
1588	Dartford No. 1				
1598		Horton	Bucks.		
		Wraysbury	Bucks.		
1605		Wooburn	Bucks.		
1610				Wookey Hole	Somerset
1612				Rugely	Staffs.
1617		Warnford	Hants.	Cark	Lancs.
1619				Old Byland	Yorks.
1625		(Unidentified)	Surrey		
1627		Glory Mill	Bucks.		
1630				Hurcott	Worcs.
1631		Sutton Courtenay	Berks.		
1635	(active)	Stoke	Surrey	Longdean	Wilts.
1636		8-9 mills	Bucks.		
		Poyle Mill	Mddsx.		
		Isleworth	Mddsx.		
	Buckland (Dover)	Hounslow	Mddsx.		
1639				Wick	Glos.
				Countess Weir	Devon
1641	(active)	Longford	Mddsx.		
		Harefield	Mddsx.		
		West Drayton	Mddsx.		
1645				Hewell	Worcs.
1645/50				Beoley	Worcs.
1648	Eynsford			Perry Bar	Warwick.
1649		Sopwell	Herts.		
1650	(active)			Langley	Salop.
				Seales	Worcs.
1651				Pincock	Lancs.
1655				Cound	Salop.
1656				Norton	Yorks.
1657	Goudhurst			Cossington	Leics.
1658		Eashing	Surrey		
		Cookham	Berks.		
1660	(active)	Catteshall	Surrey	Leeds	Yorks.
1663		Hatfield	Herts.		
		Curdridge	Hants.		
1664		Dernford	Cambs.		
1665	Barton (Canterbury)				
1666		Bedhampton	Hants.	Great Bolas	Salop.
	(active)			Monk Bretton	Yorks.
1669				Exwick	Devon.
1670				Armetriding	Lancs.
1671	Forstal				
1672		Wolvercote	Oxon.		
1673	(active)	Byfleet	Surrey		
1674	?			Bulwell	Notts.
				Farnworth Bridge	Lancs.
1675		Bentley	Hants.		
1678	Millhall Mill ?			Chewton Keynsham	Somerset
1679	Dartford No. 2	Stoke	Surrey	Croxdale	Durham
1680	Start of the Maidstone	Tottenham	Mddsx.	Thornton-le-Dale	Yorks.
1681	conversions			Ambleside	Westmorland
1682		Stanwell	Mddsx.		
1683		Eynsham	Oxon.		

In several cases Shorter's evidence for the first appearance of these mills is of a tentative nature; some mills, as will be seen later, had been in existence for several years, even decades, prior to the dates shown. In other cases some of the mills listed had a brief existence only and had disappeared before the end of the period covered. Since the lists are based mainly on information from one source (dated 1957) more recent research could alter the distribution shown above significantly. For comment on its general reliability see opppsite. The Table is used here purely for purposes of comparing the general magnitude of the different regions.

(ii)   The change in status of the paper maker on the one hand; and his origins and training on the other.

The Growth of the Industry in Kent

To help us understand this situation Table I illustrates the early paper mills of England in order of their appearance and divided into 3 groups: those in Kent; those opposing them in the London market in the West Region; and those dispersed elsewhere in England.

Even when taking into consideration the limitations of the table (set out below it)[3] it is obvious that in the early part of the 17th C. the paper mills, Brown and White, of Buckinghamshire outnumbered those of any other county in the country by a very large margin; and, if one adds to these the paper mills of Middlesex and Surrey, the difference from Kent becomes so great (ca. 22 : 2 ca. 1640) that one wonders whether Kent was entitled to call itself a papermaking county.[4] Even by 1660 when Forstal mill (Kent) had come into service[5] the margin (now ca. 26 : 6) was still very large. In terms of quality and output these differences may have been less significant. Many of the West of London mills would have made Brown paper in the corn–cum–paper type of mill, some of them falling into decay by the end of the century. However, these differences in number are of interest at this point not so much for any significance they may have in terms of output and quality but rather for the differences in potential that they offered for the further enlargement of the industry and, in particular, for the training of paper makers to implement this.

First, it has to be shown that this growth of the industry in Kent was significant; and, second, in which direction it lay. Both of these trends are illustrated in Table II. There are several points to note about these figures:

(i)   The same limitations apply as to the numbers of paper mills given here as to those in other general sets of figures in this work; it is reasonable to draw certain conclusions only where the margins between one set of figures and another are very large.

(ii)   The figures in this Table represent the number of mills making all types of paper i.e. Brown or White or both and they in no way indicate capacity.

(iii)   The division into periods is quite arbitrary; this can affect the results shown in the growth column quite considerably. For example, up to 1740 Berkshire (according to Shorter) had only 7 paper mills giving a growth factor of 3.5 compared to the 5.5 shown in the Table. Likewise Kent, according to these figures, only just manages 6 mills by 1675, so that its growth factor really lies somewhere between 4.2. and 5.0.

(iv)   Whereas Kent can be considered as an isolated Region on its own, relative to the London markets, the counties lying to the West are arbitrary geographical divisions unrelated to the locations of the industry or indeed to some of the markets some of the mills may have served. Shorter's maps (Figs.3–6) indicate the

[3]   The Note below Table I will be seen to be especially relevant later in this chapter. Recent searches have shown that quite a number of Kent paper mills had an earlier origin that those shown by Shorter. But since the Table is used here for comparative purposes only (and even this on an approximate scale) this factor could apply equally to the mills in the other columns. So in these circumstances it has been decided to stick mainly to Dr. Shorter's figures for this purpose.

[4]   Postulating the existence of one or two as yet undiscovered mills that may have operated in Kent in this early period would clearly reduce this differential; but as noted above the same assumption could apply equally to the West of London Region.

[5]   The early history of Forstal mill, Kent, is discussed in greater detail later in this Chapter and in App.III.

TABLE II

Illustrating growth in the numbers of paper mills round London in 25–year periods
between 1651–1750. Figures taken from Shorter, A. Bib.12, Maps, Figs. 3–6.

County or Region	Arbitrary Date Brackets				Growth Factor in 100 yr.	Line
	1651–1675	1676–1700	1701–1725	1726–1750		
Herts.	2	2	3	4	x 2	1
Hants.	4	6	10	14	x 3.5	2
Berks.	2	4	7	11	x 5.5	3
Middsx.	5	7	6	6	x 1.2	4
Surrey	4	5	8	12	x 3.0	5
Bucks.	12/13	15	20	25	x 2.0	6
West Region	~20	~27	~39	~48	x 2.4	7
60 mile Radius	~28/29	~37	~52	~67	x 2.4	8
KENT	6	15	23	27	x 4.5	9
MAIDSTONE	1	8	13	14	x 14	10

NOTES

1. It should be noted that the figures for the numbers of mills in these regions given in Chapter I (note 70) refer to a period ending in 1740 so that in some cases the totals will differ from those shown above.

2. Bedhampton mill has been included in the Hampshire line shown above. Shorter indicated this mill as doubtful; but documentary evidence (see App. IV under Thomas Willard) suggests that it may have been active in 1666.

3. The Hertfordshire line (1) has been compiled from other, later, sources (Bib. 69).

4. The Surrey line (5) has been amended to conform with figures published by Professor A.G. Crocker (1988) omitting two mills classified by Shorter as belonging to Hampshire.

mills lying within a 60 mile radius of London (line 8 of the Table); but this includes a number of mills that clearly served other markets than London, for example, 2 mills near Oxford and probably Dernford mill near Cambridge.[6]

The Table, therefore, includes a selection of mills (line 7) in the West Region whose production was more likely to have been oriented towards London. But even this is only an approximation because it does not include some of the mills in South Hampshire that shipped their paper to London via Southhampton.[7]

It should only be regarded then as an *approximate* indication of the relative growth of the industry round London. Nevertheless it shows clearly that the growth in Kent was above average and quite spectacular for the Maidstone area, exceeding that of each of the counties shown in the top section of the Table (lines 1–5).[8]

It can thus be seen to answer one of the points made earlier. It shows that after 1675 the direction of the expansion in Kent, which embodied a high proportion of White paper manufacture, was almost exclusively towards the Maidstone area. The latter in itself represented by 1740 a very important sector of White papermaking in a county which in Chapter I was close to being, if not actually, the most important centre for this in England.

It is clearly to the point to discover how and why this came about. But before considering this question it will be more appropriate to address the other point referred to, namely, the origins, training and status of the paper makers concerned. These figures belong unmistakably to the new ascendant generation of Master Paper Makers that "came on stream" during the 17th C. and whose origins in the case to be considered were quite different from and owe nothing directly to the declining régime of entrepreneurs.

It is beyond the scope of this work to try to trace Kent papermaking to its absolute origins; but it is very relevant to bring the situation in the Maidstone area towards the end of the century into as sharp focus as possible. Because of the shortage of information already referred to one has to resort to inductive methods using genealogical data, where this can be found, and the association of certain names with papermaking districts in order to form any sort of meaningful picture. Consequently, the rest of this chapter will be concerned very much with names that can either be attributed with certainty or by inference to persons connected with papermaking, the detailed evidence supporting these attributions being found in Appendices III & IV. Later in this chapter Table III and Map 2 summarises this information;

---

[6]   In Chap.I note 69 it was suggested that Cambridge perhaps obtained its supplies of English White paper from the West London Region; no mention was made there of Dernford paper mill, which had been active from 1664 (Shorter, A. Bib.12 147) and whose lease as a prospective White mill had been considered by one William Tubb of Middlesex ca.1726 (Shorter ibid.57). Whether Tubb took up this lease or not is not known. Shorter, however, does refer to one or more paper mills in the vicinity of Cambridge during the 16th C. and early 17th, only one of these being identified, Fen Ditton after 1550 (ibid. 147 see refs. under Fen Ditton). There is no evidence, however, that any of these mills other than Dernford survived and even this was not considered a very desirable mill site. On balance then it seems probable that White paper came from elsewhere and that Dernford supplied the Brown. (Crocker, A.G. priv.comm. on History of Ewell mill, Surrey, [1989] has suggested that the William Tubb, referred to above, may have been William Jubb snr., the distinguished manufacturer of White paper, who founded Ewell mill ca.1732)

[7]   Coleman, D.C. Bib.15 56, 58.

[8]   The number of paper mills in England virtually doubled between 1690–1710 and continued to increase after this. Table II accounts for only part of this expansion, albeit the main concentration of the industry. Elsewhere the expansion was more dispersed. Significant growth occurred in Nottinghamshire, Yorkshire, Lancashire, Shropshire, Worcestershire and Devonshire.

it is important that the reader should familiarize himself or herself with these names which recur and interconnect throughout this book. But there is a lot of rough ground to be covered first before one reaches this point.

THE ORIGINS OF THE EARLY KENT PAPER MAKERS

General considerations

Sufficient has been said in the preceding pages to show that the art of papermaking was not just a change in direction within some seemingly similar industry such as, for instance, the fulling industry.[9] It was an industry that required both original and exceptional skills and specialised equipment like the papermaking mould, to give one example. The question that arises from this is, in a county with a disproportionately low quota of paper mills for the first half of the 17th C., where did the trained personnel, the know–how and equipment come from to bring about the dramatic change shown in Table II ?

Taking the mills listed in the Kent column of Table I, we can only be reasonably certain of one, possibly two, of these paper mills being engaged in White paper manufacture before 1680, and one of these, Barton mill, Canterbury, would have made it only intermittently at that time, if at all. Even after 1680 the number of White mills would still have been quite small. It would not be too much to say, then, that the source of the skill and know–how required for this level of manufacture could *in theory* be attributed directly to Dartford No.1 mill (Spilman's mill) and its progeny; and later, after 1690, to the reinforcing influences of the COMPANY and to individual paper makers such as Johannot at Eynsford. However, the remaining Kent mills, with the exception of Goudhurst, all survived into the 19th C. and some beyond this, suggesting that some of these mills were of substance even at that time and might therefore have been engaged in making the cheaper sorts of White paper on an intermittent basis; indeed by the end of the 17th C. at least 8 mills were doing just this. When one takes the development of this first generation of mills into consideration together with the expansion of the Maidstone sector in the 1680's, there were too many paper makers involved to be able to assign their training solely to Dartford No.1 mill, even if this had been the case. Where else then could they have been trained ?

One solution to this problem would be to suggest a migration of paper makers from the greatly superior number of paper mills to the west of London to Kent. But what would have attracted them to a county with so few mills and isolated from it geographically by substantial areas without any paper mills at all (East Surrey, Eastern Hertfordshire and Essex) ? Lateral expansion is not a feasible solution to this question; it is not as though paper makers would have had to move only a few miles at most to find new work. Kent lay on the other side of London like an island anything from 45–90 miles away. In a situation like this it would not

---

[9]   It is probably quite true to say (and excerpts below are quoted from the literature) that the conversion of a fulling mill into a paper mill might not have been too difficult an operation "because the machinery for fulling consisted of great wooden hammers raised by a waterwheel which beat the dirt out of the cloth"; but it is a picturesque notion to equate this conversion with the conversion from the fulling to the papermaking process by saying that "they (the hammers) could equally well be used to pulp rags for paper" simply because "at this time the pulping process was the only part of papermaking to be mechanised". With very low quality materials the converters might have got by with this equipment in a Brown paper mill assisted by edgerunners, ropecutters, etc. (see Chap.VI); but pulp preparation, important though this is, is only part of a very complicated process.

be unreasonable then to look first for a Kentish origin for many of the paper makers whom we are concerned with here. The problem in fact lies in trying to trace the origins of those that we know of.

The procedure adopted for discovering the origins of the Maidstone paper makers may seem complicated at first sight. In the main it is because there are serious gaps in our knowledge of the true situation. In many cases the occupants of these mills are known from ca.1670–1680 onwards, but existing accounts do not tell us where they came from or where they received their training. The first question, therefore, is to ask if some, if not all, of them might not have come from the Maidstone district itself on the assumption that paper mills had existed in the district *before* 1670 ? The first task then will be to examine *briefly* what is known at present about any early paper mills that may have been active in the area. If this fails to provide a solution, the next task will be to discover what if anything can be learnt from the 5 Kent mills (outside the Maidstone district) known to have been active before 1670 to see if they provide any leads; and then to proceed from there. It will be seen that helpful information comes from 2 of these mills; but it still leaves many unanswered questions when an attempt is made to fit the evidence into what we already know about the Maidstone district after 1670–1680. To try to resolve some of these problems a more detailed examination of these external sources and those that may have already existed in the Maidstone area follows. It is only then that one can begin to take a look at the reasons why Maidstone became the papermaking centre that it did after 1680.

THE EARLIEST MAIDSTONE PAPER MILLS :
FORSTAL (BOXLEY) AND MILLHALL (DITTON)

Forstal mill is the first paper mill to have been identified in the Maidstone district.[10] It has not been discovered when it was built, but it was active in the 1660's, if not earlier than this. Thomas Taylor is the first recorded occupant; during the 1670/80's the names of several other paper makers appear on the Boxley scene, some who can be placed like Thomas Willard, Peter Musgrove, George Gill and Peter Archer; and others who cannot like Thomas Newman and some like Thomas Radford who may or may not have been paper makers at all. Taking the point made earlier, is one to assume that a long tradition of papermaking at Forstal might account for the presence of some at least of the paper makers listed above ? If not, what alternatives were there ?

The situation is more complicated than this. Recent work by the author provides tentative evidence of the identity of paper makers who preceded Edward Middleton (act.1695–1724)[11] at Millhall mill, Ditton, on the opposite bank of the River Medway to and not far from Forstal. If these proposals are correct, this would take the first operating date of Millhall back to 1677 (the earliest records to be found) and maybe further back than this. In this context perhaps the most important point to emerge is the fact that James West (occupant certainly

---

[10] The question as to whether Forstal had an earlier existence than this or whether there may have been another mill, e.g. Millhall mill that preceded it, will be examined later in this chapter. Details of Forstal mill will be found in App.III; and the early occupants in App.IV together with a discussion of the evidence relating to Millhall mill.

[11] Fuller, M.J. Bib.13.

from 1688–94) was, it is believed, one of the Ancient Paper Makers[12] whose sphere of operation has not previously been located. If this belief is valid (and there is no particular reason to doubt this), this would make Millhall a White mill for the duration of West's tenure at least; the reputation of subsequent occupants tends to confirm that the lower categories of White paper may have been made here. As a start then one has to bear in mind in this investigation into the origins of the early Maidstone paper makers that there were two mills there rather than one.

At present there is no documentary evidence of any paper mill active in the Maidstone area before 1665[13] and yet the names of several paper makers have already been mentioned, all of whom, except Middleton, had made their appearance between 1676(?)–89. Though some of the later ones could have been trained within the area, with one or two exceptions, none of the others was born in the district. As a result of this not only must one ask the question, where then did they come from ? but, also, since there are far too many of them to have been trained in such a short space of time within the district, where did they receive their training ? And this, of course, leads to a further question: if they were born and trained outside the area, why did they come to Maidstone ?

If one is to look then for Kentish origins for some of these paper makers outside the Maidstone district, consideration must obviously be given to the facilities that may have existed for training at the other early mills in the county, of which there were 5 active before ca.1660. These are examined briefly below in the order of their appearance as we know it.

Dartford No.1 Paper Mill (1588–1724)

This was Spilman's mill and (see the Paper Makers' and Paper Sellers' Petition, 1690) is believed to have been in continuous operation from 1588 until its closure in 1724. This mill could, therefore, be considered as an important source of these earliest founder paper makers, whoever these may have been. One might legitimately speculate that perhaps its close neighbour, Eynsford paper mill (see below), may have owed its existence to paper makers who had been trained at Dartford. At a later date, in addition to providing its own paper makers (known from 1670) and possibly influencing the establishment of Dartford No.2 mill (1679), Dartford No.1 must have provided George Gill with his training in White paper manufacture. He is the only named paper maker from this mill who can be connected directly with papermaking at Maidstone at this time.[14]

Buckland Paper Mill, Dover (before 1600–present day, albeit modernised)

Situated so close to the Continent and in a port which from Norman times onward had been the principal gateway to England, one cannot help feeling that this paper mill may have been

---

[12] Existing accounts locate only 12 out of the 14 Ancient Paper Makers (e.g. Shorter, A. Bib.12 35). The case for James West as a candidate for one of the missing ones is made in App.IV under "James West".

[13] With one possible exception (discussed p.67) it is unnecessary to postulate the existence of any other early paper mills than those listed. Certain paper mills like Snodland (and Sittingbourne) may have been operating at earlier dates than known at present; to illustrate this Shorter gives 1741 as first mention of Millhall; Fuller, 1684; whereas it might have dated back to 1668 or earlier(?).

[14] For details see App.IV under George Gill.

founded by an immigrant, either a chance one or a settler.[15] No evidence has been found to support this suggestion, but it makes sense in terms of papermaking geography since the Dover mill was out on a limb by itself. The first evidence of its existence may be inferred from a survey carried out in 1660 which reported that the paper mill in Buckland "has been quiet for 60 years" (this does not mean that it had been inactive for this period as the Abstract of other surveys and leases prove this point).[16] Although the name of only one paper maker[17] can be linked to this mill in the 17th C., being out on a limb reduces the chances of any paper makers from there migrating to Maidstone; no evidence has been found for this. Instead, Canterbury (see below) is a much more credible candidate for migration, if this flow was not sometimes the other way. (Although the suggestion has been made that nearby River mill might also have had an early 17th C. origin., there is no documentary evidence for it working as a paper mill before 1689.[18] In any case the same conclusions would apply to this mill as for Buckland).

Eynsford Paper Mill

Nothing has been discovered about the early history of this mill apart from the fact that a paper mill is mentioned there in a Deed of conveyance dated 1648.[19] A search through the parish registers does not reveal any of the names of the early Maidstone paper makers (or families bearing the same name)[20] with the exception of Harris. A Richard and Elizabeth Harris were having a family there in the 1650's, but with no sign of a William whom one might suggest as the future occupant of one of the early Maidstone paper mills, Gurney's mill in Loose. Nevertheless, the possibility of a Harris link between Eynsford and the Maidstone district is not entirely ruled out by this and the significance of the Richard Harris "paperman" who was buried in Loose in 1703 in this context is discussed elsewhere.[21] Due to its

---

[15] As in the case of Maidstone (see Chap.I note 72) both Canterbury and Sandwich (for which one might read Dover, as another of the Cinque Ports) also granted asylum to refugees from the Netherlands in the 16th C. among whom may have been some paper makers.

[16] Lambeth Palace Library Surveys T.C.3 1660. T.C.10 an Abstract of Surveys (17:Jul:1799) refers for instance to a survey of 1641 and to a paper mill, a mill house, a dwelling house with lodges to dry paper valued at £14. The mill collapsed in 1669 and had been rebuilt by 1676 as the list of Fines shows "by reason of great charge for building new mills". (Search carried out on behalf of the author by Mr. Simeon Clarke, A.G. & R.A. and by kind permission of the Librarian).

[17] A marriage licence dated 31:July:1638 shows that Thomas Chapman of Buckland near Dover, papermaker, bachelor about 23, son of Richard Chapman of Shropshire was to be married to Elizabeth Palmer who came from River (nr. Dover) in Buckland. (Inf. Miss A.M. Oakley, Archivist for Canterbury Cathedral, City and Diocesan R.O.). There were no paper mills listed for Shropshire before 1650 (the names of three are known 1650–65) though there were early paper mills in neighbouring counties where Chapman might have trained. In view of his age it seems more probable that whether previously trained or trained at Buckland he worked for, rather than as, a Master Paper Maker, the inference being that other paper makers had preceded him there; further evidence for the early date of this mill.

[18] Welby, Douglas "The Kentish Village of River" (1977 Crabwell Publications).

[19] Shorter, A. Bib.12 182.

[20] For information the searches included the names of the following paper makers – Willard, Wilson, Manktellow, Archer, Ashedowne, Taylor, Hillier, Richardson, West, Middleton, Musgrove, Russell, Burnham and Harris. Details of all these will be found in App.IV. The Eynsford PRs (both the originals KAO P 139 1/1 and 1/2; and the transcripts TR 2322/22) showed only that a Thomas Taylor was baptised there in 1660, too late for the Boxley one; and a Richard and Elizabeth Harris having a family there in the 1650's, but with no sign of a William (see note 21 below).

[21] The birthplace and birthdate of William Harris, the Ancient Paper Maker and paper maker of Gurney's mill, Loose, have not been discovered, but his birth has been estimated for 1663 or earlier. The Richard Harris at Eynsford (if a paper maker) could in theory have been his father as also the unexplained "paperman" buried in Loose, 1703. This notion would do much to account for the appearance of William as a paper maker and an Ancient Paper Maker at that. (Further details see App.II under the Whatman/Harris Relationship and the Harris Family Paper Makers (n.20): and re Ancient Paper Maker status see App.IV under The Russells).

proximity to Dartford (5 miles further down the Darent) an early origin for this mill is not unexpected. One might go even further than this and postulate a much earlier origin for Shoreham mill (a few miles upstream) than 1690, the first date given by Shorter.[22] But here again, apart from a family of Archal (1626–1639) and Willard (ca.1623)[23], the parish registers do not reveal any of the names we are looking for. The uncertainty is aggravated by the fact that no ratebooks or church accounts have survived from this period for either of these parishes, so that one cannot trace the occupants back from Andrew Johannot (Eynsford, 1694) and Alexander Russell (Shoreham, 1692). With the possible exception of Harris, mentioned above, it seems fairly certain that none of the paper makers who appear in the Maidstone district later came from either of these mills directly.

Goudhurst Paper Mill(s) 16th (?)–17th Cs.

It has been discovered in the course of this work that this Cinderella of paper mills supplied the Maidstone district with a significant succession of paper makers during the latter half of the 17th C.; in addition it may have been an important nursery or staging post in the case of others on their way to Maidstone, a case for which there is no certain evidence. Because of its importance in the present context it will be discussed separately later in this chapter together with suggested reasons for the migration of some of the paper makers.

Barton Mill, Canterbury (A paper mill from the 17th–19th Cs.)

Finally there is Barton mill at Canterbury, a mill which is mentioned as early as 1151 A.D. and which probably remained a corn mill throughout its life though at some point it incorporated facilities for making paper as well, just when is not known. If the fact that James Gilmore, paper maker, purchased his freedom in Canterbury in 1664/5 can be connected with the existence of the paper mill there, then this would obviously point to the mill's being active before this date. Though Canterbury was one of the main centres for the settlement of the Netherlandish refugees in 1567, unlike Maidstone, no paper makers were mentioned in the Petition.[24] On the other hand, like Dover, papermaking may have been started there by a chance immigrant. Alternatively, one might look for a paper maker who had moved there from Dover; or, just possibly Sittingbourne.[25] It is perhaps worth noting that the family who leased Buckland paper mill, Dover, for at least 2 decades, mid–17th C., (though they let it

---

[22]   Shorter, A. Bib.12 182. His evidence for this date is not clear. The first paper maker identified there does not appear until 1692, Alexander Russell, one of the Ancient Paper Makers; and there is no documentary evidence of the existence of the mill until 1716. This subject is discussed in some detail in App. IV under "The Russells" and also Chap.VII p.297.

[23]   The search here as in Note 20 above (Shoreham Transcripts KAO TR 2322/62). A Richard Willard m. Anne Mosier in 1623; James s.o. James Harris bapt. 1617; William & Elizabeth Archall m. 1625 and had 7 children bapt. 1626–39, but no Peter. Beyond indicating a presence of families with these names in Shoreham there appears to be no connection with any of the Maidstone paper makers.

[24]   Letter (3:July:87) from Miss A.M. Oakley, Archivist, Cathedral, City and Diocesan R.O. comments, "There were no papermakers that I know of among the Canterbury refugees, and I think I know them fairly well. Most of them were silkweavers. Some came in from Sandwich in 1574 and they were joined by thousands of others in the ensuing years. There is a problem though; since none of these refugees were allowed to be free of the City, they could not trade as master craftsmen and would not show in the records as these or apprentices".

[25]   Coleman, D.C. Bib.15 58 note 1 cites Port Book evidence of paper, mainly Brown, being shipped from Faversham in 1662/3. This might have come from either Barton mill, Canterbury, which must have been working by that date; or, possibly, Sittingbourne, particularly if the outlet to the Swale channel had silted up by that date and a paper mill had existed there at that time.

go to ruin) were domiciled in the parish of St. Martin's, Canterbury (ca. 1.25 miles from Barton mill).[26] The number of apprentices listed in the City's Roll of Freemen increased rapidly towards the end of the 17th C., no fewer than 7 apprentices passing through the hands of the two Richard Wellards, the paper makers there between 1693-1714.[27] It is possible in view of their number (surely greatly in excess of the needs of Barton mill itself) that some of them found employment either in the Dover area;[28] or at Sittingbourne.[29] As things stand there is no evidence that Barton mill supplied any Master Paper Makers to the Maidstone area: possibly paper mill employees but we do not have the names of these.

The foregoing may appear at first sight to be a somewhat summary examination of the early Kent paper mills, but the search has been extensive and in order to keep the text as uncomplicated as possible the detail has been relegated to Appendix IV (and the findings *are* complicated).

Out of the five paper mills considered in the previous pages only Dartford and Goudhurst have emerged positively as direct external sources of paper makers for the Maidstone mills of the 1670-80's, with tentative links suggested in the case of Eynsford. These sources are examined more fully below. In the meantime, and still keeping to general considerations, one cannot assume that these sources alone would account for the origins of all of the early paper makers at Maidstone; there are complications within this situation that need special consideration in order to prepare the way for a credible account of the industry's establishment and growth around Maidstone.

In the first place, can one be certain that none of the other early Maidstone paper makers was recruited from within the district, bearing in mind that 7-8 paper mills were operating in it *before* 1690 ? After 1690, and indeed as early as the 1670/80's, the area could in theory have become self-generating in the supply of its paper makers. It is unfortunate that so many key records such as the Poor Ratebooks for Boxley and Ditton do not go back further than 1693 and 1677 respectively (even in the case of Aylesford, the midway point between the two, the first complete assessments only date from 1657 and the Registers from 1654). This creates obvious difficulties when one attempts to trace the history of the two earliest mills in the district, Forstal and Millhall.

[26]   Documents in Lambeth Palace Library : Com.XIIa (1647) lessee Bridget Pownall; Survey T.C.4 (1664) lessee Mr. Pownall; and TA 560/1 (1669) lessee Jane Pownall of St. Martin's near Canterbury. (Search carried out on behalf of the author by Mr. Simeon Clarke, A.G. & R.A. and by kind permission of the Librarian).

[27]   The question as to whether Thomas Willard of Goudhurst (and later Forstal) and the Richard Wellards of Canterbury were related is discussed in App.IV (see Willard/Wellard Genealogy); the chances of this being the case are considered to be very slight.

[28]   In support of this there are indications of newly-trained paper makers, probably not Masters, moving from the Canterbury to the Dover area. One of Richard Wellard jnr.'s apprentices, Thomas Bannister *from* River (nr. Dover), was made free by apprenticeship in 1714. Shorter, A. Bib.12 199 refers to him under "River" mill, but provides no evidence of his return there; but there is later evidence (see Chap.VII p.342) of his being described as a paper maker of River. There may have been others; in the 1750's, and even as late as 1789, other individuals from River (Thomas Cooper s.o. a paper maker and William Karby s.o. a silkweaver both from River) were freed by Patrimony in Canterbury; and yet others described as from "Dover" appear in the Canterbury Roll of Freemen (inf. Miss A.M. Oakley 1987).

[29]   Peter Archer jnr. is known to have been at Sittingbourne paper mill in 1708 and the inference from this (discussed in Chap.IV) is that the mill was active before this date, suggested late 17th C. or even earlier (see ref. to Port Book evidence note 25).

Table III sets out the early occupants and Map 2 the location of the Maidstone paper mills. The content of the table is important as a basis for understanding the later development of the industry in this area and, more especially at this juncture, the environment in which the elder Whatman and his close friend, Richard Harris, grew up. The task of trying to determine the early succession at these mills (col.4) has been a very complicated exercise; and in many cases the results remain at present tentative. The data that has led to the conclusions set out here is intricate and often confusing and it would be quite inappropriate to consider such details within the text. Despite the fact that alternative solutions are sometimes possible, it is suggested that these findings are accepted for the time being; future research may resolve some of the uncertainties. The specialist reader, who may wish to follow the reasoning behind the proposals, should consult App.II–IV.

Certain general considerations may be mentioned here. There are instances as in the case of Thomas Taylor and James West where origin and training have not been determined and where one has to postulate that they may have come to the Maidstone area from another district or another region altogether; and much also depends on the motives for their migration. For example, is one to assume that very early paper mills may have existed near Maidstone and that they made their move there to succeed paper makers as yet unidentified ? Or, unlike expansion in the region to the West of London, is one witnessing the *establishment and growth of an industry in virgin territory* ? In the first case they could have moved untrained and learnt their papermaking under unidentified paper makers; in the second it presupposes that the paper makers in question were already trained. Whichever solution one adopts there is a further question to be considered, namely, what would prompt paper makers to move to a district without paper mills and lacking in specialized millwrights and mould makers necessary for their operations ? One could hypothesize that such paper makers might have migrated from Dartford (or even Eynsford) to found mills like Forstal and Millhall, but nothing has emerged from these searches to support an idea of this kind.[30]

With William Harris the interest lies in quite different directions, but like the others his origin is not known;[31] nor where he trained;[32] and, in addition, how he managed to qualify as an Ancient Paper Maker when the first instance of his making paper is at Gurney mill in 1687/9 only a couple of years before he made his mark on the Petition of 1690. He is of special interest because not only was he the brother–in–law of the elder James Whatman's father but, more important, the father of Richard Harris, paper maker (referred to again in Chap.III, IV and VI).

Alexander Russell of Shoreham has been included in this Table because, as will be seen later, a problem exists in trying to determine whether the various papermaking Russells one encounters, including another Ancient Paper Maker William Russell at Tredway mill, Buckinghamshire, and the Maidstone paper makers John Hillyer (who married Constant Russell) and the Russell successors at Forstal, were in any way related.[33]

The problems do not end with the examples cited above. In the 17th C. very few of the mills listed (col.1) would have had names recognizable to-day. For instance, the first reference discovered so far to "Forstal" as such is not until the 19th C.[34] Not only is it necessary to discover the location of these mills but also when they were founded or converted, not always a straightforward task.

Secondly, it has to be recognized that clearly not all of the paper makers named in this Table were necessarily of the same status. In Chapter I it was claimed that early in the 18th C. the control of the paper industry was now in the hands of the Master Paper Maker in contrast to an earlier dependence on the fluctuating fortunes of Entrepreneurs

---

[30] This subject is discussed again in this chapter; and detailed data in App.III & IV.

[31] See App.II under (a) The Whatman/Harris Relationship and (b) the Harris Family Paper Makers.

[32] In 1684 when William Harris married Lydia Whatman he was described as "of Maidstone" showing that he was living in the area possibly having just completed his training. The fact that his eldest son, William jnr., moved from Loose to Millhall mill (1724), which he and his descendants occupied for the next 40 years at least, might be an indicator that his father had trained there in the 1670/80's(?)

[33] See App.IV Alexander Russell; App.IV Hillyer and App.III the Boxley RB. extracts; and further references to the family and Shoreham Chap.IV 147 and Chap.VII 297.

[34] See App.III.

and this change was already in an emergent state in the latter half of the 17th C. The search for the origins of the new paper makers of the Maidstone area has provided very positive evidence of Masters now making their way to the forefront; and not only there but paper makers like the Quelchs of Dartford (and maybe the Russells as well) were to produce more than one generation of noteworthy successors. From very limited evidence one can see that George Gill was at the top end of the league. Both on account of his social background and from the very size of his mill with its 3 waterwheels made it most unlikely that he would have undertaken the manual duties of the paper mill himself.[35] Others like Willard, Archer, West, Manktellow and Harris may have participated more closely in the papermaking operations; whereas the role of the residue is far less certain.

Musgrove, for example, did not work a paper mill of his own until he had been in the district for 8 years; he might have come to Maidstone as a paper millwright and helped Gill convert his mill or worked as an employee at Turkey until he saw an opportunity to work a mill of his own.[36] There are many others whose origin and function are even more difficult to place; Burnham, the Master of Great Ivy which may have been a Brown mill from the date of its conversion until late in the 18th C.;[37] Richard Harris, Paperman buried Loose in 1703, may have been William's father and had come from another region possibly as a maker of White paper (no paper mills or Harris in Loose prior to William);[38] and others like Newman, Ashedowne, the Richardsons and Smith(s)[39] none of whom can be dismissed lightly since they all represent the first threads that were to be woven into a papermaking structure which was to become one of the most important centres of the White paper industry in the country. *It is a significant indication of the standing of this new district that no fewer than three, possibly four, Ancient Paper Makers were connected with it only a matter of years before signing their Petition. It is not as though they were representing a long and well established centre of the industry, but instead affirming a new sense of direction.*

Before leaving the subject of their identity an attempt has been made to set out hypothetical training or apprenticeship dates for these early paper makers,[40] assumed here to have been for 7 years and starting at the age of 12. This has been done solely for the purpose of providing some sort of base to start from and can be discarded or accepted as the case may be. With the exception of Willard and the Richardsons their birthdates are not known, although one can make further attempts to approximate the proposals more closely from our knowledge of other events such as marriages or the occupation of a paper mill. The Table below, arranged in date order groups, indicates the *latest* period thought likely, though some of them could have been a decade or more earlier. For example, there are 2 possible birthdates for Taylor, assuming he came from Goudhurst. So his theoretical apprenticeship term is shown twice and because he preceded Willard at Forstal the earlier period is shown as the preferred one.

Group	Paper maker	Latest apprenticeship period
1	Thomas Taylour	1624–1631
	Thomas Willard	1645–1652
	(Thomas Taylor)	(1652–1659)
2	James West	1659–1666
3	The Richardsons	1660's
	Stephen Manktellow	1662–1670
	Peter Archer	1664–1671
	George Gill	1667–1674
	Peter Musgrove snr.	1667–1674
4	Alexander Russell	1673–1680
	William Harris	1675–1682

[35] See App.IV for George Gill's pedigree; and under the Peter Musgroves a footnote on the likely date for the installation of 3 waterwheels.

[36] See App.IV under the Peter Musgroves reasons for suggesting that Musgrove snr. may have worked at Turkey mill. Lower Tovil mill is referred to again in this chapter, Chapters IV & VII.

[37] For Burnham see App.IV and for Great Ivy mill see Chap.VII Table XII and p.317.

[38] See this chapter n.21 and App.II under Harris Paper Makers.

[39] See App.IV for further information on all of these.

[40] The claim was made by the Ancient Paper Makers in their Petition that "above a thousand families of paper makers (who) have served their apprenticeships.....", no doubt an exaggeration but nevertheless an indication.

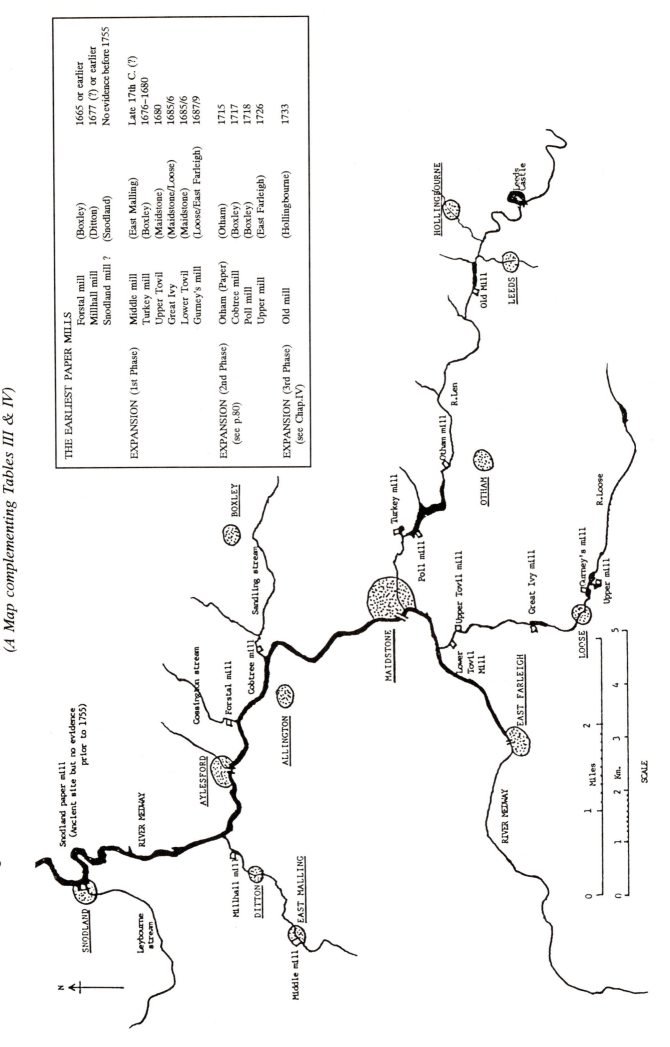

Map 2 – EARLY PAPER MILLS OF THE MAIDSTONE DISTRICT (17th /Early 18th Cs.)

(A Map complementing Tables III & IV)

THE EARLIEST PAPER MILLS

	Forstal mill	(Boxley)	1665 or earlier
	Millhall mill	(Ditton)	1677 (?) or earlier
	Snodland mill ?	(Snodland)	No evidence before 1755
EXPANSION (1st Phase)	Middle mill	(East Malling)	Late 17th C. (?)
	Turkey mill	(Boxley)	1676–1680
	Upper Tovil	(Maidstone)	1680
	Great Ivy	(Maidstone/Loose)	1685/6
	Lower Tovil	(Maidstone)	1685/6
	Gurney's mill	(Loose/East Farleigh)	1687/9
EXPANSION (2nd Phase) (see p.80)	Otham (Paper)	(Otham)	1715
	Cobtree mill	(Boxley)	1717
	Poll mill	(Boxley)	1718
	Upper mill	(East Farleigh)	1726
EXPANSION (3rd Phase) (see Chap.IV)	Old mill	(Hollingbourne)	1733

TABLE III 59

Illustrating Paper Mills in the Maidstone District during the last quarter of the 17th C.;
and their Occupants and earlier connections.

PAPER MILL	DATE	PAPER MAKER	ORIGIN & COMMENT
FORSTAL	before 1665	Thomas Taylor	suggested as Goudhurst mill (and bapt. there 1612)
	1668/9	Thomas Willard	bapt. Goudhurst 1633; last entry PRs. 1666 Master Paper Maker at Goudhurst paper mill.
	1684(?)/93	Peter Archer	Master Paper Maker Goudhurst paper mill 1680/83; possibly an immigrant.
	1693/1725	John Hillyer	not found; probably West of London, Surrey (?).
MILLHALL	before 1677	John(?) & James Smith(?)	Not found; suggested only, a James Smith, paper maker bur. Snodland 1705. John Smith bur. Ditton 1703.
		William Richardson	bapt. Allington 1649; may have occupied paper mill but was he a paper maker ?
	1682/7	John Richardson	bapt. Allington 1651; almost certainly occupied paper mill but was he the paper maker ?
	1688/94	JAMES WEST AP	Not found; suggested Buckinghamshire and moving to Aylesford via Goudhurst. Occupant paper maker from 1688, but may have acted as paper maker for previous occupants from 1668+. (see App. IV).
	1694/1724	Edward Middleton	Not found, but very probably local.
	1724/1741	William Harris jnr.	Loose; eldest surviving s.o. William Harris snr. see below under Gurney's mill.
EAST MALLING	17th C.	Unknown (Ashedowne ?)	Local: Roger Tomlyn proprietor d. 1704. A Thomas Ashedowne was paper maker at Goudhurst after 1697; bur. there 1709.
TURKEY MILL	–1680	GEORGE GILL AP	Dartford : could have left there at any time after 1676. Suggestion that Peter Musgrove snr. (arr: Boxley 1678) and Thomas Newman, paper maker (bur. Boxley 1702) worked at this mill, the former moving to Lower Tovil. (See below and App. IV)
UPPER TOVIL	–1680	Stephen Manktellow	Immigrant : Master Paper Maker at Goudhurst 1669–1679.
GREAT IVY	1685/6	Richard Burnham	Not found : possibly Maidstone, may even have been son of former occupant, a fuller, Henry Bruman ?
LOWER TOVIL	1685/6	Peter Musgrove snr.	probably Goudhurst/Marden area : see above under Turkey mill.
GURNEY'S	(1687)/9	WILLIAM HARRIS snr. AP	Not found; his family might have had a link with Eynsford mill (see Note 21). Possibly trained in Maidstone area.[1]
(SHOREHAM)	1690's	ALEXANDER RUSSELL AP	Not found; could have been Goudhurst or Buckinghamshire ? might have had Maidstone connections (see text).

AP signifies ANCIENT PAPER MAKER, signatory of the 1690 Petition.
1. Alternatives could have been Forstal or possibly Dartford (see text). [For location see Maps 1 & 2]

The difficulties encountered in trying to trace the origin of these paper makers become clear as each individual case is examined (see App.IV). Seen as a body they include lost parish registers; the effect of the Commonwealth, Nonconformism and epidemics like the Plague[41] on entries in those documents that have survived; the possibility that a child may have been baptised in another area, e.g. in the mother's parish; the loss of Ratebooks; the absence of Settlement Examinations in this area; and commonly found names. With the less common names, like Musgrove, one stands a better chance of finding the general location of the paper maker one is looking for; and, equally, the total absence of a name in a district more or less confirms that the paper maker's origins are unlikely to be found there. Finally, Russell claimed[42] that the Clement Taylor Smythe MSS. contain a complete list of the Freemen of Maidstone from 1538–1838 (Vol.I fo.264). Though this is true, only the names are given and not the Trades, the original Borough Records have not been found so that one cannot get further forward along this route.

In spite of all these shortcomings a fairly clear picture of the early Maidstone papermaking scene has emerged, the paper mills and their occupants. Goudhurst, in terms of numbers, was the most important source for these paper makers, three certain; one very probable, Musgrove; and a further three possible either trained or passing through there, Taylo(u)r, West and Russell.

The founding or conversion of these Maidstone mills, this subject will occupy most of the remaining pages of this chapter and will be considered in conjunction with the reasons for the migration of these paper makers and for their setting up mills in the Maidstone area.

FURTHER CONSIDERATION OF THE FOUR PRINCIPAL SOURCES

A preliminary examination has resulted in whittling the main sources of the early Maidstone paper makers down to four. To provide a firmer basis these now need to be examined in greater detail. Despite the fact that significant gaps remain, the results as they stand may be useful to others as well as providing a valuable insight into the motives that led to the formation of the paper industry in the Maidstone district.

Dartford No.1 Mill

The origins of this are known; it was active from 1588–1724; and it produced a number of identifiable paper makers for *itself* in the 17th C. Eynsford paper mill may have owed its origin to it. It was also claimed that it had continued to make White paper ever since Spilman's days. So far as the future was concerned it is of interest on two counts. First, it may have inspired the founding of a second mill there, Dartford No.2, in 1679. The motive for this probably came from a sudden increase in the demand for White paper arising from the embargo on French goods that came into force in 1678. Holland, as an alternative source of supply, initially filled the gap.[43] Nevertheless, it seems more than a coincidence that so many Kent paper makers made their moves and founded new mills during this same period (1678–85) and not to link this activity with increased expectations of making higher classes

---

[41] Among the exogenous factors that could have affected the lives and movements of these paper makers and disrupted records were epidemics like the Plague of which no fewer than 8 serious outbreaks are recorded in Maidstone between 1544 and 1666/7, some of these lasting for more than a decade and so serious was the one in 1562 that All Saints' Church was closed and children were taken to Otham for baptism. In the course of the searches carried out for this book, it is clear that at various times there were epidemics of some sort in other parishes in the locality.

[42] Russell, J.M. Bib.41 192 makes the claim, but on investigation the related records are no longer found.

[43] Figures for the quantities and sources of White paper imports into London between 1662–1720 are given in Coleman, D.C. Bib.15 21 Table II. This shows that for 1679 Holland effectively plugged the gap created by the embargo on French goods; but no figures are given for the years 1680–1685 leaving one in some doubt as to whether any significant imports were made during these years.

of paper. In this context one has to remember that not only were feelings against the French high at this time, but England had also only just concluded the third Anglo–Dutch War (1676) and the memory of De Ruyter's trouncing of the English Fleet in 1666 and the bombardment of Chatham in the following year must have been still fresh in the minds of the people of Kent. It will be seen (Chap.IV) that Dartford No.2 mill, although not specially noted for the quality of its White paper until late in the 18th C., was to play an important role in the development of the manufacture of this commodity.

Second, Dartford No.1 mill must also have been the place where George Gill underwent his training, evidently, as events showed, to very good effect. Here again, the planning and construction of Dartford No.2 mill, which must have taken place a year or two before 1679, may well have prompted Gill to break away from Dartford and find a suitable place of his own. If he had completed his apprenticeship in 1674 (or earlier), then after his marriage in 1676 he is not likely to have hung about in Dartford, if there were no opportunities for him there; it is quite reasonable to suppose that he had moved to Maidstone *before* 1680.[44] So far as the development of papermaking in the Maidstone area was concerned, Dartford No.1 mill appears to have made only a limited contribution in terms of numbers,[45] but a very important one in terms of White paper manufacture.

The Origins of Goudhurst Paper Mills

There is little doubt that a paper mill was operating in Goudhurst in the 1650's and it may have been founded a great deal earlier than this. The suggestion will be made that, if this was the case, the mill may have undergone a change of direction in the 1640's. The mill was sited on a small tributary at its junction with the River Teise at a point midway between the villages of Horsmonden and Goudhurst and very close to the meeting point of the boundaries of these two parishes and that of Marden to the North. It lay within 6 miles of Cranbrook to the East and within 3 miles of Brenchley to the West.[46] In fact it was placed centrally on the northern edge of the High Weald of Kent right in the middle of what was then Whatman family country. Documentary evidence shows that by 1684, at least, it was designated as "Papermills" and to judge from the number of paper makers known to have been there this designation might well have extended back to its foundation or to a change in direction whichever the case may be.

In order to appreciate the significance of this mill, its location and the relationship of this to the development of Maidstone as a papermaking centre, it is necessary to digress at this point from the subject of papermaking. Political and religious disaffection during this period were factors that particularly influenced the course of events in the whole region, including Maidstone, and although the consequence of these events may not have affected paper makers personally one cannot always be sure that they did not obstruct their operations.

---

[44] For further details see App.IV under "The Gill Family".

[45] Mention has been made earlier in this chapter (note 21) that a Richard Harris, who might have been the father of William, does appear in the Dartford PRs. during the 1660's; there is thus a possibility that William also might have come from Dartford.

[46] A more detailed account of this mill, its identification and a sketch-map (Map 8), is to be found in App.IV.

In spite of being defended initially by the Royalists in what has come to be regarded as the fiercest battle of the Second Civil War (1648),[47] Maidstone was strongly Parliamentarian in its allegiance as indeed were the cloth weaving districts to the south of it, in the Weald of Kent. Whereas the policies of the Commonwealth may have provided a relatively stable environment for this population, the effects of the régimes before and after this period were decidedly adverse. But the root causes of the situation that we find go back much further and to understand the importance of the High Weald in this, one has to consider briefly the history of the Kent Cloth Weaving Industry. The history of the rise and decline of this industry forms only a part of the very varied fortunes of the history of the woollen industry as a whole which is an extremely complicated subject in itself. It will be appreciated that in a work devoted to papermaking it is not possible, indeed it is not the proper place to present here anything beyond a highly simplified picture of these events.

Despite this proviso, since no regional account exists of the fluctuating fortunes of the Cloth industry in the High Weald that is in any way relevant to the subject of this book, and because the consequences of these were of such importance to the future course of the paper industry in Kent, it has proved necessary to anatomize its history in more detail than would have been the case had such an account existed. Many factors influenced this situation dating from much earlier periods and derived from relatively obscure sources. For the *general reader* then who may be more interested in conclusions than in seeking the causes that underlay this situation it is suggested that he should proceed to p.67, the end of this section of smaller print.

Although woollen cloth of a poor quality had been woven in Maidstone, and very probably in the High Weald as well, from the 13th C., activities of this sort were completely overshadowed by the trade in wool exports to the weavers of Flanders who produced greatly superior cloth. Appreciating the advantages that would accrue from the manufacture of the cloth in this country, provided the quality could be improved, it had been the aim of successive Plantagenets as far back as Henry III in 1271 to bring this about. But real success was only achieved in 1331 by Edward III who, with the knowledge of the troubles that were then affecting the Flemish industry, encouraged weavers to leave Flanders and settle *in selected districts* in this country. Apart from wool these weavers needed water power and supplies of fuller's earth to produce the improved cloth.[48] Cranbrook and the surrounding district (which included Goudhurst) provided an ideal location for this industry which in the event became firmly established there by 1400.[49] It had an abundance of sites for watermills (although there were other demands for these as, for instance, from the very important wealden iron smelting industry) as well as veins of fuller's earth in the underlying Hastings beds.

Although there is ample evidence for the introduction and development of these facilities in the Cranbrook district[50] the fact should not be overlooked that the Maidstone district was another very important centre of the fulling industry.[51] For instance, Spain lists no fewer than 12 fulling mills working on the tiny River Loose by 1500 with a further 2 on the River Len; and at least another 4 before 1600 on the latter.[52]

[47]   Russell, J.M. Bib.41 Chap.XI.

[48]   Formerly the cleansing and shrinking of the woollen cloth by pounding it with soap or fuller's earth had been performed laboriously using the feet in a process known as "tramping" or "waulking". The mechanical process, harnessing water power to raise and lower hammers, had been used in Europe as early as 1185; but, it has been claimed, this innovation was brought to England in the 14th C. by the Flemish immigrants. The English did not take too kindly to this process at first; in fact its use was prohibited on several occasions in order to protect the waulkers from unemployment.

[49]   Pile, C.C.R. "Cranbrook Broadcloth and the Clothiers" (Cranbrook and District Local History Society 2nd Ed. 1967. 4).

[50]   Pile, C.C.R. "Watermills and Windmills of Cranbrook" (Cranbrook and District Local History Society 1979).

[51]   The Sandgate beds (Lower Greensand) also contained rich veins of fuller's earth in the Maidstone area, especially in Boxley and in the parish of Leeds near the site of Hollingbourne Old Mill.

[52]   Spain, R.J. Bib.11 173; Bib.8 99.

Ever since Roman times England had been famous for the quality of its wool and by the Middle Ages foreign weavers had become very dependent on the exportation of it. This dependence was an important political weapon in English hands. At the same time since the English relied so heavily on the export of wool or, as became the case later, woollen cloth,[53] their economy was correspondingly vulnerable to political interference from either side of the water. Naturally a shift from exporting wool to exporting cloth to the great Flemish weaving centres and cloth markets was not a matter to be accepted lightly. During the 15th C. the aim of the Merchants based in England[54] was to exploit the current situation in the Low Countries and to defeat the Flemish weaving industry and by the 16th C. it had achieved complete supremacy in the export of *undyed and undressed* cloth, these last operations together with the finishing being left to the Flemish clothworkers. All the ingredients are here then for marked fluctuations in the fortunes of such an important industry and for the decline of various segments within it, the Kent broadcloth industry being the one which is of special interest here. The prime qualities of cloth came from Wiltshire, Gloucestershire and Worcestershire; next in quality were Kent and Suffolk cloths and it has been said of these that the majority were dyed before weaving *but not dressed or finished.*

It has been claimed that the cloth industry in Kent suffered its first major set-back, a large drop in exports, as a result of Wolsey's foreign policy which interrupted trade with Flanders in the 1520's; the debasement of the currency was another reverse during Henry VIII's reign that had serious consequences for certain sectors of the cloth industry.[55] During his reign also the exportation of cloth concentrated increasingly from London at the expense of the outports to a point where the latter ceased to be outlets of any consequence, a trend that was to have important repercussions on the state of the trade under James I. There were many other factors that affected the general health of the industry but which it would be difficult to disentangle from one another and attribute the influence of any or some of them specifically to the state of the industry in Kent. Some of the more important events are discussed briefly below.

For example, at the point of the Merchants' sale several parties were involved with conflicting interests, the Merchant Adventurers versus the Hanseatic League and other foreign merchants operating from London, some obtaining favoured export licences denied to others who, like the Flemish, compensated for this by taking advantage of a remission of Duties provided they shipped their goods in English bottoms;[56] and the Merchants of the Staple who meanwhile continued to export wool, although in ever diminishing quantities but who were nevertheless capable of exploiting situations where the cloth merchants may have been at a disadvantage as, for instance, when for one reason or another the importation of their cloth was prohibited by the Netherlands government;[57] wool was then at a premium. Further back along the line there were the powerful Clothiers who, among others, had a firm grip on the Kentish industry. It was they who organised the combing, carding and general preparation of the wool for the spinning of the yarn and the subsequent weaving of the cloth. It will be immediately apparent that with such a large and important industry as this any adverse fluctuation in the export of the cloth could be the cause of unsold stock and in turn serious unemployment and social unrest which had manifested itself on more than one occasion in the past and the consequences of which were constantly in the mind of later governments.

Thus on the one hand one has the interests of the domestic clothworkers to bear in mind (and the political clout of the London clothworkers was very considerable) and ways and means of promoting these; and on the other the problems that these pressures, amongst other things, created for the Merchants. For instance, as far back as Edward III with the aim of acquiring as large a share as possible of the processes for domestic clothworkers the export of unfulled cloth had been prohibited. This Statute was re-enacted in 1467 by Edward IV with Henry VII adding to it

---

[53]   In the 16th C. the value of the exported woollen cloth accounted for 70% of the country's total exports.

[54]   These included The Merchant Adventurers (a regulated Company), the Hanseatic League, Flemish and other continental merchants; they exported cloth as distinct from the Merchants of the Staple who dealt in wool.

[55]   Pilgrim, J.E. "The Cloth Industry of East Anglia" (The Wool Textile Industry in Great Britain edited J. Geraint Jenkins: Routledge, Kegan & Paul 1972). He claims that this debasement of the currency led to a decline in the south-east Anglian Broadcloth industry from which it never recovered.

[56]   This situation altered towards the end of Queen Elizabeth's reign and that of James I to conflicting interests between several new regulated companies to whom Charters had been granted, notably between the Merchant Adventurers and the Eastland Company.

[57]   The role of the Staplers changed once they were ousted from Europe and though their Charter was renewed for a further 7 years in 1584, the Company resorted more and more to woolbroking in England, a practice that led them into further conflict with the Clothiers who accused them of forcing up the price of wool. This situation was to some extent resolved when James I granted them a Charter in 1617 which recognized officially their position as brokers (Rich, E.E. "The Ordinance Book of the Merchants of the Staple" Cambridge 1937).

in 1487 further stages of the clothmaking process, namely, that cloth for export must now be rowed, barbed and shorn. Since none of these Acts was enforceable in practice, Henry VIII re-introduced this measure in 1512 but with more teeth to it; by better regulation of the Customs[58] and the appointment of inspectors and using a licensing system the imposition was made marginally more effective. The measure was fought fiercely by both the English and the foreign merchants who in spite of it managed to export the bulk of their cloth still in the unfinished state. Nevertheless it appears to have had an indirectly adverse effect on the trade.[59] Clearly the pursuit of a policy of this nature would lead to the unemployment of Flemish clothworkers and in retaliation to restrictions on the importation of any English cloth that had been dyed and finished. It remained, however, for Sir William Cecil (later Lord Burghley) under Queen Elizabeth to take this policy a step further, a policy that was to achieve its ultimate fulfilment under James I with disastrous consequences for the cloth industry.

In the course of Elizabeth's reign radical changes took place in the whole set-up, both at home and abroad, which affected the actual and future prosperity of this vitally important industry. Not all of these events had an immediate effect; nevertheless the seeds of decline for many of its components were then being sown. During this period new markets were being developed in other parts of Europe and in the outside world, new Regulated and Joint Stock Companies created to serve these and with their differing interests, new sources of friction arose in their struggle to secure monopolistic powers. Cloth was now to be standardised, an important innovation, and due to the debasement of the currency to make the revenue from Customs more remunerative, new and much higher rates of Duty were imposed on cloth, these being based on the weight of wool used in the make-up of the textile.[60] These rates were not applied equitably and together with other factors led not only to much resentment on the part of the buyers[61] but also to the progressive exclusion of foreign merchants, who had handled 50% of cloth exports at the beginning of the Queen's reign and only 3% at the end of it. On the home front, the perennial complaint from the London Clothworkers that they were being deprived of work led to further measures designed to give them employment by pursuing the policy already attempted without great success by previous monarchs, namely, to forbid the exportation of cloths not "rowed, barbed, first coursed and shorn". The new Statute, 1566,[62] did not supersede the earlier ones but supplemented and modified them in a way that made the measures more effective. It was obligatory now that for every 9 unwrought cloths exported 1 must be ready wrought and dressed. There was, however, another important provision in this Act specifically affecting the export of Kent and Suffolk cloths. In their case *every cloth exported had to be ready wrought and dressed; there were to be no exceptions.* In the event the Kent and Suffolk clothiers managed to secure sufficient dressers to do this work before sending the cloth to London for shipping.[63] This measure could not, therefore, have been of much help to the London clothworkers and moreover, as pointed out earlier, the import of cloths of this kind would be resisted by the authorities in the Low Countries to the detriment of this particular trade. It has all the character of a punitive measure and it has been said that it was aimed by Lord Burghley against the rising power of the Clothiers in these regions,[64] an attitude that seems somewhat paradoxical compared to his assiduity (see below) in encouraging the settlement of refugee craftsmen from the Continent in this country and especially those destined for various parts of Kent and East Anglia.

Turning now to foreign events affecting the industry, the most important of these were connected with contemporary religious unrest in the Low Countries and to a closely related matter, the growing hostility between Spain and

---

[58]   Even so no hard and fast regulations governed the English Customs system before the 17th C.

[59]   The export of cloth which had shown phenomenal growth in the 15th C. remained largely stagnant during the early part of Henry VIII's reign, only picking up towards the end of it, giving an overall increase of some 42%. (Friis, Astrid "Alderman Cockayne's Project and the Cloth Trade", Levin & Munksgaard & OUP 1927 45).

[60]   For fear of objections only 2/3rds of these new rates were applied initially with a further concession that 1 cloth in 10 could count as a wrapper. Foreign Merchants other than the Hanseatics paid double rates (Friis, A. ibid. 49/50).

[61]   These increased impositions were passed on to the Flemish Buyers increasing their costs by 400%, an act that was not well received.

[62]   8 Eliz.c.6. (Repealed 1822, an Act 3 Geo.IV c.XLI repealing divers Ancient Statutes relating to the Importation & Exportation of Goods).

[63]   Friis, Astrid ibid. 59.

[64]   Another possible reason for the restrictions affecting Kent may have been a measure to penalize the wool producers there for smuggling considerable quantities of wool over to Calais and thence to the Flemish and French weavers. Yet another suggested reason may have been an early manifestation of the anti-Puritan campaign which reached its zenith later under Burghley and Archbishop Whitgift; the cloth-weaving districts of the Weald were certainly noted for their strongly non-conformist religious attitudes, especially concerning the role of the Crown.

England. Both of these, together with many side issues,[65] contributed to major disturbances in the cloth trade and the channels through which it normally operated. A deeper motive lay behind these troubles which stemmed basically from the Roman Catholic Alliance and from Cardinal Granvelle's personal hatred of the English and their arrogance, his desire being to bring Protestant England to its knees. To achieve these aims his weapons were not openly religious ones but ones concealed behind commercial activities. Knowing the importance of cloth exports in the English economy he planned to disrupt this flourishing trade by fostering a revival of Flemish weaving, claiming that the English had deprived them of this industry. He suspected that English merchants had been behind the religious revolt in Antwerp in 1561 and his first opportunity to retaliate came in the next year when he prohibited the importation of English cloth on the grounds that it was infected by the plague that was then raging in London. This led to a temporary trade war, each side banning the other's exports, and though this situation improved after the departure of Granvelle, the real motives behind this quarrel became clear to all the parties concerned. There were two important consequences of these events (a) the increased persecution of Protestants in the Low Countries that followed and the atrocities of Alva's army culminating in the sack of Antwerp in 1576 led to many Flemish craftsmen seeking asylum in England; and (b) the exodus of the English Merchants from their traditional markets in Bruges and Antwerp to alternative trading centres.[66] Affairs were not helped either by the various measures, described above, that had been introduced at home. In spite of all this and the eventual war with Spain, cloth exports increased considerably during Elizabeth's reign, the Merchant Adventurers still managing to export nearly 80% of its cloth *in the undressed state;* all the same the cracks were already appearing in the Kentish sector of the industry.[67]

Some of the refugees referred to above[68] found their way to Kent via the Cinque Ports; and Maidstone (together with other places) petitioned the Crown in June 1567[69] for permission to admit "the number of three score families of the straungers peregrines and artificers of the severall faculties hereunder mentioned", and these included the makers of a variety of woollen and linen textiles, leather and metal workers; and, it will be recalled, of special interest the *"Makers of white and browne paper"*. Sir William Cecil saw to it that Letters Patent were speedily granted to this end, in fact by November of the same year.[70] The main Kentish settlements were in Maidstone, Canterbury and Sandwich; but it has been said that only a few of these settlers found their way into the Weald. The Dutch textile workers, however, soon made a significant contribution to the prosperity of Maidstone;[71] but whereas they had initially been occupied in making the New Draperies together with linen and silk weaving, these activities had largely ceased by the second decade of the 17th C. with thread–making their only lasting contribution to the economic life of Maidstone[72]. However, this is a subject that will be raised again in a rather different context later in this chapter.

The fatal blows to the Kent cloth industry came in the first half of the 17th C. There were three of them, two of which may be said to be contributory and the third direct and decisive in its effect. The first, which seen in retrospect might have been avoided by the Kent Clothiers, resulted from the change in demand from broadcloth to the lighter

[65] Rich, E.E. "The Ordinance Book of the Merchants of the Staple" (Cambridge 1937) Chapters III, IV and V include an account of many other factors, some of them no more than irritants, that contributed to the ups and downs of commerce at this time e.g. the Crown's coffers were virtually empty when Elizabeth came to the throne and she inherited many of the bad debts incurred by her predecessors who had borrowed from merchants abroad; there was extensive piracy on the high seas; the stipulations of various Navigation Acts to stimulate English shipping led to retaliatory measures by the Spanish and Netherlanders; there were higher tariffs and measures to export dressed cloth; increased competition from continental weavers and their acquisition of wool from sources other than England; and there was the incident of Elizabeth arresting a Genoese ship on its way to the Netherlands with bullion aboard to pay the Spanish troops which led Alva to confiscate in turn the property of English merchants in the Low Countries.

[66] Both the Merchants of the Staple and the Merchant Adventurers tried many different trading centres to the north of the Low Countries. Some proved unsatisfactory, others, like Hamburg, satisfactory but periodically unstable.

[67] Although some respite resulted from Lord Cobham's Petition, permission to export 2000 unwrought cloths per annum, the fulling mills in Cranbrook, the main centre for this in the High Weald, had ceased working by 1600 (Pile, C.C.R. op.cit.).

[68] Some had gone to the German States and others found their way to various English ports including London, Southampton, Colchester and the Cinque Ports.

[69] S.P.D. 9 Eliz. Vol.43 No.19. See also previous reference Chapter I note 72.

[70] Patent Roll Eliz. Part 4 No.1033 4:Nov:1567.

[71] For a full account of this see Morant, Valerie "The Settlement of Protestant Refugees in Maidstone during the 16th C." (Economic History Review Vol.IV No.2 1951 212 ff.).

[72] Some of these manufactures had by this time been learnt by English craftsmen. In general, however, the foreign community in Maidstone had dwindled to a very small population possibly connected with the mass emigration of Kent Clothworkers in 1616 resulting from Cockayne's disastrous project (see Text).

and more fashionable New Draperies. Although some of these were initially manufactured in the Maidstone area towards the end of the 16th C., they eventually became concentrated in Essex and Norfolk. It has been said that the ultimate decline of the all powerful Merchant Adventurers[73] was due to the fact that they had depended for too long on the export of cloth and had neglected the new and lighter materials which, incidentally, were favoured by later governments because they yielded more duty than broadcloth. Even as early as 1615 a third of English wool was used in making them.

The second blow, which has been described as "the greatest blunder in economic policy during the reign of the first of the Stuarts",[74] became known as Alderman Cockayne's Project. The causes that led to this are too complex to enter into here,[75] but basically one is back again with the complaints of the London Clothworkers and Cockayne's exploitation of these to serve his ends. Under Elizabeth they had obtained employment from the 1 cloth in 10 prescribed by the 1566 Statute, but early in the 17th C. they were once again without this work.[76] This was useful ammunition for Cockayne, a prominent member of the Eastland Company who were going through a difficult period and could not obtain a licence to export undressed cloth to the Baltic ports where they were meeting with stiff opposition from the Dutch (selling some of our own cloth there). His aim was to destroy the power of the Merchant Adventurers who at that time not only had an almost complete monopoly of the undressed cloth trade but were also hated by the London clothworkers. Cockayne had the King's ear and the latter was always interested in anything that might increase his revenue. Superficially Cockayne's scheme was based on *prohibiting the export of undyed and undressed cloth.* This would solve the London Clothworker's problems and the revenue from this measure would come from a proposal that the clothworkers paid 5/- on every cloth processed producing a sum estimated at £40,000 p.a.[77] But behind this his aim was to acquire in addition a proportion of the trade in undressed cloth and in this lay a challenge to the Merchant Adventurers who he calculated would reject any plans made for them to co-operate in this scheme. The net result of all this was that in the absence of Parliament and with an ineffective Privy Council Cockayne got his way with the King in 1613/14 to the exclusion of the Merchant Adventurers who had refused, wisely, to participate. In fact in 1615 James granted a Charter to a new company called the "King's Merchant Adventurers". It is not difficult to guess the outcome of this ill-thought-out project. It was a disastrous failure. In spite of every contortion by the Privy Council and the new company to get out of this mess it met with strong opposition from abroad and swingeing retaliatory measures; sales dropped dramatically and the clothiers in all districts were up in arms with unsold cloth on their hands. Attempts were made to bring the new and old companies together, but they were like oil and water to each other. On the 1st January 1617 the King restored the old Company and they got their Charter back. But, although all appeared to go well for a time, the damage had been done. Competition from the Dutch and the French had increased significantly; the 30 Years War which began in 1618 was to affect general trade in Europe adversely, leading to a serious recession by 1620. In fact cloth exports had come to a standstill by 1617. Among the casualties was the Kent cloth industry. It has been claimed that the Cockayne episode led to a mass exodus of their clothworkers to the Palatinate after 1616.[78]

With the Kent cloth industry already in decline the *coup de grâce* was delivered in the reign of Charles I. Another influence had been coming progressively to the fore since the beginning of the century. Seen in retrospect the religious pressures behind the Reformation had not yet expended themselves fully and even in Elizabeth's reign the relatively tolerant State Church did not satisfy the more extreme Protestant aspirations; indeed there were elements that did not recognize the Crown as head of the Church. The result of this was an ever-growing leaning towards greater religious dissent culminating in the Puritan movement.

---

[73] They lost their monopoly to trade with the Low Countries and Germany in 1688 and were finally wound up in 1807.

[74] Friis, Astrid ibid. 223.

[75] Friis, Astrid ibid. Covered in Chapters II, III & IV.

[76] In 1597 the Hanseatic Merchants made a last desperate attempt to undermine what they claimed were monopolistic powers given to the Merchant Adventurers. This led to an interruption in the cloth trade as well as to a division within the Company. In an attempt to resolve this stoppage, freedom to trade was granted to all on the Elbe and the Weser. Following this upset (1601) a licence was granted to the Earl of Cumberland for the export of a very large quantity of undressed cloth, which the Merchant Adventurers eventually succeeded in leasing, the Patent for which contained a clause which enabled the licensee to dispense with the provision in the 1566 Statute that 1 in every 10 cloths exported should be dressed.

[77] As seen, some (if not all) of the Kent cloths were already dyed and dressed *in situ.* The only operations left for the London Clothworkers to carry out were folding, tacking, measuring, pressing and ticketing. It is by no means certain that all of these were executed in London.

[78] Morant, Valerie Economic History Review Vol.IV No.2 (1951) 213.

By the beginning of the 17th C. then one has a situation where Maidstone had earlier welcomed Protestant Refugees from the Netherlands, had given them a church[79] and had allowed them to retain their own ecclesiastical discipline. The weavers of the Weald likewise through long association with Protestant merchants abroad, particularly with those of the Netherlands, had also acquired strong leanings towards nonconformism. (To judge from the numbers that eventually emigrated from there it seems clear that over the years the clothworkers must have received considerable reinforcements from the Low Countries). This rapid extension of religious dissent in both of these areas meant that a clash with episcopacy was inevitable, a situation that was particularly aggravated by the intolerant attitude of the Stuart monarchy and the harsh measures introduced by Archbishop Laud. In 1634 Laud noted that Maidstone had "divers professed separatists" and took action against them accordingly; at the same time he tried to restrict the privileges previously granted to the 16th C. Dutch Settlers now firmly established there. They resisted and, as a consequence, were subsequently debarred from worship in the town. This led to the dispersion of several of these immigrant families; just where they went is not known. The effect on the Wealden clothworkers was far more serious. Rather than submit to Laud's restraints many of the weavers left for Holland (some of them, ultimately, emigrating thence to America).[80]

After this major set-back the production of cloth continued in the Cranbrook district, but on an ever-diminishing scale, for another 100 years;[81] and with the parallel demise of the wealden iron smelting industry the prosperity of the region decayed to a point from which it never recovered. Moreover, after the Restoration in 1660 further harsh measures were taken against the dissenters by Charles II and these particularly affected areas like Maidstone and Cranbrook.[82] To what extent these last proceedings affected the paper makers whom we are concerned with in this Chapter is a matter for conjecture; undoubtedly they would have had to contend with the effects of very divergent religious persuasions on the parishes in which they worked.[83]

It would be logically admissible at this point to ask the question what conceivable connection has this rise and fall of the Kent cloth industry with our concern here with the early history of papermaking in Kent ? The short answer to this question is that had there been no cloth industry here the development of papermaking in the county would have evolved along entirely different lines, probably very much more slowly and, lastly, never involved a Whatman, the paper maker we are chiefly interested in. The events that had taken place and

[79] St Faith's Chapel as it was then; the present church of St Faith's was built on the same site in 1871.

[80] The Kentish Petition of 1640, against Laud's provocative romanizing policies, claimed that "Multitudes, both clothiers, merchants and others, being deprived of their Ministers, and overburdened with their pressures, have departed the Kingdom, to Holland and other parts, and have drawn with them a great part of the manufacture of cloth and trading, out of the land, into places where they reside; whereby Wool (the great Staple of the Kingdom) is become of small value, and vends not.....".

[81] Pile reports that Goudhurst still had 30 looms in 1725, but that shortly after the number was reduced to a dozen. (Pile, C.C.R. op.cit.23).

[82] The Act of Uniformity (1662), enforcing the use of the Book of Common Prayer, led to the ejection of Crump, the vicar of Maidstone; equally, Dr. Calamy reported "10 Ministers cast out of this town (Cranbrook) and places adjacent", many of the Ministers being very moderate in their views. The Conventicle Act (1664) applied more to the laity and forbade meetings of more than 5 persons for religious worship not consistent with the precepts of the Prayer Book. As a result of these measures many local nonconformists were thrown into gaol, some left to die there and others imprisoned for more than 20 years. The Quakers were particularly harshly treated; their founder, George Fox, visited Cranbrook in 1655 and after the Restoration a lot of his followers, both in Cranbrook and Maidstone, were gaoled. Maidstone also had at this time congregations of Presbyterians and Baptists, who were persecuted. One of the most influential of the Baptists was Simon Pine, a fuller of Tovil, whose descendants became prominent Maidstone paper makers in the 18th and 19th Cs. He gave land in Tovil as a burial ground (still there) for the Baptists after the Declaration of Indulgence (1672), when they were able to obtain a licence for a meeting house in Tovil. (See also "The Vicars of Boxley etc." App.IV).

[83] The paper makers may well have been affected more by the strictures of the Puritans than by others. Under Robert Barrell, the incumbent of All Saints' Maidstone (ejected ca. 1643) it was still acceptable for people to work in the local fulling mills on Sundays. Thomas Wilson, a severe Puritan and successor to the incumbency (1643-1653), soon put a stop to this practice. A reflection of this may be seen in Thomas Heymes' comment in the Boxley Parish Register, written probably between 1667 and 1677, on Thomas Willard "Goodman Wellard at the Paper mill quia non frequentat Ecclesiam". Heymes, described as "a creature of the Puritan party" was vicar there from 1648-1678. (For further details see section on Willard/Wellard in App.IV).

which were still unfolding both in the Weald and in the Maidstone area following the decline of this industry had a profound effect in shaping the future course of the paper industry in these districts. To appreciate this, three points that emerge from the previous pages should be noted:–

(1)   A very extensive fulling industry had been established at an early date in both the High Weald of Kent and along the rivers converging on the Medway at Maidstone, the Rivers Loose and Len. The capacity of the River Loose for mill sites had already been saturated by 1500; and the same might be said for the River Len by 1600.[84]

With the decline of the Woollen Cloth industry the fulling mills became progressively redundant. No fulling mills were active in the Cranbrook area after the 16th C.[85] A similar sort of picture is given by Spain for the Maidstone area; many of them had disappeared or been converted by the end of the 17th C. and very few survived as fulling mills after the first decades of the 18th C. The importance of these redundant mills will be discussed later in this chapter.

(2)   Probably because of the longstanding links between the Kentish Weavers and the Netherlands and their struggle for freedom, correspondingly strong liberal attitudes to religion and politics thrived in the Maidstone and Wealden areas. In the case of Maidstone these trends were inevitably influenced further by the settlement of the Protestant Refugees there in the 16th C. One has then two industrial areas that would have been receptive to other Protestant immigrants escaping from persecution by Richelieu in France during the first half of the 17th C.,[86] harassment that was to continue throughout the century culminating in 1685 with the Revocation of the Edict of Nantes. Many of these refugees were craftsmen who would have brought with them new ideas and methods.

(3)   The demise of the Wealden Iron Smelting Industry in the 17th C., resulting partly from an acute shortage of wood, the fuel used for this, and partly from the importation of Swedish iron;[87] and the decline of the Cloth industry, stemming from political intervention and the debasement of the currency in the 16th C. and religious persecution in the 17th C., together with further post–Restoration religious intolerance, collectively created pressures that either led to emigration or the local movement of the population to more prosperous areas.

Having looked at the historical background of this region one can now revert to the examination of Goudhurst paper mill in the light of this and ask the question, why should anyone have built a paper mill in this remote and rather inaccessible district and when and what kind of paper was made there. It has already been pointed out in this chapter that one

[84]   Spain, R.J. Bib.8 99 fig.11.
[85]   See this Chapter note 67.
[86]   Both before (under Elizabeth) and after (under Charles I) the Edict of Nantes (1598) the English had been helping the French Protestants actively.
[87]   It is of interest to note that, in an attempt to keep the industry going, even as late as 1637 John Browne of Brenchley set up a very large new foundry there. (Another large works was also set up at the same time in West Kent at Cowden).

cannot explain the building of a mill here simply as a lateral expansion of an existing papermaking district such as those that had grown up to the West of London.

One of the first points to note is that the paper mill appears to have been built as a paper mill and not converted from some other function. The site of many other mills, furnace mills, fulling mills etc., have been identified; but there is no hint that the paper mill site had ever been used for anything previously.

Secondly, although the Weald was undoubtedly an industrial area and might therefore have had a general requirement for paper, with the state of the domestic industry at that time, these needs in the normal way would have been met by purchasing imported paper. However, it is a fact, certainly for a later period than this, that paper mills were often built in districts manufacturing woollen cloth to supply the industry with what were known as Press papers, glazed papers used in the processes for finishing the cloth. These papers were in effect Brown papers subsequently hammered or burnished with a glazing wheel to give them a smooth surface. Just how far back this kind of paper was manufactured in this country is not known. There is evidence from which one may infer that it was being made in England before the end of the 17th C.;[88] and perhaps much earlier than this.[89]

With the above in mind there seem to be three possible solutions to the questions asked here regarding the origin of Goudhurst paper mill:-

(i)   that the mill was built to provide Press papers for the Cloth industry and that the decline of this industry eventually led to the closure of the paper mill (ca.1700).

(ii)   that the mill was originally built to make Press papers, but that production changed direction later in favour of mixed papers, possibly including the manufacture of White paper.

(iii)   that the mill was built in the first place to make White paper.

There are, of course, other possible alternatives to these proposals; but since absolutely nothing has been discovered yet about the founding of this paper mill one can do no more at present than speculate on its early history and products. In the light of what we have learnt about this region the second proposal seems to offer the most plausible solution, though not without its difficulties.

It will be recalled that prior to 1566 it was customary to export cloth from this country in the undressed state and that a new Statute (8.Eliz.c.6) forbad any person "to carry into Parts beyond the Seas.....any Cloth....made or to be made in the Counties of Kent and Suffolk, unwrought and undressed within this realm; that is to say, not rowed, barbed, first coursed and shorn". Kentish cloth was usually dyed in the wool so that all that remained would have

---

[88]   Robert Fuller's Patent of 1684 (discussed in more detail in Chapter V note 66) refers to "the art and mistery for making paper and pastboards in whole sheets without piecing for hott and cold pressing of cloath.....". The hot-pressing of cloth was certainly an established process in England by this date. An early Stuart engraving illustrates a hot press as used in the wool industry.

[89]   Shorter, A. Bib.12 42 mentions the fact that some of the earliest paper mills in Surrey (possibly near Guildford and Godalming) may have made Press papers; an unidentified mill may have existed near Godalming ca.1625; other mills were established at Stoke (1635) and Eashing (1658).

been to dress it, i.e. to "row" the loose fibres of the cloth with teazles to raise the nap, which was then cropped to give it a smooth surface; and, finally, to *press* it to give it a durable lustre. It seems that Kent clothworkers were able to obtain facilities for dressing the cloth, but whether these included a supply of Press papers or not is not known. In parts of the country where cloth was "finished" in the 16th C. it seems that a hot iron may have been used;[90] indeed from what we know about the English paper industry there can only have been very few paper mills active at that time from which papers of this kind could have been obtained.

With the arrival of new immigrant clothworkers and paper makers in or around 1567 bringing with them the New Draperies the situation created by the recent Statute could have led to the Clothiers commissioning the construction of a paper mill in a central position on what must have been one of the few sites left not being used for other purposes.[91] On this basis one might postulate a late 16th C. origin for a Press paper mill at Goudhurst; an enterprise started on a date much later than this would have had to face a situation with the Cloth industry in a state of steep decline. Pursuing the first solution proposed above for the origin of the paper mill one might envisage that this decline was reflected in a decline in the fortunes of this mill resulting in its closure at the end of the 17th C. But the character of the paper makers who have been identified there and the timing of their ultimate move out of the district does not support this idea; it looks more as if there might have been a change in direction at some point about the middle of the 17th C., in other words following the course suggested in the second solution proposed above. Moreover, the notion that Goudhurst paper mill had been built to make Press papers for a famous cloth industry that was still flourishing fits these facts better than the idea that it had been founded without any apparent reason in a region that was remote and in decline just to make paper whether White or Brown (and with no obvious outlets), namely, the third of the proposed solutions. On balance then the second solution is the one favoured here, but it has its difficulties in that no obvious candidates for a founder paper maker in the late 16th C. has emerged.[92]

---

[90] A carved pew end in Spaxton Church, Somerset, illustrates a 16th C. cloth finisher using what appears to be a flat–iron.

[91] As mentioned earlier the industries of the Weald quite possibly absorbed a steady flow of refugees both from the Low Countries and after the Massacre of St Bartholomew (1572) from France as well; these may well have included paper makers who not only found their way there but possibly to other parts of Kent. (See Note 111)

[92] A search of the Goudhurst and Horsmonden (the parish on the opposite bank of the Teise to the paper mill) parish registers, in particular the Marriage Registers (though baptisms were searched also), showed that during the period 1560–1600 Horsmonden (KAO TR 1042/8) showed no obvious "foreign" names; but Goudhurst (KAO P 157 28/1 bapt. 28/2 marr. and 28/12 bur.) on the other hand quite a number. There is nothing to indicate what trade they followed and one cannot be absolutely certain that the names are those of immigrants. They occur mainly between 1560–1595; after this there are no obvious "foreign" names until one comes to Manktellow (spelt variously) for which see later in the text. The Goudhurst names are as follows:–

1560–61	Hovinden, Janson, Vousden, Degoye, Hoiccarde
1568	Drotche
1571	Vousden, Hovinden
1579	Totche
1582	Stempe
1594	Homsbe m. Godlie Hollan
1595	Huesteepe

Early in the 17th C. Richard Rode (bapt. 1615) whose father, Edward, lived at Broad Ford very close to the paper mill site; Robert Wilson (bapt. 1624); and Thomas Willard (bapt. 1633) are names of the first paper makers known to have come from Goudhurst. Thomas' father was not born in Goudhurst, but there had been a previous generation of Willards

(continued...)

As the absolute origins of papermaking in Kent are outside the scope of this work, the solution of this must be left to others; interest here lies more in the origins of the first paper makers who came to Maidstone and this takes us to the period where there might have been a change in direction.

The idea of a change in direction comes from an assessment of the later performance of paper makers who occupied it in the 17th C. such as Willard, Manktellow, Archer and perhaps Musgrove. Some of these may have ended up making Brown paper but who, like Peter Archer a paper maker of some substance, may have made White at an earlier stage. Where and from whom could they have learnt this ? With this in mind one looks back at Goudhurst mill to see if there were any reasons for thinking that any of these proposals might have taken place. The cases of Thomas Taylor[93] and Willard will be considered separately under the heading of Forstal mill later in this chapter; the only point *of mentioning the latter here* is that it is known that Willard left Goudhurst 10 years before any of the others, possibly for different reasons. The only point to make about him here is that since he was born in Goudhurst, and assuming that a Press paper mill was operating then, he could have served his apprenticeship there without one having to recourse to the idea that he had to leave the district to learn his trade, bearing in mind that there would have been *very few* mills where he could have done this.[94]

In pursuing the hypothesis proposed above interest centres now on the Manktellow family; but this interest must be considered in conjunction with the fact that towards the end of the 1670's, and after, there was a dramatic expansion of the paper industry in Kent, the opening up of new mills in new districts (see Table II), greatly in excess of the expansion found in other areas. This applied particularly to the Maidstone area. Some of this expansion could no doubt be accounted for by the natural growth of the industry; but to account for the balance some other explanation must be sought. As already mentioned, it seems more than a matter of chance that this burst of activity in the Maidstone area should have coincided with the embargo on French goods (and have been influenced perhaps by other international events as well). The paper maker in the small corn–cum–paper type of mill is not likely to have seen an opening here or have had the capital to take advantage of it in contrast to paper makers of the calibre of George Gill, trained in a centre with a long tradition for making White paper. Likewise, immigrant paper makers would undoubtedly have been much more alive to the opportunities that a situation of this kind presented them with, particularly if they already

---

[92](...continued)

    there. It is possible, therefore, to conjecture an earlier member of one or other of these families having had an association with this mill. But it seems more likely that, if the notion of a 16th C. origin for the mill is accepted, ultimately one would expect to find an immigrant founder. A late 16th C. origin could have placed it earlier than Dartford No.1 and Eynsford; Dover, it has been suggested, may also have been founded by an immigrant.

[93]   Thomas Taylor is mentioned here because, if in fact he was born in Goudhurst in 1612 and trained there between 1624–31 (see this chapter), he would have been the earliest identifiable paper maker that we could associate with this mill, preceding even Richard Roads and Robert Wilson. Whereas we know that Roads and Wilson came from Goudhurst, Taylor's case is one of surmise. Though later in date Willard is the best documented figure and we know for certain that he moved from Goudhurst to go to Forstal mill.

[94]   If one considers the case that Willard could have learnt his trade at, say, Dartford or Eynsford, then one has to find a reason why he, the eldest son, was motivated into learning a trade foreign to that district (i.e. assuming no paper mill existed in Goudhurst then) and then returning there either to found a new paper mill or work in one recently erected by some unidentified person. The notion that a paper mill already existed in Goudhurst with a tradition of papermaking makes much better sense and takes care of other paper makers like Roads and Wilson.

possessed the capability and skills for making White paper. Indeed, we have seen earlier that it was just at this time that immigrant paper makers like Peter le Gaultier and Dupin were entering this field themselves.

It must be pointed out, however, that the influence of these better known immigrants on Kent papermaking was not seen until the COMPANY took over Dartford No.2 mill in 1693, 15 to 20 years later. Apart from George Gill and the Dartford tradition one has to ask the question, were there other immigrant influences at work in Kent capable of exploiting this situation. It is at this point that the Manktellows attract interest.

It is a fact that Stephen Manktellow was a paper maker and that he moved to Maidstone late in 1679; it is known also for certain that he was the occupant of Goudhurst paper mill from 1675 (when the Ratebook starts); from other facts we know about him[95] it would not be unreasonable to assume that he succeeded Thomas Willard when the latter left for Forstal, suggested as being ca. 1668/9.

As it happens the name Manktellow (the spelling adopted here for convenience) is unique in its occurrence in English Records for that period. It certainly has not been found at all in the course of a wide search of parish records in or near paper mill districts in Kent and there is no entry of it in the Great Card Index of the Society of Genealogists (and in other similar records) earlier than 1750.[96] The conclusion may be drawn then that Stephen, if not an immigrant himself, was not likely to have been removed from being one by more than one generation. Looking further back in the Goudhurst parish registers one finds that an Alexander Manktellow appears there for the first time in 1644, an entry for the baptism of a daughter. Several other daughters were baptised later, up to 1669, but there are no baptismal entries for a "Stephen" or an "Alexander jnr." (the latter m.1676 : bur.1709). From this and other information, it would seem that both Stephen and Alexander jnr. (perhaps his younger brother) were born *after* 1644. One must assume then that either they were sons of Alexander snr. (bur.1673) whose baptisms were not entered in the register or that they had arrived in this country from another branch of the family at a later date than Alexander snr., possibly because the latter needed an heir to whatever business he was engaged in. It may be noted that the incumbents of whatever parishes the Manktellows moved to had great difficulty in spelling the name. Taking the variations as a whole, the suggestion that the name may originally have been "Mantelleau" and French is acceptable.[97]

So one has the situation of an Alexander Mantelleau arriving out of the blue in Goudhurst ca. 1644 (there are *no other* contemporary references to a Manktellow or variants in any of the surrounding parishes).[98] It is assumed here that he was a French refugee and one asks what made him and his family choose Goudhurst in the first place and then decide to stay there? Since it has been demonstrated that Stephen was a paper maker, one might also ask was Alexander one too and, if so, did he found or put new life into a paper mill there? On present

---

[95]   For details see App.IV under Stephen Manktellow.
[96]   Not in Soc. of Genealogists' Great Card Index; Huguenot Society's list of denizations 1509–1700; International Genealogy Index of the Utah Gen. Soc.
[97]   The name is apparently not a Dutch name as has been suggested elsewhere in the literature. See App.IV for further details.
[98]   These include Cranbrook, Horsmonden, Marden, Lamberhurst, Benenden and others.

evidence it is quite impossible to answer these questions; there are many alternatives and yet at the same time one has to account for the presence of several paper makers already associated with Goudhurst at this time and the probability that some of these at some time acquired the know–how for White paper manufacture, when up till then Goudhurst paper mill can only have been a mill capable of making Press papers. There is, for example, a Robert Wilson, baptised in Goudhurst in 1636 and subsequently married in Maidstone in 1657, described as a paper maker of Goudhurst.[99] There was a Thomas Willard, possibly not the one we are concerned with, who was described as a "paperman" in the Marden Register in 1655;[100] and our Thomas Willard who was certainly the Master Paper Maker at the mill in 1666, the evidence for this to be found in a deed that brings one into contact with yet another paper maker, described in the document as Richard Roads, a paper maker of Bedhampton in Hampshire and who was baptised in Goudhurst in 1615[101] and born at a place very close to the paper mill site. Finally, at some point in its history one has to recognize that there were two paper mills there, an upper and a lower. There are then a lot of loose ends to try to tie up with no real evidence as yet to help put these together to form a clear picture.

Before concluding this section on the paper mill at Goudhurst, there is no harm in speculating on the answers to these questions and seeing where this leads one. Stephen Manktellow had almost without doubt an immigrant origin and he may have been in charge of Goudhurst mill as early as 1668; one might safely deduce from this that he would have been conversant with continental papermaking practices, which he would have imparted to his successors. Peter Archer was in fact his immediate successor and one can make out for him also a fairly convincing case that he too was an immigrant.[102] One can propose with some confidence that the immigrant influence that we have been looking for emanated from Goudhurst as from ca. 1670. Could it have originated there earlier, for instance, with the arrival of Alexander Manktellow in 1644 ? If this was the case, it seems unlikely that Alexander would have been particularly interested in making Brown paper (though he may have been compelled by circumstances to do this); nor in continuing to make Press papers for an almost defunct woollen industry. One might even envisage the proprietor of Goudhurst mill,[103] assuming it had an earlier existence, welcoming someone who might put new life into a dying business, perhaps building a new mill there at the same time. If Alexander had done this in 1644, one could in theory accommodate the training of Thomas Willard there and the employment of both Wilson and Willard during the period of his tenure. Lacking a successor of the right age Alexander may have then temporarily ceded the lease to Thomas Willard; and, when Stephen came of age, Thomas had to move on.[104] The known facts about this situation are satisfied

---

[99] See App.IV under Robert Wilson. After his marriage Wilson seemingly disappears from the records; no trace of him found.

[100] There were 4 contemporary Thomas Willards in the adjoining parishes of Marden, Goudhurst and Horsmonden. For identification see App.IV under "The Willards of Goudhurst".

[101] KAO U 1406.

[102] The case for this is given in App.IV in a special section under "The Archers: Their Origin and Relationship discussed". A case can also be made out for an English origin, at Hatfield in Hertfordshire; see App.IV as above.

[103] The suggestion has been made that the Rode family at Broad Ford (less than a mile from the mill site) may have had interest in or even owned the paper mill and adjoining land; certainly Willard had to pay rent to Richard Rode in 1666. For discussion see App. IV under Goudhurst Paper Mill.

[104] Acceptance of this theory means that Willard almost certainly would have taken some experience of White paper manufacture with him to Forstal. The Ightham PR (KAO P.202 1/2) is made up of very highly glazed second quality unwatermarked White paper made prior to 1654 which could easily have been made at Goudhurst, especially if it had had long experience in making Press papers.

by this explanation, which is lent some further support by the continued residence of the Manktellow family there for a period of some 36 years.

Whether there is any substance in this theory or not, it has been demonstrated in the previous pages that:–

(a)   Goudhurst provided Maidstone with three Master Paper Makers; probably another, Musgrove; and conceivably others like West and Russell (though alternatives for these exist) and Taylor. It may well have supplied in addition under–papermakers and journeymen, as yet unidentified. It was undoubtedly one of the most important sources of papermaking expertise for the emerging Maidstone paper industry.

(b)   The timing of the paper makers' migration from Goudhurst strongly suggests that this was connected with an intention, if not already realised at Goudhurst, of manufacturing White paper.

(c)   To account for several paper makers active in or emanating from Goudhurst in the first half of the 17th C. a mill had probably been operating there as far back as the late 16th C. and making Press papers for the cloth industry. It has been suggested that this may have been initiated by an immigrant from the Netherlands; but with the decline in the demand for these papers following the demise of the cloth industry an effort seems to have been made, to judge from the continuing activity there until the end of the 17th C., to keep the paper mills in business. It has been proposed here that the impetus this time came from French immigrants having experience in the manufacture of White paper.[105]

---

[105]   Shorter, A. Bib.12 38–43, 74–5 lists many agencies that affected the siting of early paper mills in this country, places not always of the paper maker's choosing. Although it appears to have been built as a paper mill, and thus presumably with an element of choice in siting it, it is an appropriate point to consider here an additional factor that may or may not have influenced the continued existence of the Goudhurst mills and the quality and types of paper made there. Mention has already been made in the text of points such as the possible requirements of the local industrial area for paper and the effect of the decline of the cloth and iron industries on the mills that produced it. In the pages that follow reference will be made to some of the other factors that determined the future of these paper mills such as the remoteness of the site from alternative markets and the difficulties that would have been encountered in transporting products to them. But Shorter draws attention to yet another factor that might more specifically have accounted for the general scarcity of paper mills in the Wealden district (p.75) because, he suggests, paper makers may have deliberately wanted to avoid sources of water that were liable to contain iron, or clay in suspension.

With Brown or Press papers it is unlikely that either of these two contaminants would have mattered unless the concentrations were very severe, in which case it is doubtful that whoever built the mills would have chosen this site and stream in the first place. In any case the mill or mills continued to operate where they were for the best part of a century, if not longer than this. So it seems safe to rule out these potential sources of trouble where it concerned the manufacture of inferior grades of paper; but they could have presented problems to anyone proposing to make White paper.

In considering this point one has to remember that the paper makers in the 17th C. would not only not have had modern scientific facilities for examining the quality of the water, and thus avoiding its use, but both they and the users of the paper would have been accustomed to a much lower standard of White paper than, say, consumers of the 18th C. A lot of so-called White paper made before the last quarter of the 17th C. would have had a greyish cast possibly due to fermented rags and contained at the same time what would later have been regarded as unacceptable amounts of shive and other extraneous matter. It is very doubtful then whether anyone would have noticed the presence of iron in any White paper made there unless it was excessive.

Recent analyses (and I am indebted to Mr. P.M. Bolas, Chief Scientist of the Mid Kent Water Company for supplying me with this information) show that the water in this region has a high or very high iron content, possibly amounting

(continued...)

The aim of this exposition of Goudhurst paper mill is not to make out that its influence was necessarily a long–term or successful one so far as the manufacture of White paper was concerned (the real achievements in this field were to come later, in the 18th C.) but rather to demonstrate that the potential for this manufacture was there, perhaps as far back as the middle of the 17th C. in the form of a rising generation of Master Paper Makers who owed nothing to the entrepreneurs described in Chapter I. This new strain helped lay the foundations of a new papermaking district, which was to become a centre of the first importance in the manufacture of White paper, namely, Maidstone.

Forstal (Boxley) and Millhall (Ditton) Paper Mills

The reader will have noticed that in company with some of the other Kent mills listed in Table I references have been made since then to much earlier starting dates than those shown there, e.g. Buckland now before 1600; a 16th C. date postulated for Goudhurst mill; and in the case of Forstal a documentary reference to 1665 and the possibility that Millhall mill may have been active as early as 1668. With regard to the evidence, allegedly supporting these last two assertions, Appendix III must be consulted in the case of Forstal and Appendix IV for Millhall mill. Only the main points will be touched on here. In each case the question is, how far back do the histories of these two mills go ? Is there anything to support the notion that one or both of them may have been operating in the 16th C. ? It is very doubtful we shall ever know the answer to this last point. The situation is a much more difficult one than has been the case with Goudhurst mill. The Table below indicates that the handicaps are from the start considerable:–

[105](...continued)

to quantities 50 times higher than that found, for example, in the water of the Maidstone district. It is difficult to arrive at a precise estimate because the amounts tend to vary seasonally and with the rainfall. An additional difficulty is the fact that the geology of the area is complicated by a number of faults, though it is fairly certain that the springs feeding the stream on which the paper mills lay would have been contaminated with iron derived from one or other of the ironstone bands lying in the Tunbridge Wells sand and the Wadhurst clay.

One can only conclude from all this that, initially, the iron content need not have been a major factor in deterring a Goudhurst paper maker from making a White paper that would have been acceptable, had he wished to do so; but, later, it could well have been a contributory factor in the demise of these mills at the end of the 17th C. as the standards of quality rose and paper makers like George Gill started drawing on the much purer spring water found in the Maidstone district.

Finally, one might query the overall validity of Shorter's suggestion, namely, specific impurities in the water as a reason for the scarcity of paper mills in the Weald of South East England. One really has to go further than this and ask the question, why were there so few paper mills in Kent as a whole at that time compared to the West of London Region? The quality of the water may indeed have been an important agent in determining the early predominance of the industry to the West of London. Shorter cites an extract from Robert Plot's notebooks (written ca.1693. loc.cit 50 note 129) "The River that crosses Hounslow heath runs many miles all upon gravel, so that the water is clear even in time of flood, for which reason it is the best River for making paper in the Kingdom of England". Once established in such a suitable environment the lateral expansion of the industry in Middlesex and the High Wycombe district of Buckinghamshire would have followed rapidly, as Shorter's Maps demonstrate (Figures 1, 1495–1600, and 2, 1601–1650). In the absence of a similar suitable surface water supply the notion of using spring water may not have been widely known then, a fact which could account for the later development of the White paper industry in Kent. Once the industry had become more widely established there, then the proximity of the markets and facilities for transporting goods would have been more important agencies in deciding the future location of paper mills than the contaminants of the waters of the Weald.

Parish	Registers	Ratebook or A/cs
Boxley	start 1558	start 1691
Aylesford (in between)	start 1654	effective from 1657/68
Ditton	start 1663	start 1677

Added to this, the entries in the Boxley PRs. are very scarce during the ministry of Thomas Heymes (1646–77); and though in theory the Aylesford accounts start early in the 17th C. the first entries are fragments only, the first complete set in 1657 and not regular until ca.1668. Some deeds and other documents take one back a little further than the Churchwardens' accounts, useful especially in the case of Boxley where the ratebook starts at a very late date. And then one comes to a standstill.

These two mills lay approximately 1.5 miles apart on either side of Aylesford village situated about half–way between (see Map 10 at end of book). They may thus be considered together conveniently. The relevant question here is whether one or both of these mills contributed to the expansion of the paper industry at Maidstone in the 1680's. It is clear from the evidence that Forstal mill was operating at least 15 years before this development got under way, and quite possibly as long as 40 years.[106] No parallel indications have been discovered in the case of Millhall mill, but there are other aspects of this situation that suggest that Millhall equally might have been operating at a much earlier date than hitherto thought to be the case; these will be considered below as part of the examination of Forstal.

For one thing both of these mills occupied unusual sites; both were constructed within the flood plain of the River Medway (as indeed seems to have been the case with a mill site at Snodland, further down the river).[107] The Forstal site was marginally more elevated than the Millhall one but because the former has long since been erased by later industrial activities one can only try to relate it to what is known about the latter. In Fuller's description[108] it was noted that extensive banking was used in the construction of the Millhall millpond to provide it with an effective head of water for its operations; and, again, in his view[109] this mill could have been built as a paper mill rather than one converted to papermaking from some other function. In other words if these mills were founded as paper mills at an early date, then obviously they cannot be seen as a material part of the expansion of the paper industry at Maidstone in the 1680's, though they may have contributed to it indirectly.

If one accepts for the moment that one or both of these mills were founded at a much earlier date, the same question arises that we have had before, who founded them in what must then have been *virgin territory for papermaking* ? and why the choice of these unusual sites ? The choice of these sites suggests that, as in the case proposed for Goudhurst paper mill, other more suitable sites were at that time saturated with mills serving other industries, especially if this had been at a time when the fulling industry was flourishing.

A second point to note is that the kind of construction required for mills in these low level

---

[106] See discussion of Sir Edward Duke's Will (P.R.O. PROB.11–183) made in 1640 in App.III under Forstal.

[107] Mr. M.J. Fuller is currently (1986) working on the mills situated on the Leybourne Stream and has kindly informed me that the site believed to have been occupied by Snodland Paper mill lies as in the case of Millhall mill (and probably Forstal mill) within the flood plain of the River Medway. But so far nothing has been discovered about its early function, no evidence of a paper mill there before 1755.

[108] Fuller, M.J. Bib.13.

[109] Fuller, verbal communication.

sites would have presented no problems to paper makers accustomed to working in low–lying districts. The further back one goes in time the fewer candidates we are likely to find with English origins who could have set up mills of this kind in uncharted papermaking territory. All the elements are here that favour a proposal that immigrant paper makers had founded these mills at a time when more conventional mill sites were in short supply and a reasonable solution to this situation is to suggest that "the Makers of White and Browne Paper" referred to in the 1567 Petition from Maidstone to the Crown for the settlement of the Protestant refugees from the Netherlands were the ones who built these mills. No documentary evidence has been found to support this proposal beyond the fact that the Patent was granted and presumably the paper makers must have settled somewhere in a place that has yet to be determined.

The names of the paper makers do not appear in Maidstone records as was the case with other settlers. But this is not surprising considering that paper mills were usually found in rural districts away from a town. If their products had been retailed locally, it is more likely that they would have been found in the market place rather than in shops (or else have been supplied directly to a Clothier). Furthermore, there was no Guild to which paper makers would have been affiliated; and very few people would have been involved in their operations. All in all these paper makers would have been difficult to trace except through parish records perhaps and deeds which either do not exist or remain to be discovered.[110] Finally, to judge from the very few and scattered references to the industry in contemporary documents, the immigrants' employment in papermaking would have passed unnoticed.

Taking all these things into consideration there is no obvious objection in proposing that one or both of these mills had been built in the 16th C. but whether they operated afterwards continuously or intermittently can only be guessed at. An alternative to this idea is that, in view of the traffic between them at a later date, paper makers from Goudhurst may have been invited over by the owners of the land to *build* paper mills for them in the Aylesford area. In such a case one still has to find motives for the landowners undertaking an enterprise of this kind, engaging a papermaker from a quite different district to build a mill on an unusual site and introduce papermaking into a place where none had existed before and which would have been without the millwrights and tradesmen necessary for constructing and operating them. The latter is a possibility; but of the two the idea of a 16th C. origin seems to fit the circumstances better than the Goudhurst one.[111] The chances of finding an answer to these proposals are remote. In spite of this the subject still has a bearing on the expansion that took place later, in that one can no longer regard it as a migration into virgin territory. If one works backwards from this event we shall see why.

In the case of Millhall mill no significant progress can be made in this direction. A map of 1684[112] illustrates a paper mill, house and pond on this site and it can be inferred from this

---

[110] In a search of the first Boxley PR covering a period of 1567–77 no obviously foreign names were noted. Unfortunately, it is not possible to make a similar check in either the Aylesford or Ditton PRs., parishes that were much closer to the river and more likely to have been chosen by immigrant paper makers.

[111] Overend, G.H. Bib.66 199, sources not given, refers to a long–standing tradition that French refugees are said to have established mills in various parts of Kent, at Maidstone, and along the Darent at an early date. (The possibility that Dartford might have been a contender has also been mooted earlier though there is no evidence to support this idea.)

[112] KAO U 49 P 4 Courtlodge Farm, A. Walter.

that the mill existed *before* this date though one cannot be certain when it was active. There were very few ratepayers in this small parish and it is thus possible to identify the 1684 occupant[113] and trace him back to 1681 at least. But one comes to a point then, too complicated to discuss here (see Appendix IV), where others like the Richardsons, Smith(s) and the Ashedownes may have been involved and, above all, James West. It is only the fact that we know the latter was present in the area from 1668 that lends credence to the idea that initially he could have been a non−resident paper maker at Millhall mill; from 1688 he *was* the resident paper maker. With Thomas Willard occupying Forstal sometime before 1671 (ca.1668/9) one has to find a home for West and it could have been Millhall mill. In any case there is nothing in the Church Book to suggest that a new mill had just been constructed on this site (although the ratable value did rise when West took it over in 1688, but then there is the *evidence of the map showing a paper mill before that date*). The best one can do is to propose, provisionally, that a paper mill had been active there as early as 1668 and that its site and construction suggest an earlier date than this.

In the case of Forstal the matter can be taken further back than this. A document[114] shows that Thomas Taylor was the occupant of the paper mill in 1665. The fact that it was described as "one other Messuage or Tenement with a Paper mill, Mill stream and Mill Pond, Workhouse, Outhouses, Buildings and Appurtenances adjoining....." confirms the view that it was an established papermaking concern with no hint of it being " a new−built paper−mill". This is the earliest reference found so far that specifies a paper mill. It was then owned by George Duke of the Manor of Cossington in Aylesford who had inherited the property from his father, Sir Edward, in 1640; he left to George, among other things, "...all other messuages, mill*s*, edifices, buildings, gardens, orchards....lying in the parishes of Aylesford, Boxley, Burham (and others).....".[115] No earlier deeds relating to the Duke family have been found; so to go back further one has to rely (as above) on Wills. No mill is mentioned in Thomas Duke's Will (1608),[116] Edward's father and the first member of the family to live in Aylesford. The mill must therefore have been built or bought by Edward or acquired through a marriage settlement. To avoid going into detail here (see App.III) the most helpful solution would seem to be that the (paper) mill had come into Edward's possession through his second wife, formerly Jane Russell, whose family came from "Ailsford, Kent".[117] At present one can get no further than this supposition.

To summarise, a speculative case can be made out for a 16th C. origin for these two mills; but, working backwards, only in the case of Forstal is there any certainty that a paper mill existed in the area before 1665 and possibly before 1640. In the present context it is really sufficient to know only that there was at least one mill near Maidstone working long before the main migration of paper makers took place. In contrast to a concept of virgin territory then there is evidence of a stepping stone already in position to aid expansion. Furthermore, the fact that so many paper makers converged later on Maidstone in such a short space of time suggests that these mills were better known than one might imagine, particularly if one

---

[113] John Richardson (see App.IV under Millhall mill).

[114] KAO U 1823/24 T3 Part (1).

[115] P.R.O. PROB. 11−183. Other parishes mentioned include Newington (nr. Hythe), Halstow and Romney Marsh.

[116] Local Court of Rochester KAO DR$_b$/PW21.

[117] No mill is mentioned in her father's Will, Robert Russell of "Ailsford" (d.1626) P.R.O. PROB 11−149. For further discussion of these Russells see App. IV under "The Russells".

accepts the notion that early paper makers like Taylor and West arrived either from or via Goudhurst. Something seems to have induced this flow which makes one think that the mills had been there for a long time.

Was there another, unidentified, Kent Paper Mill ?

The reason for asking this question is not so much a concern in finding another source for paper makers who came to Maidstone as one of trying to explain the apparent disappearance for a period of two prominent paper makers, Peter Archer snr. from Goudhurst between 1673–80 and Alexander Russell, the Ancient Paper Maker, between his marriage in 1683 and his arrival in Shoreham ca.1690. With large numbers of fulling mills becoming redundant in the High Weald during the 17th C. it is not difficult to imagine that one or two of them might not have been converted as a temporary measure to papermaking until more favourable opportunities presented themselves elsewhere, albeit the existence of such mills has not come to light yet. Such a conversion could account for the absence of these two paper makers.

In the case of Peter Archer the 7 missing years are an important element in assumptions made later in this book.[118] In theory he and Elizabeth could have had a family that included Richard, Elizabeth, possibly Robert and Mary during this period. The first two would certainly fit in well here; Robert is an altogether unknown quantity; and all we know about "Mary" is that a Mary Archer was buried in Brenchley (quite close to Goudhurst) in 1679, but we know nothing about her age or status except that the name is not otherwise found there at all. Brenchley was a very large parish in those times (since subdivided into three) and without doubt would have had many potential mill sites for conversion.[119]

In the case of Alexander Russell, if he had connections with Goudhurst then he too might have followed Archer to this "unidentified mill" and worked there from the time of his marriage (1683) until he appeared at Shoreham, the first documentary evidence of his presence there being not until 1692.[120]

THE EXPANSION OF THE PAPER INDUSTRY IN KENT AND ITS MIGRATION TO MAIDSTONE

Earlier in this chapter the growth of the paper industry in Kent, especially during the latter part of the 17th C., has been demonstrated; in addition it has been shown how this expansion centred on the Maidstone area during the last quarter and who the paper makers concerned initially in this were. Finally, so far as this has been possible, the origins of these paper makers have been determined. The results show that the majority of the first wave (Map 2 inset), if not all, converged on the Maidstone district from other areas. It may be added here that this expansion continued on into the early 18th C. (as Table IV demonstrates) and this aspect will be considered further below; but before doing this it would be as well to look at the reasons for this expansion and the initial migration.

---

[118] See Chap.IV pp.139–143 and App.IV under "The Archers : Their Origin and Relationship".

[119] If in fact they did operate an unidentified paper mill in the High Weald, factors such as iron contamination of the water and isolation from markets may not have suited paper makers like Archer for a long-term stay.

[120] See App.IV under "The Russells".

TABLE IV – KENT PAPER MILLS ACTIVE BETWEEN 1670–1734

AREA	Before 1680	1680	1690	1700	1710	1720	1733	(Line)
MAIDSTONE DISTRICT	Forstal Millhall	Turkey U. Tovil	Lower Tovil Great Ivy Gurney's E. Malling ?	?- - -	Otham Snodland ? Cobtree Poll Mill	Upper Mill (Loose)	OLD MILL (Hollingbourne)	
TOTAL	2	4	8	8	12	13	14	(1)
WEST KENT	Dartford 1 Dartford 2 Eynsford	?- - -	Shoreham			Basted		
TOTAL	3	3	4	4	5	5	4	(2)
NORTH KENT		? - -	- - - - - -	- - - - -	Sittingbourne			
TOTAL		?	?	?	1	1	1	(3)
EAST KENT	Buckland (Dover) Barton (Canterbury) ? - - -	River (Dover)					CHARTHAM	
TOTAL	2	3	3	3	3	3	4	(4)
SOUTH KENT	Goudhurst							
TOTAL	1–2	1–2	1–2					(5)
GRAND TOTAL	8–9	11–12	16–17	15	21	22	23	(6)

1. This Table has been compiled from various sources e.g. Shorter (Bib. 12) : Spain (Bib. 8, 10, 11) : Fuller (Bib. 13) : and from the author's own searches and amended in the light of the consideration given to this subject in the foregoing pages.

2. The Grand Total differs slightly from the Total given in Chapter I (n.70) because the latter takes one up to 1740 (though it does not include Hamptons and Conyer mills, 1740; or Dartford No. 3 under construction in 1741/2).

3. The information is a best estimate only. For instance, the first evidence for Sittingbourne mill is a marriage licence of 1708, when it might have been active 40–50 years earlier. No early parish records have survived for Sittingbourne (and neighbouring Milton is of no help either). East Malling has been given, tentatively, a slightly earlier date than the first documentary reference to it. Shorter proposes ca. 1700 for Otham; Spain ca. 1715, first mention of William Keeble in RB. But in neither case does this necessarily mean that he was the first paper maker there. 1715 seems the more likely date in view of Harris' comment (Bib. 4) that it was still a fulling mill i.e. sometime before 1719. (publ: date).

Figures for the steady rise in the imports of White paper[121] and the growth in the number of paper mills in this country during the first three–quarters of the 17th C. are undisputed facts.[122] Coleman lists a number of reasons for this increased demand for paper.[123] He points out that from the 14th C. onwards paper had progressively replaced parchment in a wide range of uses for printing and writing; and over and above these there was an ever–increasing demand for Brown paper used for wrapping all kinds of commodities. The number of printed books rose and at various times during the 17th C., particularly during the Civil War and immediately after, there were floods of tracts and pamphlets coupled with the issuing of news–sheets and other publications like the London Gazette (1665), all of which contributed to the growing demand for Printing paper. In the case of Writing paper this replaced parchment in many, but by no means all,[124] official uses such as the State Papers as well as in a multitude of local and personal documents like municipal and parish records, merchants' accounts and private correspondence etc.

One might expect, therefore, that in one form or another this nationwide expansion might be reflected in the size of the Kentish industry which was small at that time compared to the paper industry in the region to the west of London. But having considered the early mills in Kent now this does not really seem to have been the case. Even if one ascribes a 16th C. origin to Forstal, Millhall and Goudhurst mills, the size of the industry in Kent remained small and its growth relatively static until ca.1670/1680. After ca.1675 the growth curve for the industry (nationally) steepens considerably and this is *more than reflected* in the growth of the Maidstone paper industry in the years that followed. Compare, for instance, line 1 of Table IV with lines 2–5 representing the other areas in Kent and national figures of ~63 (1675), ~100 (1690) and 209 (1712).

The main reason for the slow development of the industry in Kent in the early stages was because it lacked, unlike the counties to the west of London, the potential in terms of paper mills and paper makers to expand. Although Dartford No.1 paper mill had clearly been a very important mill in the 16th C., the district in which it was situated evidently did not offer facilities for an expansion of this kind because most, if not all, of the mill sites were already occupied by other industries in contrast to other areas to the west of London. This restraint would have applied to many other areas in Kent. Consequently one finds that, as a base from which to start, the Kent paper industry was highly dispersed and lacked any recognizable structure, so that in addition to having a low potential in material terms to expand there would have been no stimulus such as one might find in an established papermaking region, like Buckinghamshire and Middlesex, where mills tended to be concentrated more or less in one closely packed area with counties all around into which the industry could expand laterally.

One has to accept the fact that at this stage the industry in Kent was disadvantaged in more than one way, but that, possibly due to the arrival of immigrants in the Weald, this state of

---

[121] Coleman, D.C. Bib.15 13 Table I.

[122] Shorter, A. Bib.12 29/30.

[123] Coleman, D.C. Bib.15 6–10.

[124] In contrast to this move from parchment to paper it is interesting to note that as a result of Thomas Cromwell's insistence records of baptisms, marriages and burials should be kept by each parish (27 Henry VIII c.25) from ca.1538 these were generally set down on paper. 60 years later, however, the order was made that these were to be transcribed onto parchment (Tate, W.E. "The Parish Chest" Cambridge Univ.Press. 1969. 44).

affairs was about to change. It has been shown here that Goudhurst paper mill, at least, was preparing the ground, as it were, quite early for such an expansion. It is not suggested that this was necessarily a consciously planned policy, but the industry was responding as a whole in the country to an increased demand for paper and at Goudhurst immigrant influence may have been quicker to recognize the opportunities for growth than elsewhere in Kent. The fact remains that, *when the up-turn came, it was in a position to provide a number of Master Paper Makers who were able to take advantage of this situation,* more so than any other papermaking district in Kent. One might ask, then, with its two main industries virtually defunct and consequently with a lot of water-mill sites now disused, why did the local paper industry not expand in the High Weald ?

Why Maidstone ?

Probably the chief reason as to why the paper industry did not develop in the High Weald was the relative inaccessibility of this region. The only means of transporting goods down from there to where there were markets was by road. Pile[125] states that the roads in the area were mere tracks, often impassable in winter. The cloth industry had devised its own method to overcome this difficulty. Paved tracks were laid down and packhorse trains used to get the goods away. Whilst this may have been a satisfactory method for transporting bales of flexible cloth, it would have been impracticable for moving paper, especially White paper. There were obviously many other contributory reasons for the failure of the industry to develop in this region and these will become apparent when we consider the advantages Maidstone had to offer.

If the paper makers decided then to move to another area, why did they choose Maidstone in preference to other districts in Kent ? Taking Kent as a whole one is tempted to ascribe this decision to causes such as the relative merits of the Kent river system (see Map 1). But explanations of this kind tend to be based on hindsight; the reasons may not have been so obvious to contemporary paper makers. There were a lot of watermills on the River Stour, for instance, but most of these were undershot[126] and it is possible also that a general uplift of Eastern Kent (due to epeirogenic earth movements) may have led to reductions in gradient of the river and hence the differentials needed for driving waterwheels; and, ultimately, to mills falling into disuse. Certainly, a lot of mills had ceased to function below Canterbury; but there were sites higher up the Stour that were used later for paper mills. Generally speaking the reputation of the Stour among prospective paper makers may not have been a particularly good one. The fact is that the Stour basin never became an important paper-making area.

At the western end of Kent the River Darent and its tributary, the River Cray, were clearly suitable for watermills, but the limitation so far as expansion of the paper industry was concerned was almost certainly related to the question of finding vacant sites. In fact this may have been the main reason for George Gill leaving the Dartford area in favour of the Maidstone one.

---

[125]   Pile, C.C.R. "Cranbrook Broadcloth and Clothiers" (Cranbrook and District Local History Society 2nd Ed. 1967. 20).
[126]   Spain, R.J. and Burnham, C.P. "Watermills" (Chap.XIII pp.197/8 "The Rural Landscape of Kent" McRae, S.G. and Burnham, C.P. publ. Wye College, Univ. of London, Aug. 1973).

Maidstone was not a particularly large town; the population at that time was less than 4000. Nevertheless it occupied a central position in Kent both geographically and administratively; and, more important from the papermaking point of view, it was situated on a navigable river and at the junction of this with two important tributaries, the River Len and the River Loose, as well as having other lesser streams joining it lower down.

The central position and general accessibility of Maidstone had been recognized from an administrative angle from the beginning of the 16th C. and confirmed by the 17th.[127] It had been a port from very early times and because of its position and the facilities it offered it had become by this time the focal point of the quite considerable commerce of the region, handling stone, timber, agricultural produce as well as manufacturing and processing textiles and other miscellaneous commodities.[128] So that when the woollen cloth trade died out towards the end of the 17th C., Maidstone and the surrounding district would have been much better equipped to withstand this deprivation than areas like the High Weald after its two principal industries had collapsed. In general terms, therefore, one would expect craftsmen and enterprising young people to have migrated northwards from the Weald to more prosperous areas like Maidstone; and this certainly seems to have been borne out to judge from the movements of the early paper makers; and one suspects also that some of their key craftsmen, whose names are not known, came with them.

From a papermaking point of view Maidstone offered a number of other advantages. The supply of rags was likely to have been larger there than in the more remote areas of Kent; and for Brown paper quantities of old ropes and sails would also have been available from the Naval Dockyard at Chatham, which had been greatly enlarged in the reign of Charles I, and from shipping in the Medway and Thames estuaries. The problem of transporting the paper to markets has been mentioned above and the difficulties which the Wealden Industries encountered in this respect. The River Medway above East Farleigh, the tidal limit then, was not rendered navigable until 1740/41; whereas by an Act of Parliament towards the end of the 17th C. the lower reaches of the Medway had been made more navigable, its banks below Maidstone improved and a towpath constructed, factors that would undoubtedly have raised the status of the mills sited close to it like Forstal, Millhall and, later, other mills like Cobtree and Snodland. Skilled workmen may have been marginally more easy to recruit in a place like Maidstone than in an area where the population was on the move. In general terms the labour requirement of the local paper industry would have been small though significant, probably less than 170 people for all of the Maidstone mills at the turn of the century and no more than, say, 250 by the 1730's, less than 10% of the local adult population.[129] Even so, though we may have accounted for the Master Paper Makers who came to Maidstone, converted and

---

[127] Maidstone became the Kent centre for weights and measures at the beginning of the 16th C. and the permanent seat of the Kent Assizes early in the 17th C.

[128] Historically, valuable building stone had been quarried in the area since Roman times and shipped to London and, later, even to Calais for its fortifications; the ragstone had also been used extensively for the manufacture of cannon balls. Great quantities of oak and elm were supplied from the Weald for shipbuilding at Chatham. The second Fruit Belt had been established just south of Maidstone at the end of the 16th C.; and hops, a very valuable agricultural product, from a similar date. Maidstone was also the home of many other industries including flax processing, the manufacture of linen and woollen cloth, linen thread; tanning and leather goods; millinery; brewing etc.

[129] Coleman, D.C. Bib.15 86–7 gives estimates for the numbers employed in paper mills of this period. In France numbers in 1–vat mills ranged from 6–17 persons (male and female). With 9 mills active by 1700 (possibly with 12 vats working) and 14 by 1733 (with, say, 19 vats) the figures given in the text are probably not far off the mark.

occupied the mills, an expansion of this order must have taxed the papermaking resources of the county severely in its initial stages; because each mill would have required several different skills from its employees, beatermen, vatmen, couchers, layers, sizers etc. and one might well ask where did all these people come from ?

Undoubtedly the main factor that shaped the course of events was the *potential* availability of fulling mills[130] which had many advantages when converting to papermaking compared to other types of mill. Because of the vertical movement of the hammers in a fulling mill it would have been easier to convert than, say, a corn mill.[131] To judge from the parish ratebook assessments many of these mills were still operating as fulling mills; but the rate at which they were converted to papermaking suggests that the proprietors were feeling the draught caused by the decline of the woollen industry and were only too anxious to find some other use for them.

Taking all these points into consideration one can see that Maidstone could undoubtedly offer many advantages to prospective paper makers coming to the district compared to those prevailing in the Weald of Kent. But clearly there must have been some other factor that influenced the decision of so many paper makers to make this move in the space of a few years.

Improved opportunities for making White paper

If there had not been a stimulus of some sort or another, one would have expected a gradual drift from one region to the other spread over many years and conforming to the national growth pattern of the industry which in Kent, in any case, had been a slow one. In addition, it is not as though the woollen industry in the High Weald, if nowhere else in Kent, had declined suddenly ca.1670. The reasons for this migration at this particular time have already been suggested earlier in this chapter. Coleman has drawn attention to the ever–growing debate that took place after the Restoration (1660) on the unfavourable balance that existed in Anglo–French trade; he refers to two much publicized calculations (1663 and 1674) showing how England lost more than a million pounds annually in its trade with France.[132] Factors of this kind together with the progressive deterioration in Anglo–French relations must have been in the minds of many English tradesmen long before the final precipitation took place with the embargo on French goods coming into force in 1678. There is absolutely no doubt that this prohibition, coupled with the wars that followed later, provided a very significant stimulus to the British paper industry and to the manufacture of White paper in particular.

The points to note here, however, are firstly that the more perceptive paper makers, particularly if prompted by immigrant influence, would have been aware of this situation and

---

[130] Apart from the adequacy of the water power generated there, an important consideration in the choice of a mill site was the constancy of the supply, one not subject to marked seasonal fluctuations nor to flooding the site etc. (See Shorter, A. Bib.12 38 ff. "The Sites and Situations of Early Paper Mills in England"). The fact that most of the fulling mill sites round Maidstone had been occupied satisfactorily for centuries would clearly commend them to prospective paper maker occupiers.

[131] Spain, R.J. and Burnham, C.P. loc.cit. (see note 126).

[132] Coleman, D.C. Bib.15 64/5.

the opportunities it might offer much earlier than 1678; the case of Eustace Burnaby exemplifies this. Secondly, the overriding factor in such circumstances would have been the state of readiness of the paper makers to exploit the opportunities when they arose; one cannot expand an industry of this kind at short notice and the fact is that some papermakers had clearly anticipated this eventuality. Whatever moves were afoot elsewhere, it has been proposed earlier that the expansion that took place at Maidstone had the manufacture of White paper as an objective. As Taylor, West and Willard were all in the area 10 years or more before the embargo came into force, one can only explain their presence as an early symptom of the expansion that was to come, probably a move prompted by the general decline in the fortunes of the High Weald. One cannot be certain that any of them made White paper at this stage; even so Willard had worked for or with the Manktellows and perhaps West too and, in addition, the latter may also have had experience of this manufacture earlier in the West of London Region. (West's later position as an Ancient Paper Maker surely confirms that he had both the training and the ambition to make it). Around 1678 the expansion proper began with Musgrove, Gill and Stephen Manktellow, Gill unquestionably skilled in the art of White papermaking; and, equally one assumes, Manktellow as an immigrant. This all lends support to the claim made in the first paper makers' petition of 1689 that the Ancient Paper Makers, if not other domestic paper makers as well, had had 20 years experience in making White paper to the COMPANY'S 3 or 4. No doubt because of the shortage of rags of suitable quality the bulk of this paper failed to match the quality of the White paper produced by Burnaby and maybe some of the newly arrived immigrants. In spite of this it would still have been classed as White paper. There is a danger perhaps of people reading into Harris' statement, made in his "History of Kent", that with the exception of Turkey mill the other Maidstone mills made only "a great deal of ordinary wrapping paper",[133] a conclusion that, though perhaps correct for ca.1715 (when it was made), did not apply to the district nearly 40 years earlier, when the migration of these Maidstone paper makers was taking place.

Encouraged then by the deteriorating international situation and jolted into action by the embargo it is not difficult to envisage that the primary motive for converting the Maidstone fulling mills was to make White paper. However, once the embargo had been lifted (1685) the bottom temporarily fell out of this market and some of the new arrivals would have been forced to make lower grades of paper while others struggled on making White during the war that followed;[134] but competing with the COMPANY during the 1690's would have made it difficult for even these survivors to have made a success of it. In the event when imports once again dominated the market even the COMPANY itself succumbed, creating a situation in the early decades of the 18th C. that justifies the comments made by Harris.

It can be seen then that when the circumstances were favourable for expansion the Maidstone area was a suitable one for this to take place; but how the news spread around is a matter for speculation. Information probably reached Goudhurst through Thomas Willard; but if James West came *direct* from Buckinghamshire instead of via Goudhurst then one has a problem on one's hands. George Gill came to the area at least 10 years later, by which time the news

---

[133] Harris, John Bib.4 191.

[134] First there is Harris' own evidence that George Gill had to make Brown paper at times; and this was at Turkey mill, the largest and most important mill in the area, where he noted that they had much unused capacity for making White paper. On the other hand since the Ancient Paper Makers made the claim in 1690 that they all made White paper, there must have been at least two other mills in the Maidstone area engaged in making it at times also.

could feasibly have spread to Dartford. All the same for news that such a large number of fulling mills near Maidstone were available for conversion to have spread so quickly is somewhat surprising. Eight of the Maidstone paper mills listed in Table IV were converted from fulling[135] and four of the others either were (Hollingbourne) or are thought to have been[136] built as new–built paper mills; but nothing certain is known about the previous usage, if any, of East Malling and Cobtree.

The initial expansion of the Maidstone industry continued on into the 18th C. and leads ultimately into the period to be considered in the next chapter and to the activities of James Whatman. The progress of this development was determined by a number of different factors, the emphasis altering as the settlement grew. For instance, excepting the earlier arrival of Willard at Forstal and West at Millhall the motives for which are problematic and may have been different, one can distinguish *a first wave* of conversions from later ones (see Map 2 inset). The first started with George Gill and Stephen Manktellow and ended with William Harris at Gurney's, the latter converting his mill *after* the embargo had been lifted; Harris has been included here on the strength of his participation as an Ancient Paper Maker. The motivation for these first conversions came from the paper makers; they would have come there with a purpose and known what had to be done to convert a building into a paper mill.[137]

Nothing is known about the early status of East Malling (Middle), Snodland or Otham paper mills. Since only one of them ever figures as a White mill and even then only late in the 18th C.[138] it seems safe to assume that during this early period they were nothing more than small Brown paper mills.

Excepting Hollingbourne Old Mill, the commissioning of the 3 remaining mills may be regarded as *the second phase* of the expansion (Map 2 inset) clearly prompted and encouraged by the New Duties (1712) and subsequent amendments to these. This time the conversions stemmed partly from the proprietors, imitating the example set by the first wave and seeking to enhance the performance of their assets by investing in a new and growing industry, and partly from other influential sources. There is unequivocal evidence for this in the case of Poll mill. In 1718 Lord Aylesford paid John Swinnock, his tenant, £300 "to build a good and substantial paper mill..." by converting Poll mill from its now out–dated usage, fulling, to papermaking.[139] More will be said about the fortunes of this conversion later in this book. Mention has already been made that nothing is known about the circumstances that led to the conversion of Otham mill ca.1715. Finally, the first ratebook evidence to show Cobtree as a

---

[135] Turkey, Upper and Lower Tovil, Great Ivy, Gurney's, Otham, Upper (Loose) and Poll mills.

[136] Forstal, Millhall and possibly Snodland.

[137] Based on Ratebook values a case could be made out for the conversion of Lower Tovil mill during Lanes' tenure (Lanes being a fuller); both of the Tovil mills were part of the manor of Maidstone and the proprietor, having seen the successful conversion of Upper Tovil, may have arranged for Lanes to convert the lower mill. If so, he did not last long there.

[138] Details of the 3 East Malling paper mills will be found in App.IV. Middle mill is the only mill we are concerned with here and it would appear that throughout its life, certainly in its later life, it never made anything other than Brown paper. No documentary evidence has come to light yet indicating Snodland as a paper mill before 1755, though there seems to have been a mill site there from early times; but, like Middle mill, no references have been discovered to show that it ever made White paper. Likewise there is nothing to suggest that Otham mill made White countermarked paper before the late 18th/early 19th Cs. (See Chap.VII p.319 and note 235.)

[139] Spain, R.J. Bib.8 83.

paper mill is an assessment for May 1717 against "Gill" (George's son, William).[140] To judge from its site it seems likely that he resurrected it from some former activity in an earlier age. It is not known who the proprietor was, but Gill held the lease and so far as he was concerned his action was part of a much bigger response to the prevailing situation, a subject examined in Chapter IV. The relevant point here is that Gill installed David Dean snr. as occupant of Cobtree; the latter's son, David jnr, was later associated with Upper mill, Loose, sometime after 1726[141] and since it is unlikely that the Deans converted this mill at their own expense and because William Gill snr. was still very active at this time expanding his other papermaking interests, it looks very much as if he had had a hand in this also. The Gills had a long association with the Dean family (up to 80 years) and William Gill jnr. was to come back to Upper mill at a later date. On this basis Upper mill has been included here as part of the second phase of the expansion of the industry round Maidstone. The first two phases of this, together with the third, will be considered again in a wider context in Chapter IV.

THE EMERGENCE OF MAIDSTONE AS A PAPERMAKING CENTRE SUMMARISED

The overriding difficulty in presenting this account has been the problem of trying to create a coherent picture of an important development in the absence of so many basic records of the period. It may have been difficult for someone unfamiliar with papermaking history, the geography of the region and the distribution of its paper mills to absorb this material. At the risk of being repetitive it may be helpful to recapitulate the contents of this chapter here, though not necessarily in the same order in which the various points have been made. It is quite possible that the facts known about this situation are capable of being interpreted in a number of different ways; all the same the claim is made that the proposals made here at least cover these facts and portray a reasonable picture of the events that took place.

1. *The small size of the early Kent paper industry and the disparity between this and the industry to the west of London*

   In Chapter I it was seen that by 1740 Kent possessed a very substantial and important segment of the British paper industry, mainly concentrated in the Maidstone district. Examination in this chapter (II) of the distribution of paper mills in England over the previous 100 years revealed that initially the size of industry in Kent was negligible (see Table I). Even allowing for the earlier existence of certain mills (Goudhurst, Forstal and Millhall) the total compared to the size of the industry to the immediate West of London is still small. Moreover, it was highly dispersed and lacked structure in contrast to the dense concentration of its counterpart. The Kent industry could provide therefore only a very limited platform from which to expand. When it did expand it did so very significantly in the Maidstone area during the last quarter of the 17th C. (Table II). This posed the questions, where did the paper makers come from and why to Maidstone?

2. *Identification of the early Maidstone paper makers*

   Table III lists the names of the paper makers known to be in the Maidstone area in the last quarter of the 17th C. but in some cases only tentatively assigned to converted mills. Their identification is examined in detail in App.II, III and IV.

---

[140] See App.III the synopsis and notes on the history of Cobtree paper mill. Boxley RB. KAO P 40 12/1.
[141] Spain, R.J. Bib. 10 48 discussed in more detail in Chap.IV.

3. *The origins of these paper makers*

Examination of Maidstone district records and those belonging to the environs of other early paper mills in the county showed that Dartford and Goudhurst were significant sources for these with others possibly migrating from the West of London Region.

4. *The two principal sources examined*

Dartford as a source is not difficult to explain (in addition to Gill, it is possible that it, or alternatively Eynsford, may have produced William Harris' father). But the case of the almost–unheard–of Goudhurst mill was a different matter. Why should there have been a paper mill in this remote district in the first place ? and how was it that a backwater of this kind managed to produce so many Master Paper Makers for the Maidstone district later ?

5. *The status of the High Weald : a suggested 16th C. origin for Goudhurst paper mill : and immigrant influence*

The main industries, and in particular the woollen industry, of the High Weald and its religious and political affiliations have been examined. The effect of Cecil's prohibition of the export of unfinished cloth to Flanders in 1566, never fully relaxed for Kent, could have led to the founding of a Press paper mill in the area, possibly built by a contemporary paper maker refugee from the Netherlands.

Whether this was the case or not, Goudhurst paper mill *must* have been in existence before 1650 (no fewer than 3 future paper makers were born in this parish between 1615–1633); and, since the region by this time must have been a haven for Protestant refugees from France, it has been proposed that Alexander Manktellow (perhaps Mantelleau), who appears first in Goudhurst in 1644, may either have built a mill at Goudhurst or enlarged an existing one, injecting new life into a declining business (the demand for Press papers would have virtually ceased by then with the demise of the Broadcloth industry).

It is a fact that Stephen Manktellow was a paper maker, the occupant of Goudhurst paper mill from at least 1675 (possibly from ca.1670); and that he migrated to Maidstone in 1679. It has not been possible to show a direct relationship between Alexander and Stephen; but it has been suggested that the latter, when of age, took over the mill from Alexander after an interregnum (see 6 below).

In any case one or both of these would have brought continental experience of papermaking there, which no doubt would have included experience of White paper manufacture.

6. *The other paper makers at Goudhurst*

The most important of these were Thomas Willard, a native of Goudhurst, and *Peeter* Archer, who may have been another immigrant.

(a)   *Thomas Willard.* His identification amd motives for moving from Goudhurst to Forstal mill are discussed in App.IV; the latter are thought to include the declining fortunes of the Weald and pressure from the Manktellow family. His move also highlights the earlier history of Forstal and its close neighbour Millhall mill and as to whether either or both of them had been founded by the Settlers of 1567.

(b)   *Peter Archer.* His origin is likewise discussed in detail in App.IV. In his case there are the unsolved questions as to whether he was an immigrant or not; and whether he was the father of Richard, Elizabeth, Mary and Robert, as well as other recorded members of his family.

7. *Expansion 1670–1733*

The expansion of the paper industry in Kent as a whole is compared with that of Maidstone for this period (see Table IV). It is clear that the expansion at Maidstone was exceptional and the motives for this are discussed:-

(a)   It is claimed that there was a latent, if not actual, potential for White paper manufacture not only at Dartford but at Goudhurst as well.
(b)   The imbalance of trade with France and the deterioration of Anglo–French relations culminating in the

embargo on French imports (1678–1685) were responsible for the sudden expansion of the industry and for the manufacture of White paper in particular, prompted by immigrant influence.

(c)   It is important to note that the paper makers were trained and ready to exploit this situation.

(d)   Conditions outside their control led to fluctuating success in this field; the lifting of the embargo (contra); renewed war (pro); the monopoly of the COMPANY (contra); the return of peace and imports (contra); and, later (1712), the New Duties (pro).

George Gill survived these changes, but even he had to make Brown paper at times. Other possible survivors in White paper manufacture, albeit limited at times, might have been William Harris at Gurney's mill in Loose and the paper makers at Forstal, Millhall and, late on the scene, Poll mills. Intermittent White paper production probably continued at several other mills especially when William Gill snr. was working them.

(e)   The expansion seems to have taken place in two distinct phases, the first during the embargo and the second after the imposition of the New Duties.

8.   *Why did the Expansion take place in the Maidstone district ?*

(a)   The decline of the Weald as an industrial area compared to the more broad–based and robust commercial structure of Maidstone together with its centrality, geographically and administratively, must have been general attractions.

(b)   Transport of goods by packhorse from the Weald compared to shipping from the port of Maidstone with improvements to the lower reaches of the Medway must have been another important factor.

(c)   Increased availability of raw materials, both high and low quality; sources of skilled and unskilled labour; local markets (wrapping papers for Maidstone products) and easier access to London markets were all other points in favour.

(d)   The close proximity of many fulling mills, the most suited of watermills, available for conversion to papermaking was perhaps the most important consideration and would account for the exceptional growth here when compared to other areas. They had had a long and reliable history as watermills. In those cases where the object was to make White paper, *the quality of the water would have been another very important factor.*

(e)   There are still many unsolved questions concerning the establishment of this new papermaking district, one of them being how the news had reached paper makers who had come from other areas; and another as to where so many skilled workmen needed for the process came from at such short notice.

Up to this point the establishment and growth of the English paper industry on a national basis has been summarised, this being followed by a similar examination of a single region, Kent. These both showed that events of one kind or another had definitely advanced the status and substance of the White paper industry during the last decades of the 17th C. Coleman has shown that, later, between 1714–1718 the domestic paper industry had reached a stage when it was producing about two thirds of our total consumption of paper, White and Brown;[142] and since imports of White paper declined in the period 1700–1720[143] the inference is that, with an expanding market, domestic White paper manufacture must have been on the increase too. More than 90% of this would probably have been, as was the case with imported White paper "Ordinary Printing and Copy" paper;[144] the best qualities of White paper were still imported.

In spite of all this progress and the introduction of highly protective Duties, which were to have an effect in the long term, the domestic White paper industry was still in a precarious position, certainly with respect to the better qualities. Publishers and printers still preferred continental papers for their more important works. Some paper makers, like George Gill,

---

[142]   Coleman, D.C. Bib.15 13 Table 1.

[143]   Shorter, A. Bib.12 29/30.

[144]   Coleman, D.C. Bib.15 6–10.

clearly had a limited entrée to this market. But the industry needed something more to get it over this hump. This then is the general setting in which the elder James Whatman, a tanner of Loose and paper maker to be, would have found himself in the fourth decade of the 18th C.

Plate 6

JAMES WHATMAN, THE ELDER
(1702–1759)

Chapter III

THE ELDER JAMES WHATMAN, PAPER MAKER :
TESTING THE EVIDENCE

In the 18th C. a great vogue was created for the silhouette portrait;[1] this form of likeness was also known as a "shade" and a similar kind of insubstantial image is about all that the currently available histories of papermaking convey to us about the elder James Whatman (1702–1759), though it must be added that we do possess an actual painted portrait of him, a unique record of a paper maker surviving from the earlier periods of British papermaking (Plate 6).[2] In the literature, however, he appears as an isolated, though later in his life as a distinguished, papermaking figure quite unrelated to the industry he was to influence so greatly. In the two previous chapters an attempt has been made to provide a papermaking background for the district into which the elder paper maker Whatman was born with the object of giving him something more of a three–dimensional setting than his image has at present and to which we can relate the few facts that are known about him. His biographer, Thomas Balston, could manage only five pages on him and most of this is concerned with the later years in his life.[3]

From the existing accounts one gets the impression that the first important date in Whatman's life was the date of his marriage, 7th August 1740, when at the age of 38 he was seemingly transformed overnight from being a Tanner of Loose, a village just under two and a half miles south of Maidstone, into a paper maker at Turkey Mill, three–quarters of a mile to the East of Maidstone and lying in the parish of Boxley; and what a momentous transformation this was to be for the future of White paper manufacture. But from what has been said, and the point has been stressed more than once in earlier chapters, can we really accept this extraordinary transformation at face value ? Even the humblest of paper makers required many years of training to master the skills needed for making paper and, although it is not essential for us to assume that Whatman ever worked at the Vat, in view of his rapid progress and remarkable achievements in this field once he had become a paper maker we are more

---

[1]   This fashion appears to have originated from the paper cut–outs created by the French politican, Etienne de Silhouette (1709–1767).

[2]   The date of the portrait is unknown. However, Dr. Rosalind Marshall (Asst. Keeper, National Portrait Gallery, Edinburgh) considers that from the style of the powdered bob wig, collarless coat and shirt with frill that the portrait was painted between 1730–40; and from the sitter's appearance, nearer to the later date of this bracket. The dress is perfectly suited to a well–to–do middle class merchant, professional man or tradesman (inf. letter Aug:89). In the author's view the portrait was probably painted for the occasion of Whatman's marriage (7:Aug:1740) when he would have been nearly thirty–eight.

How do we know that it is a portrait of the elder Whatman ? Apart from the dating based on his dress, there are two inventories of the contents of Vinters made in the 19th C. (1854 and 1887) that refer respectively to it as "A portrait of James Whatman 175 ? (artist unknown)" and "A portrait of James Whatman ob.1756[sic] (artist unknown)". In addition, the last members of the Whatman family to have lived at Vinters (James d.1887) were certain that it was a portrait of their ancestor (inf. Maj. Edward Trousdell 7:Oct:89). It is also unlikely that Thomas Balston would have accepted it as such had he any doubts.

Painting relined and revarnished in Mr. Simon Blackwood's workshops (Hawick) in Jan.1990.

[3]   Bib.1 12–16.

or less forced to conclude that he must have had some experience of papermaking prior to 1740.

The *raison d'être* for this book on the elder Whatman and his Hollingbourne paper mill is not a straightforward one. The author's curiosity was first aroused by the recent discovery by Dr. Frederick Hudson, in 1977, of a Whatman countermark (which will be discussed more fully later in this chapter) for the year 1740 in paper which may or may not have been made prior to this "transformation", but obviously so close to it that it makes little difference. This discovery has made it clear that, seen in the context of the paper industry at that time, the elder Whatman, by some means or other, had established a position of pre–eminence from the very beginning of his papermaking career and the most unusual occurrence of a portrait is further testimony of his status. Shortly after this (1978–1980) the author was engaged on his study of the Development of early Wove papers.[4] This undertaking to make Wove paper must have been conceived sometime between 1754–1757 and proved to be one of the elder Whatman's most remarkable achievements, very much more the case than has been realised to date. The development of this new kind of paper, now in almost universal use, was a technological feat requiring very considerable expertise and inventiveness in papermaking and clearly needed accounting for in much greater depth than ascribing it to a mere act of chance. In the light of these revelations, and others which continued to turn up, it was considered a matter of prime importance that the subject of this apparently sudden transformation from tanner to accomplished paper maker should be examined more closely. The question was how to approach a study of this kind when so little was known about the papermaking career and particularly the origins of the elder Whatman. It so happened that in the course of the investigations connected with these discoveries one or two items had come to light that suggested a way round this difficulty by narrowing the scope of the work, certainly in its initial stages.

Before considering these points in detail it would be as well to restate the limited information we already had to work on. In retrospect one can see that no attempt had been made to try to relate the scattered data to each other. It was known, for instance, that the James Whatman in question was born in Loose in 1702, the only son of another James Whatman, a tanner, who had moved to Loose in 1688 from the village of Brenchley in the High Weald of Kent.[5] The latter died in 1725, his widow in 1726, leaving his son as sole heir to the tanning business in Loose and to various other properties. Reference is made in the father's Will to various family beneficiaries and, among others, to his brother–in–law, William Harris and his son, Thomas. The conclusion was drawn, correctly, that this must have been William Harris, the Ancient Paper Maker;[6] but exactly how he was related by marriage to the James Whatman from Brenchley had never been established.[7] Neither for that matter had Richard Harris' position in this story been clarified; Richard appears later, in 1733, as tenant of a paper mill (Old Mill) in Hollingbourne "owned" by Whatman.[8] Finally, we follow Richard

[4]   Bib.76
[5]   See App.II under "The Whatman Paper Makers' Pedigree".
[6]   See App.II under "The Harris Family Paper Makers" for the identification of William Harris snr. Having identified and located him in Gurney's paper mill Loose and active in 1690 with no other William Harris paper makers to be found in Kent, there is only one conclusion to be drawn, namely, that he was William Harris, the Ancient Paper Maker.
[7]   See App.II under "A Diagram of the Whatman/Harris Relationship".
[8]   Balston, T. Bib.1 10.

Harris' move to Turkey mill in 1736, and his acquisition of this mill from a certain James Brooke in 1738 by means of "a conveyance to two trustees, James Whatman of Loose, tanner, and Thomas Harris of Wrotham, tanner".[9] Richard Harris died during the rebuilding of Turkey mill "on a more curious and extensive plan" on 22nd August 1739. Just under a year later James Whatman married Richard's widow who, by her marriage settlement (2:July:1740), conveyed Turkey Mill "to trustees to the use of Whatman and herself during their joint lives and to the use of the survivor and the heirs and assigns of such survivor for ever".[10]

All these facts will be brought together again later in their proper context. There is not a great deal to add to this information, but a much closer examination of all the available data leads one to ask further questions and a result of this is that further facts emerge so that in the end one finds that one can build up a reasonably coherent picture of Whatman's early life and the influences that helped shape his papermaking career. To do this, two items connected with paper and papermaking are to be examined closely in the pages that follow, *testing the evidence*, with the object of establishing Whatman's early contact with the paper industry more precisely. To help the reader follow the argument with greater understanding the appropriate Appendices, indicated in the footnotes, should be consulted. The two items referred to are:–

(1)   The discovery of an "IW" countermark in a printed document dated December 1740, the earliest Whatman countermark discovered and similar to that illustrated by Thomas Balston.[11]

(2)   The building of a paper mill, Old Mill, Hollingbourne, by James Whatman in 1733 seven years before he made what has hitherto been regarded as his first recognized appearance as a paper maker at Turkey mill.

---

[9]   ibid. Bib.1 8.
[10]   ibid. Bib.1 11.
[11]   Bib.1 157 fig.1.

(1) *THE 1740 "IW" COUNTERMARK*

In 1977 Dr. Frederick Hudson[12] published a paper in the Music Review[13] entitled "The earliest paper made by James Whatman, the Elder (1702–1759) and its significance in relation to G.F. Handel and John Walsh". This showed conclusively[14] that the first edition of Walsh's publication "Select Harmony Fourth Collection" was in print by 11th December 1740. Exemplars had been located in Edinburgh, Oxford and Paris and these contained a number of sheets bearing an "IW" countermark similar to the hitherto earliest known Whatman countermark found in documents dating from 1747 onwards.[15]

Earlier bibliographical investigation of Handel's works by Dr. Hudson in 1959[16] had shown the presence of many "IW" countermarks in printings originally advertised in 1741. Mr. Thomas Balston's attention had been drawn to this discovery and it was considered as quite feasible for the paper bearing these marks to have been made in 1740, the year in which Whatman was believed to have started his papermaking career. However, as a result of a further seventeen years extensive and systematic work in this field, using modern techniques including β–radiography for comparing laid mould covers and watermarks, Dr. Hudson was able to publish a great deal more information on the occurrence of "IW" countermarks in 1977, embracing the example cited above. Two points of some considerable significance for English Papermaking History of that period arise from these findings and call for comment.

First, whereas one had been concerned originally with a publishing date of 1741 in the case of Dr. Hudson's discovery of "IW" countermarks in 1959, their appearance in a printed work dateable with certainty to December 1740 at once raised the question that Dr. Hudson asked, would it have been possible for Whatman to have made and delivered the paper in between the times of either the marriage settlement of 2nd July, or the date of his marriage on 7th August, or the date when he first insured Turkey mill on 19th August and the time when it appeared in a printed work issued on 11th December, 1740 ? The feasibility of this will be discussed below.

---

[12] At that time Reader in Music at the University of Newcastle upon Tyne.

[13] Bib.2.

[14] Dr. Hudson presents a great deal of evidence of the occurrence of the "IW" marks in the edition of "Select Harmony, Collection IV" first advertised by Walsh in the London Daily Post and General Advertiser of Thursday 11th December, 1740. Eight sets were located and he shows that the part books in Edinburgh, Oxford and Paris are first editions, the others reissues of 11th November, 1741. In view of the very early date of these marks in relation to Whatman's commencement of production in July or August of the same year, Dr. Hudson stated that he would have had very grave doubts about the truth of this discovery if convincing proof had not been available in the Bodleian set of parts, where he discovered the signature of the first owner and the purchase date (illustrated Bib.2 Plate I) 1740.

[15] Thomas Balston (Bib.1 157) discusses this countermark and mentions the fact that not only has this countermark been located in the SPD files of the PRO for the year 1747 but in other documents dating from 1748–1750 as well as one used in 1756, adding that in his view Whatman probably changed from "IW" to "JW" around 1750. It may be of interest to note that Thomas Gravell discovered a single line "IW" mark in a Philadelphia document dated 1773 (Bib.16 letter 31:Mar:1981 and discussed in App.V p.282 under "Some Notes on "W" countermarks"; and a double–line block letter "IW" very similar to Dr. Hudson's examples in a New Castle, Delaware document of 1785 (Bib.68 No.417–418). The latter example is accompanied by a Fleur–de–Lys in the other half of the sheet. The inter–chainwire mark spacing is similar to Dr. Hudson's examples, namely, ca. 26mm.; but the Fleur–de–Lys is wider and more elongated ca. 41 x 68mm.

[16] The works examined were published by John Walsh, father and son, between 1734–1752 and the countermarks discovered in the 3rd Edition of the six "Oboe Concertos" Op.3, originally advertised in 1741. Hudson, F. Music Review Vol.20 1959 7–27 and the British Paper Trade Journal 1959 May 64–69 and June 38–43.

There is, however, the hint of a further problem in that Dr. Hudson's later examination was extended to a larger sample of Walsh's printings of Handel's music spread over a period of approximately two and a half years (1739–1741), 24 works comprising 976 folios, one of these containing "IW" countermarks dated by the late W.C. Smith, the leading Handel Bibliographer, as early as 28th February 1739, and four others as belonging to the first half of 1740. Dr. Hudson does point out that Smith "had paid little heed to filigrany as an additional aid to investigation" and as a consequence in his later paper he re–examines these datings and makes tentative suggestions for revising these to a later date; but some of these are based on the assumption that they are later simply because Whatman could not have made the paper early enough to match Smith's datings.[17] He does qualify this by saying that to draw conclusions from the investigation of this sample would be both foolish and dangerous. So one is left with a question mark as to just how early Whatman started making paper; does one still regard the 2nd July 1740 or the other dates immediately after this as the definitive date for the beginning of Whatman's papermaking career or not ? And it also raises another question as to whether one can be certain that the "IW" countermark was Whatman's ?

Second, if we can be reasonably certain that the countermark was Whatman's, we are still left with the problem of his apparent transformation overnight from a "Tanner of Loose", a description applied to him up to the date of his marriage, into an accomplished paper maker and one who was using a personal mark at a time when the use of such marks by British Paper Makers was rare. Although nothing has as yet been resolved by this, the fact that Whatman had built a paper mill some seven years earlier does provide an opportunity for the resolution of these problems; and additional scope is supplied by information resulting from the current search which has thrown more light on the environment in which the young Whatman must have passed his early years.

"IW" as a Whatman Countermark

Prior to an examination of the mark itself and the questions it poses, how certain can one be that the marks Dr. Hudson has discovered emanated from Whatman ? From the information available to the author at the time of writing, no piece of paper bearing this double line block letter "IW" mark has been discovered that can be associated unequivocally with the elder Whatman himself. Nevertheless there are a number of indirect pointers that make it practically certain that this mark was used by him. Some of these are listed below; maybe there are others unknown to the author:–

[17] Hudson, F. Bib.2 The Table on p.26 and the discussion pp.30–31 isolates Prints 4; 10 & 17; 12; 11, 13 & 14 as containing paper with "IW" marks. The rest he assumes were printed on Dutch paper and that there were no grounds for disputing Smith's dates. Smith's datings for prints 4, 10, 17 and 12 provide loopholes in one form or another which enable Hudson to suggest the parts containing the "IW" paper could have been printed after 11:Dec:1740; but in the other three, 11, 13 & 14 Hudson's suggestions really rest on little else than the fact that Whatman could not have made the paper for an earlier date, that is if we assume that Whatman did not start making paper before 2:July:1740. Smith dated 11 as 15:Mar:1740; 13 simply as 1740; and 14 as 13:May:1740.

(i)   An English origin for the mark. Dr. Hudson expresses the view that at this time, ca.1740, the Dutch paper Walsh used and preferred was in short supply, if available at all. Supplies of both French and Dutch paper had been largely cut off by the War of the Austrian Succession (1739–1748) and Walsh would have been looking round for a domestic supplier. In other words the chances are that a search for the author of the "IW" mark can be limited to the British Paper industry as a source particularly in view of the fact that the occurrence of these marks continued in Walsh's printings for some time after the war had been in progress.

(ii)   No other candidate, European or British, has come to light yet for this period other than James Whatman. James West (Ancient Paper Maker) died in 1694; John West, another Ancient Paper Maker, is unlikely to have been active still for this period or after (see iii below).

(iii)   Continuity of the mark. The fact that, to the best of our knowledge,[18] this mark first appears ca.1740 and continues to ca.1750, and thereafter is changed to "JW" which we can associate with Whatman, lends further support to the proposal.

(iv)   The elder James Whatman's use of *single line* "W" marks with Loop either as solitary "W"s or in association with "I" or "J". This is perhaps the most unequivocal indicator of Whatman using this form of "IW" mark from an early date (generally used in these cases in the smaller sizes of paper). It can be shown without any doubt that the elder Whatman used this particular and distinctive kind of solitary "W" as a countermark and exactly similar "W"s were used in conjunction with both "I", for early marks, with "J" for later marks; and with "A" as Ann Whatman's countermark during the interregnum following the elder Whatman's death. These marks and their occurrence are discussed more fully in Appendix V.

(v)   The dimensions of the sheets of paper bearing the double line block letter "IW"s discovered by Hudson do not appear to be those of a size of sheet known in Holland, suggesting once again that the origin of this paper was English.

---

[18]   Heawood, E. Bib.35 under "IW/JW" No. 3139 illustrates an "IW" found in an Amsterdam document of 1676 in association with a Dutch Lion. Though both block letters, they are totally different from the "IW"s found in the Walsh printings. The "W", for instance, is made up from 2 unconnected "V"s one superimposed on the other. Churchill, W.A. Bib.3 illustrates 3 "WI/IW" countermarks. No.16 (top) and No. 34 are clearly "WI" marks found in documents dated 1678 and 1698 respectively, the former in a Dutch document. No. 54, however, is shown as an "IW" mark in a document that Churchill dates as 1742 but unfortunately does not give its provenance. It is associated with the Arms of Amsterdam, which at that time may equally have been used by a Dutch or an English paper maker. Churchill suggests that the "IW" should perhaps be "WI" as in his No.16. This idea does not seem at all plausible, if he has drawn the "W" in No.54 correctly in relation to the "I" unless the mould maker was incapable of forming a "W" correctly in reverse. If it is in fact an "IW" mark, then No.54 could conceivably be another early Whatman countermark.
Finally, 2 solitary double line block letter "W"s have been discovered by the author in documents dated 1725 and in the 1730's (the former in a Leeds Village paper). Though nearer to Dr. Hudson's "IW" marks, these "W"s are quite distinctive and different. (See in App.V under "Notes on "W" countermarks").

(vi)   Finally, a small point of difference, Hudson has pointed out that the "IW" countermarks would have been readable on the face of the mould, whereas with some of the other papers, without "IW" marks and believed to be Dutch, the mirror image of the marks is found on the mould cover. This is merely a point of difference and in no way indicates the country of origin.

When all these points are taken collectively, there is a very strong case for believing that the "IW" marks in question were Whatman's. Provided an investigator has sufficient experience, coupled with remarkably good eyesight, it is possible to dissect the wire profiles into their component parts from an examination of the marks in the sheet of paper and to show how they were sewn on to the cover.[19] Following such a course one might be able to link the "IW" countermarks found in Walsh's printings with those found in the State Papers, Domestic, for instance; but it is only a "might" and really sufficient reasons have been advanced above to give one reasonable grounds for regarding the 1740 marks as Whatman's without having to recourse to this method.

There are certain papermaking details arising from Dr. Hudson's examination of Walsh's printings that may be of interest *to the specialist reader* and can be mentioned at this point (*the general reader* may prefer to pass on to the section dealing with the problems the "IW" countermark poses):

(a)   *The dimensions of the sheets used*

> Hudson shows (Bib.2 20) that sheets used for the Select Harmony Collection IV, in which the confirmed 1740 "IW" mark was found, averaged approximately 34 x 50cm. With the exception of 1 sheet, one without an "IW" mark, all the other sheets had been halved, printed on and then stitched together again later; the undivided sheet was used to assist turning over the page at a difficult place in the music. In another copy a sheet in the same place had been halved, but the two halves placed together showed that no part was missing. The assumption is made then that the half sheets containing the "IW" marks would produce whole sheets with similar 34 x 50cm. dimensions; but, unfortunately , it has not been possible to identify the other halves of the "IW" sheets.[20] However, exact photocopies of the Balfour Collection Exemplars, Hudson's extended examination, had among them, fortunately, a half sheet from Print No. 13, made up entirely of "IW" folios and which Smith had dated 1740, which appears to have preserved its deckle edges; all the other specimens had been trimmed, some quite extensively. The dimensions of the half sheet with deckle edges was 34.3 x 23.5–23.7cm.or brought to full size 34.3 x 47.0–47.4cm., dimensions which agree reasonably closely with the Select Harmony Collection IV sheets, a size which Hudson noted was not thought to be one known in Holland.

> The dimensions suggested for the Whatman paper are 34.3 x ca.47cm. (English Printing Foolscap in 1713 had dimensions of ca. 34.5 x 44.5cm. Gaskell). As these dimensions are approximately the same as the other papers used, the question has to be asked were any of them Dutch ? There are two reasons for discussing the dimensions of the sheet here in such detail; first, alleged to be an unusual size unknown in Holland, this fact supports the proposal that the "IW" papers were English in origin; and second, the size of sheet is a

---

[19] See also Loeber, E.G. Bib.45 Text pp.31 ff.; and Plates 79–81,117.

[20] Four types of half sheet were identified, three with marks (Fleur–de–Lys), (IV) and (IW); and one with no markings. The Laid Wire counts and the inter–chainwire mark spacings were really too close to one another in all the examples illustrated by Hudson to say that one or other kind of half belonged to another. The only whole sheet discovered had a Fleur–de–Lys in one half and IV in the other and, on balance, of the examples illustrated all the other Fleur–de–Lys/IV examples show the closest match in wiremarks. In other words the suggestion is that the "IW" half–sheets were paired with the half sheets without marks. (For full details of all measurements see "Working Papers").

Plate 7a

ILLUSTRATION OF THE "IW" COUNTERMARK
LEFT SIDE

Discovered by Dr. Frederick Hudson in Walsh's Printings of
Handel's Select Harmony Fourth Collection published on the
11:December:1740

Tranchefil wiremark (left side of sheet just out of picture)*

Ex. 14

In this illustration it
will be noticed that the
Tranchefil wiremark is
to the left of the
Countermark

Ex. 15

Reproduced here by kind permission of Dr. Frederick Hudson
(Full particulars to be found in the Music Review, Vol.38, Feb. 1977 15–32)

* For an explanation and illustration of the Tranchefil Wire see Chapter I, Plate 5 and p.43.

ILLUSTRATION OF THE "IW" COUNTERMARK
RIGHT SIDE

Discovered by Dr. Frederick Hudson in Walsh's Printings of
Handel's Select Harmony Fourth Collection published on the
11:December:1740

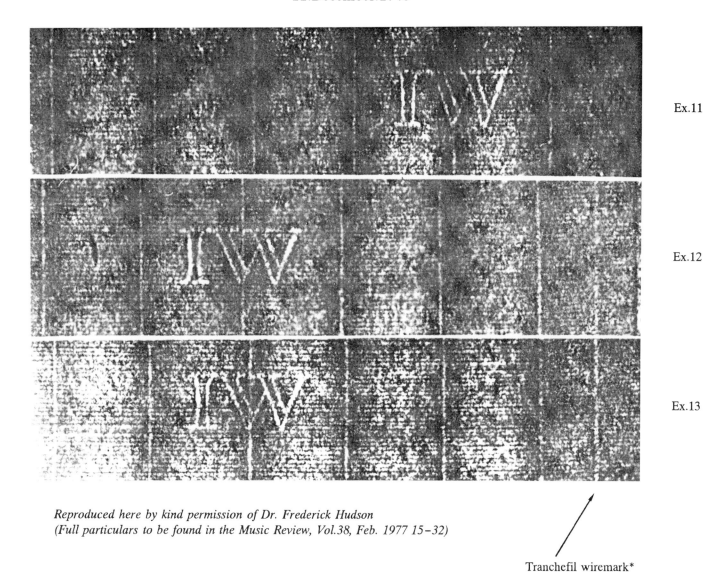

Ex.11

Ex.12

Ex.13

Reproduced here by kind permission of Dr. Frederick Hudson
(Full particulars to be found in the Music Review, Vol.38, Feb. 1977 15–32)

Tranchefil wiremark*

In this illustration it will be noticed that the Tranchefil Wiremark lies to the right of the Countermark (the right edge of the sheet being just out of the picture); but this does not necessarily indicate that this is the right–hand side of the Mould as has been suggested in Dr. Hudson's paper. An alternative proposal has been advanced here and is discussed in the text on p.100, Method 2.

* For an explanation and illustration of the Tranchefil Wire see Chapter I, Plate 5 and p.43.

Figure 1

Illustration showing two methods of positioning the countermark in a pair of Moulds (A & B) so that, after rotating one of the sheets (B in this case) through 180° (keeping the sheet in the same plane) to counteract the effects of *la bonne rive*, the countermarks in the two sheets will be readable from the same view point.

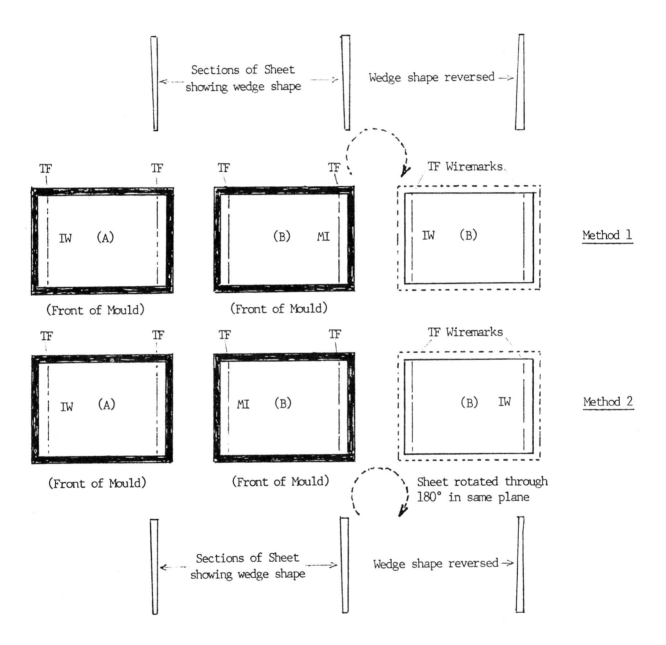

Method 1, after rotating sheet B through 180°, will produce countermarks nearest to the left hand tranchefil in both sheets A and B.

Method 2, after rotating sheet B through 180°, will produce one countermark (sheet A) nearest the left hand tranchefil wiremark and the other (sheet B) nearest right hand tranchefil wiremark.

consideration in the subject to be discussed in (b) below. (For a word of caution on dimensions see footnote).[21]

(b)   *The position of the "IW" Marks*

Dr. Hudson also observed five variants in the positioning of the "IW" Countermark, see Plate 7; three, at first sight, placed nearest the right side of the mould and two nearest the left, this being on the assumption that the countermark was readable on the cover. However, as will be explained below, these may not necessarily have been the actual positions of the countermark. By superimposing the β−radiograph negatives he established differences in the moulds themselves, differences too large to be accounted for by the contraction of the sheet on drying (and, seen in Note 21, because of the regularity of the chainwire spacings in all the exemplars unlikely to have been distorted during printing). He thus came to the conclusion that Whatman had used more than one vat to make his paper; it will be remembered that each vat makes use of a *pair* of moulds.

There are at least three explanations that would account for these variants; the use of twin moulds; the use of three pairs of moulds with "IW" countermarks sewn one on the right and one on the left of each pair (one on the left is missing in these exemplars); or, as illustrated in Fig.1, Method 1 with one countermark on the left and the other on the right but sewn on the other way up (not to be confused with upside down as a mirror image); and Method 2 with both countermarks sewn on one side, illustrated as the left side here, but again with one of them upside down; Method 2 seems to be the most likely explanation.

With regard to these alternatives, there is evidence that the use of twin moulds had been practised in Holland from the late 17th C. onwards.[22] But on his own evidence these were not used here, according to the Younger James Whatman, until 1768.[23] But this evidence can be seen as being slightly ambiguous in that his assertion that the paper in question was "made in a mould which is the first mould in which two sheets *of this kind of paper* was made at once. I am the first person who made it double, two sheets at once; this was in January 1768". Dr. Gaskell is of the opinion, however, that Demy Printing papers were made on such moulds in England as early as 1712. However, there must have been at least three vats working at Turkey mill where Walsh's "IW" paper appears to have been made, so there is no special reason to invoke the use of twin moulds to make what may have been Foolscap in this case.[24] Moreover, as Povey and Foster point out[25] the advantages of the twin mould appear to be somewhat dubious with heavier moulds, slower out−put and possibly greater damage to the fragile sheet. In any case we cannot tell whether a tranchfil mark appears for certain in the other half of sheet to that of the "IW" Countermark; in a twin mould the tranchefil wire would have been used only on the outer edges of the mould, the two covers being separated by a dividing bar or wire. On the whole, then, the view held here is that Whatman made use of single moulds.

Turning to the other proposals one has to find a good reason as to why the "IW" countermarks should appear some in the right half of the sheet and some in the left. It is suggested here that the reason for this

---

[21] Paper expands on wetting and contracts again on drying. Leaving aside the variations that might arise between sheet and sheet during the sheetmaking and drying process, paper used for printing at that time was dampened before the actual printing took place and would thus have been in a partially expanded and pliable state, so it is conceivable that distortion could occur in the printing press and in the subsequent drying of the paper, but to what extent is not known. The chainwire spacings in Dr. Hudson's exemplars are regular, but this may not always be the case. There have been cases of unexplained distortions across the face of the mould.

[22] Povey, K & Foster, I.J.C. Bib.73.

[23] Balston, T. Bib.1 23.

[24] A twin mould is a mould capable of making 2 sheets of a standard size e.g. Demy; each sheet is separated by a bar or thick wire. These standard sheets should not be confused with sizes known as Double Demy, Double Medium, Double Foolscap which are sheets with one dimension approximately doubled, but made on a single mould.

[25] Povey, K. & Foster, I.J.C. Bib.73 199/200.

may have been due to what Le Francois de Lalande has called *la bonne rive*[26] or the tendency for a sheet of paper to be thicker along the back edge of the mould than the front, making it slightly wedge–shaped. To compensate for this difference it was certainly the practice in modern times to place watermarks and countermarks one way up in one mould and the reverse in the other (both readable on the face of the mould i.e. not a mirror image in one case) Thus by placing all the watermarks in the *finished* paper facing in the same direction the effect of the thicker edge is eliminated when stacking the paper or possibly when making up a book. Whether this method was practised earlier or not is not known; Le Francois de Lalande certainly commented on *la bonne rive* in 1761 and this comment may well have been assimilated from M. Desbillettes' account of the paper making process (now lost)[27] of 1706. So it would not be unreasonable to propose that Whatman may have taken steps to compensate for this irregularity.[28] If this was the case then by sewing the countermarks all on the same side of the mould but with half of them reversed (as in Method 2), when one of the sheets is rotated through 180° the stacked or collected paper will all have their countermarks facing one way, one on the right side and one on the left, and the effects of *la bonne rive* eliminated or at least reduced.

The questions that the "IW" countermarks of 1740 pose

From what has been said in the foregoing pages one can accept with reasonable certainty that (a) the "IW" countermarks in question belonged to the elder Whatman; (b) that they appeared in paper used for printing in December 1740; and (c) to judge from Dr. Hudson's β–radiographs possibly as many as three pairs of two single moulds, with the likelihood that this meant three vats in operation. We are now faced with the problem of explaining how this could have taken place bearing in mind that on present evidence the elder Whatman only started his papermaking career in August 1740. Each of the three points mentioned requires separate comment: (a) the very unusual practice at this time for English paper makers to use their own personal marks; (b) would it have been possible for Whatman to make, size, finish and deliver the paper to Walsh in four months ? This question in turn raises yet another question: How did Walsh know where to turn for the paper he required at such short notice? Finally, (c) poses the question as to where one would have found a mill at this time that was equipped with three vats ?

The use of countermarks

Reference has been made in Chapter I to the fact that the use of countermarks by English or foreign entrepreneurs and English paper makers seems to have been prompted by continental paper makers working for and with them and that towards the end of the 17th C. this had become such a noticeable feature that the new generation of English Master Paper Makers, specializing in the manufacture of White paper, no doubt felt it in their interests to follow suit. Even so the incidence of countermarks belonging to English paper makers at the beginning of the 18th C. seems to have been rare, particularly when one takes into account the fact that by 1710 there were probably between 150–200 paper mills operating in this country, by 1738 278 in England and Wales and that by this time, it has been claimed, we

---

[26] Le Francois de Lalande, J.J. Bib.23 Art.76 last para. "La Partie de la forme que l'Ouvrier tient de la main droite, s'appelle les Mains : le côté opposé s'appelle les Pieds : la mauvaise rive est le côté qui est contre l'estomac de l'Ouvrier : le bord opposé s'appelle *la bonne rive*, parce que le papier est plus fort de ce côté là; c'est par la bonne rive qu'on pince le papier, quand on enlève les feuilles".

[27] Gachet, Henri Bib.24

[28] Private communication. Mr. E.G. Loeber has informed the author that the positioning of Watermarks in early Dutch papers was often reversed.

were producing significant quantities of White paper, the only sort of paper likely to have carried countermarks or stereotypes of any kind.[29] Thus, by any standards, Whatman's use and moreover immediate use of a countermark is a remarkable feature. This state of affairs was to continue for another three decades; the changes that took place then will be discussed later in this book.

There are two aspects to this use of countermarks by Whatman that require comment. First, it demonstrates that from the very beginning of his operations he must have had unusual confidence not only in the quality of his products but also in himself and his ability to maintain these standards. That this was so is shown by his continuous use of countermarks throughout his life and by the proliferation of their design,[30] both of these practices carried on by his son. Second, one has to ask whether there was any particular influence that may have prompted his use of countermarks. It has been alleged that some English paper makers of this period who made White paper made use of stereotypes such as "IV" or even "LVG"[31] or the initials of other famous Continental paper makers, possibly with a view to deceiving their customers into believing that the paper had been imported, English papers not having been regarded in a very favourable light before; but, more probably, it was used as a mark of quality. Whatman also could easily have made use of these pirated marks (and did so on occasion), but clearly he must have had special reasons for adding his personal mark to the paper. Four possible sources of influence suggest themselves. One may have been a continental source, for instance, knowing someone who had learnt his papermaking abroad; another may have been the insistence of a stationer telling him that he must countermark his paper to enable him to penetrate the market; or he might have inherited this practice from a former owner of the mill; or, finally, he may have made the decision himself for the same reasons, perhaps, that had made him decide to make an investment in the paper industry.

From the evidence available there are no certain pointers to any one of these four suggestions as being the real or the sole reason for this practice of Whatman's use of countermarks at such an early date. Taking them in the order given above, the notion that the elder Whatman had learnt his papermaking in Holland has now been largely discounted;[32] but, as will be discussed later, there are perfectly credible reasons for thinking that his close friend, Richard Harris, may have been trained abroad; or, at least, that he, perhaps together with Whatman, had been in contact with Dutch craftsmen or people familiar with Dutch practices from which this unusual use of countermarks may have stemmed.

Next, after citing the inclusion of the phrase "printed on fine Dutch paper" in an advertisement of 1734 as an example of Walsh's decided preference for paper made in Holland, Hudson has pointed out that the printer was almost certainly *compelled* to look for alternative supplies of *printing* paper because of the effects of the War of the Austrian Succession. That war could have a drastic effect is demonstrated by a similar interruption of

---

[29] See Preface to the Appendices I & II, Notes on Countermarks page v, n.15, for definition and mention of "Stereotypes".

[30] See App.V "Some Notes on "W" Countermarks" for evidence of Whatman's proliferation of personal marks.

[31] See App.V "The Whatman Ream Stamp" and the use of "LVG". With the lifting of restrictions on printing the use of countermarks etc. in papers made and sold in the provinces may have been optional due to the absence of foreign competition in contrast to more important markets e.g. the early use of personal marks by John Durham (Postlip mill, Gloucestershire) may have been because his papers were destined for, say, London, Oxford or Bristol.

[32] Balston, T. Bib.1 App.I 143–146. The idea is not entirely ruled out here, but instead considered improbable. An alternative to this is discussed later.

supplies in 1689 which produced the contemporary comment that "Paper became so dear that all printing stopped";[33] but, to have turned to Whatman at such short notice presupposes that Walsh knew where to turn for an alternative supply, a point which will be considered later. Having located a supply it is conceivable that he might have insisted that the paper should bear some mark by which he could distinguish it from the paper that he normally used. This suggestion is a possibility, but it would not really account for Whatman's continued disposition towards the use of countermarks or the proliferation and sophistication of their design.

The third suggestion takes one back to the former occupants of Turkey mill, that is prior to Richard Harris. These were William Gill snr. and his father and founder of the mill as a paper mill, George Gill, who not only made "very good White paper"[34] but, it is believed, used the countermark "GG". Possibly in earlier national crises John Walsh's father, who had been in the publishing and printing business since 1695 (his son did not take over until ca.1730), may likewise have looked for a good domestic supplier and discovered George Gill. His son may have remembered this and knew where to look in a later crisis. There is, however, no evidence or even a hint that William Gill used countermarks (or his successor Richard Harris)[35] so that the suggestion that Whatman may have inherited a tradition of using countermarks from George Gill is a remote one. Nevertheless the idea cannot be easily dismissed, because it is quite possible that Whatman knew George Gill and had been impressed by this very considerable paper maker and wished to perpetuate a tradition in the mill that he had now succeeded to.

Lastly, there is the suggestion that this practice of using countermarks may have been a decision of his own making. To judge from the circumstances surrounding the building of a paper mill in Hollingbourne, the second item of evidence "to be tested" here, it is clear that the basic motives for this investment were deep−seated in origin and longstanding (Chap.IV *The Challenge*) and that Whatman, as a result, was determined by all the means at his disposal to ensure that his venture was a success from the outset, and the use of a personal mark would have added another string to this bow.

When considering this investment in more detail, it will become apparent that this practice of using countermarks may well have originated from a combination of influences arising from the first, third and last of the suggestions made here, namely, an element of continental influence; an element that emanated from the experience of the Ancient Paper Makers of whom George Gill was one; and from his own personal convictions.

To conclude this section it should be stressed that the intention of testing this piece of evidence so closely has been to try to convey something of the singularity of this use of a countermark by Whatman so early in his career; but at the same time not to suggest that it

[33]   Hazen, A.T. Bib.5 329 quoting the diary of Edmund Bohun.
       The designation of the class of paper referred to here as "printing" is emphasised in the text above because there seems to be some evidence of continuity of quality in the paper used in the Handel autographs between ca.1710–1752 (letter 1:Mar:90 Dr. Donald Burrows, Senior Lecturer in Music, Open University) in contrast to the papers used by Walsh for his printings. If these observations are confirmed, a possible explanation may lie in the substantially different quantities of paper that would have been needed for two such distinct uses.
[34]   Harris, J. Bib.4 191.
[35]   See App.I the countermark section to the Synopsis of the history of Old Mill, Hollingbourne.

was in any way unique. It so happens that for this period the use of countermarks by English paper makers appears to have been very uncommon[36] in spite of the fact that more White paper was being made then in this country than ever before. Consequently it is important to try to discover some of the reasons that led Whatman to employ them. It will be seen that the use of countermarks by British paper makers became increasingly more common during and after the 1760's.[37] At this point it is sufficient to note that Whatman's use of a countermark at this time was very unusual and that his practice of employing them may have resulted from a combination of three separate influences connected with the circumstances that surrounded his investment of 1733. The credibility of these suggestions will become apparent when this investment is discussed later.

---

[36] The subject of countermarks crops up from time to time in this book. The author has redefined for the purposes of this book the countermark and distinguishes it from other types of watermarking such as emblems, mottoes, stereotypes etc. (see Preface to App.I & II); and, the incidence of "W" marks is discussed in a special section in App.V as well as other countermarks which are treated as and when they arise in the text; but he has not had the facilities or time for making a detailed study of the subject as a whole. All the same, whether it may be due to the fact that they are still waiting to be discovered or due to unidentified contemporary restraints, it is a curious feature of this period that, whereas English countermarks do not appear to have been uncommon towards the end of the 17th C. and for the first decade of the 18th, they seem almost to disappear during the period approximately 1730–1750 and not to be commonly used until after 1760. In the earlier part of this period, for a smaller total of mills than for the later one, there are examples of countermarks that have been attributed to Eustace Burnaby, Peter le Gaultier, Thomas Quelch, Rice Watkins, Denis Manes, Thomas Meale, Nicholas Dupin, the COMPANY with at least 4 different subscript countermarks (Gravell, T.L. Bib.16 12:Dec:1984), Elliston & Basket, all occurring within the last quarter of the 17th C. Early in the 18th C. we may possibly have George Gill, William Harris (?); an unidentified "SP" (Irish): a Dupin Braid and another unidentified Scottish mark (Shorter, A. Bib.9 252 fig.32 a–c); Durham; and an "RA" (suggested as Richard Archer : Author); as well as quite a number of unidentified marks, which may or may not be English but have not been identified as Continental.

In contrast to this, when one comes to the later period (1730–1750), the only countermarks identified so far for Kent are those of the Elder Whatman, who used a surprising variety. Elsewhere Shorter (Bib.9 56/7) has identified Richard Ware (Middlesex, 1746); John Crowder (Buckinghamshire, 1745); Durham was still active at Postlip mills (Gloucestershire); and Richard Heath (Worcestershire) was making "watermarked" paper ca.1743. The first "William Jubb" countermark that has come to the author's notice is in a document dated 1754, Ewell mill, Surrey (Gravell, T.L. Bib.68 452–3), not a very noteworthy total.

Clearly there must have been several other makers of White paper at this time, but either they did not identify themselves or their marks have not been discovered yet. One might have expected countermarks from:–

Henry Portal	(Bere; or the Laverstoke mills, Hampshire)
Daniel Roussillon	(Up mills, Hampshire; formerly COMPANY)
John Beckford	(Wolvercote, Oxfordshire)
Edward Band	(Wookey Hole, Somerset)
Joshua Carby	(Quenington, Gloucestershire)
Joseph Lloyd	(Gun's mills, Gloucestershire)
Henry Cotton	(Bristol mill, Gloucestershire)

and possibly two or three other mills that had installed "engines" to make Writing paper such as Colthrop mill (Berkshire); Hay mill (Herefordshire); and Stoke Holy Cross (Norfolk). Gravell, T.L. (Bib.68) illustrates the following unidentified countermarks, which may be either English or Continental, unknown. 187–188 "DP" (1714); do. (1716); 224–225 "EVH" (1741); 281–282 "GHD" (1707); 394 "IGB" (1704); 395–396 "IKM" (1739); 405–406 "ISRB" (1750); 469 "LA" (1730); 581 "RH" (discussed App.I countermarks to Old Mill, Hollingbourne); 606 "SC" (1746); 612 "SL" (1758). It is now thought that "SL" (1758 and later d.o.ds.) refers to Samuel Lay at Sittingbourne. (See Chap.VII note 195). All dates refer to the d.o.ds of American documents.

[37] Chap.VII n.357.

The Feasibility of supplying Walsh with paper within 4–5 months

The next question, could Whatman have made and delivered paper for Walsh's printing of 11th December 1740 during the period between this event and either the marriage settlement of 2nd July 1740 (five months) or the date of his first insurance policy on 19th August 1740 (four months) ? The short answer to this is that with certain important assumptions, namely that Whatman took over a going concern; that the mill was suitably equipped (*and this includes the use of the new Hollander Beating Engine*);[38] and that he had good weather, such an undertaking would have been feasible. Though the Insurance Policy indicates that Whatman must have been firmly established in the mill by 19th August[39] it would be as well in this feasibility exercise to limit it to a period of four months to allow time to cover the event of his marriage, his move to Boxley and the receipt of an order for this paper. For the reader interested in the grounds that have led to this conclusion, the assumptions made are discussed in some detail below.

A Going Concern

This is the first of the three basic assumptions that have been made to cover this situation. It will be recalled that after Richard Harris had acquired Turkey mill in September 1738 he pulled it down and began to re-erect it "on a more curious and extensive plan" and his Will (22:Aug:1739) shows that this rebuilding was still in progress then.[40] No evidence has survived to indicate when this work was completed and the new equipment commissioned and considered to be operating smoothly as a production facility. One has no alternative, therefore, other than to assume that by the time Whatman took over the mill all this had been achieved, by no means a minor assumption.

This concept of a "going concern" also implies that there must have been some continuity in the supply of rags as well as an outlet for its products. For instance, in the hypothetical case described below it seems most unlikely that roughly 1.5 ton of rags would have appeared at short notice from local sources.[41] To avoid complicating the present issue the question of outlets for the products and Whatman's means of entreé to the London market will be discussed later; the fact is that Walsh got his paper so, clearly, the means were available for this to be achieved. Similarly, there is the problem of the availability of skilled labour to man Turkey mill and operate its new equipment, a subject that

---

[38] The "Engine" or Hollander Beater was a new and revolutionary method of washing and converting rags into stuff that had been introduced into England in the 1680's from Holland where it had been invented and developed earlier in the 17th C. The rags were ground rather than hammered and reduced to pulp much more quickly than in the traditional stamping process. It would be inappropriate to discuss this new equipment here. References to its introduction and development occur in the chapters that follow; a full account is reserved for Chap.VI.

[39] SFIP No.85207 (Guildhall Library MS.11936/57) dated 19:Aug:1740 shows that James Whatman was described as "of Boxley in the County of Kent, *Papermaker*" and that he insured his Dwelling House (£200), Utensils and Stock in Paper Mill called the Old Turkey Mill near his dwelling house now adjoining (£400); Stock in the Raghouse (£500); as well as a House in Loose in the tenure of Joseph Charlton (£300); Tan House, Barn etc. (£100); and a Barn and Stable adjoining each one (£200). This Policy provides useful information about the elder Whatman. He is described as a paper maker; the Stock in his Raghouse was insured for a greater sum than the Stock and Utensils in the paper mill; and his house in Loose was insured for a greater sum than Turkey Court. For us the Policy shows that by this date Whatman must have been in a position to supply paper and that he had a considerable stock of rags for this purpose.

[40] Balston, T. Bib.1 10–11 citing Hasted's "History of Kent" (1782); see also his note 1 commenting on Hasted's statement. (Harris' Will KAO PRC 17/91 Part I fo.4).

[41] Harris, John Bib.4 191 had made the point (ca.1716) that at Turkey Mill "they could easily make much greater quantities of Paper, if there were demands accordingly. The Rags they use they have mostly from straggling persons, which bring them to the Mill; *and some they have from London*". This was in George Gill's day when they made Brown paper as well as White. Since that time the demand for White paper had increased, especially from domestic sources, and accelerated as a result of the War of the Austrian Succession (1739–48). When Whatman started making paper at Turkey Mill the problem of obtaining adequate quantities of suitable rags would have become more acute. In the event the Insurance Policy (see note 39) shows that he must have inherited a considerable quantity of rags from his predecessor or foreseen the need for these at a much earlier date than his formal accession to the mill.

will also be treated later. Taken overall then the assumption of a "going concern" is a very considerable one which, at the same time, one has to accept as a *fait accompli*.

A Mill suitably equipped

The two main factors under this heading are the size of the order itself and the order of the mill's throughput; one has to remember also that almost certainly the mill would have been dealing with other orders than Walsh's during this period. Taking the size of the order first one has to make an inspired guess at this and, if possible, *overestimate* it (to allow for contingencies) and then see whether Whatman could have coped with it in the time allotted. To cover not only Walsh's requirement for the Select Harmony Fourth Collection but others (viz. Prints 4, 10, 12, 17, etc.) to be on the safe side an allowance has been made here for supplying 3000 lb. of paper (for calculations see Working Papers). It is reckoned that, given a 3-vat mill equipped with two Hollander beaters with a capacity of 100 lb. rags each (coupled with a suitable backing of rag-breakers)[42] and remembering also the greatly enlarged drying shed at Turkey mill (rebuilt 1738/9) and the fact that Printing papers were *not* finished, this order could have been completed and ready for dispatch within three months. This reckoning is discussed below.

Certain assumptions have been made above that are inseparably linked to another factor, namely, the throughput of the mill. Starting with the number of vats, Shorter estimated that at least 50 out of the 200 mills in Great Britain in 1711 had two vats. Although he goes on to say that this proportion does not appear to have altered significantly by 1738,[43] one has to account for the fact that at some point in its history Turkey mill became a 5-vat mill. On the basis of the younger Whatman's accounts Thomas Balston came to the conclusion that before the elder Whatman died (1759) Turkey mill had become the largest paper mill in the country and, further, that there was no evidence that his son's establishment in 1771 was appreciably larger than what he had taken over from his father.[44] The conclusion is that Turkey mill had five vats by 1759, if not before this date. Moreover we have Harris' evidence of ca.1715 that the mill was *"a very large work, and they could easily make much greater quantities of paper if there were demands accordingly".*[45] That it was indeed a very large work is borne out by his statement that the mill was powered by three waterwheels. So, viewing these remarks collectively, it is not unreasonable to propose that even by ca.1716 Turkey mill was already a 3-vat mill; and this much more so the case by 1740.

Taking all the other conditions into consideration, such as dealing with orders other than Walsh's, to have completed the latter's order within three months one also has to assume the use of a Hollander beater; to have used the old stamping process and mortars would have added, at a guesstimate, another 2-3 months[46] to the production time of three months already suggested, taking one back at a minimum to a starting date early in June (i.e. long before the marriage settlement). In addition one is not concerned only with a three-month production period here. Though the order may have been ready by then for despatch, it still had to be shipped to London, delivered and used by 11th December. Under these circumstances it is both essential and legitimate to assume that Whatman made use of Hollander beaters to process this order. Indeed, in view of the radical rebuilding programme undertaken by Harris in 1738 and with the knowledge that the Hollander Engine had been introduced into this country towards the end of

---

[42] As Rees (Bib.50) pointed out some small mills at the beginning of the 19th C. with limited water supplies "frequently have but one Engine, and use it both for washing and beating"; but, as will be seen later, Chartham mill had two Engines and 2 Vats by 1738. It is not known, however, whether Chartham had other means of preparing Stuff or indeed what the quality of the rags used there was and whether they needed the prolonged treatment necessary for White paper manufacture. We do know that in 1771 Old Mill, Hollingbourne, with only 1 waterwheel serving probably no more than 2 vats at the most was equipped with 2 rag-washers and 1 Beater (See App.V). It is not unreasonable, therefore, to assume that Turkey mill with its 3 waterwheels and almost certainly 3 vats would have been equipped with at least 2 Beaters and probably 4 supporting rag-washers.

[43] Shorter, A. Bib.9 68.

[44] Balston, T. Bib.1 13

[45] Harris, John Bib.4 191

[46] Harris, John Bib.4 191 stated that fine rags required 36 hours beating (presumably breaking and beating is meant here); Le Francois de Lalande, J.J. Bib.23 Art.50 and 51 gives the same figure. These figures may be compared with 10 hours breaking and beating time with the new Engine, which handled much larger quantities of stuff. Whether it is to be believed or not Richard Herring "Paper and Paper Making, Ancient and Modern" (Longman 1855. 60) states that "no fewer than forty pairs of stamps were required to operate night and day in preparing one hundredweight of material". To the rag preparation times for the older system one has to add the fermentation period which may have lasted from anything between, say, 10-20 days for strong rags.

Figure 2 – Illustrating a Hypothetical Production Schedule
For the 100 Ream Order

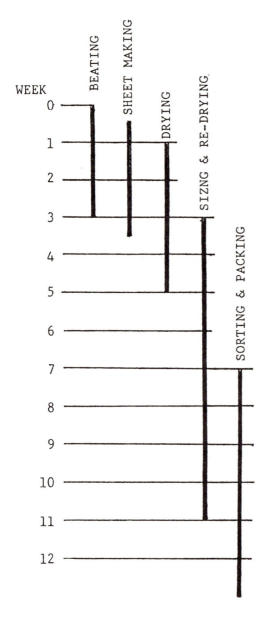

The diagram (left) represents a purely hypothetical schedule but makes sufficient allowances for work to have been interrupted and continued again later.

For instance, it has been calculated that the Beating time for Walsh's order could have been in theory 7½ days working a 12–hour day. The beater floor in some mills worked a 24–hour day, so that the work could have been completed in less than 7½ days had this been the practice. On the other hand material loss, which could be considerable, has not been taken into consideration in these calculations. On this basis 7½ days seems a reasonable compromise; but to allow for contingencies the beating period shown in the diagram has been more than doubled to 3 weeks.

Similarly, sheetmaking at 5 reams per day per vat would in theory take about 7 days to complete. Some of the smaller size sheets could be made at the rate of 8 reams a day per vat (Desmarest, N. Bib.21 511 Table); * but, as above, material losses have not been allowed for and to take care of contingencies as well 3 weeks have been allowed to complete sheetmaking for this order.

The Drying Capacity of the mill both in space and drying time are both quite unknown. As shown in the diagram the periods indicated, if they were in fact directly related to beating and sheetmaking output, would have led very quickly to a major imbalance in production. Under normal circumstances this was probably not the case and the drying times shown here have clearly been overestimated by a considerable margin. Once production had really got under way i.e. not under the conditions following Whatman's start it is probable that paper for sizing and re–drying would have been taken out of a store

and perhaps made several months earlier. To judge from the size of the new drying lofts at the mill it would appear that they had ample capacity to dry the order in much less time than indicated here, leaving periods which could take care of interruptions.

Finally, the period for sorting and packing would have been dependent on the rate at which the sized paper was coming through to the Salle. As stated, it is unlikely that Walsh's paper would have been pressed.

*See also "Instructions to be observed by Officers in the Country employed in charging the duties on Paper" (1720) p.14. Number of Reams usually made per day......Crown and Foolscap 8 Reams etc.

the 17th C. and that two such "Engines" had been installed at nearby Chartham mill, Kent, in 1733 (a subject discussed later), one cannot imagine any alternative. The other conditions needed to satisfy this order in time, namely, that the Engines were capable of holding 100lb. rags, beating them in 6 hours[47] and working a 12–hour day,[48] are also considered as acceptable. Taking this together with a greatly increased capacity for drying paper,[49] it is considered that the throughput of this mill would have been quite adequate to have coped with an order of this size with time and resources to spare.

To execute this order one has to take into account the following processes: rag sorting, rag breaking, beating, sheetmaking, drying, sizing and re–drying and, finally, sorting and packing. These processes would have run concurrently and, because paper in those days was air–dried, the paper maker would not have been faced with the modern problem of conditioning and maturing the paper. Fig.2 opposite summarises the production schedule envisaged for the execution of this order. In view of what has been said above about the concurrent nature of these processes the rag sorting and rag breaking have been bracketed with Beating.

The final component needed to complete this picture of a mill suitably equipped was the availability of skilled labour. This point has been referred to earlier under the heading of a "going concern". It has been demonstrated in Chapter II that by the time Whatman came onto the Maidstone papermaking scene, the paper industry had become firmly established in the district and that Turkey mill had been operating for at least 60 years by 1740. One would not imagine, therefore, that the availability of skilled labour would have been a problem for Whatman in all the processes he needed to make the paper with except one, the working of the Hollander Engines. Taking into consideration the state of development and the use of these engines at this time, a new process, this is a very serious proviso to have to make. It is not the intention to discuss this subject here, but it must be borne in mind. It has already been said that Walsh's order was executed and the paper delivered so that the problem must have been surmounted by one means or another.

Weather

Due to difficulties encountered in drying sized paper the completion of orders could be seriously delayed by bad weather. Weather could, of course, affect other operations adversely. For example, with some paper mills drought or floods could interfere with the power supply from the waterwheel; or affect the shipping of goods from the mill to the market. To judge from the number of watermills that had been situated on it for centuries one might safely assume that only under very exceptional weather conditions might the River Len have failed. The normal method of transporting the paper from Turkey mill to London would have been by the hoy that travelled regularly down the Medway from Maidstone and up the Thames Estuary to London; this service could have been delayed by fog or bad weather. But it is more likely that the drying of sized paper could have been a more serious cause of delay in this case than the others.

That the weather was an important consideration in the sizing of paper is evident from the number of references to it in the literature and the need for "chusing a fine, dry temperate day" for it. But the effect of the weather in the drying of paper is less well documented. The Société Typographique de Neuchatel, for instance, would obtain during the summer the paper they were going to need the following winter, so acute had this problem become in the 18th C.[50] So clearly the weather is a factor one cannot overlook.

---

[47] Le Francois de Lalande, J.J. Bib.23 Art 51 gives a beating time of 6–7 hours. This time may well have been reduced, if sharper beating tackle than that instanced by Lalande had been used. Mid–Century criticism (Roy.Soc.Arts Guard Book 1755) of English beating practice suggests that this may have been the case. (See also App.V pp.227 ff. Whatman's Beater bars in 1771).

[48] Le Francois de Lalande, J.J. Art 47 indicates that in some mills the beating operation continued throughout the day and night (remembering, if this was so, that the state of the stuff would have had to be judged by candlelight; so possibly not applicable to Fine papers).

[49] Balston, T. Bib.1 The Drying House is illustrated in Plate 2(b).

[50] The author is indebted to Dr. Philip Gaskell (letter 8:Aug:1977) for supplying him with this information, obtained in turn from M. Jacques Rychner. Coleman, D.C. Bib.15 163 n.2 citing P.R.O. CO 391/90 which states that ca.1700 contemporaries reckoned not only a working year of 200 days but that paper makers could not work during frost nor size during the winter.

Though no figures are available for the Maidstone area those given below for the Tonbridge area[51] (ca.12.5 miles SW of Maidstone) should give a reasonable picture of the weather experienced at Turkey mill in 1740. After 3 exceptionally wet years (1737–1739) with annual totals of 30.32, 30.38 and 35.08 inches of rain, 1740 was the first of a series of dry years with an annual total of 23.77 inches. The rainfall for August 1740 was higher than the 10-year average, 3.60 inches as against 2.40 inches; but September and October were much drier than average, 1.74 inches as against 2.83 and 1.13 inches as against 3.22. The indoor temperature for September 1740 never fell below 60°F. (unfortunately the records kept for October were too uncertain to be of any value here). On this evidence one should at least be able to say that there appears to have been nothing catastrophic in the way of weather that might have delayed Whatman from supplying paper to Walsh at such short notice, if this indeed had been the case.

Was a 3–Vat mill involved ?

Dr. Hudson's evidence suggested that 3 pairs of moulds were used to produce the paper employed for the Select Harmony Fourth Collection, but due to the cost of the process he was unable to obtain sufficient β–radiographic evidence to demonstrate unequivocally that 3 pairs were in fact used on these and other printings on Whatman paper made at the same time, although in all cases the "IW" marks were similarly placed on a chain line. But 3 pairs of moulds does not necessarily signify the use of 3 vats; if the making period was long enough, they could all have been used at one vat. But the notes accompanying Fig.2 indicate that the entire order could have been made in 7 days at the vat and in view of the short period in question taken together with a reasonable assumption that Walsh made his printings of the Select Harmony from reams produced at approximately the same time, i.e. not printed on some sheets made at the start of a lengthy making and others at the end, supports the view that 3 pairs of moulds were used to execute his order at 3 vats.

There cannot have been many mills in this country at that time, if any other than Turkey mill, that were equipped with 3 vats. Taking this then and all the other points collectively, namely, that the "IW" mark was Whatman's, that the mill in question was Turkey mill and that Whatman took it over as a going concern, one can be pretty certain that Whatman manufactured and delivered the paper Walsh had ordered between 17th August and 11th December 1740 without undue difficulty.

It will be seen from the first piece of evidence tested here, the 1740 "IW" countermark, that a close examination of this subject has revealed a host of other issues that have to be taken into consideration when attempting to explain the occurrence of this mark, issues that extend far beyond the mere attachment of two letters to the face of a papermaking mould by a given paper maker and then only after a certain date. Perhaps the most important of these, and one which embraces many of the others, is the now obvious fact that Whatman cannot have occupied his new position in 1740 without having had some earlier contact with the papermaking industry both locally and in a wider context. Some of these issues will arise again when the next piece of evidence, Whatman's investment in a paper mill, is tested, and it will be seen then that examination of the latter will throw even more light on them. It has been demonstrated here, however, that given certain conditions, Whatman could have made the paper used by Walsh for his printings of 11th December 1740 after he had assumed control of Turkey mill in August of that year. The one point that has not been resolved is the

[51] Acknowledgement is made here to the kindness of the Librarian of the National Meteorological Library, Bracknell, Berkshire for supplying statistics on the weather for these years and from which the information above has been extracted. (Ref. AF/M64/77).

question as to whether any papers bearing his countermark were made earlier than this, remembering that some of the late W.C. Smith's datings of certain publications of Handel's works, printed on paper containing the "IW" mark, suggested dates prior to August 1740, one even as early as 1739. It is true that Dr. Hudson has proposed alternative datings for some of these printings; but in the event that some of these suggestions are still open to doubt, the question remains, could Whatman have put his mark into paper made at an earlier date ?

(2) *WHATMAN'S PAPERMAKING VENTURE IN HOLLINGBOURNE*

It has been known for a long time that the two Whatmans had had a paper mill in the parish of Hollingbourne, about 4 miles to the East of Maidstone and sited on the River Len. Thomas Balston gives a general account of this mill;[52] but, presumably either because the information was not fully known to him or because the significance of this fact escaped him, he treats its early history very summarily.

Dr. Shorter goes somewhat further than Thomas Balston and states that Hollingbourne Old Mill had been "established" by James Whatman.[53] Mr. R.J. Spain, in his paper on the "Len Watermills",[54] actually quotes a passage from the recital to the Indenture Tripartite of 1762 in the Whatman Archives concerned with Sir Roger Meredith's demise of land in Hollingbourne "with free liberty for the said James Whatman to erect a new Dwelling House and Paper Mill on the said land etc. ..." on the 30th July 1733.[55]

In none of these accounts, however, is reference made to the fact that according to this same indenture Whatman "did *act* and *build* on the said leasehold lands and premises a dwelling house, water mill etc. ...." in 1733.[56] This is a highly significant fact. It immediately raises questions such as why should a tanner of Loose want to build a paper mill at all ? Why in Hollingbourne ? It is true that an empty site existed there, formerly occupied by a fulling mill that had long since disappeared;[57] all the same Hollingbourne was some distance from Loose and the site an obscure one. Why, instead of converting an existing fulling or corn mill, should he want to build *an entirely new paper mill* ? This would appear, perhaps, to have been the first new mill to have been built in Kent since Dartford No.2 in 1679.[58] Finally, why did he install his friend, Richard Harris, in this mill ? A lot of questions have been asked here which will be examined more closely later. In the meantime it would be fitting to see if any other evidence has survived, which would confirm the claims made in the Indenture Tripartite of 1762.

In the absence of a Hollingbourne Poor Ratebook for the period in question evidence for the construction and occupation of Old Mill depends, apart from the information to be found in the Deed referred to above, on the details given in the Insurance Policy taken out by "JAMES WHATMAN of Loose in the County of Kent Tanner", No.61845 dated 25th September 1733 with the Sun Fire Insurance Company,[59] which showed that "a New-built Dwelling House and Paper Mill being one entire building in the parish of Hollingbourne" was then in the Occupation of Richard Harris paper maker; and on indirect evidence such as payments made

---

[52] Balston, T. Bib.1 Chap.XV. Some of the statements made later in this chapter (XV) are incorrect. The necessary corrections have been made and will be found now in App.I under the synopses of the histories of Old Mill and Eyehorne mill, Hollingbourne.

[53] Shorter, A. Bib.7 (May) 54.

[54] Spain, R.J. Bib.8 61. (see note 55 for corrected reference to this document).

[55] KAO U.289.T34.

[56] loc.cit.

[57] Spain, R.J. Bib.8 61. See also the synopsis of the history of Old Mill, Hollingbourne, App.I.

[58] Dartford No.2 paper mill appears to have been built specifically as a paper mill in 1679 and not converted from some other function as was the case at Chartham mill (1733). Other possible candidates, though there is no particular reason to suppose that they too had not been converted from some other function, are Shoreham (ca.1690); East Malling (end of the 17th C.); Sittingbourne (early 18th C.): and Cobtree mill (1718).

[59] Guildhall Library (London) MS 11936 Vol.39. SFIP No. 61845, quoted in full in Preface to App.I & II n.11.

by Richard Harris from 1733-1739 (first half year) for assessments made by the Leeds Parish Overseers against the osier beds within the parish and lying along the southern bank of the River Len and the mill pond[60] on land originally leased to Whatman by Sir Roger Meredith and always sublet to the occupier of the mill, in this case Harris. Various other pieces of evidence, of a slightly later date, confirming Harris' residence in Hollingbourne are to be found in the entry for his marriage at St. Saviour's, Southwark, in November 1734;[61] and the baptism of his daughter in Hollingbourne in 1735;[62] as well as Insurance Policies for 1734, taken out by Harris himself;[63] and for 1736, taken out by Whatman,[64] the house and mill still being in the occupation of Harris. There is no need to take this subject further at this juncture; sufficient evidence has been supplied to show that the mill was built by Whatman in 1733 and occupied, for a period at least, by Richard Harris.

Before considering the nature of the investment and the motives that may have led to it, it would be instructive to place it in a perspective appropriate to the period to see how the conditions governing a decision of this kind have changed from those that exist to-day and, for that matter, during the intervening two and a half centuries; and, at the same time, expose the problems it might have presented the would-be investor with.

If as a resident in this country (U.K.) one was planning to invest in a paper mill to-day, that is towards the end of the 20th C., to make the kinds of paper that we have been considering so far, namely writing, printing and wrapping papers, then one would have to think of this now in *international* terms due to a much altered situation. Historically, because of the start that this country had in the first half of the 19th C.,[65] we still retained an important share of the world's production of these papers until well into the 20th C., so that 50 years ago, and perhaps even less than that, one could still think of such an investment in *national* terms. Even after World War II, for a short time and by a small margin, we still had the fourth largest paper industry in the world; but the writing was already on the wall. The rapid growth of integrated pulp and paper mills in countries that had previously supplied us with pulp, or the wood itself, put paid to much of our domestic production; and the substitution of brown (wrapping or sack) Paper with cheaper plastic film decimated the production of Kraft paper

---

[60] KAO P 222 12/4. For Leeds parish see Map 2 (Chap.II) and Map 9 (end Vol.II).

[61] Greater London R.O. P 92/SAV/3039. The entry for 2:Nov:1734 describes Richard Harris as of Hollingbourne in Kent and his bride, Ann Carter, as of Leeds in Kent. (See also App.II Notes on Ann Carter).

[62] KAO P 187 1/1. Anne bapt. 7:Oct:1735.

[63] Guildhall Library (London) MS 11936 Vol.40 SFIP No.65053 7:Oct:1734.

[64] Guildhall Library (London) MS 11936 Vol.47 SFIP No.72264 27:Dec:1736.

[65] After the licensing for sale of production models (1807) of the papermachine together with numerous improvements that followed (detailed account Clapperton, R.H. Bib.75) the output of handmade paper declined in contrast to a rapid increase in machine made (Coleman, D.C. Bib.15 fig.9). The net result was that by the middle of the century Britain had become the greatest paper exporting country in the world (see Coleman ibid. Chap.VII "Mechanization" and Chap.VIII "The Period of Expansion, 1800-1860").

Production, however, was still based on rag furnishes which obviously became more and more a limiting factor as expansion proceeded. Though alternative materials had been used successfully on a manufacturing scale as early as 1800 (Matthias Koops in London: see also Index Paper Makers, Koops), it was not until the period 1840-1860 that new materials (ground wood, Manila hemp and, later, esparto grass) were developed and used on an ever-increasing scale. New processes for extracting the materials were also being developed successfully and the 1880's saw the introduction of chemical woodpulps, which in retrospect can be regarded as a major turning point in the history of the paper industry. But for another 70 years the British Paper Industry, in spite of the fact that it had to import all its raw materials now, continued to hold its own, albeit on an ever-dwindling scale. (For this contraction see Shorter, A. Bib.9 181 fig.18).

also. Hence the need for the would–be investor of to–day to plan new papermaking ventures in international terms.

In a sense the position for the would–be investor in the 18th C. was quite the reverse of this. During the 17th C. the infant paper industry of this country struggled to compete with imports from the Continent, successfully at first in the field of Brown paper and marginally towards the end of the century in White paper. However, at the beginning of the 18th C., with the assistance of increased Duties on imported paper, the tide was slowly beginning to turn, especially in favour of would–be investors in the manufacture of White paper.

There were many obstacles to this progress such as loopholes in the regulations governing the duties on imported paper, greatly exploited by the Stationers importing paper; but there is evidence that though the consumption of paper in this country was increasing[66] imports showed no corresponding rise during the first 35 years of the century and thereafter went into a steep decline.[67] Even so domestic production, though clearly higher than at the end of the 17th C. appears to have remained relatively static for this early period but, later, rose and had increased four–fold by the end of the century. The industry as a whole was, therefore, definitely on the upward path by 1740; in fact Blue and Brown paper imports for 1743 were negligible.

Coleman has shown that throughout the 18th C. roughly 50% of domestic output consisted of Brown paper (in actual fact it declined from ~53% to 47%). Initially, much of the rest consisted of the cheaper sorts of printing and writing paper. It follows then that the volume of these lower grades of White paper also increased significantly (i.e. ca. four–fold by the end of the century). By inference, then, the opportunities for the manufacture of the residue, namely the better qualities, became correspondingly greater both in volume as the century progressed and in proportion to the total as imports of this class of paper declined.[68] In general it may be said then that, unlike the latter part of the 20th C., conditions increasingly favoured investment in the domestic industry, including the manufacture of White paper, from about 1740 onwards.

In the case of White paper it has been claimed, and referred to earlier under Walsh's requirements, that the War of the Austrian Succession (1739–1748) interrupted supplies of the better qualities, still imported from the Continent, and so provided an opportunity and corresponding stimulus to the domestic production of this class of paper.[69] It could also be argued for those who were alert to the implications of this situation, probably in the main the Stationers and Printers, that the time was also ripe for those who might wish to invest in this

---

[66]   Coleman, D.C. Bib.15 100 ff. The subject of the increased demand for paper is examined here. Though the population of England & Wales increased by ca.60% during the 18th C., the increase in paper consumption was governed by other factors such as the increase in national wealth, the growth of other industries, more complex commercial intercourse and documentation, more goods to wrap etc., slow at the beginning of the century, but gathering pace especially during the last three decades.

[67]   Coleman, D.C. Bib.15 fig.2 (opp.p.90).

[68]   Coleman, D.C. Bib.15 91–94. Quoting contemporary sources shows that imports were in decline; more White paper was being made in England and used for writing and printing. Table IV (p.94) shows that a total of 42,000 reams of White paper were imported into England & Wales during 1743, a figure that may be broadly compared with anything from 100,000–over 200,000 reams at the end of the 17th C. and up to 1710 to meet a smaller demand (ibid. Table II opp.p.20).

[69]   Balston, T. Bib.1 12.

field. That the elder Whatman, and no doubt other paper makers as well, benefited during these war years is not open to doubt; but, on the other hand, it is difficult to assess just how far this opportunity to invest was pursued.

Initially, increased production of White paper may have come more from existing mills either in the form of taking up the slack in their potential for the output of top quality paper; or by increasing their productivity; or in up–grading their mills by one means or another to make White paper where inferior grades had been made before rather than by investing in new mills. Investment in new or conversion of old mills seems to have been a much slower affair. 5 + 1 (?) paper mills make their first appearance in Kent in the 1740's, a further 4 in the 1750's and only 2 of these producing White *uncountermarked* paper, probably common printing. The national picture looks even less promising; Shorter's research[70] has only identified the appearance of a further 30 mills (all types) between 1745 and 1755, with the growth gathering pace in the next decades, 52 mills between 1755–1765 and an additional 55 in the next.

On the face of it Whatman's appearance at Turkey mill in 1740 seems to have been a timely one in these circumstances; but in his case one really has to look further than this. It was shown earlier that Whatman made his investment and built his new mill in 1733, that is *seven years before the effect of the War of the Austrian Succession began to show itself* and he must have come to a decision to do this at an even earlier date. Even Harris' conversion of Turkey mill antedates the effects of this war, an event he could not possibly have foreseen. As a consequence future investigation will have to be directed towards finding other, or at least additional, motives for this investment rather than explaining it simply as a case of his being inspired by a general notion that the prospects of making and selling White paper were improving; and his project was certainly not aimed at the manufacture of any other kind of paper. However, the motives for Whatman's investment is a separate issue to this comparison of conditions past and present for decisions of this kind and will be dealt with later.

Summarizing these conditions briefly, in contrast to the situation existing in the United Kingdom in the second half of the 20th C., as the 18th C. progressed so also did the circumstances that favoured investment in the domestic paper industry improve, though slowly to begin with despite the fact that nationwide the number of new paper mills increased by just under 70 between 1712 and 1738. But many of these would have been little more than cottage industries engaged in producing Brown or, at most, the lower qualities of White. Production remained relatively static for the first 35 years of the century and then increased steadily from ca. 1740 onwards including within it an increasing proportion of the best qualities of White paper. But it seems that for reasons that have not yet become apparent, Whatman anticipated those conditions that specially favoured this growth, namely the war, by more than a marginal span of years.

The intention so far has been to try to convey to the reader who may have difficulty in projecting his or her imagination into the overall circumstances in which the industry found itself in the 18th C. the differences a prospective investor would have had to face at that time compared to the situation he would find himself in today. This can be a very real difficulty,

[70]   Shorter, A. Bib.9 76.

particularly when this comparison is extended to cover the means at the disposal of a paper maker, because we have all become so used to the facilities available to us nowadays that one can easily overlook the effect of their absence when considering an early 18th C. setting (in the author's experience the number of misconceptions surrounding the details of early papermaking that continue to prevail is quite extraordinary).

To implement his investment the modern investor would have to consider the vast capital outlay needed to equip a new paper mill. Quite apart from the cost of the buildings, often of similar dimensions to that of a cathedral, and the machinery, another massive capital item, he would have to take into account all the ancillary services that go with this installation. The power consumption of a large modern paper mill, for instance, sometimes demands generating plant of a magnitude capable of supplying the electricity needs of a large town; the consumption of water is formidable and carries with it the attendant problem of effluent disposal. It is not difficult to imagine either the problems of supplying pulp, water, steam and fuel (for power and steam raising) to just one machine of enormous width capable of making more than 30 miles of paper per hour, 24 hours a day and, virtually, non-stop for the whole year round. All this to be followed by conversion and shipping this endless stream of paper to the customer.

The planners to-day would have at their disposal all the modern aids to help them decide where to site a paper mill and how big it should be; they would also have a good idea of the market size and what competition they were likely to face, all based on a mass of computerised statistics and coupled with a world-wide communication network. From a technical standpoint they would employ highly sophisticated production plant and instrumentation for control;[71] and have their own engineering, maintenance, research, development and quality supervision facilities; and so on. Sufficient has been said here to show that the modern investment decision really bears no comparison at all with one made, say, 250 years ago apart from one common aspect in that one might say that in both cases the final decision would always be a bit of a gamble.

Considering some of the points made above and in the same order, the capital requirement for a paper mill in the 1730's would probably seem to us to be very small. No figures have survived to show what Whatman's outlay might have been. Coleman has suggested[72] that towards the end of the 18th C. £2,000 would have covered the value of an average mill. Hollingbourne Old mill was probably of average size when first built, but it may have contained more expensive machinery than other contemporary mills, requiring rather different building construction as well. Even though it might have been a 2-vat mill, one could probably safely envisage an outlay of less than £2,000, possibly something more like £1,000. The house and mill were insured for £600 in the first Policy (1733), but this would obviously not take into account the expenditure that had gone into all the "Bridges, Floodgates, Bays, Penstocks, Sluices and all other proper conveniences for the use and supply of the said Rivers and Watercourses", items that clearly would not have been included in a Fire Policy.

[71] In some cases this would involve closed-loop computer operation of the paper machine supported by a largely automated stock preparation system and linked to computerised stock control and despatch of orders.
[72] Coleman, D.C. Bib.15 150 Note 5.

With regard to financing the operation of a mill of this kind one might assume a wage bill of not more than £200 p.a.[73] amounting to about 20% of the running costs[74] and leading to an estimated total running cost of ~ £1,000 p.a. of which raw materials would have been by far the largest item, accounting for 50% of this.[75]

Working backwards from the modern scene, the 19th C. had seen the introduction of steam power on a scale which freed the paper mill from the restrictions imposed on its siting and on its capacity, both of which were dependent on either water or wind as a source of power.[76] The arrival and development of the paper machine in the early decades of the 19th C. not only increased the potential for output but led in time to the demand for new raw materials, materials that had to be imported and chemically processed; and, in addition, the energy required to run the mill came from steam that had to be raised by coal firing. Consequently, mills tended to be sited no longer on streams but near estuaries allowing for dock facilities and in many cases they also shifted to places where the chemicals and fuel they needed were nearer to hand. As one goes back in time then one can see that the industry moves from its modern integrated pulp and paper mill site in the countries where the raw material grows to the 19th C. concentrations of industry in this country and then back to the rural sites that it originally came from; and, moreover, to a source of power that strictly limited the positioning, capacity and performance of the paper mills. The extent of this limitation can be seen when one considers that the average overshot waterwheel of those times generated no more than 3–5 h.p. and its operation was, of course, dependent on the constancy of the supply of water i.e. not subject to fluctuations brought about by drought, flood or ice.[77]

In this very generalised comparison, the financing, siting and power generation of a paper mill present and past have been considered. Turning now to the materials required for the process, it is well known that papermaking, whether ancient or modern, requires very large quantities of water and in the case of White paper manufacture in the 18th C. two sources of water, water to drive the waterwheel and water used in the process. The latter had to be the cleanest available and in the case of a mill that was to be sited on the River Len, it would have had to come from springs close to the mill and would have been used in the rag washing and beating processes as well as in sheet formation. To give one an idea of the quantity of water required for sheet–making in the handmade process, the ratio of water to cellulose could have been as high as 100 : 1 (Vol./Wt). Although possibly as much as 50% of this water drains

[73] Balston, T. Bib.1. 13 shows that the younger Whatman's wage bill at Turkey mill was about £1,000 in 1762. As Turkey mill was almost certainly a 5–vat mill by then, it is not unreasonable to assume that the wage bill for Old Mill, Hollingbourne was ≯ a quarter of this.

[74] Coleman, D.C. Bib.15 169 gives 2 examples (Keferstein, 1765; and Whatman 1784–5) of paper mill running costs. In Whatman's case Excise accounted for 21.5% of these costs, only 7% in Keferstein's case. It seems reasonable to assume that Excise costs for Old Mill in 1733 would have been nearer to the latter than the former; and in Keferstein's case wages formed 21% of the running costs.

[75] In the examples quoted in Note 76 above Raw Materials formed 50% of Keferstein's costs; 59% of Whatman's.

[76] The first major example of this was William Balston's Springfield mill, Maidstone, a mill which he built deliberately in the middle of a field, but with access to ample supplies of spring water, in 1806–7. (For an account of this see Balston, T. Bib. 74)

[77] Of the more practical sources of power for a paper mill of that period tidal and wind power were alternatives. Whereas wind was extensively used in Holland, very few examples of its use in this country are known. Shorter, A. Bib.9 38 refers to three examples of the use of wind power, two of these being in Kent at Deptford and Horn Street, Cheriton (Chap.VII p.346).

back into the vat from the mould, the 50% removed has to be replaced to maintain the consistency of the stuff; and this water was not recoverable as in a modern mill. So a source of substantial quantities of clear spring water would have been required by the prospective manufacturer of White paper.

Right up to the last quarter of the 19th C. the cellulosic raw materials used by the British paper industry had always been in short supply. In the case of 18th C. White paper the material had to be the best quality of linen rag available, much more difficult to obtain than the lower grades and one that would have been required in quantities greater than local sources could provide.[78] This shortage and the reasons for it are discussed in Chapter V of this book; it is enough to note here that a would–be manufacturer of White paper in the Maidstone district would sooner or later have had to rely on contacts in London for his supplies of this quality of rag. Dr. Harris' comments on this subject, after visiting Turkey mill (ca.1716), have already been mentioned[79] and the equivocal nature of the supplies that they relied on there would have been even more restrictive in the case of a smaller and more remote paper mill such as Hollingbourne Old Mill; though there may have been mitigating circumstances in this case because Turkey mill (further down the River Len) just then was up for sale possibly with reduced requirements. In Whatman's case the other raw materials required by a paper mill, such as gelatine and alum, would not have presented him with any problem as both these materials were either derived from or used by the tanner in his trade.

There is little that can be said at this point about the equipment used in the paper mill involved in this particular case. In the ordinary course of events the special items required by a paper mill would have been Stampers, Moulds and Presses, all of which could have been supplied from local or well tried sources in an area that had had an established paper industry for more than 50 years (a rather different situation to the one that existed when it was founded). In the case of Old Mill, however, it is for all intents and purposes certain that it was built to house the new "Hollander" Engines in place of the conventional Stampers and this presents us with a special rather than a general problem in this comparison between past and present. This will be looked at again when the actuality of Whatman's investment is examined. One must take it for granted that his other, lesser needs would have been satisfied through local channels, at least initially.

---

[78] Coleman, D.C. Bib.15 fig.2 (opp. p.90) illustrates curves for paper output in England and Wales and also for Rag imports covering most of the 18th C. including the period with which we are concerned here. Using these figures the author has made very rough calculations (assuming a 60% yield of paper on raw material weight and an 8% gelatine content in paper), which show that for 1750 and 1800 83% and 75% respectively of the raw material needed for the outputs shown for these years came from domestic sources; the figure is nearer 90% for the 1730's. However approximate these figures may be, and however crude the assumptions, they show that domestic sources of material were comparatively large in relation to the quantities imported. (If one assumes a 70% yield later in the century, it does not make a very significant difference e.g. 80% for 1750 and 71% for 1800)
It has to be remembered that ca.50% of this output was in the form of Brown paper where very low grade rags, tanned sailcloth and tarred ropes would have been used. Consequently, one would not only expect imported rags to be of a high quality but that the quantity of these imports would be more closely related to White paper production than to the total output of paper. In other words the prospective manufacturer of White paper would almost certainly have had to rely on significant quantities of imported rags as well as on rags collected from more highly populated areas than the Maidstone district in Whatman's case.

[79] See this chapter note 41.

Again, in an area with an established papermaking industry there would normally have been a pool of skilled labour to draw on; transport and shipping facilities to move products as well as markets to sell them in would also have existed, otherwise the would-be investor would not have been interested. However, Whatman's case was a special one; first, in the Maidstone area there would have been no pool of labour skilled in the operation of the new Engines at that time to draw on; second, according to Dr. Harris,[80] the majority of paper mills in that district, other than Turkey mill, made "a great deal of ordinary wrapping paper for Tobacco, Grocery Ware, Gloves, Milliner' goods etc." and, in view of his subsequent career in White paper manufacture, it is hardly likely that Whatman would have invested in an absolutely new mill to make this sort of product range, his markets would undoubtedly have been further afield; and third, he would have needed some means of entrée to such markets, especially as the best qualities of White paper were still being imported and it would have taken a great deal to persuade a London Stationer to alter his ways in favour of a domestic product. Since these are all special issues, they would be best left for discussion as and when they arise.

Whatman's investment in 1733, seen in a contemporary perspective, bears no resemblance to its modern equivalent. The reader might regard a capital outlay of £1,000 and an equal sum for running costs as so insignificant as not to warrant further consideration; a modern undertaking would be a multi-million-pound affair financed by a corporation and not an individual. To make the comparison more realistic, an attempt, little more than a cock-shy, is made below to arrive at a very approximate estimate of the cost of setting up and running a 1-vat mill in modern terms. For instance, in the 200 years between the 1780's-1980's a vatman's wages have gone up (at minimum) 200-fold; rags probably somewhere between 28-56-fold; and because of strong inflationary pressures towards the end of the 18th C. one could safely increase these factors when covering the 250-year span. Because labour and site costs are such big elements in to-day's expenditure, Whatman's capital outlay for a "custom-built" mill could have been ~ £200,000-£300,000 *at minimum* at to-day's values (with inflation, possibly much higher), a very considerable sum for a local tanner to find. One might also expect the running costs to be of the same order (see also Chapter VII Part II).

In other areas too the early 18th C. investor would have been faced with difficulties that were disproportionately greater than they would be to-day. No Trade Associations existed in those days to guide him; communications would have been slow and an assessment of the market very difficult, if not impossible. In addition, without established contacts, and in an area with a substantial industry demanding all they could get, rags would have been in short supply and clean ones very difficult to obtain; similarly, suitable outlets for his products would not have been easy to come by. Having considered Whatman's position in general terms one can now return to the questions asked earlier about the reasons for this investment, the choice of site and so on.

The questions asked earlier were, briefly, why should a tanner of Loose involve himself in building a paper mill in Hollingbourne or, indeed, in a mill at all ? Why a *new* mill ? And why install Richard Harris as paper maker there ? In view of the fact that Whatman's investment decision appears to have been made at a time which, when seen in retrospect, seems to have offered no obvious incentive for this suggests that the motives for his action

---

[80] Harris, John Bib.4 191.

may have stemmed more from events that had taken place much earlier within the locality and even, perhaps, on a nationwide basis than on a snap decision of a purely speculative character, although there may also have been contemporary factors that helped precipitate his plans to build a paper mill. As a result, whereas one may be able to identify some of the reasons in this present chapter, when testing the evidence, the subject will recur and be considered in more detail in later chapters in the context of the local and national papermaking scene. For the moment investigation will be limited to examining some of the circumstances that surrounded this investment; the site; and some of the people immediately involved in this undertaking.

The Circumstances surrounding the building of Old Mill, Hollingbourne

The first point to note is that it was a very bold investment for anyone, paper maker or not, to have made at this time and it says a lot for the extraordinary confidence Whatman must have had in his own judgement and abilities. It is not without interest to note in this context Dr. Shorter's description of the papermaking situation for this very period.[81] He wrote as follows:–

"To judge from the number and distribution of bankruptcies which occurred among English manufacturers of white paper in the period 1723–1746, several of the master makers in the *South East* of the country suffered most from financial difficulties. In their attempts to establish and develop the manufacture they may well have overstretched their resources, and their trade may have suffered particularly because of the competition from imported paper in the London Market."

Literally on his own doorstep there had been two examples that might have deterred a more timid investor. At Poll Mill, on the opposite bank of the River Len to Turkey Mill, Lord Aylesford had commissioned John Swinnock, a fuller and occupant of this ancient mill, to convert it in 1718 into "a good and substantial paper mill, with six troughs (mortars), a good and sufficient pond or mill pond with floodgate etc. ..." for which he was paid £300.[82] In 1727 Swinnock was made bankrupt. Mr. Spain comments "apparently the transition from fuller to papermaker was not easy". One might add, why should it have been any more easy for a tanner ? In passing it may be noted that Swinnock had been commissioned to build a *traditional* paper mill where rags were still fermented and then hammered in the old–fashioned mortars; this was in 1718.[83] William Gill snr. succeeded Swinnock at this mill in 1727.

As to William Gill snr., he could well be considered as a throwback to the 17th C. entrepreneur.[84] Among other interests, which included both property and brewing, during his papermaking career he either owned, attempted to secure the freehold of, or was tenant of no fewer than five paper mills in the Maidstone area. He owned Forstal mill (1716);[85] held the

[81] Shorter, A. Bib.9 55.
[82] Spain, R.J. Bib.8 83.
[83] In his account of the Maidstone scene, with its detailed description of Turkey mill, Dr. John Harris (Bib.4 191) makes no reference to Poll mill (on the opposite bank of the River Len) as a paper mill or, indeed, any mention of a mill at all. The inference is that Harris must have visited Turkey mill prior to 1718, when Poll mill was converted to papermaking and probably before 1716, because the "Mr. Gill" mentioned clearly refers to George Gill. (See also Chap.II Table IV n.3 re conversion date of Otham mill, 1715).
[84] For a fuller account of William Gill snr. see Chap.IV and Appendix IV.
[85] See synopsis of history in App.III.

lease of Turkey mill (1716) and later tried to acquire it; he set up Cobtree as a paper mill (1717);[86] he was tenant of Lower Tovil mill (1722);[87] and Poll mill (1727); and it seems likely that he had a hand in the conversion of Upper mill, Loose, (after 1726).[88] Like Swinnock he too became bankrupt in 1729 and then again and finally in 1731.

How was it then that Whatman and Harris succeeded where Swinnock and Gill had failed ? The point will be made again later, but, on the face of it, one reason for this could have been the incorporation of more modern equipment in the new mill at Hollingbourne compared to that which was in service at either Poll or Turkey mills. This would certainly have contributed to the success of this venture and paved the way for Whatman's achievements in the future. Moreover, it would also explain why immediately after acquiring Turkey Mill Harris had pulled it down and re–built it "on a more curious and extensive plan". In spite of these failures Whatman went ahead with his investment, an action which one can see in retrospect went against the grain of events and lends even further weight to the suggestion made above that his motives for this were deep–seated and longstanding rather than the outcome of a quick decision made on the spur of the moment.

How did Whatman become involved ?

To answer this question it is necessary to go back a generation.[89] The salient features of this situation are the move by the elder Whatman's father from Brenchley (just over 8 miles South–West of Loose, a village on the outskirts of Maidstone) in 1688; and the connection of the two families, Whatman and Harris, through marriage. The elder paper maker Whatman's father, also a James Whatman, was the *second* son of yet another James Whatman also of Brenchley and who died there in 1672 (no Will found). He left a widow, Lydia, later buried in Loose (1702); two sons, Thomas (18) and James (16), the future tanner; and two surviving daughters, Sarah (14) and *Lydia* (8); another daughter, Anne, had died, aged one, in 1670. The eldest son, Thomas, appears to have been the first to make a move ca.1677[90] to the Maidstone district, Boxley, about two miles North–East of Maidstone. There were other Whatmans in the Maidstone area as well; but it is not known how or even whether they were related to the Brenchley family, although it seems highly probable that they were.

Chronologically the next event to occur in this situation was the marriage of the daughter, Lydia, to William Harris, then described as "of Maidstone", in 1684 at Brenchley. It is possible that William met Lydia through the Whatmans living in the Maidstone area or even in Maidstone itself.[91] Lydia died two years later and was buried in Brenchley. This link between the two families seems to have been a memorable event, having a lasting impact on

[86] See synopsis of its history and accompanying notes as well as extracts from the Boxley Poor Ratebook (KAO P 40 12/1) in App.III.

[87] Spain, R.J. Bib.11 178.

[88] See earlier reference to this proposal in Chap.II p.87. Upper mill and the Dean family and the later history of this mill are discussed in Chap.IV and VII in greater detail; and the Dean(e) family App.IV.

[89] For a detailed account of this relationship see App.II under Whatman/Harris and Ann Carter.

[90] Thomas and Bridget Whatman had a daughter, Lydia, baptised in Boxley in 1677; she was niece of James, the Tanner of Loose, and a beneficiary under the terms of his Will. More than one family of Whatman had lived in Boxley for most of the 17th C., but their occupation has not been discovered.

[91] Two families of Whatman appear in the All SS.' Maidstone parish registers (baptisms) from 1679 onwards (see App.II).

Map 3

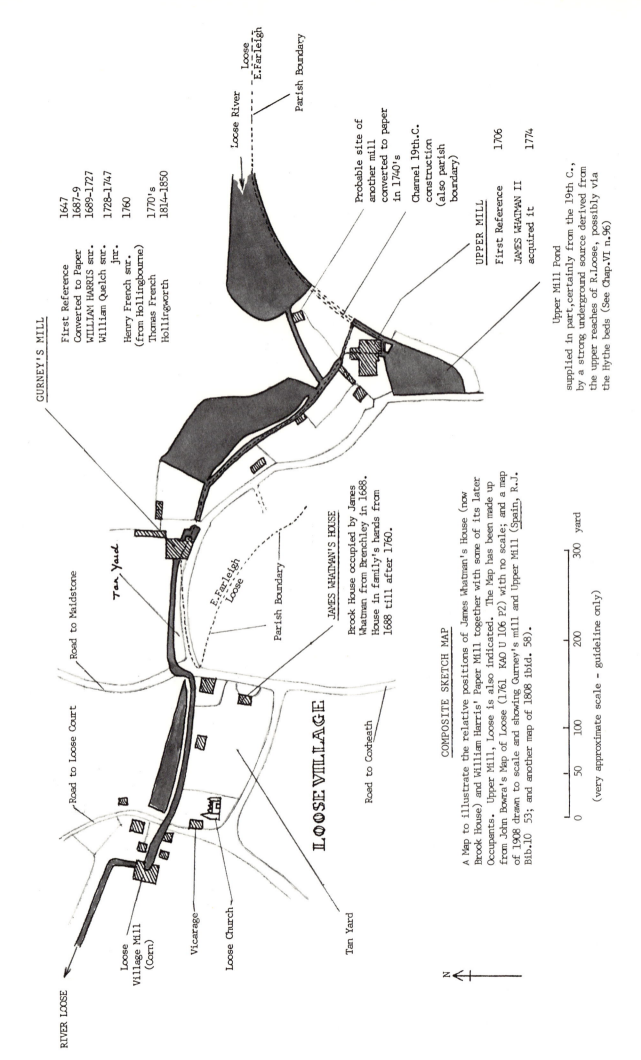

RIVER LOOSE

Road to Loose Court

Road to Maidstone

Loose Village Mill (Corn)

Vicarage

Loose Church

Tan Yard

Road to Coxheath

LOOSE VILLAGE

Tan Yard

E.Farleigh Loose

Parish Boundary

GURNEY'S MILL

First Reference	1647
Converted to Paper	1687-9
WILLIAM HARRIS snr.	1689-1727
William Quelch snr.	1728-1747
jnr.	
Henry French snr.	1760
(from Hollingbourne)	
Thomas French	1770's
Hollingworth	1814-1850

JAMES WHATMAN'S HOUSE

Brook House occupied by James Whatman from Brenchley in 1688. House in family's hands from 1688 till after 1760.

Loose River

Loose E.Farleigh

Parish Boundary

Probable site of another mill converted to paper in 1740's

Channel 19th.C. construction (also parish boundary)

UPPER MILL

| First Reference | 1706 |
| JAMES WHATMAN II acquired it | 1774 |

Upper Mill Pond
supplied in part, certainly from the 19th C., by a strong underground source derived from the upper reaches of R.Loose, possibly via the Hythe beds (See Chap.VI n.96)

COMPOSITE SKETCH MAP

A Map to illustrate the relative positions of James Whatman's House (now Brook House) and William Harris' Paper Mill together with some of its later Occupants. Upper Mill, Loose is also indicated. The Map has been made up from John Bowra's Map of Loose (1761 KAO U 106 P2) with no scale; and a map of 1908 drawn to scale and showing Gurney's mill and Upper Mill (Spain, R.J. Bib.10 53; and another map of 1808 ibid. 58).

N

0 50 100 200 300 yard

(very approximate scale - guideline only)

both sides;[92] and clearly having a very important formative influence on the first papermaking Whatman.

As the other daughter Sarah had died in 1685 this left only Lydia (the mother) and James at Brenchley after 1686. They decided to move to Loose in 1688, when James would have been aged 32. Unfortunately, there are several unknowns in this situation. It is not known, for instance, what prompted this move. At some point, date unknown, James married Mary Peene whose father was a tanner in Loose (d.1684). One would have thought that at the age of thirty–two James had already married before he and his mother made the move to Loose. One might speculate also that he had, perhaps, been apprenticed to Richard Peene earlier, met Mary there and married her later. This explanation has the double advantage of accounting for his involvement in the tanning industry and, possibly as a result of a marriage settlement or the terms of Richard Peene's Will, the move to Loose and the occupation of what had probably been Richard Peene's house and tan yards.[93] The house in question was Brook House, which remained in the hands of the Whatman family from 1688 to sometime after 1760 (see Map 3, a composite sketch map of Loose). There may have been other reasons for this move also, better prospects for James in the Maidstone area than in a small country village or because of pressures from family and friends within the Maidstone district. If we knew a little more about James' marriage to Mary Peene,[94] it might resolve this uncertainty. There was no issue from this marriage; Mary died some time prior to 1695, by which time James had remarried, Mary Charlton, the mother of James, the first of the paper makers.

The village of Loose then is the setting for the next stage in this narrative. James Whatman of Brenchley moved there in 1688 and settled in Brook House with its adjoining tan yards (see Map 3). Exactly contemporary with this Gurney's mill was converted from fulling to papermaking between 1687–1689 and the first paper maker to occupy it was William Harris, already identified as one of the Ancient Paper Makers and brother–in–law of James, the tanner. One is confronted here once again with a number of unknowns. Who owned the mill which lay partly in the parish of East Farleigh and partly in Loose (Map 3)? And who instigated the conversion ?[95]

William Harris must have had previous experience of papermaking (a) in order to run a paper mill successfully for 38 years; and (b) in order to qualify as an "Ancient Paper Maker" he

---

[92] On the Whatman side both William and his son, Thomas Harris, were beneficiaries under the terms of James' Will; and in the next generation there was a close link between James Whatman, the paper maker, and Richard Harris. On the Harris side, if names can be said to have any meaning in this context, "Lydia" was used for one of William's daughters and persisted in two later generations (see App.II under "Harris").

[93] In the maps of Loose Village (KAO U 106 P2 of 1761 and Spain, R.J. Bib.10 58 of 1808) Brook House and the adjoining tan yards, which Whatman was to occupy in 1688, are described respectively, as belonging to Mr. William Pienes and Mr. Peenes. It is presumed here that both before and after Whatman's occupation (1688–1760's) this property was in the hands of the Peene family.

[94] See Chap.VII n.225 for a suggestion that the Pines of Tovil, 1.5 miles downstream of Loose, may have been related to the Peenes of Loose. Simon Pine (1634–81) was a prominent and pioneer Baptist. The question is, were the Peenes of Loose also Baptist ? might not this account for the marriage entry not being found ? The Baptist Historical Society and the Soc.Gen. were unable to throw any light on this.

[95] Spain (Bib.10 55) has shown that the last entry for Henry Maplesden, a fuller of Maidstone, in the East Farleigh Ratebook is 10:July:1687 and that the first for William Harris is 2:June:1689. The entries for both the marriage and the burial of Lydia Whatman/Harris in the Brenchley PR (KAO P 45 1/2) describe William Harris as of Maidstone i.e. that in 1684 and 1686 he was in the Maidstone area and thus in 1687 could have begun the conversion of Gurney's mill.

must have had through his family a longstanding connection with the industry; so it is reasonable to assume that with this background he carried out the conversion of Gurney's mill (which remained a paper mill, and later a board mill, for another 226 years). To account for his training it has been suggested that either he learnt his trade at Millhall mill, Ditton, which his descendants were to occupy later; or under his father (possibly the "paperman" buried Loose 1703) who might have been a former papermaker at Eynsford or even Dartford.[96] Although this is speculation, it does account for the facts and gives a credible backing to William's claim to have been an Ancient Paper Maker. Whatever the truth, William Harris became the paper maker occupant of Gurney's mill which, as the composite sketch map of Loose shows, was situated little more than 200 yards from Brook House. James and his brother-in-law, William, were thus close neighbours. In addition, since paper mills required gelatine (and alum) to size their papers with, the gelatine coming from the tanner's trimmings, James would not only have been in touch with the needs of Gurney's mill but also with those of other paper mills in the district who used these materials.

James, as mentioned, remarried sometime prior to 1695. His third, and only surviving child, was James the future paper maker born in 1702. William had also remarried ca.1689 and produced a family of nine children,[97] William jnr. (the second child) in 1691, the future paper maker of Millhall mill, Ditton; Thomas (the third child) in 1693, the future tanner of Wrotham, possibly apprenticed in Whatman's tan yard and, later, co-trustee in the conveyance of Turkey mill to his brother in 1738; and Richard (the seventh child) in 1703, the future paper maker at Old Mill, Hollingbourne and, later, at Turkey mill, and the husband of Ann Carter of Leeds village, who eventually became Mrs. Whatman in August 1740.[98]

In retrospect one can see now the close relationship, not a blood one, that existed between the Whatman and Harris families over a period of two generations together with a close physical proximity within the parish of Loose to all of which may be added their connections in trade. Looking at the events that were to occur later one can also see that the relationship between the children, James and Richard, with only one year's difference between them, must have been very close too. James being the only surviving child in his family and with a father aged about 50, would inevitably have sought the companionship of his contemporary. It is not difficult to imagine then that as they grew up together the two boys would have been in and out of the paper mill constantly. The young Whatman would thus have acquired a useful knowledge of the papermaking process at an early age; and, further, he would also have become well equipped to handle the problems that bedevil the difficult process of sizing the paper so important for the successful manufacture of good quality White paper. When one takes into account James' successful career as a paper maker later in his life, these are perfectly valid assumptions to make and go a long way towards explaining his apparently sudden transformation from tanner to paper maker in 1740; but they do not supply us with any precise reason for his making an investment in a paper mill in 1733 beyond showing that he must have been familiar with the papermaking process by then and knowledgeable about the state of the local industry. Very few facts have come to light about James' early years that can help us and none at all about Richard.

[96]   See Chap.II n.21 and App.II n.20.
[97]   See App.II Pedigree for the papermaking descendants of William Harris.
[98]   See App.II Ann Carter of Leeds Village, Kent.

James' father, the James from Brenchley, died in 1725, his widow in 1726, leaving his son as sole heir at the age of 24. His father's Will[99] shows that he inherited the dwelling house (Brook House) and tan yard at Loose, providing him with what one might regard under normal circumstances as a cut and dried prospect for his future career. He also inherited property at Marden. There were other substantial bequests including a tenement in Loose for his niece, Lydia. From all this one might judge that his father had been reasonably well off, perhaps as a result of one or other of his marriages, and that, as a consequence, his son was too; there is no evidence to show that the latter had inherited wealth from any other members of the Whatman family, so the assumption is that the "£1,000" used for his investment came directly from his parents' resources. The investment apart, and its attendant interest in a papermaking venture, Whatman was all set to continue his father's career as a tanner of Loose, a title he in fact retained, in name at least, until his marriage in 1740; but, as things turned out, the papermaking venture is too important an exception to overlook.

So far as Richard Harris is concerned, one can only presume that he served his papermaking apprenticeship under his father at Gurney's mill and had completed it by ca.1723, a year before his eldest brother, William jnr., moved to Millhall mill, Ditton.[100] But nothing factual has been discovered about his training, a subject that is wide open to further speculation. With regard to William jnr. it is thought that since a vacancy had evidently occurred at Millhall mill, with the departure of Edward Middleton,[101] he felt that at the age of 33 it was time he set up on his own. Seen in retrospect it is likely that there was some other factor in this situation that perhaps caused both William jnr. and Richard to come to a decision at this time on their futures. Their mother had died in 1719 and William snr. may have become a difficult person to work with. He carried on at Gurney's mill until 1727, when he must have been about 60 years old, and then disappears from the scene. According to Shorter[102] William's name continued to appear in the Loose Ratebook for some years after this; but at present it is not known when he died or where he was buried. The main interest in this situation, however, is what happened to Richard ? What had he been doing all this time ? Did he continue to work under his father at Gurney's mill ? and, if so, why did he not carry on making paper there ? He would have been aged 24 at the time his father left off. There is an alternative to this. After completing his apprenticeship (ca.1723) and, perhaps at the time William jnr. left, he may have decided to move with the times and gain experience elsewhere, possibly in Holland, for example.

This suggestion is not as outrageous as might seem at first sight. There are two reasons which lend support to this idea. First, a general one, there was a legend current in the 19th C. that "Whatman" had learnt his papermaking on the Continent "where he had worked as a journeyman in most of the principal mills". Thomas Balston gives an account of this legend

---

[99] KAO U 289 T56. Beneficiaries in order were Mary (wife); James (son); Liddea Catt (niece, formerly Whatman); Robert Peene (servant and kinsman); James Castreet (brother–in–law); William Harris (brother–in–law), Thomas Harris (his son) and Liddea Harris (his daughter); and Liddea Catt (widow).

[100] See App.II The Harris Family Paper Makers : William jnr.

[101] See App.IV under Millhall mill and Edward Middleton.

[102] Shorter, A. Bib.12 193. There are three points to note about this reference. (1) The reference to Little Ivy Mill is incorrect; see App.II n.81; (2) A William and Frances Harris were living in Loose, certainly by 1737 and possibly earlier; see App.II p.48; (3) During searches of a wide number of Kent parishes no William Harris burial was noticed, certainly not in any of the villages surrounding Loose, nor in Maidstone, Ditton or Brenchley.

and discusses it at some length.[103] James Whatman, the younger, is known to have made two trips to Holland and it is possible that this gave rise to this legend. For a long time it was not realised by the later historians and commentators that there had been two papermaking members of the family. Whereas Thomas Balston largely discounts this story, he does still ask the question, could it have been true of his father ? He asked the obvious question as to how the elder Whatman had become such a highly accomplished paper maker so quickly after 1740 and he added "there is nothing among the very few facts known of his early life to make it improbable that he had studied the craft in Holland, possibly as a member of the suite of our Ambassador". One of the main arguments against this theory is that we know now that Whatman *had built* a paper mill of his own in Hollingbourne. So one might ask, if he had had all this experience in Holland, why did he not set up as the Master Paper Maker in his own mill ? He may have had personal reasons for not doing so; but it would make more sense in this case, if one assumed that he installed Richard Harris there as paper maker (which is what he did) partly because he had confidence in his papermaking ability and partly, perhaps, on the grounds that Richard had acquired experience somewhere of the new technology in papermaking, a development that had been penetrating the British scene slowly for some time past from Dutch and French sources. This "somewhere" could, of course, have been somewhere in this country; but in view of the legend, which seems to have clung to the Whatmans, it may well have been Harris who went to Holland.[104]

Second, it was suggested earlier that one of the reasons why Whatman and Harris had succeeded, where Swinnock and Gill had failed, had been the result of incorporating modern equipment in their new mill. Not only are there good reasons for thinking that this was so but the New Technology was so radically different to the traditional method of making paper that neither Harris nor Whatman could possibly have adopted it without some previous experience or external help. So, once again, one asks the question was it Harris that went to Holland to train ?

Why was Hollingbourne chosen as a site for the new mill ?

One's first reaction to this question is that Whatman evidently knew at some point in the history of this venture that there happened to be a vacant site there which he could use; but was this the real reason, and in any case how would he have come to hear about this isolated and derelict site ? What were the alternatives ? Were there any sites nearer to James' and Richard's homes in Loose either vacant or capable of being converted to papermaking ? Spain has pointed out that the River Loose was already congested and had been ever since the beginning of the 16th C., the density of the watermills along its short course was one of the greatest in England.[105] It seems though that in the 1730's there were still six mills on this river that had not been converted to papermaking; three of them were actually converted later

---

[103] Balston, T. Bib.1 App.I 143–146.

[104] There are various versions of this legend in the literature, some being more specific in that they suggest that Whatman had learnt his papermaking in Lubertus van Gerrevink's mill. There is the unsolved question as to how "LVG", an abbreviated form of Gerrevink's countermark, came to be incorporated in the Whatman Ream Stamp and whether Whatman was the first English paper maker to use "LVG" in his papers. These subjects are discussed further in App.V under "The Whatman Ream Stamp" with a special note on the "LVG" mark. In view of what has been said in the text above, it is possible that Harris may have worked in Lubertus' mill. If so, did Whatman incorporate "LVG" in his Ream Stamp in memory of Harris' contribution ?

[105] Spain, R.J. Bib.10 43.

but not until the 19th C.[106] Either their owners had no wish to change their business then or else for one reason or another they were not suitable for Whatman's purpose. Having lived all their lives close to that river, James and Richard probably knew all the drawbacks that existed there. Was there anywhere else in the district, other than on the River Len, where they could have built their mill ? There is no question that there were other streams on which paper mills had yet to be built or converted but it is unlikely that any of these sites or mills would have met their criteria taking into account the current state of water power technology.

Although Spain lists as many as 29 watermills on the River Len and its tributaries (some of these were defunct by or had not been built in 1733)[107] against 13 on the River Loose, the effective length of the Len is about three times greater as well as having a larger drainage area. The net result, therefore, was a much lower density on the Len compared to the River Loose. At the time that Old Mill was planned there were only three paper mills on the River Len, Turkey Mill, converted ca.1680; Poll Mill opposite Turkey Mill converted in 1718, both of them roughly 1 mile from the centre of Maidstone; and one of the Otham mills, converted ca. 1715, about another mile further upstream. The site for Old Mill was 4 miles upstream from Maidstone. (See Chap.II Map 2).

What was so special about the Hollingbourne site and how did Whatman or Harris come to hear of it ? Consequent on the proposals already made it is clear that Whatman or, more probably Harris as the paper maker, was looking not only for a site that would satisfy the needs of a White paper manufactory but one where the waterwheel could generate sufficient power to drive the new equipment that they planned to install in the mill. As will be seen in Chapter VI it is possible that they may have overestimated their requirements, but the new Engines certainly required a powerful source of energy and in their country of origin, Holland, windpower had provided the paper makers with such a source, with a margin considerably above that of the average waterwheel. Although at that time the Old Mill site may not have had quite the potential that it had at a later stage in its life, Spain has described Old Mill "as the most powerful mill the Len valley has ever seen".[108] The other factor in this situation is that soon after he was installed in the Hollingbourne mill Richard Harris married Anne, the daughter of Thomas and Sarah Carter of Leeds village at St. Saviour's Church, Southwark on 2nd November 1734.[109] Thomas Carter appears to have been either a builder or a timber merchant in Leeds in which parish part of the Old Mill site lay.[110] One might surmise here that Richard had perhaps been courting Ann before 1733 and had made it known that he and James were anxious to build a new and rather special mill and that Carter had mentioned this vacant site. It might also be argued that in those days prospective millers would have been far more aware of mill sites than people would be to-day. Even so, for anyone who knows it, the site is an obscure and isolated one. Moreover, if Whatman was looking for a paper mill, why had Turkey mill not been chosen ? It had been advertised for

---

[106] Spain, R.J. Bib.11 173. The 6 mills were Little Ivy (Corn); Bockingford (Fulling); Hayle (Fulling); Upper Crisbrook (Corn); and Lower Crisbrook (Fulling). The sixth mill, Loose Village mill, remained a corn mill throughout its life; the first 3, however, were converted to papermaking early in the 19th C. but only Hayle mill survived as a paper mill after the 1860's and was, indeed, a handmade paper mill until recently; Messrs. Barcham Green ceased production in July 1987.

[107] Spain, R.J. Bib.8 33.

[108] Spain, R.J. Bib.8 60.

[109] See App.II under Ann Carter of Leeds for details.

[110] For a description of the site see Preface to App.I & II pp.xii ff. with sketchmaps and photographs.

sale in 1731 and was still unsold on 17th January 1734.[111] It is true to say, however, that between June 1732 and June 1736 the mill was leased to Cordwell, first, of Poll mill and, later, to "Mr. Musgrove"[112] and in addition, the freehold was still split between James Brooke, the London Stationer and chief mortgagee (of whom more will be heard later) and the Cripps family.[113] This state of affairs clearly did not suit Whatman's requirements and, indeed, his funds were perhaps insufficient at that time to have bought this large mill *and* converted it into a modern one. Equally, he and Richard may have lacked the technical experience to have done it then. In the event they settled for the Old Mill site.

Earlier in this chapter the normal requirements of a paper mill of those times have been outlined. In terms of water power there should have been no problems. Clean water for the process might have been a more formidable obstacle to overcome. The River Len, as a supply of process water, could not match spring water for cleanliness. Dr. Harris had specifically noted this point when he visited Turkey mill: "Mr. Gill told me when I went to see his mill that he could not make his paper *fine and white* till he brought into his work a collection of *fine clear water* from two or three springs, which rise in a field adjoining to the mill".[114] It is not known how, or even if, Whatman overcame this difficulty. Similar springs to those at Turkey mill were available at the Hollingbourne site; the geology is essentially the same as that at Turkey mill.[115]

It is inconceivable that Whatman would have built this mill merely to have made common wrapping paper, but circumstances may have been such that Harris was compelled to do this for some of the time. No papers known to have been made by Richard Harris have been discovered yet, but this does not necessarily signify that he might not have been engaged in making the cheaper sorts of printing and writing paper referred to earlier in this chapter and which, according to Coleman, were characteristic products of the better class domestic mills during that period.[116] For the former category of paper Harris could no doubt have relied on the Naval Dockyard at Chatham for supplies of old ropes and sails and, initially, supplies of the best qualities of rags may not have been as critical for him as at a later period after he had overcome the teething troubles of his new equipment. Nevertheless, if his and Whatman's objective was to break into the White paper market, sooner or later he would have had to establish contacts in London capable of obtaining the best qualities of rags for his paper. In the meantime with Turkey Mill, probably the only other major consumer of these rags, more or less *hors de combat* he may have been able to pick up sufficient supplies to meet his needs. Whether he succeeded in making the best qualities of paper or not, the fact is that he kept Old Mill going and then proceeded from there to the much larger-scale operations of Turkey mill. It is self-evident, therefore, that he was able to obtain the raw materials he needed and, more or less to confirm that he and James had established sources for these, it

[111]   Balston, T. Bib.1 7.
[112]   See App.III Extracts from the second Boxley Ratebook.
[113]   Balston, T. Bib.1 loc. cit
[114]   Harris, John Bib.4 191.
[115]   Wyatt, R.J. (Letter G/O/288 21:Aug:1981) Springs rising from the Hythe Beds/Atherfield Clay junction. The 1864/5 6 inch Ordnance Survey map also shows a well at the Old Mill site, presumably for the use of the house if nothing else. Nothing is known about the depth or flow of this well; but, apparently, it was perfectly practicable in those times to have pumped water from an underground source to supply the mill. Something ~600 gallons, at minimum, would have been needed every 6 hours. (Correspondence Institute of Geological Sciences).
[116]   See description and comments on an "RH" countermark illustrated in App.I p.8.

will be recalled that when Whatman first insured Turkey mill the insured value of his rag stock was greater than the utensils and stock in the paper mill and two and a half times that of the dwelling house (see note 39). It is true that this might reflect the difficulty they had in obtaining them. There should have been no problems for Harris in obtaining the other materials he needed for his papermaking.

According to the Indenture Tripartite of 1762 Whatman was permitted to build his mill as from the 30th July 1733 and he insured his new–built dwelling house and paper mill on the 25th September 1733, two months later. Unless one assumes that the preparation of the site was well under way before the agreement was signed or else that the mill was not fully commissioned by the end of September, two months does appear to be a very short time indeed to have completed the whole project. In the next SFIP Policy (65053) made just over a year later (7:0ct:1734) Harris insured *for the same sum* (£600) "his household, goods and stock in Trade in his dwelling house, Mills, Drying Loft and Storerooms all under one roof". The fact that the sum insured had not increased suggests that work may have started prior to the 30th July. If Thomas Carter was in fact a builder, he may have helped in the construction work or, at least, supplied the timber for the mill.

With regard to the equipment used for the Hollingbourne mill much of it would have been standard for the normal paper mill of the time. All the indications so far point to the installation of one or more of the new Engines for washing and beating the rags in this mill, Engines that came to be known later (19th C.) as "Hollanders". The whole subject of their introduction into this country, their application and the problems they would have created for the contemporary paper maker are set out in some detail in Chapter VI. It is sufficient to note here that to operate them they would have needed a more than average supply of energy which the Old Mill site could provide; two Engines had been installed at about the same time, only 20 miles away by road, at Chartham mill which had been converted to papermaking that same year, 1733. When the motives for building this new mill are examined later, it will be seen that this would have been the logical course of action for Whatman and Harris to have taken in the circumstances; and moreover, it would also account both for the fact that they had built an entirely *new* mill as well as Harris' reconstruction of Turkey mill when he managed to acquire it in 1738. Seen in retrospect the whole venture suggests that the paper mill was a small one conceived with the object of operating it on an experimental basis; there was clearly more to this investment than the erection of just another paper mill.

In other words the principal feature of this investment was to try out *and improve* what was seen then as a new and revolutionary papermaking process, an act that we can see to–day was to transform the technology of papermaking, the quality of the paper and the economic performance of the industry in this country. But James and Richard could not have undertaken this project without one or other of them having had some previous experience in operating the new equipment; hence the suggestion that, after serving his apprenticeship, Richard may have spent some time working in Holland. Experience of this kind would also have enabled him to train beatermen in the new techniques required by these Engines, because there would have been few, if any, in the district at that time capable of operating them.[117] In addition it is most improbable that these Engines could have been constructed locally. It is known that in some of the earlier installations in this country the equipment had been imported; but, at the same time, others had by this time probably been built in this country albeit perhaps more primitive versions than those we are considering here. Obviously, with an ever-growing demand for them someone at some time would have set up an establishment to make them or, at least, the more difficult parts. The impression gained here of the Whatman/Harris venture is that one is looking at a more advanced model than had been employed hitherto, but just where it was built and by whom is not known.

If one assumes that Hollingbourne mill was a small 1-vat mill, then with the new equipment the chances are that the total employed would have been less than 17.[118] With operations at Turkey mill in an uncertain state during the early 1730's Harris in theory should have had no difficulty in recruiting labour for his mill, both skilled and unskilled; he most likely supervised the working of the new Engines himself. However, whereas the labour employed at Turkey mill could have come from the outskirts of adjoining Maidstone, the Old Mill site was an isolated one over 5 miles further out by road. Accommodation locally may therefore have been a problem as indeed the movement of raw materials out to the mill and the transport of finished goods in to the port of Maidstone. Hasted, in his History of Kent, has frightening descriptions of horses floundering up to their girths in mud on so-called roads of almost unlimited width.[119]

In 1733 the Maidstone to Ashford Road, which later ran quite close to Old Mill, was not one of the Turnpiked roads, but was possibly better maintained than its lateral offshoots. A search through the Quarter Session Order Books, which covered the maintenance of Highways, from 1730-1750 revealed nothing that affected this stretch of road between Hollingbourne and Maidstone. This is not to say that it was in good condition or that it would always have been easy to convey paper from the mill to the wharves of Maidstone. The journey from there to London by hoy had been made a great deal easier for shipping by measures taken in the 17th C. to improve the condition of the River Medway. It can be seen that whereas in some respects the Old Mill site had advantages for Harris, it also had its disadvantages.

Finally, there is the question of outlets for the Old Mill products. It has been suggested above that initially Harris, both for experimental reasons and because he lacked the necessary contacts in London, concentrated on the cheaper sorts of printing and writing paper, products that he was already familiar with and made formerly by his father at Gurney's mill and as well now by his eldest brother at Millhall mill, Ditton. Although during the 1730's total paper output for England and Wales remained static it was nevertheless just under three times higher than the quantity of imported paper[120] and of this rather less than 50% was White paper, the greater part of it being the cheaper sorts, qualities unlikely to have been too

---

[117]   No evidence has been found of the names of foreigners e.g. Dutch in the parish registers of Hollingbourne or Leeds for this period. Towards the end of the 17th C. what appear to be Dutch names do appear occasionally in the All SS.' Registers in Maidstone but this is much too early for them to have influenced operations at Old Mill. The possibility that other paper mills in Kent were equipped with a primitive form of Engine is examined in Chap. IV.

[118]   See Chap.II note 129.

[119]   Melling, E. Bib.14 vii. has written "If any part of the normal right of way became impassable, it was legally permissible to travel over adjoining land even to the extent of trampling down crops and removing fences".

[120]   Coleman, D.C. Bib.15 Fig.2 opposite p.90.

difficult to sell. Well-used channels for its disposal would have existed. This was obviously not James' and Richard's ultimate objective and no doubt as they mastered their new process they became more and more competitive and would thus increasingly attract attention from the Stationers in London in search of alternative supplies of the better sorts of White paper. It will be seen in the next chapter how this may have come about.

Examination of the evidence presented in this chapter has fleshed out the silhouette of Whatman that we started with into a more substantial image. It has become clear that to have made an investment in a paper mill on the scale indicated earlier that he must have been something more than an ordinary tanner. One has only to look carefully at his portrait to see that it conveys the impression of a much more thoughtful, resolute and distinguished figure than one would expect to find in an 18th C. village tradesman. The family pedigree can be traced back to the 15th C.[121] but there are no signs of any person of distinction in his ancestry. Thomas Balston pointed out[122] "for many generations the Whatmans had intermarried with yeoman families of their neighbourhood", on occasions rather above this.[123] It is plain that there must have been some external influence that developed the potential of this man. Was he educated privately ? or did he attend the Maidstone Grammar School ?[124] Questions such as these remain as yet unanswered. No evidence has survived either to indicate where his wealth came from, possibly from his mother or else from Mary Peene, his father's first wife and daughter of the owner of the Loose tan yards, which he in time inherited. But he was under no obligation to spend his fortune other than on himself. He was unmarried at the time and yet he chose to invest it in a new paper mill. The motives for Whatman's involvement in this have not been discussed here; the question as to how he became involved has been addressed instead.

Had the "IW" countermark, identified by Dr. Hudson, been dated just a year later then the discovery might easily have passed unnoticed. The fact that it can be dated with certainty to 1740 has forced us to re-examine the conventional image that we obtain from existing sources; and to have produced the paper bearing this mark in the time that he did proves without doubt that Whatman had Engines at his disposal with which to prepare the stuff for this paper to be made from. These facts have compelled us to go back even further in order to discover where he could possibly have learnt his papermaking and how the practical knowledge of using Engines had been acquired. The proximity of the papermaking Harris family and his relationship with Richard Harris provide us with a plausible answer to the first of these; and the investment in the building of a paper mill in Hollingbourne, on land leased from Sir Roger Meredith, in 1733, furnishes us with an explanation for the second. The site

[121] See App.II The Whatman Paper Makers' Pedigree.
[122] Balston, T. Bib.1 17.
[123] See App.II The Social Standing and Family Distribution.
[124] There is no particular reason to suppose that Whatman's father was any more literate (though he might have been) than William Harris, his brother-in-law, who could only manage to make his mark on the ANCIENT PAPER MAKERS' Petition of 1690. From what is known of Whatman's achievements later in life it is clear that not only had he received a good education but one that stimulated his technical and business acumen. The village school is unlikely to have brought this about. The Maidstone Grammar School on the other hand has had a long and distinguished history in producing scholars. During Whatman's boyhood it was under the headmastership of Charles Walwyn (act. 1696-1741), a Fellow of King's College, Cambridge. Though he may not have produced as distinguished scholars as his immediate successor, Rev. Deodatus Bye (1741-1746), he nevertheless had a number of noteworthy pupils during his term in office. Unfortunately, no attendance registers have survived.

of the mill was an unusual one, one capable of generating much greater water power than, say, a mill on his own doorstep which he could have acquired as soon as Richard's father had retired or, failing that, one further upstream. The conclusions to be drawn from this are (a) that Engines which required greater power to make them work effectively than the traditional hammers and mortars were to be installed there; and (b) that the small scale of this venture points to its being used as a pilot plant to gain experience of these new Engines and master other elements of the New Technology. The site was by no means the best in other respects, which supports the notion that the primary objective was of an experimental nature rather than ideal for normal manufacture. In addition, Whatman's and Harris' goal would not have been to make Brown or other low grades of paper, but the very best in the White line, as the former's use of a countermark at a later date demonstrates. This is all borne out by Richard Harris', the occupant's, subsequent activities, his move to Turkey mill, a three-vat mill, and after acquiring it pulling it down and rebuilding it "on a more curious and extensive plan". It is important to note too that the decisions for this enterprise and the execution of these plans all took place *many years prior to* the War of the Austrian Succession, often claimed to be a landmark in the advancement of the domestic White paper industry's fortunes.

Although Whatman's motives have not been investigated here, at least an explanation has been put forward to account for his apparently miraculous transformation from tanner to paper maker overnight. It is clear, then, that one has to go still deeper into the circumstances that prevailed locally to unravel the motives for this project and the consequences of his venture. In the chapters that follow, various aspects of both the local and the national papermaking environment will be examined to account for this undertaking as well as the effects it may have had on the manufacture of White paper in Kent.

Chapter IV

INFLUENCE ARISING FROM OTHER PAPERMAKING ACTIVITIES IN KENT DURING WHATMAN'S EARLY YEARS

The early history (17th C.) of the paper industry in Kent was examined in Chapter II; and in the previous chapter the object was to discover from very limited evidence what was known about the elder Whatman's background. The task now is to try to relate these two subjects in order to determine whether any of the contemporary activities of other paper makers in this environment may have influenced his actions; and also to see how he and Richard stood in relation to their papermaking neighbours. Attention will be concentrated in this chapter on the paper makers and their mills; discussion of the role of paper technology will, as far as this is possible, be avoided here and confined instead to Chapters V and VI.

It was noted how the expansion of the industry in the Maidstone district had taken place in two phases, the first coinciding with the embargo on French Goods (1678–1685); and the second after the introduction of the New Duties (1712–14). The second included Otham, Cobtree and Poll mills at Maidstone, and Basted mill (1716) near Wrotham in the West Kent Region. In retrospect this phase could also be seen to cover the conversion of Upper mill, Loose (1726)[1] and, in some respects only, the conversion of an adjoining mill between 1742–45[2] on the grounds that these two had formerly been fulling mills. Upper mill was converted to the traditional process but it is arguable that the second mill, because of its late date, might have contained elements that characterise the third phase considered below. Indeed Basted mill, as will be seen, was just such a hybrid of two separate influences.

1733 saw the beginning of yet another phase, a new type of paper mill that came into existence not directly influenced by the New Duties but rather as a result of further developments in the New Technology. It included probably a paper mill at Chartham converted to papermaking by Peter Archer jnr.; and an entirely *new mill* built by Whatman and occupied by Harris at Hollingbourne.

Isolated facts about the existence of paper mills or the names of their occupants do not

---

[1]   Spain, R.J. Bib.10 48 shows that the ratable value of this mill was increased in 1726 to what might be regarded as a paper mill level in the name of "Daniel Purlis his aires". It is not thought that Purlis had any connection with papermaking. David Dean appears as occupier 1728–32; Joseph Deane 1733–39; Mrs. Deane 1740. (KAO P 233 5/2). In the Will of David snr. of Boxley, made in 1732, it was stated that the lease of this mill was "of Mr. Arnold's". (PRC 17/96 f.364). See also this chapter under Cobtree mill and Note 62.
The David Dean who occupied Upper mill Loose in 1728 was David jnr. bapt. Boxley 1700 (KAO P 40 1/2), so it would be safe to assume that it was working as a paper mill from this date, if not from 1726. The subject of Upper mill will crop up later in Chap.VII when it passed into the hands of the younger James Whatman (1774/5).

[2]   Spain, R.J. Bib.10 45 has identified a mill, for want of a better name, described as "beside Leg–o–Mutton Pond", so named because of its shape (see the most easterly pond in MAP 3 Chap.III). A fulling mill had probably occupied this site from before 1570. There is evidence that sometime between 1742–1745 John Farley, a paper maker and successor to the Dean family at Upper Mill, converted it to papermaking, probably incorporating an early form of Engine (See Chap.VII p.313).

usually tell one very much about the state of the industry and they tell nothing about its technology. Dr. Shorter has, of course, shown[3] that this kind of information can indicate concentrations of the industry in certain localities and the reasons that favoured these such as the availability of suitable sites for generating power, the right quality of water for making White paper; the proximity of markets and facilities for transport. But the kind of information to take one beyond this point is much harder to come by for this period (and even more so, as we have seen, for earlier ones). One has to rely in these circumstances on informed speculation and inference.

For example, this kind of procedure has to be employed to follow up the questions posed in the previous chapter. What sort of pressures led Whatman into building a new mill in an out-of-the-way site with an excessive potential for generating power, when he might have been contented with a mill on his own doorstep ? And, more important, *what led him to expect that he might succeed in an area where others had failed* ? The facts, summarised in the previous chapter, can assist us in arriving at answers to these questions when no other sources of information have survived to help us.

Whatman's later achievements, both financial and technical, and the confident manner in which he emerged as a paper maker in 1740 refute any suggestion that he made his investment in Old Mill in a spirit of foolhardiness; this would have been quite out of character. Clearly he undertook this venture for a *very good reason*. Was this a purely financial one ? Or had it a technical objective as well ? Bearing in mind the quality of his later products and, in contrast, the abundance of that sort of paper mill in the district it cannot have been to build yet another one for making Wrapping paper.[4] One may safely conclude that "the very good reason" lay in some important technical innovation that would place him and his proposed mill in an advantageous position for the manufacture of White paper. On reflection his intention can only have been to install an "Engine" there, either an improved model of the ones already in use in this country or to employ it more effectively than had formerly been the case or both.

By using informed speculation one can see how various documented facts fit into and support the assumption made above. A prototype of the Engine had been introduced and used in this country more than 40 years earlier and the number of installations following this, sporadic at first, was on the increase. One can be certain then that a paper maker who a few years later was in the van of the industry would have known about these Engines when he was planning his new mill. We also know, as a fact, that only 20 miles away by road from Hollingbourne, Peter Archer jnr. had incorporated two of these Engines in his "new-built" paper mill at Chartham. In addition, prior to Richard Harris' occupation Turkey mill had been equipped with the old-fashioned stampers which he had got rid of when he pulled down and rebuilt it in 1738.

Finally, evidence of a later date shows that the younger Whatman installed an even newer version of an Engine in 1771 at Hollingbourne where other earlier *Engines were already in*

---

[3]   Bib.12 41-43
[4]   Harris' (Bib.4) reference to the mills in the Maidstone district that made "a great deal of ordinary wrapping paper". This comment must have been made ca.1716.

situ.[5] Cumulatively this circumstantial evidence[6] makes it certain that some technical advance related to the Engine had been incorporated in the construction of his new mill. Not only would the absence of such an innovation require a great deal more explaining than the assumption made here of its presence but we should be at a loss to account for a lot of later events that led to resolving the impasse that currently faced the White paper industry of this country.

The technical aspects of this new Engine, and the advantages it offered, are discussed in detail in Chapter VI. For the moment it is sufficient to know that one is entering a third phase in the expansion of the local industry embodying improvements whose effects on the papermaking process, economically and technically, and on paper mill design and operation extended far beyond the mere installation of a new mechanical device.

The rest of this chapter will be devoted to searching for influences within Kent that might throw light on these achievements. Just as found in Chapter II the clues are scarce and often far apart; but the sometimes conjectural conclusions that link them *have not been reached lightly*. They embody the consideration of facts about paper makers, and the survival of their mills, that span a wide period of papermaking history; the starting and finishing points are known and there are islands in between to help one bridge the gaps.

INFLUENCES ARISING FROM PAPERMAKING IN KENT BETWEEN 1670's–1730's

Reverting to Table IV in Chapter II illustrating the paper mills that were active in Kent between 1670–1733 and taking the regions shown there in the reverse order, they can be divided up broadly into areas of greater or lesser significance as sources of influence to Whatman and Harris as follows:–

(a) *South Kent* For the time being this region can be regarded as having no relevance to the present issue. Goudhurst mill had almost certainly closed down before the end of the 17th C. and the next mill in this region does not appear until the 1750's.

(b) *East Kent* The only development of any significance in this area was the conversion of Chartham mill by Peter Archer jnr. in 1732/3 to papermaking, a conversion that incorporated two of the new Engines. In the present context, however, it would be best to consider this event in relation to earlier ones that took place in the West Kent and Maidstone regions.

(c) *North Kent* As for East Kent and Chartham.

(d) *Maidstone & West Kent* There remain two districts to consider which, as it happens, were the two principal centres of White paper manufacture and also the regions in which all the Ancient Paper Makers of Kent were to be found.

---

[5] For details see App.V. Two Drawings by James Whatman, the Younger.

[6] It must not be thought that the reasoning presented here is the *only* evidence suggesting the use of the Engine at Old Mill.

During the early years of Whatman's and Harris' lives Maidstone was still in the process of becoming the principal papermaking centre in the county and it is here that one would expect to find the main influences that were to shape their futures. Undoubtedly it was the most important source for these; but it was changes that had taken place in the West Kent Region towards the latter part of the 17th C. that demand our attention first in spite of the fact that the expansion of the industry there had been negligible.

THE WEST KENT REGION

Dr. Harris, as well as commenting on the "very good white Paper" made at Turkey mill, had noted that "they also make very good white Paper upon the Darent River".[7] At the time he made this comment, probably ca.1716, Richard Archer had been at and had owned Dartford No.2 mill since 1701; Andrew Johannot, a refugee from France and a member of a very famous papermaking family in the Auvergne, had appeared at Eynsford mill in 1694; and Alexander Russell, an Ancient Paper Maker, had been at Shoreham since ca.1692 (possibly earlier). Dartford No.1 mill, Spilman's original mill, had clearly been in decline for a number of years. Since 1702 it had been occupied by William Quelch snr., a mill that was assessed during his tenure at half its previous ratable value and which he vacated in 1716 to convert Basted mill at Wrotham from a corn mill to papermaking. The low ratable value of Dartford No.1 mill (£12, formerly £24) suggests that it had been outmoded by Dartford No.2 whose normal ratable value was £40.[8]

For the period under consideration, then, there were four paper mills in the West Kent Region whose occupants and practices could have influenced Whatman and Harris. As in the case of the early paper mills in Kent, there is little to go on apart from knowing who the occupants of these mills were and, possibly, what their political colour may have been. One feels that if any influences did originate from these sources, they would not have been transmitted as a result of direct contact but rather that they had percolated through the system by word of mouth, through people like Stationers or Journeymen moving from one mill to another. So one cannot be certain as to precisely where an influence originated.

To take an example, early in Whatman's career as a paper maker (that is after 1740) there is unmistakeable evidence that he was producing papers of a greatly improved quality compared to normal output, undoubtedly a result of knowledge he had acquired of new methods practised elsewhere coupled with the use of the New Technology. One has to assume either that Richard Harris had perhaps trained in Holland, or somewhere else where the New Technology was practised, and brought with him to Maidstone the know-how needed to make these improvements effective; or to assume that some of these innovations filtered through gradually from local sources. When the technical aspects of these innovations are considered in the next two chapters, it looks as if both of the solutions proposed here played a part in these developments.

---

[7]   Bib.4 191
[8]   Shorter, A. Bib.12 181. When newly built in 1679 the ratable value of Dartford No.2 mill was £40; at a time when it may not have been working, 1692, it was only £20. When re-occupied in 1693 it was £40 again; for part of 1698, when under George Hagar, it was £60 reverting to £40 from 1698 to, probably, 1740.

Taking the Engine as an example it is known that their use had been increasing slowly during the first three decades of the 18th C.; there are four documented examples of installations before 1730[9] and obviously there must have been other unrecorded instances, some of them in the COMPANY'S mills. Consequently, word concerning these developments could well have reached Whatman and Harris indirectly; but the translation of these ideas into practice can in no way have been achieved without practical experience of operating them. Apart from the almost simultaneous installation of Engines at Chartham and Old Mill, there is no documentary evidence to date to show that any other mill in Kent possessed one where Harris, at least, could have learnt how to use them; and, as mentioned, the message that has emerged in his case is that an improved model was used at Old Mill. It is probable, however, that one of the more primitive Engines had been introduced by the COMPANY at Dartford No.2 mill during their occupation, in which case news of this could have passed from the West Kent Region to Maidstone in a roundabout way.

One can only guess then at what sort of influences may have stemmed from the West Kent Region. Three possible sources for these attract attention; first, the occupants of Dartford No.2 mill; second, the first signs of what was to become in time the Quelch empire; and, third, methods of improving the quality of White paper that the Johannot family brought with them when they arrived in this country from France.

Dartford No.2 Paper Mill (1679–19th C.)

For close on the first hundred years of its history, either by association or under their direct control, this mill seems to have been the principal stamping ground of the Quelch papermaking family and will be considered again below as part of their empire. But there were periods, particularly in its early history, when it passed into other hands, enemies one might say. This is because Edward Quelch, though never assessed himself for the mill, must have been the Ancient Paper Maker there in 1690 only to be followed in three years by the COMPANY and one can scarcely believe that they had patched up their differences by then. The early Quelch succession at Dartford No.2 for this period is too complicated a subject to enter into here;[10] it is sufficient to know that the mill passed out of Quelch control in the early 1690's until late 1698 when it was briefly in the hands of a John Quelch and then it was bought in 1701 and occupied by Richard Archer for over 30 years. In 1736 the Quelchs acquired it again but left Richard Archer there as tenant until he was bankrupted in 1740. It is the intervals between the Quelch occupants that are of interest.

Why did the COMPANY take over this mill ? Who managed it for them ? Did they or others install new equipment during this interval ? What role did Hagar play in this ? and how did Richard Archer become involved in it ? For the moment one can only theorize about this changing situation. Careful consideration of these isolated facts does enable one to provide a reasonable solution to the questions asked above. All the same it is conjecture and only further discoveries will show whether it will stand the test.

---

[9]   Shorter, A. Bib.9 40.
[10]   For details see App.II

Plate 8

PETER ARCHER of CHARTHAM MILL

The Chartham Mill Lease Book shows that Peter Archer took over the lease of this mill in 1732 "now a paper mill" (Letter from Miss A.M. Oakley, Archivist to the Cathedral, City and Diocesan Record Office, Canterbury, 22nd December 1981). The mill belonged to the Dean and Chapter of Canterbury. Peter Archer first insured the paper mill "on the other side of the river" in Chartham Parish on 10th July 1733 (Shorter, A. Bib.12 197 quoting SFIP No.61335). The advertisement below indicates that the mill was "new–built", so that conversion from fulling to papermaking must have taken over six months to complete; water plentiful.

Immediately to be SOLD,

A Very good new-built Paper Mill, fituate and being in the Parifh of Chartham, where is plenty of Water, two Miles diftant from the City of Canterbury, built by Peter Archer, late deceafed, containing two Engines, two Fats, and all other Utenfils and Conveniencies fitting and neceffary for the making of Paper; together with a very good Dwelling-houfe adjoining to the faid Mill.

Enquire of the Deceafed's Widow, who lives at the faid Mill, or of John Dean of the City of Canterbury, Miller.

The John Dean of the City of Canterbury, Miller, referred to in the advertisement above was Peter Archer jnr.'s brother–in–law; he insured Barton paper mill in 1736. Peter Archer was buried in Chartham on 5th January 1737 (corr:date). The implications of this relationship are examined later in Chapter VII under Barton mill (p.331); Chartham mill (p.333); and as a family relationship with other possible extensions in Appendix IV (note 64).

The advertisement appeared in the Kentish Post and Canterbury News Letter for 3rd May 1738 and is reproduced here with the permission of the Kent County Library, Canterbury.

One thing that we can be certain of, this is the only documented instance of the COMPANY penetrating into Kent,[11] an event that must have had an impact on the local paper industry, both short- and long-term in its effect. In 1693 the COMPANY was prospering, a good reason for taking over another relatively modern mill.[12] They made a lot of paper[13] and they were evidently well organised, showed great energy and in some of their mills, at least, they had introduced a very early model of the Engine into their papermaking operations (Chap.V). Because of the relatively late take-over date it is proposed here that Dartford No.2 be included in this number.

Dartford No.2, in addition to being a new mill, was a large one, if its ratable value is anything to go on, more than twice that of Turkey mill, for instance, though the circumstances may not be directly comparable; and Harris described Turkey mill as "a very large work". From 1679, when it was built, it had been assessed in the name of William Wood; in 1691 this became "Mrs. Wood and paper mill"; and in 1692, when the ratable value dropped to £20, the entry was "late Mr. Wood and paper mills". From this one might safely conclude (although there were three other Wood families in Dartford) that William had died, had no successor and that the mill was vacant, which together with its recent construction and size would help explain the COMPANY'S taking it over. It is presumed that Edward Quelch can only have been William Wood's paper maker and brother-in-law and not a candidate as occupant.

The next question is, who managed the mill for the COMPANY ? The mill was assessed in the COMPANY'S name *and not that of an individual* and it is here that the subject becomes one of pure conjecture. To follow the reasoning behind the suggestions made below it is necessary to digress and consider the activities of the papermaking Archers. The interest here, it should be noted, is not so much in the question as to who operated Dartford No.2 mill for the COMPANY between 1693-7, but, as in the case of Whatman and Harris where the same question arises, what led Peter Archer jnr. 40 years later to convert Chartham mill, sited on the Great Stour near Canterbury, into a paper mill "containing two Engines" (see Plate 8) most probably powered by a breast wheel when on the face of it no other installation of this kind in Kent is known to us up to that time ?

---

[11] Shorter (Bib.9 26) suggested that Eynsford mill under Andrew Johannot may also have been another of the COMPANY'S mills in Kent; but since there is no Eynsford Ratebook for this period, it is not possible to confirm this. His name does not appear among the COMPANY Petitioners, though it is just possible that, when he arrived in this country, the COMPANY may have appointed him to manage this mill. (A similar suggestion is made in the text for Peter Archer snr. see Text. On the other hand the Johannots' later association with an Ancient Paper Maker tends to discount this suggestion [see p.147]).

[12] Scott, W.R. Bib.43 Vol.III 63 points out that the COMPANY's share prices, nominally 50, oscillated between 41–120 during the 1690's. He uses Houghton, J. Bib.20:July:1694 as his source where it is claimed that between 1692–4 the COMPANY were doing particularly well.

[13] There is some dispute about the precise quantities of paper made. Coleman, D.C. Bib.15 73 note 1 discusses this subject. He regards the claim that they made 100,000 reams of paper per annum as wildly improbable and even an amended claim of 50,000 as unlikely. Obviously much would have depended on the number of mills the COMPANY controlled. There is some evidence to show that it was 20 (See Chap.V p.174 for this); on the other hand some claim that no more than 8 can be identified. Another consideration is the length of the working year. Coleman (op.cit. 163 n.2) produces evidence that at the end of the 17th C. the working year was no more than 200 days; but the COMPANY may have insisted on more. Clearly one has to strike a balance. 8 x 2-vat mills could have produced 40,000 reams of Foolscap in a 300-day year and ca.27,000 in a 200-day year and depending on the number of vats 20 mills might have raised the total to 40-50,000 for a 200-day year.

An interval of 40 years is a long time and the claim will be made later that during this period other installations of an Engine would inevitably have taken place in Kent, almost certainly models of the earlier kind. All of them point to a common source, namely, Dartford No.2 mill and the COMPANY. The circumstances surrounding these other installations will be examined later, but it can be said here that they appear to have stemmed from paper makers working in Dartford itself. But our concern at this point is with Peter Archer jnr. and the question as to how he or, as it turned out, his family came by the operating experience that enabled him to make the conversion at Chartham and use these Engines when, as pointed out in the case of Richard Harris, practical experience was an essential requirement when employing a method that was so totally different from the traditional process. One can postulate various ways in which Peter jnr. might have acquired this knowledge e.g. a chance encounter with a Dutch paper maker or from a journeyman who had worked at Dartford No.2 etc.; alternatively, can one connect him more directly with this mill ?

A very extensive search has been made for the origins of the papermaking Archers. The name is commonly found, but even so "Peter Archers" have proved to be very hard to find indeed.[14] The papermaking Archers described here need not have been related to one another at all; but, if the assumption is made that they were, one obtains a much more rational picture of their activities and this is what will be presumed to be the case, namely, that they were all descended from Peter Archer snr., who married in 1673 at Goudhurst.

A reference has been made in Chapter II to the fact that the Goudhurst Archer may have been an immigrant.[15] The pros and cons of this suggestion are discussed at some length in Appendix IV, an Immigrant v an English origin. The fact that he appeared out of the blue at Goudhurst with no known connections with this district and following Stephen Manktellow (undoubtedly an immigrant) at the paper mill there favours this notion[16] though there are equally good reasons for thinking that he might have had an English origin.[17] In neither case is there any positive evidence pointing one way or the other.

If one accepts, for sake of argument, that "Peeter" Archer was an immigrant, his next move was to follow Stephen Manktellow to the Maidstone area in 1683, where he settled in Boxley, three of his children being baptised there between 1684–89, one of them being Peter jnr. in 1685. It is presumed that he took over Forstall mill from Thomas Willard, uncertain because the Boxley ratebook does not start until 1691 where he is shown as the occupant. According to the same source, he left Boxley about May 1693, thereafter disappearing completely, no further record of him being found. The COMPANY meanwhile took over Dartford No.2 mill in April of the same year.

In this situation, with the proposal that Peter snr. was an immigrant paper maker, it is not an unreasonable suggestion to make that he might have been offered the job of managing the COMPANY'S operations at Dartford, the dates certainly tie in with this theory and there are several other proposals that fit in with this also.

The first of these is the assumption that Richard, later owner and occupier of Dartford No.2 mill, was Peter snr.'s eldest son. If born sometime between 1674–80 (Peter snr.'s "missing" period and the only feasible date bracket for this) he would have been too young to have bought and worked the Dartford mill after the COMPANY'S demise in 1697/8, although he could well have served his apprenticeship there which, in turn, would account for his interest in this mill. Attempts have been made to link this acquisition with Richard's in-laws, the Whitewoods, but it has not proved possible to discover who they were and whether they had the means to finance it.[18] Whatever the truth Richard Archer snr., to judge from local records, was a person of some standing and one wonders how this could

---

[14] See App.IV "The Archers : Their origin and relationship discussed".

[15] See Chap.II Table III.

[16] Both the Records of the Huguenot Society of London and the Registers of the French Church (Threadneedle Street), London, contain 17th C. references to Archer/Arche and Larcher/L'Archer, one family coming from the Ardennes (see App.IV).

[17] Two Peter Archers were buried in Hatfield, Hertfordshire ca.1606 and 1656, but there are no baptismal records there until a date well after our Peter would have been born. That there may have been some sort of a link with Hatfield cannot be entirely ruled out (see App.IV under John Archer bapt., Boxley 1689).

[18] There is no reference to Whitewoods in the Dartford Registers nor any mention in either Dunkin, J. Bib.46 or Keyes, S.K. "Dartford, Historical Notes" (1933). Their domicile not found.

Figure 3

Drawings from Dylux Prints of 3 COMPANY Countermarks with a subscript "A" under a Posthorn in Shield reproduced here by kind permission of Mr. Thomas L. Gravell, Wilmington, Delaware, U.S.A. In addition, an "RA" Countermark found in an All Saints', Maidstone, Kent Parish Document dated 1712 (KAO P 241 12/8).

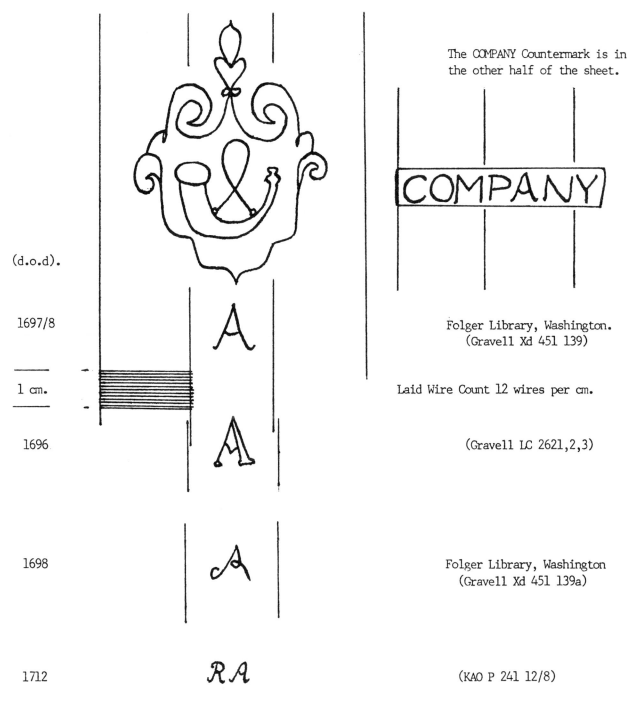

The COMPANY Countermark is in the other half of the sheet.

(d.o.d).

1697/8   Folger Library, Washington.
                                         (Gravell Xd 451 139)

1 cm.   Laid Wire Count 12 wires per cm.

1696   (Gravell LC 2621,2,3)

1698   Folger Library, Washington
                                         (Gravell Xd 451 139a)

1712   *RA*   (KAO P 241 12/8)

The direction of the Posthorn varies in different COMPANY examples. The one illustrated above (1697/8) is similar to the 1698 "A" example (and in another case with "CL" subscript). In all other cases known to the author, four others, the Posthorn faces in the opposite direction.
No other mark was found with the "RA" countermark.

have come about without some earlier family contact with the mill.[19] His own family, if not the others too, was evidently a very close knit one.[20]

The second assumption is related to the first in that several, as yet unclaimed, countermarks have been discovered that belong to the two periods in question. Gravell has discovered three COMPANY papers with "A" subscripts below a posthorn mark in the other half of the sheet to the usual COMPANY mark (see Fig.3);[21] and the author has found an "RA" countermark in a Maidstone document dated 1712. So far it has not been possible to ascribe any of these marks to other known paper makers. In addition, it has been suggested earlier that the use of countermarks at this time pointed to immigrant influence based on continental practice. Associating them with Peter and Richard would therefore accord with the proposal that they were immigrant in origin and related and that both had occupied the Dartford mill from which the marks could have emanated.

To connect the above with Peter jnr.'s conversion of Chartham there is one further important assumption to make, namely that after the demise of the COMPANY Peter snr. moved to or set up a mill at Sittingbourne in 1697/8, taking his family with him and installing an Engine there. This is the simplest explanation, though not necessarily the only one, which would accommodate all the known facts in this situation.[22] Working backwards from the conversion of Chartham in 1732/3 it is clear that (a) it was Peter jnr. and not his father who undertook this;[23] and (b) in order to accomplish this he must have had prior practical experience in the use of the Engine at Sittingbourne from where he had made his move.[24] It is known that this mill possessed an Engine in 1737[25] and by inference it must have been there long before this, Peter jnr. having left there in 1732 and worked there from 1708 (aged 23), if not before this date.[26] This picture is complicated by an unknown quantity, namely, Robert Archer.[27] In all this it is possible to postulate Robert and/or Peter jnr. gaining working experience of the Engine under Richard at Dartford, but when one takes *all the factors* into account i.e. explaining Richard's appearance at Dartford in 1701; the countermarks; the documented reference to Peter jnr. at Sittingbourne as a relatively young man and a paper maker; the possibility of Robert there as well, the involvement of Peter snr. as a common factor in this sequence of events provides a more

[19]   No Archers found in the West Region to whom Richard snr. might have been related (see Archer Genealogy App.IV).
[20]   For evidence of this compare Archer baptisms in the Dartford PR between 1704–40 and the Archer burials at Darenth between 1713–84; the entire family bar one daughter were buried there (see App.IV and working papers for full details). In the Darenth entries Richard snr. was variously described as "Gentlemen", "Mr. Archer of Dartford" etc.
[21]   Gravell, T.L. Bib.16 3:June:1981 (example 139 1697/8); Bib.16 12:Dec:1984 (examples 139a 1698 : LC 2621/2/3/ 1696). The last communication contained in addition "V" and "L" subscripts. All of the foregoing were in documents located in the United States.
[22]   A less satisfactory alternative is discussed in App.IV note 62. Another reason for thinking that Peter snr. might have moved to Sittingbourne is that had he been a COMPANY man he might still have had a hostile reception elsewhere; the COMPANY were still active and Sittingbourne was about as isolated a site from the Ancient Paper Makers as one could find.
[23]   Shorter only identifies one Peter Archer. The fact that Peter jnr., son of the paper maker, was bapt. Boxley 1685, married in Canterbury in 1708 making him 52 when undertaking a revolutionary conversion at Chartham undoubtedly favours him as the candidate for this against his father who would have been ca.84 at the time.
[24]   His status and his previous domicile are confirmed (i) by the Canterbury Marriage Licences 5th Series 1701–25 describing him as a paper maker of Sittingbourne; and (ii) An insurance Policy SFIP 61335 (10:July:1733) in which he is described as a paper maker from Sittingbourne insuring his paper mill sited "on the other side of the river" in Chartham.
      A search of the Chartham PRs has shown that there were no Archers there prior to Peter jnr. There were several families of Archer in nearby Canterbury but none appear to have been connected with him. Peter jnr.'s wife, however, was the eldest daughter of Robert Deane, a millwright of Canterbury, who must have known the Chartham district well. (See also Chap.VII p.333 and App.IV note 64 for further details).
[25]   The inventory (KAO PRC 11/81/166) of 1737 relating to Robert Archer's possessions, a paper maker of Sittingbourne, may be divided into three categories: the chattels in his house; the contents of his paper mill; and the contents, his musical instruments, in the accommodation above it (App.IV p.147). The contents of the paper mill were 30 reams Pott paper £7–5; 40 reams Hand £8; 4 ton rags £24; 2 post felting, 5 pr. moulds, 1 ENGINE, 3 presses, copper basins, white rags etc. £34–6–0. The important point to note here is the reference to an Engine and the absence of any reference to Mortars or Troughs. If the valuation of the papers is at all realistic, then one might legitimately assume that the papers itemized were White; but the rags possibly not the best cf. Fig.6 illustrating Price of Rags and Chap.VII note 35.
[26]   See Note 24 above. The Marriage Licence identifying him with Sittingbourne is dated 1708 and by inference he must have been there before this.
[27]   If an elder brother, he is unlikely to have been more than four years older than Peter jnr. The fact that he remained at Sittingbourne after Peter's departure might indicate this seniority. (Further details App.IV).

satisfactory solution and at the same time takes care of his apparent "disappearance". It is a most unfortunate fact that *there are no contemporary Sittingbourne records to help* and a search of the nearby Milton records does not illuminate the subject either.[28]

From the above it can be seen that if we are to explain the appearance of the Engine in Kent and the extension of its use, in view of the very limited size of the contemporary industry in the county' one inevitably sees the COMPANY at Dartford No.2 as the source of its introduction and an indispensable link in the chain leading to their introduction into Peter Archer's "new-built" paper mill at Chartham. The following summarises the proposals put forward here for connecting the two and taking care of all the known facts:-

(i)   that the papermaking Archers, of whom there were seven (possibly eight with yet another who may have been married to a paper maker), were all members of the same family. (Alternatives pose more problems than they solve).

(ii)   that Peter Archer was an immigrant.

(iii)   that, whether he was an immigrant or not (though the former provides a fuller picture of events), he managed Dartford No.2 mill for the COMPANY between 1693/7.

(iv)   that, after the demise of the COMPANY there in 1697/8, he and his family moved to Sittingbourne to occupy or set up a paper mill there.

(v)   that Peter jnr. subsequently worked at this mill and, later, moved to Chartham in 1732 partly with the object of setting up on his own and partly to obtain greater power from his water wheel.

The precise motives for Peter jnr.'s move to Chartham are not known but it could have been a step forward into the New Technology with a requirement for greater water power, a factor in common with the Whatman installation at Old Mill. If this was the case then Peter jnr. must have worked independently of Richard snr. who never managed to upgrade his beating facility though it is clear from later events that a close relationship must have existed between these two mills; Richard, who was bankrupted in 1740, may have been deterred for financial reasons. On the other hand one has to ask the question, did Peter jnr.'s advance match that of Harris and Whatman ? On balance this seems doubtful. It is true that Archer died before he could make his mark and no countermarked paper from Chartham has been discovered before the 1760's. Certainly the performance of his successors never matched the progress of Whatman at Turkey mill.[29] Nevertheless one thing emerges from all this; the Engine, probably in an embryonic form, had been introduced into Kent and the COMPANY is seen as the agency for this. This was an important innovation that other forward looking contemporary paper makers would have noted although at that stage of its development it evidently offered no special advantages over the traditional process. By all accounts it had not been introduced at Turkey mill at the time of Dr. Harris' visit (and indeed, to judge from Hasted's comments, not until Richard Harris pulled the mill down) nor at Poll mill where Swinnock had been commissioned to install "six troughs". In the case of Peter jnr. one must suppose that after several decades of practical experience in its use he would have been alerted to any new developments in this field and, as a consequence, his installation may have touched on the fringes of the New Technology.

---

[28]   For search of the Milton PRs see App.IV n.64.

[29]   There were no fewer than 3 lessees and 4 paper makers at Chartham in the 15 years following Peter jnr.'s decease and it could well be that they were not sufficiently familiar with the New Technology, that is to say if it had been introduced, to make effective use of it. (Further details see Chap.VII table XIV).

The next question, what was George Hagar doing at Dartford in 1698 ? There is little doubt that he was the same Hagar referred to in Chapter I where he was seen to have been in conflict with the COMPANY and his Patent the subject of much intrigue. Nothing precise is known about his activities after the early 1690's. He had claimed in 1689/90 that he had an interest in several mills in Surrey and one in Middlesex which he had set up sometime between 1682–91. So it is entirely feasible to see him still active in 1698 and also in opposition to the COMPANY. It is suggested here that his interest in the Dartford mill could have been prompted as a rescue operation by the Quelch family.

The reasoning behind this suggestion is that Hagar is reputed to have set up Eynsham mill (Oxfordshire) sometime after 1682, but was not the active paper maker there; this was Thomas Meale.[30] During the latter part of the 17th C. (from the 1670's to at least 1694) Thomas Quelch was the paper maker at Wolvercote mill, Oxford.[31] Both of these mills supplied paper to the University Press, so one might legitimately assume that Hagar and Thomas Quelch knew one another. As no evidence has come to light of any Quelchs found in Kent before the arrival of Edward in 1673 and since the main colonies of Quelch for that period were to be found in Oxfordshire and Berkshire, it is more than likely that Edward came from the West of London Region. That there were two of them with this unusual name making paper at the same time suggests a family connection between Thomas in Oxford and Edward in Kent. From this one might presume that Hagar was known to both of them and that Edward, as an Ancient Paper Maker, would have been familiar with Hagar's battle with the COMPANY.

It will be recalled that Edward Quelch was not assessed himself for Dartford No.2 mill; he may not have had the financial resources for this, in which case one might suppose that with the COMPANY'S demise at Dartford in 1697, the Quelch family invited Hagar to rescue the mill from any further attempts by the COMPANY or their successors to take it over again.

Although the reasoning behind this suggestion may seem tortuous, it does account for Hagar's unexpected and fleeting appearance in a Kent paper mill. It receives some further support from the fact that Hagar was succeeded there by John Quelch, quite possibly the brother of William Quelch snr. who was to occupy Dartford No.1 mill about three years later.[32]

Hagar during his career had undoubtedly been more in the fray than any other contemporary paper maker in Kent and thus would have brought additional papermaking experience to that already introduced by the COMPANY. This, together with his Patent for whatever its worth

30 Shorter, A. Bib.12 226.
31 Ibid.
32 The Quelch genealogy at Dartford is complicated and the question of a relationship between John and William snr. is examined more appropriately in App.II (q.v.) than here. In passing mention may be made of a reference in the Dartford Library (inf. Mrs. J. Stirk) which alleges that John erected a paper mill at Brooklands, Dartford, ca.1694 which was unsuccessful the mill being converted to Zinc processing. Unless there were two John Quelchs in this district this seems questionable. If the Dartford No.2 John had been born in 1677 (App.II TABLE XXIII) he would have been only 17 in 1694. It has been suggested that John and (?) William may have come from another branch of the family e.g. there were contemporary Quelchs in London but of a different trade. A John Quelch also appeared later at West mill, Berkshire (Chap.VII pp.305/306). Richard Archer snr., John's successor, bought Dartford No.2 in 1701; if Peter snr.'s eldest son, he would have been ca.26 making him 71 at the time of his death in 1746.

may have been,[33] would have filtered through to the Maidstone district by the time that Whatman had grown up.

To conclude this section on Dartford No.2 mill, it may be said that, in spite of the much greater expansion of the industry at Maidstone and the move of George Gill there also, the activities at Dartford were undoubtedly an important though indirect source for motivating and influencing Whatman's and Harris' future plans; and, indeed, those of Peter Archer for his move to Chartham. Two points remain that might be conveniently mentioned at this juncture.

First, whether one accepts the suggestion or not that a primitive model of the Engine had been installed during the COMPANY'S tenure of Dartford No.2, it will become clear later[34] that the real impact of the New Technology did not reach this mill until William Quelch snr. rebuilt and divided it into two in 1741/42.

Second, it seems an extraordinary coincidence that Engines were installed first at Chartham and a month or two later only 20 miles away at Old Mill, Hollingbourne, the former described as "new-built" but in reality a converted fulling mill and the latter entirely new, for there not to have been some common factor, but so far this has not been discovered. The time interval between the two would have been much too short for Whatman to have copied Archer's installation, besides the one at Old Mill may have been technically more advanced or else better managed than the other.[35]

The Quelch Empire

This subject will only be touched on briefly here, because the empire in question was only in its infancy during the formative period in Whatman's and Harris' development. William Quelch snr., the occupant of Dartford No.1 mill at the beginning of the 18th C., was really the architect of this empire. William snr.'s origin, and connection with the earlier Quelchs at Dartford, has not been established with any degree of certainty beyond the fact that he must have been related to them in some way.

It will be seen from Table XXII (App.II) illustrating the papermaking network built up by the Quelch, Terry and Clement Taylor families, that William snr. made his first appearance, presumably as a fully trained paper maker, at Spilman's mill in 1702. This mill was obviously nearing the end of its life and by 1716 (*significantly, after the introduction of the New Duties*) William had moved his papermaking temporarily away from Dartford and converted the corn mill at Basted into a paper mill.[36]

---

[33] Chap.V p.193.

[34] Chap.VII p.281.

[35] Seeing that Whatman, Harris and Peter Archer jnr. were all born in the Maidstone area and that the latter's wife, Margaret, may have been connected with the Boxley paper maker Deanes (App.IV note 64) it is possible that through mutual acquaintances Peter's activities may have become known to and alerted Whatman. The fact that a branch of the Whatman family had lived at Chartham at the end of the 17th C. does not appear to be relevant in this case (App.II under Whatman).

[36] Following the COMPANY's example Quelch may well have installed a similar type of Engine at Basted in 1716 (Chap.VII pp.276/77, 281).

William snr. was the driving force behind this empire (he lived to the age of 96); but his second (William jnr. b.1704), third (Eleanor b.1711) and a later child (Sarah b. ca. 1720) were instrumental in expanding the papermaking activities of the family, Eleanor marrying John Terry, a journeyman at Basted mill; and Sarah marrying Clement Taylor snr. Even William jnr. lived to the age of 73. Between them, they and their progeny occupied an ever–increasing number of paper mills in Kent, from which even more paper makers sprang in the course of time.[37] This empire was to dominate the Kent papermaking scene, in numbers rather than in technology, for the rest of the 18th C.[38] In spite of the fact that the older Quelchs at Dartford must have inherited their share of the White papermaking tradition initiated by Spilman, no (Kent) Quelch countermarks have been discovered in documents earlier than the 1780's and these must have stemmed from William jnr.

William Quelch snr. undoubtedly made White paper of a sort, but not the kind that would have made a name for himself. One gets a very strong impression from his activities and movements that he was an ambitious man but not an innovator, although perhaps keen to learn from others by imitation. With Ancient Paper Maker connections he may have been friendly in his disposition to Whatman and Harris (though much later a bitter enmity developed between the younger Whatman and the Clement Taylor side of the family), but it is most unlikely that he contributed anything technically significant towards the evolution and execution of the Whatman enterprise at Old Mill; at a later stage the flow of information was manifestly in the other direction. On the other hand, after his move to Gurney's mill in Loose in 1728 (replacing William Harris), he would have been living on Whatman's doorstep. The latter must, therefore, have had ready intelligence of what had been going on at Dartford, although one has to remember that at this time Whatman was still a tanner supplying the paper trade with materials for making size and had not yet made his investment.

When Quelch snr. moved in 1728[39] he left William jnr. to manage Basted mill. In 1732 the latter also moved to Loose but by this time John Terry would have been 21 and old enough to look after Basted mill in their absence. The successive moves of father and son to the Maidstone area are symptomatic of the programme of expansion that the Quelchs were to pursue. The stimulus that the New Duties gave to the industry provided Quelch with just the impetus he needed for this and Maidstone was the only region at that time where he could see an opening for himself. Moreover, the mill he was to occupy was more favourably placed and perhaps better equipped for their purpose than their mill at Wrotham, though the Clement Taylors retained the latter up till 1802. The reason for Harris' departure is not known, but in all probability it was his age that determined this; he would have been at least 64 by then and added to this his eldest son had left and was then firmly established at Millhall mill, Ditton, and the young Richard was evidently no longer interested in this type of mill; indeed, at this

[37]   See App.II, The Quelch family et al.

[38]   There is some evidence that this influence spread further afield e.g. a John Taylor of Wrotham, a cousin of Clement's, appeared at Carshalton mill, Surrey, in 1744 and rebuilt it in 1746 (see App.II p.62 iii).

[39]   Although Elizabeth Quelch's burial has not been found, it seems from the Loose Prs. that William snr. had married again, Eleanor, and yet there is an unexplained "Elizabeth w.o. William Quelch" buried in Dartford 1771 [see App.II TABLE XXIII]. Whether Elizabeth or Eleanor was the mother of Sarah has not been discovered. Possibly Elizabeth's death may have been another contributory reason for Quelch snr.'s move.

The subject of Gurney's mill at this time is discussed later in this Chapter, the Maidstone Region.

juncture he could have been in Holland or wherever it was he acquired his knowledge of the New Technology.

For the time being, then, further consideration of the Quelch empire will be left to Chapter VII, where later developments in the Kent paper industry will be examined. It is enough to note at this point that the Quelchs were establishing themselves in the Maidstone area, in Loose itself, just at a time when Whatman and Harris were about to enter the arena.

Eynsford and Shoreham mills and the Johannots

As mentioned in Chapter II nothing has been discovered about the previous occupants of either Eynsford or Shoreham paper mills on the River Darent before Johannot and Russell appear at them in the 1690's. No ratebooks have survived at all for either parish which makes the investigation of the history of these two mills extremely difficult. One of the very few documents that have been discovered relating to Shoreham mill[40] shows that certainly by 1716 Andrew Johannot was the occupant of this paper mill as the undertenant or assignee of Alexander Russell. Both mills must have made White paper, a practice handed on to their successors,[41] which later led to the long and sustained reputation that these mills had from the late 18th–20th Cs. for the manufacture of the best qualities of White paper. So far as their contribution to the advancement of papermaking then, attention may be confined to the Johannots who came, it is believed, from a distinguished papermaking family in the Auvergne and brought refinements to the process when they arrived in England and to Kent in particular.

Nothing is known about the circumstances surrounding the Johannots at Eynsford. The first indication of their arrival is the baptism of a child of Andrew's there in 1694. Shorter mentions the presence of a Samuel Galliot,[42] who may have worked with Andrew and later corresponded with the Treasury on frauds, practised by paper makers avoiding the Excise. The Johannots at Eynsford were obviously well thought of as paper makers as they figure in the 1720 Issue of "Instructions to be observed by Officers in the Country in charging duties on Paper".[43] The notion that they might have worked for the COMPANY may be discounted; there were several other immigrant paper makers contemporary with them who retained their independent status, some actively opposing the COMPANY.[44] Beyond these few facts little is known about their activities or just when they arrived in this country. The fact that their

[40] KAO U 1007/E 128 Draft Lease and Release 20/21:Nov:1716 between the Polhills of Otford (vendors) and John Borrett of Shoreham relating to a Messuage and Paper mill etc. in Shoreham then in the occupation of Andrew Johannett (sic), paper maker, as undertenant or assignee of Alexander Russell who had leased the property on 25:Oct:1700 for 20 years. The document is in the Sevenoaks Library and I am indebted to Mr. Michael Carter, West Kent Area Archivist for making the search (17:Feb:1987). (See also St Mary Cray mill Chap.VII n.196).

[41] The first Eynsford mill countermark known to the author is "Floyd & Co." in an American document of 1791 (Gravell, T.L. Bib.68 260/1); the first Shoreham mark "TW" (Thomas Wilmott) d.o.d. 1783 (KAO Q/RP1/338). "AI" countermarks have been recorded by Churchill (Bib.3); Cameron (Bib.18); and Gravell (Bib.16) usually attributed to Abraham Janssen, but might also have belonged to Andrew Johannot.

[42] Shorter, A. Bib.12 182.

[43] A sample form is illustrated on p.20 of this issue which reads "Ensford, Mr. A......Johannot". Later issues refer to Anthony Johannot.

[44] For example, Peter Gaultier, Gerard de Vaux, Denis Manes, Berreau; and possibly, but indirectly, Theodore Janssen; and perhaps many others. See also this chapter note 11.

business here was in papermaking makes it virtually certain that they were related to the family at Annonay.[45]

This is more or less endorsed by the fact that, apart from other refinements to the process, Andrew Johannot must have been familiar with an innovation known as the Exchange and said to have been developed by Matthieu Johannot of Annonay.[46] Unfortunately, this subject (which the author has treated in much greater detail elsewhere)[47] is surrounded with a great deal of uncertainty as to when it was first introduced. Matthieu Johannot's dates have not been discovered at the time of writing this, but there are two pieces of evidence to support the idea that Andrew knew of this process which was, in effect, an extension of the Pack–pressing operation. Without doubt the Whatmans knew all about it by 1760 and to judge from the esteem in which the elder Whatman's Writing papers were held he obviously must have known about it too, indeed, in all probability from the very beginning of his career as a paper maker.

Second, there is anonymous evidence in the form of a contemporary remark made indirectly about Andrew, as we know now,[48] at Eynsford, that "the manufacture of *Writing paper* was greatly improved by one Johannot, a French refugee, *whose son Josias* succeeded him in that business".[49] Josias himself was active as a London Stationer in the early 1730's; so, once again, the inference is that the remark quoted above must refer to a process that was practised much earlier than this (Andrew died in 1737). In fact Andrew is not likely to have acquired this art after his arrival in England in 1694.

The technical aspects of this innovation will be considered briefly in the next chapter under the heading of the papermaking Felt (and, as mentioned, in more detail elsewhere). For the benefit of the non–papermaking reader it may be helpful to explain at this point that during the Pressing stage of the sheet-making process the surface features of the woollen felt become imprinted on the wet sheet producing a rough surface known as the Grain of the paper. If the sheet is allowed to dry in this state, the rough surface becomes a permanent feature, an undesirable property in paper to be written on. In the pack-pressing stage, the surface of one damp sheet is pressed against the surface of another and the roughness is thereby "softened". By repeating this process so that sheets present different surfaces to each other each time they are pack-pressed, the grain can be reduced even further, thus improving

---

[45]   Shorter, A. Bib.12 under various headings mentions Andrew snr. (bur. Eynsford 1737); Andrew jnr. bankrupted there in 1746; Anthony may have succeeded them there later. Josias (see also in text and notes 48 and 51 below) insured his Cray Valley mill, Kent, 1742; a Patent of his dated 1747 describes him as "Stationer, late of London". Israel insured his Tottenham mill, Middlesex, in 1735. Beyond noting these papermaking activities, however, it has not proved possible to determine their relationship with the Johannots of Annonay. The Huguenot Society of London hold no pedigree or manuscript material on the Johannots.

[46]   Coleman, D.C. Bib.15 77 Note 1.

[47]   Balston, J.N. Bib.76.

[48]   Miss Mary Pollard has kindly drawn my attention (2:Feb:86) to an entry in McKenzie, D.F. "Stationers' Company Apprentices 1641–1700" Oxford Bibliographical Society, 1974 Entry No.3918 "Josias Johannot, apprenticed to William Herbert I; son of Andrew, papermaker of Eynesford, Kent. Bound 6 May 1723 etc....". (See Text following this note for context; for other references to Wm. Herbert see Index under Paper Makers and Stationers)

[49]   HOW Aspley Guise Papers Acc. 809 Bedfordshire Record Office MK42 9AP.

the quality of the Writing paper; and it is this variation in the process that has been attributed to Matthieu Johannot, but on what evidence is not known.[50]

Although the influence in question cannot be proved, if as seems certain Andrew brought this innovation with him to England and used it at Eynsford, then by one means or another the knowledge would have reached Whatman and Harris, barely 20 miles away by the time they undertook their venture 40 years later; an important influence that was to have far–reaching consequences for him.[51]

Summing up the potential sources of influence on Whatman and Harris likely to have emanated from the West Kent Region the policy adopted here has been to go back and examine the situation that existed there in the period before they were born. This had been a very critical time in the history of domestic White paper manufacture. It had seen the COMPANY operating a monopoly in this business with considerable success under initially favourable circumstances that had enabled them to extend their dominion into West Kent, a stronghold of their opponents, the Ancient Paper Makers. Although all of this took place before Whatman's and Harris' time, the effects of the COMPANY'S methods and improvements would not have penetrated the Maidstone area immediately. One of their innovations had almost certainly been the introduction of an early, but not very efficient, model of the Engine into their mill at Dartford, producing side effects on the Archer family's papermaking, possibly on William Quelch snr., as well as on the more receptive elements in the Maidstone district.

This situation, however, was an unstable one. Imports, which had been at a negligible level during the war (1688–1697), flooded the market again once peace had been declared; this brought about the downfall of the COMPANY and bad times for the industry as a whole. Nevertheless the opponents of the COMPANY were more firmly based and had less far to fall so that during the first decades of the 18th C., aided by the New Duties, they were clearly in a more favourable position to take on opposition wherever it might have come from.

Just as methods and technical improvements used by the COMPANY would have taken time to filter through to Maidstone and a new generation of paper makers, so the resurgence of the

---

[50] This process of repeated pack–pressing was known as the Exchange and the puzzling feature about its introduction is that Nicholas Desmarest in a communication read before the Académie Royale des Sciences on the 20:Feb:1771 on Dutch papermaking techniques explained that the Exchange process was borrowed from the Dutch and until his communication "n'est pas bien connue en France". Moreover, he adds (Bib.21 513–515) "MM. de Montgolfier ont été les premiers à adopter l'échange, même sur des papiers fabriqués avec matières pourries. Je trouvai dans leur fabrique un atelier d'échange tout monté en 1779". And yet Mr. Voorn (Bib.28 PAHIS 790444 of 21:Mar:1979) said that they had no information in the Hague Papermaking Archives on this subject earlier than Desmarest's reference. Where then did it originate? As mentioned in the Text, the Whatmans were plainly aware of this technique before 1760.

[51] If Andrew Johannot's improved Writing papers were available in the market place by the beginning of the 18th C. then one must assume that Stationers like James Brooke would not have taken long to pick this up and, in turn, pass on this information to either George or William Gill snr. If one assumes that the passage of this information took longer than this, then there can be little doubt that by the early 1730's when Josias Johannot had established his Stationer's premises on London Bridge, not far from Brooke's, the message would have got through by then (for Brooke's role as mentor and Stationer to the Gills, see later in this chapter).

The consequences arising out of Whatman's high quality paper, referred to in the text (equal, if not superior to imported paper) were such that the reputation of these eventually led, amongst other things, Whatman into the development of Wove paper (Balston, J.N. Bib. 76).

local industry would have taken time to manifest itself. The New Duties would not have brought instant relief. All the same one can see new forces emerging and amongst these was one that has been called here the Quelch empire, not yet in an effective state but germinating. Thus the West Kent Region can be seen as a source not only of technical improvements of varying significance, to be considered in the next chapter, but of foreign elements that were to stimulate new forces within the local industry, particularly in the still expanding Maidstone division of this. More specifically, details, so far as they are known, are given of the activities of the Archer family and the ultimate conversion of Chartham mill; the first move of the Quelchs, soon after the introduction of the New Duties, to Basted mill and later extending their activities to Gurney's mill in Loose; and, finally, the Johannots at Eynsford and their knowledge and use of the Exchange process leading to improved surface quality in Writing papers.

THE MAIDSTONE AREA

Whereas the influences of the West Kent Region on the young Whatman and Harris were most likely to have been technical in character, those originating in their home territory were more probably concerned with the expansion of the industry within the Maidstone zone itself and with the movements and personalities of its paper makers and the opportunities that arose from these. Apart from the very good White paper made by George Gill at Turkey mill and the refinements he had introduced there to produce this, it is most improbable that any of the paper makers round Maidstone had anything radically new to contribute towards technical progress in the process during the period leading up to Whatman's investment. The first task then will be to examine the movements and expansion that took place after the first wave had been completed.

If Table III, setting out the Paper mills in the Maidstone district and their occupants during the last decades of the 17th C., is extended to cover the period up to 1733, and the significance of the changes assessed, it will be found that after examination the relevant features in this phase can be reduced to two or three important elements. The changes listed below (in the same order as the mills in the Table) can be classified as either significant, of interest in one way or another, or of no relevance. The list also includes the mills converted in the second wave (see Chap.II Map 2):

Forstal Mill

Peter Archer snr. was replaced in 1693 by John Hillyer, the husband of Constant Russell. It is not known where he came from, but he may have had paper maker antecedents and anti–COMPANY leanings.[52] He married in Boxley seven years before he took over the mill. His wife's origin has not been traced either, it could have been Horsmonden (the parish next to Goudhurst); and, being in the same age group, she could have been related to Alexander Russell, the Ancient Paper Maker at Shoreham (a notion supported by a shared opposition to the COMPANY).[53] The later succession at Forstal was essentially a Russell one, followed by Hillier Russell and ending in the 19th C. with Clement Taylor Russell.[54] These changes are of general interest only; the mill undoubtedly continued to make White uncountermarked paper throughout the 18th C.

This mill is, however, of considerable interest in another direction. By 1716 it was owned by William Gill and, in fact, was still in the hands of a branch of the Gill family as late as 1826. This subject will be considered separately.

Millhall Mill

James West died in 1694. It is just possible that he and his mill had become a casualty of the COMPANY'S activities, because he was succeeded by Edward Middleton, an undistinguished paper maker. The fortunes of the mill were perhaps restored by his successor, William Harris jnr. (Richard's eldest brother) in 1724 and it remained, by direct descent, in Harris hands until at least 1763, the death of Thomas. Thereafter, the Mary Harris who married Thomas Golding, the next occupant (1776–1816+), may have been a daughter.[55] Here again the mill for most of its life probably made the same sort of White paper as nearby Forstal, uncountermarked lower grades of Printing.

---

[52] The problem of Hillyer's origin is discussed in some detail in App.IV.
[53] For further discussion of this subject see App.IV under Alexander Russell.
[54] For the Succession here see App.III under the Synopsis of the History of Forstal mill.
[55] See App.II under the Harris Family Paper Makers.

It is of interest in that it demonstrates the continuity of the Harris family papermaking tradition, a tradition that might have extended as far back as the mid–17th C. Also, as seen in Chapter III, Richard may have used the same sales outlets for the experimental products from Old Mill, Hollingbourne, during the 1730's.

One might say that this mill had some significance in so far as its occupant would have been an ally of Whatman and Harris at the outset of their venture.

East Malling (Middle Mill)
William Middleton, the son of the former paper maker at Millhall mill, had moved in here by 1723. This mill is not relevant to our subject.

Turkey Mill
The circumstances surrounding the possession of and the succession at this mill prior to Richard Harris' occupation and ultimate acquisition of it are of the utmost importance in this case and will be considered separately later in this chapter.

Briefly, control of the mill passed from George Gill to his son, William snr., in 1716. By 1729 the latter had acquired a moiety of the freehold and an undertaking that the rest would come into his possession later. In 1731, however, he was bankrupted for good and although in March of the same year the mill was advertised "to be lett" technically, because of his involvement in the freehold of the property, it was up for sale. Despite further transactions it remained in this state of suspense until it was eventually acquired, seven years later, by Richard Harris in 1738.[56]

Meanwhile, after William Gill's demise, it was first occupied by Mr. Cordwell, the tenant from Poll mill on the opposite bank of the River Len, from 1732–35; then for one year (June 1735–June 1736) by a "Mr. Musgrove", who will be referred to again below. Richard Harris was first assessed for it in Dec. 1736.

Upper Tovil
Stephen Manktellow (from Goudhurst) was replaced at this mill in 1721 by Peter Musgrove jnr. Stephen, it has been reckoned, must have been at least 70 by then. Whether he had ever made or still made White paper there is unknown. If he had, initially, he may not have been able to compete with the COMPANY after 1690. The mill does not figure among the top class mills until it was rebuilt in 1772 by Clement Taylor jnr.

The only point of interest here is the presence of Peter Musgrove jnr. who occupied the mill for the next 20 years, having moved from Lower Tovil (see below), and it seems likely that he was the "Mr. Musgrove" who occupied Turkey mill in 1735, possibly because his father may have started his Maidstone career there.[57]

Great Ivy Mill
Thomas Manktellow, son of and formerly apprenticed to Stephen, took over this mill from Richard Burnham. It is not relevant to our subject. Certainly, later, this mill was engaged in making "Shop" papers.

Lower Tovil
Peter Musgrove snr. had arrived in Boxley in 1678, but it was not until 1686 that he occupied Lower Tovil mill, by which time the embargo on French goods had been lifted, so that, even if he trained under George Gill, he probably never had an opportunity of making White paper. He died in 1701 and was succeeded by Peter jnr. who may have been more ambitious.

As seen above Peter jnr. moved to Upper Tovil mill in 1721 and William Gill snr. occupied the lower mill in his place from 1722–28. This mill is of interest to us only on account of Gill's tenure and will be discussed separately.

---

[56] App.IV under William Gill snr.
[57] See App.IV under the Peter Musgroves, Musgrove snr. and jnr.

Gurney's Mill

William Harris was replaced at this mill by William Quelch snr. arriving from his Basted mill, Wrotham, in 1728. In retrospect this can be seen as a significant event. He was joined there in 1732, at the latest, by William Quelch jnr.

William Quelch snr., prompted partly by the opportunities that he saw stemming from the introduction of the New Duties and partly from the resurgent forces within the industry following the collapse of the COMPANY, had converted as stage 1 a mill at Basted in 1716 and now saw further opportunities for expansion in the Maidstone area and moved there. There is evidence that the ratable value of this mill increased significantly in 1729, Quelch's second year,[58] which makes one wonder if he had modified this mill in any significant way. For instance, the question posed earlier, did he install one of the early Engines there ?

At the moment no other motives for his move to Maidstone have come to light. But, as he was living right on Whatman's doorstep (Map 3), by the early 1730's he must have become aware of new developments in the offing. It is not impossible that the stimulus was mutual in that Quelch may have been instrumental in bringing Whatman up to date on recent developments at Dartford and pointing out the opportunities that lay ahead. But it is not thought that any of these would have been factors that determined Whatman's decision to invest.

The activities of the Quelchs will be discussed again in Chapter VII. They continued to occupy Gurney's mill until 1746, by which time the Quelch empire had expanded in other directions.

The above concludes the account of the main developments that had taken place in the mills converted or operating during the first phase of the expansion of the industry in the Maidstone area. The second phase has been referred to briefly at the beginning of this chapter and the mills included in this were:

Cobtree Mill

To judge from its site it seems fairly certain that some sort of mill had existed here before and had either fallen into disuse and was being revived by constructing a new mill there for paper manufacture (as was the case with Hollingbourne Old Mill) or, less likely, that it was a working mill converted to papermaking from some other unknown function. There is no obvious evidence of a paper mill having been there. In fact, the relevant entry in the Boxley Poor Ratebook is "£4 Gill for ye new paper mill" May 1717 and this entry is sandwiched between the names of Jobe Potter (above) and John Springate (below). It is to be noted that no entry is to be found between Potter and Springate for the November 1716 assessments.[59] The Gill in question must have been William snr. The question of proprietorship of this mill is discussed in some detail in App.III. It is unlikely to have been Gill himself; no insurance policy has been found for it as was the case with his Forstal mill.

Within six months of William Gill snr.'s final bankruptcy the mill was insured by a London Stationer, Edward Rowe, but still in the tenure of David Deane.[60] There is a parallel to this situation in the case of Forstal mill, namely, James Brooke, also a London Stationer, took care of this mill.[61]

Reverting to the early years of the mill, Gill's assessment was replaced in October 1718 by "£30 Mr. Deann, for the Paper Mill". David Dean had been described as a "paperman" in the Boxley PR. as early as 1700.

---

[58] Gurney's mill was assessed in both East Farleigh and Loose parishes (Harris clearly resident in Loose and Quelch as an Outdweller in both parishes until 1740 when he is listed among the Loose parishioners). Some of the entries are missing but *at an annual rate* (both parish assessments combined) Harris was assessed for £36 in 1724, £42 in 1726; and Quelch, initially, £50 in 1728, and £64 in 1729, a rise of 52% on Harris' rates. (KAO P 142 5/2 and 12/1 E. Farleigh. P 233 5/3 and 12/5/1-2 Loose).
     For further rises see Chap.VII p.281 and note 88.
[59] See App.III Boxley Poor Ratebook Extracts and the Synopsis of the History of Cobtree mill.
[60] SFIP 54351. For further details (as in note 59) see synopsis.
[61] See later in this chapter p.164

As there was no unoccupied mill there and because he was later installed by the Gill family in the new mill, it is highly probable that he had been working for them at Turkey mill and acquired a reputation for reliability.[62] In May 1743 Thomas Dean replaced David snr., the former insuring his goods in the mill in 1742 and being replaced in 1750 by Mrs. Dean.[63] At some point in the mid–18th C. the proprietorship of the mill either reverted (as in the case of Forstal mill) to William Gill jnr. or was acquired separately by another member of the family in whose hands it remained until ca.1810.[64] The history of this mill is, therefore, of decided interest in the present context.

Poll Mill
Lord Aylesford commissioned Swinnock to convert this mill in 1718 from fulling to a conventional paper mill with 6 troughs. Swinnock was bankrupted in 1727 with William Gill succeeding him as the tenant in name, but is not known who the paper maker was there. After Gill's bankruptcy the occupants were brothers William and Joseph Cordwell, and it remained in Joseph's hands until 1756.[65] It was a two–vat mill and Shorter believed that White paper may have been made there from 1736–7;[66] although, if the conversion was related to the introduction of the New Duties, one would have expected that Lord Aylesford's intentions had been aimed at making White rather than Brown from the outset and that Gill, during his tenure, had similar objectives.

In the period leading up to Whatman's investment this mill, because of the out–of–date methods used there to make paper, cannot have influenced or interested him. At a much later date, when this mill became part of the "Quelch empire", it became of greater interest and will be considered again in Chapter VII.

Upper Mill and Mill by Leg o' Mutton Pond, Loose
The details of these two mills have already been given at the beginning of this chapter,[67] Upper mill being occupied by David Dean, the son of the Cobtree David Dean, in 1728, the other mill being converted ca.1742.

The former is of interest on two counts; first, it was sited not much further away from Whatman's house and tan yards than Gurney's mill and presumably, had he wished to do so, he could have invested in this mill by converting it to papermaking. Instead, he can only have noted that the mills surrounding him, including Gurney's, were passing into strangers' hands. Second point of interest in contrast to the first is that the younger Whatman acquired and rebuilt this mill in 1775, a subject that will be considered again in Chapter VII.

Whether William Gill snr. had a hand in this conversion as well as in Cobtree is not known. A Mr. Arnold appears to have been the proprietor, but one senses that it was Gill's influence, directly or indirectly, that contributed to its conversion. The points that suggest that Gill may have lent a hand are (a) that the Dean family were occupants, later replaced by John Farley; and (b) William jnr. and his brother-in-law, Thomas Wright, insured this mill in the tenure of John Farley in 1770 indicating more than a passing interest in it by the Gill family.[68]

---

[62]   David Deane makes his first appearance in the Boxley parish registers in 1697, the entry of a son, John, under baptisms (KAO P 40 1/2) followed by the comment "but not baptised". In 1700, the entry of a son David, Deane is described as "paperman" and is again followed by the comment "but not baptised". The Deanes then disappear from the records until 1718 when "Mr. Deann" (David) appears in the Poor Ratebook as occupant of what turns out to be Cobtree mill. It is not known what occupation the eldest son, John, pursued, but he was still alive in 1728. David Deane snr. left the lease of Cobtree to his son, Thomas; and that of Upper mill, Loose, to David jnr. and Joseph (PRC 17/96 f.364).
The question as to whether the Boxley Deans were corrected with the Canterbury ones, Peter Archer jnr.'s in-laws, is discussed in App.IV Note 64.

[63]   See App.III Synopsis of History of Cobtree.

[64]   See App.III under Extracts from the Boxley Poor Ratebooks and Land Tax Returns; and James Brooke's Will (App.IV p.172).

[65]   See App.III Boxley Poor Ratebooks Extracts.

[66]   Shorter A, Bib.12 p.57.

[67]   See this chapter notes 1 & 2.

[68]   See Chap.II p.87; see also App.IV under James Brooke's Will.

Otham

This was converted from a fulling mill sometime before 1719, probably 1715 when William Keeble first appears in the Otham RB, into a paper mill and might thus be included in the "second phase" of the expansion.

As a result of examining the state of the Maidstone paper mills between the end of the 17th C. and the time when Whatman made his investment, it can be seen that some of the original paper makers had merely consolidated their positions; others had faded from the picture altogether; and there were still others, of whom it might be said, that they were imbued with a new determination to exploit the opportunities that they saw in the protection offered them by the New Duties for the manufacture of White paper.[69] In the event, the last group met with varying degrees of success or none at all. They include the incipient empire of the Quelchs which, maybe because it was only in its infancy and had, perhaps, less ambitious aims than the others, came through this period unscathed; the empire of William Gill snr., which ended in disaster for himself; and the partnership of Whatman and Harris that went from strength to strength.

So far as formative influences on the young Whatman and Harris are concerned, it has been suggested that any that might have originated from the Quelchs, or other changes that had taken place in Loose, would have had only a superficial effect on them, if any at all. If they had wanted to they could have converted Upper mill at any time from 1726 onwards. By this time Whatman would have inherited his father's estate and it seems unlikely that his financial circumstances would have altered significantly between then and 1733. Or they could have retained Gurney's mill, if William had intimated that he was about to retire and Richard had wanted to continue there. In retrospect one can see that these actions would have been quite out of character with the course that they were to pursue. In other words by this time they had evidently made up their minds to break new ground. Harris must have been training elsewhere. It seems safe then to set any of the changes in Loose on one side, though Whatman might well have picked up useful tips from the newly arrived William Quelch about papermaking in the West Region. Despite the fact that Quelch had very probably installed an early version of the Engine in 1729, Whatman's and Harris' plans to install an improved model must have been well advanced by then so that it would have had little effect on them.

We are thus reduced to two other sources of influence; first, the Ancient Paper Maker background supplied by Richard's father, who in turn had been closely associated with James' father, and the imposing figure of George Gill; and, second, the later activities and demise of William Gill snr. The first of these will be dealt with under the heading of "The Challenge"; and the second "The Papermaking Empire of William Gill snr. and its Aftermath".

---

[69] It has to be understood that it was the opportunities offered by this situation that are under consideration here rather than any practical achievements in White paper manufacture that might have resulted from the courses of action pursued by these groups. The market may well have been unready for this expansion and hence forced some of the paper makers into making the cheaper sorts of paper or out of business altogether. What is not in doubt is that a driving force was now acting on the manufacturing end of this chain.

The Challenge

It is obvious from what has been said already in both this chapter and the previous one that between ca.1680–1733 new technical developments of one sort or another had either been adopted or were still in the process of evolution, these being particularly applicable to the manufacture of White paper in this country. They would in their time, as we shall see in the next two chapters, improve the economics of the process and the quality of the paper. It is also clear that Whatman and Harris had got wind of many of these innovations as they grew up; and sometime before 1733 they had committed themselves to a project of an unusual character which embodied some or all of these. But it is a fact, well known in our own age when new ideas are two a penny, that one does not necessarily equip oneself with these novelties unless there is some underlying motive for doing so. In the case of the two young men there must have been something fundamental that motivated them over and above a predisposition to continue the expansion of the industry in their locality because the protection now afforded by the New Duties provided them with better prospects for their trade, especially so in the case of Whatman who was not even a paper maker and who in the event was to make the investment. Had this not been so, Richard might have continued to make paper at Gurney's mill after his father had retired, consolidating his position like the others in the district; and Whatman might have carried on working his tan yards after his father's death in 1725 as indeed he did. In any case any improvement in the papermaking climate would have applied equally to anyone else in the Region who was prepared to take advantage of it. Or, again, to account for their undertaking this project one might postulate the existence of some hypothetical "salesman", as it were, persuading them to invest in a new idea; but, even so, one still has to look for a reason as to why they should listen to and act on his advice, and then to go off at a tangent from the others in the district.

The motivation that we are looking for came unquestionably from the problems that had beset the domestic White paper industry ever since the embargo on French goods had been enacted in 1678, or maybe the symptoms were there even earlier than this. The hopes of those paper makers who had struggled to compete in this field before, and others who had joined them later, had been justifiably raised only to be dashed again in their unsuccessful confrontation with the COMPANY; and where else was this frustration likely to have been felt more than in Maidstone where the greatest expansion had taken place ? The maximum opposition to the monopoly, granted to and operated successfully by the COMPANY, came from the Ancient Paper Makers, who had been in the business longest and were likely to lose most from it. The Cases they had presented to Parliament in 1689/90 show that they were fully aware of the threat to them posed by both imported paper and the alternative to this, a monopoly to be granted to newcomers making the paper *in their own country*. It was enough to make anyone's blood boil.

In Kent we have seen how, apart from Alexander Russell at Shoreham mill (ineffective from 1716), William Blackwell, the Ancient Paper Maker at Dartford No.1 mill, had faded from the scene by 1698; Edward Quelch had been displaced by their enemy, the COMPANY, at Dartford No.2 mill by 1691; at Aylesford James West had died in 1694, which left only George Gill and William Harris still active in the field at Maidstone, together with William Quelch snr. saddled with an obsolete mill at Dartford, to continue the struggle. This is precisely the situation that we have found in a more detailed examination of the area from which the future at Maidstone was to develop.

In retrospect one can see to-day that the COMPANY had ceased to be an effective force by the beginning of the 18th C. But the contemporary paper makers would not have known this with any degree of certainty. The problems of the domestic White paper industry were by no means over. White paper of high quality from Holland had replaced for the most part paper formerly imported from France; it would have been just as difficult as it had been before for domestic manufacturers to have persuaded the Stationers to buy British goods; in the minds of paper makers with memories, like the Ancient Paper Makers, feelings would have lingered on of the possibility that another group of paper makers might obtain some form of privilege or advantage, fraudulent or otherwise, similar to those acquired by the COMPANY; and, if the proposals made earlier concerning the papermaking activities of the Archer family have any substance, then Richard Archer at Dartford No.2 mill could be seen as a survivor of the enemy régime there before.

It was in this rather hopeless environment that James and Richard would have started their lives. Richard's father, William, cannot be seen as an outstanding paper maker despite the fact that his family had probably been making White paper of sorts for more than one generation. He, like the others in the district, had converted his mill and run it, so far as we know, efficiently for nearly 40 years; but, like the others, he seems to have done no more than hold his position.[70] In addition he was illiterate to the extent that he was unable to sign his name. Although earlier in his life he had married into the Whatman family, unlike his brother-in-law, he left no Will or property that we know of to his family. Richard, who was obviously of a very different calibre, cannot have seen much future for himself in the business as it stood; and, evidently, James must have shared his doubts also.

George Gill, on the other hand, can be seen to-day as one of the most distinguished paper makers of the period operating one of the largest paper mills in the country. But even Gill must have had his difficulties in trying to make and sell White paper in a market that was unreceptive to domestic papers. Dr. John Harris pointed out the fact that not only was Gill forced into making inferior papers at times but he clearly had much spare capacity in his mill, "Tis a very large work, and they could easily make much greater quantities of Paper *if there were demands accordingly*".[71] Since we know that Gill made good countermarked (?) White

---

[70] As an Ancient Paper Maker William Harris snr. must have made White paper at some time in his career, but it is not known whether he used a countermark. A number of "H" countermarks have been noted by the author and, whether this is a coincidence or not, all of these (see fig.4) have been found in English documents, 4 of them in Maidstone documents of 1702, 1705, 1715 and 1729 (KAO P 241 12/4–14); a further one in the Wrotham Overseers' Accounts, 1706–20 (KAO P 406 11/17). Gravell, T.L. (Bib.16 4:May:1981) found another of exactly the same dimensions in a Folger Library document of English origin dated 1703/4; Heawood, E. (Bib.35) also noted two, Nos.364 and 2942, in a Kent and a London document of the early 18th C. These marks appear to be quite distinctive from other "H" marks found in 17th C. documents. It has been claimed, however, that "H" marks are quite commonly found in 17th/18th C. continental papers, not seen by the author, but whether they resemble the above mentioned or not is not known. None of these has been attributed to a given paper maker as yet.

[71] Harris, John Bib.4 191.

Figure 4

"H" and "GG" Countermarks observed in Maidstone Documents
of the early 18th C. (KAO P 241 12/4–12/14)

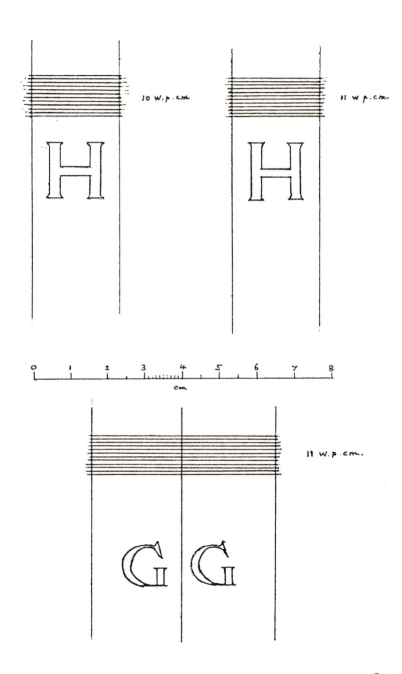

For details see notes 70 and 72.

paper,[72] Harris' verdict does sound as if this spare capacity was not due to any shortage of rags but rather to a shortage of orders.

The position, in fact, was still unsatisfactory so far as the domestic manufacture of White paper was concerned in spite of the COMPANY no longer standing in their way and Duty on imports having been raised substantially on several occasions between 1690–1704.[73] Coleman has pointed out that in 1698 and 1699 there had been two strong pleas from different quarters that the rate of Duty on imported paper was wholly inadequate and should be raised, the later of these two being a Petition from the Principal White Paper Makers to the House of Commons in which it was pointed out that whereas French goods had formerly been subjected to complete embargoes or very high rates of Duty, it was the other sources of imports, from Holland, Italy and Germany, that were destroying English manufacture. In 1703 and 1704 the rates were raised once again and this time on *all imports*, to be followed by the New Duties in 1712, which now included Excise on home production. Finally, a further rise in 1714 led to what Coleman has described as a "markedly protective" state of affairs, in which French imports were penalised with even higher rates of Duty again. It was manifestly these Duties that had stimulated the responses we have seen from William Quelch snr. and William Gill snr. No doubt it also brought new hope to paper makers like William Harris and, although Richard would have been only 11 at the time, the message would not have been lost on him either. But in spite of this protection was the paper industry at that time really any better off ?

There is no doubt that the New Duties, as well as other contributory factors such as the War of the Austrian Succession (1739/40–1748), were decisive in consolidating the position of the British White Paper industry *in the long term* and that the quantities of imported paper declined rapidly from the 1730/40's onwards. Coleman has pointed out that the total imports of White paper had already shrunk by 1743 to 42,000 reams compared to quantities of well over 100,000 reams before 1720.[74] However, during this transitional period when James and Richard would have been formulating the plans for their venture, domestic production was still in the doldrums. It must have been apparent to these two that some blockage in the system was impeding progress. Technologically the Dutch paper industry was now in a leading position and however much protective Duties might help it was going to need something more than these to unblock the system and persuade the London market that British papers were not only competitive but equal in quality, a goal which they had yet to achieve.

One of the principal battles of the past had been fought around the nature of White paper itself. By the early 18th C. the Dutch were producing very superior paper, preferred as we

[72] See Fig.4 for illustration of the "GG" countermark. In addition to Shorter's tentative attribution of this mark to George Gill (Bib.9 248 fig.c) the author has found two, as illustrated, in Maidstone documents of 1706 and 1710 (KAO P 241 12/4–14); in addition Churchill (Bib.3 No.25) illustrates a somewhat similar one found in a document of 1690; and Gravell, T.L. (Bib.16 4:May:1981) found two more in Folger Library documents dated 1686 and 1697. To date these distinctive marks have not been allotted to any paper maker. Other forms of "G" have been noted, sometimes in association with an "S" shaped mark (see App.V. Fig.13).

[73] The subject of Duty on imported paper for this period is an unusually complicated one. For further information the reader should consult Coleman, D.C. Bib.15 66–68 for a general discussion; and 122–126 for a detailed one.

[74] Coleman D.C. Bib.15 cf. p.95 and Table I p.13.

have seen by English printers like Walsh.[75] All the same, though the distinction in theory between "White" paper and other classes of paper may seem to be a clear one, in the period under consideration the borderline between White and the Whited–Browns was obviously much more blurred than this.[76] The flexible attitude adopted by contemporary paper makers and stationers to the differences between White and not so white paper confirms this assertion. Reverting to an earlier period, in their counterclaim to the COMPANY'S declaration that they had brought with them from France a New Invention, that of making White paper, the Paper Sellers had replied by saying that White Writing and Printing Paper "is but a degree of goodness from the Courser Sorts and the making thereof no new invention"; and indeed there had been paper makers in this country then who were capable of making very good White paper, but uncompetitive in an open market and possibly variable in quality and unreliable as a source of supply. Though conditions were more favourable for the domestic manufacture of White paper after the Duty had been increased, the prejudices, now held by the importers, remained; and at the same time the Dutch had improved the quality of their papers markedly by employing the New Technology which they had practised for more than a quarter of a century. There was, therefore, a very real blockage to further progress, a situation exacerbated further by the evasive tactics of the Stationers.

This ambiguity in the definition of White paper coupled with the complexity of the regulations governing the various rates of Duty was turned to advantage by both the paper makers and the stationers in evading the New Duties required of them under the Act of 1712 simply by switching inadequately specified classes of paper from rated to unrated categories. This inevitably led to a very confused state of affairs and did nothing to advance the domestic White paper industry. Coleman has shown that so far as the importers were concerned the quantities of unrated paper rose from ca.4.6% at the end of the 17th C. to 11.6% between 1706–10, 13.3% in 1719–23 and reaching a peak of 49.3% in 1724, when an Act was passed rating previously unrated categories.[77] The less scrupulous paper makers for their part used

---

[75] Chap.III pp.103/104.

[76] One has to recognize first of all that White paper of the late 17th C. was quite different in make–up and character to that of the late 18th C. as indeed the latter was from the White papers of the 19th and 20th Cs. Technically, therefore, it is incorrect to try to group all of these under one convenient heading. (For further discussion see App.V pp.251–260). The only thing that can be said collectively about them is that they represent the better qualities of paper for common uses such as writing and printing, the former generally regarded in the earlier periods as being the best.

In the late 17th and for a great part of the 18th C. White paper in the marketplace would have included all sorts of categories ranging from Superfine and Fine through Ordinary to lower categories such as demi–fine, Seconds and demi–seconds. In the absence of modern physical and chemical quality control standards one can only assume that these distinctions were based primarily on appearance, substance, surface, tear by hand, the incidence of dirt and the paper's ability to bear ink without feathering, a classification probably determined by the manufacturer and put into effect by his sorters and packers, who graded paper as good (bon), retree or slightly defective (retrié), irregular in weight or dimensions (chantonné, court) and broken (cassé); the last categories, if irretrievable, being used either as "outsides" when packing up reams or for separating quires (these terms all had modern usage, but were also used in 18th C. France). The purchaser may, of course, have had different views of quality standards and been strongly influenced by the price being asked.

Although these different qualities were bought and sold as such, the real distinction between one sort and another may not have been so clear. Apart from classifying paper somewhat vaguely as "FINE" or "SECOND" (a distinction whose origins are unknown but which were employed when drawing up the Excise Act of 1712, 10 Anne c.18, based probably on continental practice, and which were used together with *the dimensions of the sheet* for the greater part of the 18th C. in determining the rates of Duty), there was really no definition of "White" paper, a commodity which in these circumstances might be subject to various interpretations when debated in the abstract as, for instance, in Parliament or before a Select Committee or Court.

[77] Coleman, D.C. Bib.15 125/6.

many fraudulent practices for evading the Excise due on their papers.[78] At least one of the paper makers in Kent (if not all of them) was prepared to expose these practices: Samuel Galliot who was at Eynsford for a time.[79]

It is against this background that one has to see what has been described here as the Challenge. James and Richard had been brought up in a White papermaking environment, albeit a provincial one but nevertheless sensitive to external events; and these events had been humiliating to those concerned. In spite of this the two young men were to continue and prosper in this trade; but to do this they must have been aware of the problems that their predecessors had had to contend with as well as those that would continue to confront them in this particular line of business. In these challenging circumstances they would have been extra receptive to innovation and in planning their venture they must have been convinced that they had a practical solution to some at least of these difficulties. This sense of conviction may seem an obvious point to make, but in this case it was a very real one; the investment, and the choice of site, was a very carefully planned undertaking. Again, it is one thing to improve a product, or even the economics of the process, but it is quite another to sell it in a market over which foreign manufacturers and their agents have a stranglehold. The events of the previous era had shown this to be only too true. So from an early period they would have sought the advice and imbibed the experience of their forerunners; their formative years were spent in surroundings permeated by the fluctuating prospects of a market strongly conditioned by a legacy from the 17th C.

The effect of the Monopoly must have left an indelible mark on Gill and Harris that persisted as a warning to the next generation, a lesson not likely to be forgotten in a small community like Maidstone. Although this was an age when technical innovation was taking place within the British paper industry and although new factors like greater Protection were beginning to have an effect, one feels that all these influences might easily have fallen by the wayside had this "challenge" never been recognized and accepted. In due course it was to provide James and Richard with a catalyst, intangible and slender as it may seem, to their early aspirations and, subsequently, to their achievement. But there was still more to come by way of example than this.

The Papermaking Empire of William Gill snr. and its Aftermath

On looking back one can see that George Gill must have been amply furnished with ambition when he decided to leave Dartford and set up a paper mill near Maidstone. The mill was indeed a very large work for those times, powered by no fewer than three waterwheels. In addition one can see that he had an unswerving aim to make good White paper, something that he had learnt at what had once been Spilman's mill. Although later in his life he probably

---

[78] Paper Makers and Stationers, when the opportunity arose, could switch papers to unrated categories by such devices as altering the dimensions of the sheet or by some other form of misrepresentation. For instance, in their Instructions (1722) Excise Officers were told "to observe that Whited–Brown is never sized, but all other Ordinary paper for Printing is sized much or little to make it bear ink". The less scrupulous of paper makers could not have wished for a bigger loophole and to judge from the quantities one finds in collections of old papers of Whited–Browns, and even Brown paper, that bore ink as well as any White paper, they were evidently not slow to take the opportunity given them.

[79] Samuel Galliot, paper maker, who appears in the Eynsford PRs. between 1695–1701 and who is believed to have been associated with Andrew Johannot (Shorter, Bib.12 182) presented a report to the Treasury in 1738 on the subject of Frauds practised by paper makers in order to avoid paying Excise (Coleman, D.C. Bib.15 131).

took no practical part in papermaking, he would have served some sort of apprenticeship at Dartford No.1 mill, estimated as during the late 1660's and early 1670's, under William Blackwell. This early start enabled him to qualify as an Ancient Paper Maker, one of those paper makers referred to in the original Petition submitted in 1689 claiming that they had had 20 years experience to the COMPANY'S 3 or 4. Further, from the accounts we have he would surely have been a leading, if not the most important, figure amongst this select band of paper makers.

It is not known, however, how George Gill came to be involved in papermaking in the first place. There does not seem to have been any earlier family connection with this industry, though George belonged to the fifth generation of Gills to have lived in Dartford. Michael Gyll, his ancestor, had moved there from Hertfordshire in ca.1570 and would have seen Spilman's mill built in his time. So no doubt papermaking was never very far away.

The family would have been classed amongst the gentry.[80] It is not known what sort of occupation his father, Thomas Gill, followed, though histories of Dartford refer to a Thomas Gill as a tailor in the High Street.[81] George married Susanna, daughter of Thomas Cox Esq. of Dartford in 1676 and moved to Maidstone between then and 1680, the first documented record of his presence there, the baptism of a daughter in Boxley. His only surviving son, William, was also baptised there in 1686.

George in the meantime was building up a reputation for himself as a maker of Fine paper. Because times must have been difficult and frustrating for him, he does not appear to have had any plans to expand his business. Indeed, when John Harris visited him, probably ca. 1715/16, he had more spare capacity than he would have wished for.

In 1716, when George must have been at least 61, William insured Turkey mill[82] and from this, coupled with the fact that the latter also insured his own Forstal mill a month later,[83] it would appear that the son had taken over the running of the business at an age of just under 31. Turkey mill, however, continued to be assessed in his father's name until 1721 possibly because his parents continued to live at Turkey Court, the house adjoining the mill.[84] William's mother, Susanna, died in 1720 and this may have prompted his father to leave and go to live with his only surviving daughter, Ann Walter, in Ditton where he died in 1726. He was buried in Maidstone.

In 1716 James Whatman and Richard Harris would have been aged 14 and 13 respectively, the latter by then serving his apprenticeship, presumably under his father at Gurney's mill.[85]

---

[80] For full family pedigree see Burke's "Landed Gentry" 1853 Edition 521–3. For an abbreviated pedigree and other details concerning George Gill see App.IV under the Gill family.

[81] Keyes, S.K. "Dartford, Historical Notes" (1933 and 1938)

[82] SFIP 7379 29:Oct:1716

[83] SFIP 7477 21:Nov:1716

[84] KAO P 40 12/1 (For details see App.III Extracts from the Boxley Poor Rate Book).

[85] This is an assumption only, based on the supposition that the father would have trained the son. In view of Richard's later move to and the rebuilding of Turkey mill there is the remote possibility that he might have trained at Turkey mill and thus been familiar with these surroundings. No evidence at all, however, has come to light yet regarding Richard's training. Neither the Society of Genealogists' Index of Apprentices (1710–1762) nor Crispe's Apprenticeship Indentures contain any references to Richard Harris, paper maker or Richard s.o. William Harris.

From what has been said about him they would inevitably have regarded George Gill as a "father figure" in papermaking, a reliable and imposing figure retiring from a soundly based, though probably not very profitable, business of manufacturing White paper. In the coming years James and Richard could not fail to contrast this image with that of his son, who was to give them a perfect example of what not to do.

William snr. meanwhile had married Elizabeth, daughter and co-heir of John Laurence Esq. of Kent in 1713.[86] Where Laurence lived, or what his social and financial status was, has not been discovered. However, Elizabeth was also the niece of James Brooke Esq. of Lewisham, a London Stationer, High Sheriff of Kent in 1731, and as will be seen later a kind of "fairy godfather" or protector of William and his family. If one takes into account George Gill's Will and subsequent events in William's life, the indications are that he had married himself into a more wealthy circle than that of his father. From 1716 onwards William snr. gives the impression of being a man of considerable means.[87]

The events of the next 15 years were probably the result of a combination of different circumstances. The facts are clear enough, but the causes can only be guessed at. James Brooke had been a London Stationer since 1702 and George Gill must have known him from an early date; in fact he must served as an outlet for the paper from Turkey mill. Whatever the truth of this may be, Brooke soon became involved in William's affairs. For one thing, Brooke, as a Stationer, would have been fully conversant with the current market situation, the implications of the new rates of Duty and the sort of opportunities these would give him, and in turn William, for buying and selling English White paper. It may have been a somewhat over-enthusiastic picture which in the end led to disastrous results for William. Brooke's first involvement with Turkey mill was his payment of the Insurance of the Goods and Merchandise in Turkey mill in 1716.[88] Does one read into this that prior to 1716 the business had not been good, that George Gill was getting too old to run it and that Brooke had persuaded him that it was time William took over and that he would help in doing this? It is possible that there may have been a scene over this or else William's later activities led to strained relations between the two, because the terms of George's Will were not exactly favourable to William. He left everything to his daughter, Ann, and her family and 5 shillings to his son to be paid twelve month and a day after his decease.

The details of William Gill's empire building transactions will only be touched on briefly here.[89] Looking back on them one can see that James Brooke must have been a very important influence acting behind the scenes. Brooke obviously had the interests of the Gill family very much at heart, possibly because his niece may have been a favourite one or because he saw opportunities for his own gain; the answer to this is not known but the evidence points more to his affection for the family than anything else. He looked after them up to the time of his death in 1750.[90] As William snr. got deeper and deeper into the morass resulting from his ever extending involvement in the Maidstone paper industry, Brooke had he chosen could at any time have said "no more"; instead he was constantly bailing William

---

[86] Information Soc.Genealogists 40607.
[87] For further details and appropriate references see App.IV William Gill snr. (1686–1754).
[88] For further details of this Policy, SFIP 7380 29:Oct:1716, see Shorter, A. Bib.12 187.
[89] See App.IV William Gill snr.
[90] See Addendum to section on William Gill snr. App.IV, James Brooke's Will and comment.

out of trouble. One can attribute all sorts of motives to explain Gill's activities but, good or bad, in the end the responsibility for these must be seen as a shared one.

It is not known when or from whom the Gills acquired Forstal paper mill. With spare capacity in Turkey mill it is most improbable that it was George's doing. By 1716 it belonged to his son, William snr. But after his demise in 1731 Brooke evidently acquired it and held it in trust for William jnr. who was later, in 1737, apprenticed to him as a prospective Stationer. After Brooke's death in 1750 the mill reverted to William jnr. who insured it as his mill in 1754,[91] a year after his father's death. Just how long after this the mill remained in his hands is not known; at some point in the 18th C. it passed into the possession of another branch of the Gill family and remained in their hands until 1826. How these other Gills were related to William jnr. has not been discovered. The acquisition of Forstal can be seen as the beginning of William snr.'s entrepreneurial activities, a throwback to the 17th C.

Almost certainly anticipating improved prospects for the paper industry resulting from the new Duties, encouraged by Brooke, Gill began extending his empire in 1717 by setting up Cobtree as a paper mill;[92] following this by acquiring property adjoining Turkey mill, first the Square, land on which he built six cottages,[93] then Christian's corn mill in 1719[94] which he later demolished. In 1720 he set about acquiring the freehold of Turkey mill (still with a lease of 16 years to run).[95] He succeeded in gaining only a moiety of this and a promise of the rest later. As his financial resources became more and more strained by his growing empire, ending in bankruptcy, so his interest in the Turkey mill estate passed more and more into Brooke's hands as mortgagee for this.

Before this took place Gill had been splashing out in several other directions, as the occupant of Lower Tovil mill from 1722–28; he might have played a part in the conversion of Upper Mill, Loose, after 1726; he became tenant of Poll mill in 1728, following Swinnock's bankruptcy; and he had, in addition, interests in brewing and agricultural property. We shall never know what were the exact reasons for this extraordinary involvement. As Thomas Balston has pointed out, his finances were already showing signs of being stretched beyond their limits in 1723 and by 1725 his indebtedness to Brooke as a mortgagee was increased even further. Whether he was a gambler or trying to rescue an ailing Maidstone paper industry one cannot tell; but, whatever his aims were, he does not seem to have seen the writing on the wall and by committing himself to the tenancy of Poll mill in 1728 he overstrained his resources and was made bankrupt in 1729 only to be bailed out temporarily by further loans from Brooke. But even this did not save him and he was bankrupted for good and all in 1731 and was still a certified bankrupt in 1753.

What could have induced all this activity, and what sort of effect was it likely to have had on James and Richard, in their teens at the outset of this extravagant escapade, and just about to enter their thirties at its close ?

[91] SFIP 142250 13:Aug:1754.
[92] See this Chapter pp.153/4.
[93] Balston, T. Bib.1 6/7.
[94] Spain, R.J. Bib.8 88.
[95] The Cripps family let Turkey mill on 4:Sept:1695 to George Gill for 41 years (Balston, T. Bib.1 4).

Dealing with the first of these questions, in the absence of any ledgers or other documents relating to these transactions, one can only surmise on the factors that led to the creation of the Gill empire. To judge from the few pointers mentioned earlier, namely, Quelch snr. converting Basted mill in 1716, William Gill entering the papermaking scene at the same time, Lord Aylesford with Poll mill and the proprietor of Cobtree following suit in 1718, the more ambitious of the paper makers and proprietors, if not others as well of whom we know nothing beyond the fact that they consolidated their positions, must have taken heart from the latest measures introduced by the Government to protect the paper industry. But it has also been pointed out that, particularly before 1725, importers were managing increasingly to get round the New Duties so that it would not necessarily have been the case that renewed efforts by domestic paper makers would meet with success, though in the case of William Gill snr. one would have expected that Brooke was in a good position to interpret the changing scene for him first hand.

Although Coleman has emphasised that too much credence should not be placed on the timing and accuracy of the figures he sets out in his Table of Imports of Paper into London, 1560–1720[96] (London receiving ~97% of the imported paper), they are the only figures available at present to go on and may be seen as a broad indication, at least, of the trends that were taking place. One has to also allow for the fact that Brooke may not have been entirely representative of the purchasers and distributors of White paper. All the same the picture that emerges is one in which imports of White paper are seen falling between 1710–20, from a 5–year average (1710–1715)[97] ~120,000 reams to (1716–1720) ~107,000 reams, this was for an *expanding* market. The actual year–to–year figures show a much greater variation e.g. a high of 158,000 reams in 1710 and a low of 87,000 reams in 1720. A similar up and down trend continued over the next few years[98] with a significant rise in the early 1720's and a sharp drop again to 1730, followed by a big rise in the early 1730's; and from then on the decline is set permanently downwards.

If one had been living at the time, the pace of events and the decisions reached would have been much more closely related to the state of the mill order book than to trends of the kind illustrated above. In short, verdicts may have been that this year, for example, had shown good results, much better than the previous one and that the forecast was good. One can understand then, to some extent, that Brooke and Gill on this basis, unable to see the real underlying trends as we can, could easily have been caught up in the unfavourable situation that they actually made for themselves. With what they thought was better intelligence of the market than would have been available to other local paper makers, they sought to take advantage of whatever opportunities came their way.

Coleman's figures for "rated" paper *output* for this period[99] gives the same jagged up and down curve. These figures, as with the others, portray the state of the paper trade seen as a whole, but the fortunes of the individual within this framework might have presented a very

---

[96]   Coleman, D.C. p.13 Table I.

[97]   Figures for the year 1712 are not shown in this Table.

[98]   Coleman, D.C. Bib.15 Fig.2 facing p.90. The curve shown for imported paper represents total imports. By this time, however, Brown paper imports were negligible compared to White, so that the curve in question can be seen as an indication of the fluctuations in imports of White.

[99]   Coleman, D.C. Bib.15 Fig.4 facing p.135.

different picture. Nevertheless one can visualize Gill's decisions being made on results that were too short term to be sound. There is another aspect to his predicament, namely, that in all his mills he still employed the traditional papermaking process and was pitting his efforts mainly against the Dutch using the New Technology; Gill's margins were obviously too small to protect him from the downturns he inevitably experienced in this business.

In this situation, following the unfortunate and humiliating experiences of the Ancient Paper Makers and the seemingly hopeless impasse in the market for White paper, one can understand the euphoric welcome given to the New Duties by some, at least, of the White paper manufacturers and the ensuing desire to capitalize on the opportunities presented as quickly as possible. Throwing caution to the winds and without realising the dangers of the fluctuating market, it is not surprising that this period resulted in so many bankruptcies.

With regard to the second question, namely, what sort of effect were these events likely to have had on Whatman and Harris ? Would they, for example, have been directly instructive ? In terms of technology the suggestion has already been made that the answer to this would have been in the negative; but in terms of business tactics and new opportunities for them, the events would have been instructive only in so far as they would have served as a warning to them to be cautious in their own undertaking; and, secondly, they may have tipped the balance in the decision as to when, and possibly where, they made their investment. They could not have foreseen Gill's demise; so really the opportunities that this created could only have come when their own plans were well advanced. It would have been the aftermath of these events that gave them their chance to develop and fulfil their ambitions.

In order to arrive at these conclusions one has to make a number of assumptions to bring together the scattered evidence relating to the participants in these events. For those readers who wish to follow the reasoning behind these conclusions the details are given below; those who have a more general interest in the subject may proceed, if they wish, to the discussion of the Aftermath.

One has to recognize first of all that Gill's transactions and their consequences took place within a very small community by to-day's standards[100] and would thus have become common knowledge in a very short space of time. For want of funds of their own most of the other paper makers would have been no more than interested spectators; but, if Gill was not the activator of the Cobtree and Upper Mill conversions, then the *proprietors* of these mills, like Lord Aylesford, would have followed Gill's example; he was obviously the most important paper maker of the district and maybe in their eyes the best informed. So far as Whatman and Harris were concerned, they would not have been in a position to take any action of their own until after 1726, by which time they would probably have been heading in an entirely different direction.

Second, in order to try to discover the sequence of events that led up to Whatman's investment and how Gill's activities may or may not have impinged on these, one has to separate Whatman from Harris and look at them individually.

Although the young Whatman may have spent much of his boyhood in and out of the Harris paper mill, he was not at this stage a paper maker but a prospective tanner. Thus from 1726, when he inherited his father's estate or possibly

---

[100] This is a subject that will recur later (Chap.VII.fig.7), but it is worth mentioning here that the adult male population of
    Maidstone and the papermaking district round it was probably ~2000 for this period.

earlier than this, he would have had to manage his own tanning business and would not have been a free agent.[101] Before this date, if the legend has any substance, it is not beyond the bounds of possibility that he might have paid a brief visit to Holland and got an idea of the advances they had made there in papermaking. After all, he had had some papermaking experience already. The New Technology, however, required practical experience before it could be put into operation and taking all the facts into consideration[102] it is highly improbable that he was the one who received this practical training. As later events were to show, the elder Whatman was a highly intelligent and inventive paper maker,[103] so in these circumstances he could have made useful observations during a visit of this kind, passed on later to Richard who, in turn, may have gone out there to acquire this knowledge practically. All this is no more than a hypothesis put forward to show how Whatman might have been involved and when, should the legend prove to have a factual basis.[104] Whether he ever went to Holland or not, it was Harris, a free agent, who was to put the New Technology into practice. So it is really to Richard that one must turn.

In 1716, when William Gill snr. took over Turkey mill, Richard would have been 13 years old and had probably just started his apprenticeship, obtaining his freedom ca.1722 at the age of 18 or 19. By this time the creation of Gill's empire was in full swing, Phase II of the Maidstone expansion had been largely accomplished and, one would suspect, a feeling of optimism was running through the district, including his father's mill where his eldest brother would still have been working (he did not make the move to Millhall mill until 1724). At this stage Richard may well have wondered what sort of future lay ahead for him in papermaking and where.

It has already been demonstrated convincingly[105] that when Old Mill, Hollingbourne, came to be built it was equipped to meet the demands of the New Technology. In view of this one has to postulate that at some stage in Richard's career news of this improved process had reached his ears; or, at least, developments leading in that direction. It is necessary here to distinguish between the first applications of the Engine which would have brought papermaking only as far as the fringes of the New Technology, in that the paper maker would have been obliged to use a mixture of new and traditional methods to prepare his rags for the vat and either more effective usage or more advanced models where this became unnecessary and the advantages of the new method could be exploited to the full. In both cases practical experience would have been imperative, but much more so in the case of the latter.

News of the first models and their application could have reached him indirectly as a result of the COMPANY'S activities at Dartford No.2 mill (or, if not from there, from some other source since installations were now taking place here and there and news of these must have got around). But with regard to the more advanced application of this technique and the newer models of the Engine, by whatever means news of these reached him, one can only propose that Richard had to go to Holland to learn more about them. The Engine does not appear to have been used in France before 1740;[106] and there had been very few installations in Britain before 1730 and it is thought that none of these would have been as advanced as those ultimately installed in Old Mill.[107] No documentary evidence has been discovered that might throw light on this subject, so at present there is no way of confirming this point. But,

---

[101] In support of this statement, the Loose Churchwarden's Accounts (KAO P 233 5/2) show a continuous assessment made against Whatman from 1725 (£11), when he presumably took over the running of the tan yards after his father's death, to and including 1741 (£11). There is no entry for him in 1742; he seems to have been replaced by William Peene, probably a kinsman through his father's first marriage.

[102] Chap.III pp.125/126.

[103] Not only did the elder Whatman make use of new methods of mould construction as well as develop Wove paper, but it has been suggested that he may have designed an Equation Clock ca.1750. This proposal was made in a letter received by the author from the Science Museum (ref. Sc.L.G. 15/4326 30:July:1981). It has not proved possible, however, to substantiate the claim made in this letter, though the clock was purchased at a sale at Vinters Park in the early 1950's.

[104] For an expression of this uncertainty see Balston, T. Bib.1 146 bottom paragraph.

[105] Chap.III and this chapter pp.134/135.

[106] Le Francois de Lalande, J.J. Bib.23 Art.52.

[107] With regard to the early "Engines" references are made in the literature (Shorter, A. Bib.9 40 and Coleman, D.C. Bib.15 109) to Thomas Watkins, a Stationer in London and a paper maker with a mill at Longford, Middlesex, who in 1713 had made "improvements with great trouble and expense in procuring workmen and purchasing Engines and other raw materials from abroad". This is some 23 years after the first known use of Engines in the British Isles, so one might expect that Watkins' Engines showed some advance on the earliest models. Watkins was bankrupted in 1723, possibly the result of incompetence. But with 10 years experience of the new process one suspects that whether his Engines were more advanced models or not he was unable to use them effectively and had to rely on the Old Technology to help him out. If his Engines had really reached the efficiency of the model used by Whatman and Harris (only 10 years later), one might ask why had their application not been more rapid than appears to have been the case ?

in view of the persistent legend that Whatman had "worked as a journeyman in most of the principal paper–mills" on the Continent, the suggestion is made here, that it was Richard Harris who went abroad and Holland at that time can have been the only place where he could have acquired the experience; this makes better sense than the other version of the legend.

Richard does not figure in James' father's Will (drawn up in November 1721) like his own father, his brother, Thomas, and his sister, Liddea; nor does he appear to have been around in 1727, when his father gave up Gurney's mill. These observations could be interpreted in a number of ways, but one suggestion is that perhaps Richard had shown a certain amount of independence during his training and had decided to leave home, just about the time he was made free, and make his own way in the world. It would have been during these years that one might envisage him training in Holland.

To secure a terminal date for his reappearance the first insurance policy for Old Mill, Hollingbourne, shows that Richard had been installed there as *Paper Maker* by September 1733. William Gill snr. was made bankrupt in January 1731 and his Estate advertised for sale in March.[108] It is most improbable that Whatman would have chosen the Hollingbourne site, made all the plans, negotiated the lease and built the mill all between 1731 and 1733 without Harris being there. (Gill's final bankruptcy, as suggested, doubtless accelerated, but never contributed to their plans.) In other words one sees Richard as having returned to the neighbourhood before 1731, possibly soon after his father's retirement.

For Richard Harris then it has been proposed that he served his apprenticeship from ca.1715–1722; seeing little future for himself at Gurney's mill, and perhaps being of an independent nature as well, he set off to work in Holland having heard of the progress taking place there in papermaking technology and having seen for himself the Fine Dutch papers that were then dominating the market. Finally, it has been suggested that he returned to the Maidstone district before Gill's irreversible demise in 1731. Whether he returned much earlier than this or not, he would have witnessed the collapse of the central pillar of the Maidstone paper industry with Turkey mill being offered for sale shortly after.

William Gill's contribution to Whatman's and Harris' venture can be seen as one of default rather than of intent. Father and son had manifestly provided leadership for the paper industry round Maidstone ever since George had arrived in the district and brought with him valuable knowledge of White paper manufacture, which he continued to develop. Now, in 1731, when Whatman's plans must have been well advanced, Turkey mill, the largest and most important in the district, was ineffective. Materials, skills and outlets that might not otherwise have been available to them must have lent impetus to their enterprise and contributed to its initial success, particularly as there had been no takers of this prize by 1733.

The Aftermath

By 1735, due to action on the part of William Gill's creditors, Brooke had become the chief mortgagee of the Turkey mill estate; and as a result of a further transaction in May 1738[109] he became possessed of the whole estate. In this situation one can see that Brooke, a Stationer, was faced either with running the paper mill himself or leasing it to a paper maker, on which subject he might have sought William's advice. Clearly Cordwell, the occupant from 1732–1735, was a stop–gap and unlikely to restore the fortunes of the mill. Possibly because of his father's earlier involvement at the mill in George Gill's time[110] and the added fact that William must have known him (when he took over Lower Tovil mill in 1722), the next

---

[108] For details see illustration of this Advertisement under William Gill snr. Appendix IV.
[109] Balston, T. Bib.1 8.
[110] See App.IV under The Peter Musgroves.

candidate was Peter Musgrove jnr. (at that time the occupant of Upper Tovil mill).[111] In the event he only lasted a year. To judge from his subsequent performance as a paper maker at Upper Tovil either Brooke did not consider him as a suitable tenant capable of returning the mill to a profitable state or Musgrove felt that it was more than he could manage. Whatever the reason Richard Harris stepped into his shoes, a very significant pointer to Harris' superior technological advantage over the other paper makers of the district.

One wonders whether this move was a result of Richard's initiative or whether Brooke had learnt of the goings on at Hollingbourne and had invited him to take the lease. Brooke, as chief mortgagee, would almost certainly have had the final say. The Policies show that Whatman resumed the responsibility for insuring Old Mill in Harris' tenure on 27th December 1736 and Harris, in the very next Policy, his Stock in Trade at Turkey mill; but who insured the mill itself has not been discovered, it might have been Brooke or the Cripps family. In less than 18 months from this date Brooke had become the owner of Turkey mill and by this time he must have appreciated that Whatman and Harris were a new force in the papermaking world and something to be reckoned with.

It has to be remembered that Harris, very probably aided by Whatman, was operating the New Technology at Old Mill and compelled to work Turkey mill under the old system, by comparison a very time–consuming and wasteful way of making paper. By 1738 both parties must have recognized that the profitability of Turkey mill was unlikely to improve under these conditions. One might see then that by mutual consent (albeit a Hobson's choice for the Stationer), Brooke redeeming the outlay he had made on William's behalf and Whatman and Harris visualizing the transformation they could make at Turkey mill, converting it into a really productive and profitable papermaking facility, the conveyance of the estate from Brooke to Harris was the only possible solution and would be advantageous to both parties.[112] The full significance of this will be appreciated all the more when it is realised that this decision and the ensuing rebuilding of Turkey mill took place at a time when the effect of the War of Jenkins' Ear and the Austrian Succession lay in the future. Whatman and Harris must have had considerable confidence in this extension of their enterprise without the foreknowledge of the Wars to which Whatman's success has so often been attributed

As Whatman and Harris were virtually newcomers to this field, one feels that Brooke must have continued to serve as an outlet for the papers from Turkey mill, which in view of its reconstruction and the early death of Richard in November 1739 would have fallen mainly, if not entirely, to Whatman's lot. Quite possibly it may have been through these channels that Walsh obtained his Whatman paper in 1740.[113] One might also speculate that in what appears to have been a combined operation on the part of Whatman acting in support of Harris whether the former may not have made "IW" countermarked paper *before* August 1740. It remains to be seen whether further work on Walsh's printings of Handel's music provides evidence one way or the other on this point.

---

[111]   Brooke became the chief mortgagee on the 23:April:1735 and Mr. Musgrove was first assessed for Turkey mill in June of that year.

[112]   Brooke became the owner of Turkey mill on the 23:May:1738 and according to Balston, T. (Bib.1 8) Brooke signed an undertaking to convey the freeholds of Turkey mill and adjoining property to Richard Harris on or before 1st August. The transaction actually took place on the 29th September and the details of this are also given in this account.

[113]   Chap.III p.104.

To complete the narrative, William Gill jnr., the youngest member of William snr's family, was apprenticed to Brooke on the 5th July 1737,[114] took up the livery of the Stationers' Company in 1747 and became a partner of Thomas Wright, his brother-in-law, as a wholesale stationer in London in 1753.[115] Later the younger Whatman used Wright and Gill not only as one of his principal stationers but as bankers through whom he paid a number of London accounts.[116] To judge from the mutual trust they had for each other, it seems almost certain that they had also acted for the elder Whatman after Brooke's death in 1750.

It can be seen from the above that it was the aftermath of William Gill snr.'s attempt to build a papermaking empire that in the end provided Harris, and subsequently Whatman, with the opportunity to fulfil their joint ambition and extend their enterprise. It was through James Brooke that this was realised and the link with the Gill family maintained. Finally, it can be seen that it was through the timely introduction of the New Technology that this enterprise progressed in the way it did, providing a solution to the impasse that had trapped the domestic White paper industry in its uneconomic clutches for so long.

---

[114] As indicated in the text William snr. took over the papermaking business from his father in 1716, but the first assessment made against him in the Boxley Ratebook is not until 1722/3, by which time it is thought that his father had left Turkey Court for Ditton and that William and his wife had taken over there. However, it has not proved possible to locate William snr.'s domicile then and even less so later. It has been reckoned that William jnr., the youngest of William and Elizabeth's family, must have been born ca.1723-5. There was an elder son named, significantly, "Brooke", who died without issue in 1744. (For further details see App.IV William Gill snr.).

[115] For further details of William jnr.'s life and the more than successful restoration of the family fortunes see App.IV.

[116] Balston, T. Bib.1 51. Further references to Wright and Gill are made in Chapter VII.

Chapter V

EXTERNAL INFLUENCE:
ADVANCES IN PAPERMAKING TECHNOLOGY (1)

The setting and the events leading up to 1740, the year when Whatman ceased to be described as a tanner and thereafter was styled a paper maker, have all been related in the preceding two chapters. The stimulus provided by the confrontation between the Ancient Paper Makers and the COMPANY together with the activities of the paper makers of the West Kent Region, and marginally those of the Maidstone area, have been presented as basic factors motivating Whatman and Harris in the conception and undertaking of their enterprise. But, beyond this, there was really no other known source of influence in Kent that could have taken them a step further than a conventional response to these influences, in other words to achieve something more advanced than the status George Gill had acquired in his time. It has already been suggested, for example, that Richard Harris might have gained experience of the New Technology in Holland during the 1720's, a suggestion that would solve a lot of the difficulties that would otherwise follow had this not been the case. The fact is that after 1740 Whatman built up an increasingly distinguished reputation for himself in the manufacture of Writing paper equal to, if not better than, the best quality of paper which had hitherto been imported. So the question has to be asked where did the technical knowledge that enabled him to do this come from, if it did not come from his locality ?

One is forced then to look for other, external forces that may have brought about the advances made by Harris and Whatman in producing papers of such superior quality. Some of these influences have already been touched on in the previous chapter and quite probably stemmed from practices employed in the mills of the West Kent Region and had reached the ears, at least, of the Maidstone paper makers during Whatman's formative years. But many of these clearly came from earlier, and sometimes more diffuse, sources and the purpose of this and the next chapter will be to examine these origins in greater detail.

In general terms it might be said that from approximately 1670 onwards significant technical improvements in the papermaking process of one sort or another, though some of them only minor ones, had been progressively introduced into the paper mills of this country, finding their way slowly in the decades that followed through the different regions and finally *coming together* most especially in the hands of Harris and Whatman at Maidstone during the period 1733–1740 in what might be regarded as a watershed between the traditional process and the new papermaking technology. The origins of these innovations in most cases are not known precisely and they may have reached their Maidstone destination by all sorts of different routes such as feed-back of information from the more sophisticated business centres like London; journeymen on the move from one mill to another; or the chance meeting of a traveller from the Continent with an English paper maker. This is after all how Dr. Johann Becher, a German Councillor and author, on his way to England in 1680, first recorded in a work published in 1682 the existence of the Dutch "Engine" (later known as the Hollander

Beater) in the Zaanland and who was to see one of these installed in a German paper mill 30 years later.[1]

Other refinements in the process obviously came from France and were employed either by organisations like the COMPANY or, more specifically, by individuals like the Johannots, Nicholas Dupin, Denis Manes, le Gaultier and many others; in addition, it has to be remembered that many Huguenot refugees settled in Holland and no doubt continued to communicate with their compatriots in the British Isles. New ideas and methods must also have accompanied the arrival of William III and his entourage in 1689.[2] Finally, as mentioned in Chapter I,[3] this period was characterised by the flood of Patents for various sorts of inventions, so that as well as continental sources of innovation one must also take into account our own domestic contribution. All would have provided fuel to fire the changes that ultimately produced the watershed referred to above, innovations born in the 17th C. and maturing in the 18th, creating a latent capability within the domestic industry which in the right hands would eventually be exploited successfully and release British papermaking from the impasse in which it still found itself. These innovations will be discussed separately, the lesser ones in this chapter and, undoubtedly the most important, the Hollander Beater in the next.

Before examining these subjects it would be as well to recall that all the worthwhile innovations were brought together in the case of Kent, if not for the United Kingdom as a whole, by Richard Harris and Whatman. Whereas Whatman provided the capital for the investment and no doubt lent moral and technical support as well, the credit for the practical application of the combined innovations must surely go initially to Richard Harris as the professional paper maker and only later its fulfilment and further development to Whatman after Harris' premature death; it certainly did not come to a halt as a result of this. Neither must one overlook the role of Ann, formerly Harris and later, Whatman in this enterprise. Although she and Richard were not married until 1734, she must have been in on the deliberations that preceded her husband's involvement. Later, evidently with close support from Whatman, she continued the operations at Turkey mill after Richard's death in November 1739 until the marriage settlement of July 1740; and, finally, during the interregnum following Whatman's death in 1759 and the succession of her son in 1762 she held the fort once again and her position as head of the business was recognized by a countermark of her own.[4]

The COMPANY'S Technical Contribution

Because of the difficulty of pin-pointing precisely the sources of innovation the impact of the COMPANY'S technical contribution can only be seen as diffuse rather than direct in its effects on the White paper industry. Collectively it undoubtedly had an effect, but separately

[1]   Voorn, Henk Bib.51 8.
[2]   Ca.1693 several Dutch names appear under baptisms in the All Saints', Maidstone, PRs. Shorter, A. Bib.9 24 also refers to Dutch paper makers coming over to this country as early as 1682 and cites the case of one Gerard Eversten (identified by Voorn) who worked as a vatman in a mill near London and to teach the others in this mill the art of making, sizing and finishing paper.
[3]   Chap.I p.7
[4]   For details of Ann see App.II under Ann Carter of Leeds Village. For her countermark see App.V fig.15.

some of the factors in this clearly had origins some years before it received its Charter in 1686. The contribution can be seen as (a) general; and (b) specific. In both cases one sees the hand of Nicholas Dupin at work. He was one of the COMPANY'S most dynamic members and was at the heart of many different enterprises.

Although the Revocation of the Edict of Nantes (1685) is often cited in the literature as a milestone in the history of various industries in Britain, many influential refugees had arrived in this country from France long before this date. In fact Nicholas Dupin had become a naturalised English subject as early as 1670;[5] Peter le Gaultier was working for Eustace Burnaby during the latter part of the 1670's. With this in mind and taking the general issue first there is evidence that Dupin and some of his colleagues were already working an unidentified paper mill in Hampshire by ca. 1685 and had imported foreign labour from France for this purpose at considerable risk to themselves.[6] At a later date, to judge from the quotation, Dupin and his associates had also found it necessary to bring out of France "excellent workmen......to set up severall new-invented mills and engines........ not heretofore used in England".[7] This partiality for foreign skills is also apparent in the inventory to the COMPANY'S Dublin paper mill made in 1690, a document that shows not only Dupin's controlling hand over this venture, but lists in addition to the two to be considered here a number of other most interesting items which will be referred to later.[8] Items (2) and (3) in this inventory read as follows:

Item (2)   For sending for Five *Dutch* White-Paper-Makers out of *Holland* and bringing them over to Ireland

> The Dutch had considerable papermaking interests in France at this time and a great deal of so-called Dutch paper imported into Britain was in fact made in France. However in 1690 we were at war with France so that Dupin may not have had any option in obtaining skilled White paper makers. Consequently the word "Holland" has been underlined here and the implications of this will be discussed below; see also under item (3)

Item (3)   For Artists, and French-Paper-Mill-Wrights brought over to Ireland to build Paper-Mills, and ten Irish Carpenters to work under them.

> The word "Artists" obviously refers here to those who pursued some practical science, artificers, craftsmen or mechanics. It will be noted that Dupin has not specified "from France" in this instance as he and his colleagues had done in the case of their earlier mill. So these mill-wrights, though French in origin, may have been refugees and come to Dublin from England.

From these two items it will be observed that the COMPANY, or more specifically Nicholas Dupin, sought skills for use both within the paper mill and for its construction, presumably because he had not been impressed by what he had seen in this country. In terms of general influence the skills of the imported paper makers would have been disseminated with time, absorbed first by the COMPANY'S own employees and, later, by other English or Irish makers of White paper. It seems unlikely that much would have been learnt about the making of the actual sheet, a skill that English paper makers already possessed, but rather in the

[5]   Pollard, M. Bib.19 footnote 3.
[6]   Pollard, M. Bib.19 224 and 226.
[7]   Shorter, A. Bib.12 32. Shorter, A. Bib.9 24 refers to Daniel Roussillon, another immigrant and, later, of Up mill (Hants) as visiting the Guelderland in 1688 to recruit Dutch paper makers.
[8]   Bagford, J. Bib.22.

acquisition of refinements in process know–how from rag–sorting to sizing and finishing and in various pieces of equipment used, such as, for example, in moulds and felts, both of which will be examined later in this chapter in more detail.

The skill of the mill–wrights is also significant, because Dupin's requirement implies that the British mills that he had seen (not only in Dublin, but his earlier one in England) were not up to French standards for the manufacture of White paper. One cannot be sure that criticism of this kind would have applied to Turkey mill. All the same, apart from the fact that the incorporation of Engines in their mills required them to build or rebuild new mills, Peter Archer and Whatman may have come to recognize too that the conventional mills of this country were not good enough for the manufacture of good quality White paper.

From the outset it was obvious that the immigrants had a high opinion of their capabilities, claiming that they made "as good Paper, of all sorts, as any made in Europe". Despite this not a great deal is known about the performance of the COMPANY beyond the fact that to start with, at least, they prospered and to have done so within the higher price bracket to which they were restricted one might assume that the quality of their paper must have been good and those samples of it that have been identified bear this out. In addition, to judge from their use of the more or less anonymous countermark "COMPANY",[9] their aim was to maintain a uniformly high standard among their various mills. Cameron has suggested that at one point they may have been operating as many as 20 paper mills; he bases this figure on notes found on the back of the Yale copy of the COMPANY'S defence in the House of Lords.[10] Both Shorter[11] and Coleman[12] place this figure no higher than 8 mills. (To these may be added their mills in Ireland and Scotland). As seen in Chapter IV one of these mills was at Dartford in Kent, this being their nearest point of influence to the Maidstone district; and, since this was not acquired by them until 1693, it is probable that the operations there would have benefited from practical experience gained in their other earlier mills.

Some of the COMPANY'S contribution, in practical terms, may also be reflected in Mr. Million's account of the papermaking process as he described it to John Houghton in 1699; this could have come from either father or son.[13] It has been suggested that this account may have been French in origin. If so, their association with either the COMPANY or Dupin himself might explain this. Both Henry Million snr. and jnr. (and a Mrs. Sarah Million) were partners in more than one of Dupin's ventures e.g. his Dublin paper mill and in the King and Queen's Corporation for Linnen Manufacture in England. Alternatively, Henry Million had been closely associated with Eustace Burnaby[14] and in 1678 had championed his "making of white paper fit for writing and printing......and brought to perfection etc.",[15] an achievement which almost certainly derived from Peter le Gaultier's expertise. So it is possible to see both le Gaultier and Dupin as the source on which this account of the process was based. As well as these contacts with immigrant paper makers, further support for a

[9]   As noted in Chap.IV fig.3 + n.21 some of their papers also carried the countermarks of individuals as well.
[10] Cameron, W.J. Bib.18 19.
[11] Shorter, A. Bib.9 26.
[12] Coleman, D.C. Bib.15 74 and note 3.
[13] Houghton, J. Bib.20 Vol.II 410 ff.
[14] See Chap.I n.31,40.
[15] Hazen, A.T. Bib.5 316.

French origin comes from the use of an obscure French term for describing the top grades of rags.[16]

The reason for dwelling in such detail on Mr. Million's account is because it is a very perceptive account of the process and one that was to remain almost unaltered in the literature for the next three–quarters of a century.[17] The process that he describes was the traditional one into which one might read a rather greater emphasis than one might ordinarily expect on certain refinements such as a more selective method of grading rags; an informative description of rag fermentation and stuff preparation (although it is curious that in view of the COMPANY'S use of Engines no mention is made of this fact, which suggests that the account may have derived from le Gaultier rather than Dupin); a fairly explicit description of pack–pressing; likewise taking down; an unusually specific account of the preparation of size; sizing and drying, and finishing, all of which are treated in an instructive rather than a purely descriptive manner (though this, of course, could have been due partly to Houghton's editing). It is not suggested here that Mr. Million's account would have been known to or read by contemporary paper makers,[18] but it is of interest in that it illustrates for us practices that would have been employed by the COMPANY and which obviously rubbed off later on to other paper makers.

More specifically than any of the examples given above of the COMPANY'S general influence, the Inventory of skilled labour and materials used for Dupin's Dublin paper mill in 1690[19] allows one to look behind the scenes, the bricks and mortar of the structure in contrast to Mr. Million's Flow Chart of the process. It is a very revealing document. Although it may reflect Dupin's own papermaking practice, since he was interested in the prosperity of the COMPANY as a whole one could take it that the matters covered by this inventory would have been applicable for the most part to its other mills. The Inventory is comprised of 37

[16] At the beginning of Mr. Million's account, in his description of rags, he uses a very unusual term for their classification, namely "grobin fine", "grobin second" and "grobin tres". No contemporary or earlier source for this term Grobin is known. However, Desmarest, in 1788, (Bib.21 573) defines Grobin as "nom qu'on donne en certaines provinces aux lots de chiffon qui résultent du travail des trieuses. On en distingue trois, qu'on appelle grobin fin, grobin second, grobin troisième". Dupin came from Saumur and le Gaultier probably from Angoulême and it would be interesting to know, if this term, Grobin, was peculiar to either of these districts.

[17] It was used, for instance, by Chambers in all editions of his "Cyclopaedia" from the second up to 1781; it appears in the first two editions, more particularly the second, of the Encyclopaedia Britannica (1771, 1781); Dennis Coetlogon (1745); Barrow (1756); Croker (1764); and even George Selby Howard (179?). It seems that Goussier's account, some 50 years later, in Diderot's "Encyclopédie" borrowed the word "tribble/treble" from Mr. Million (Labarre, E.J. Bib.36 65 note 4). Although it is known that from 1693 onwards the Académie des Sciences were intent on preparing an account of the papermaking process, not realised until 1706, no contemporary French account remotely resembling Mr. Million's has been discovered. In any case the Académie's account was lost.

[18] Professor Coleman has remarked that Mr. Million's name has a certain fascination about it (Bib.15 76/79). It appears to have been a very unusual name also. There are only 5 entries for Million/Millian in the Society of Genealogists Great Card Index during the 17th C.; 3 in Nottinghamshire, 1 in New Brentford and 1 in Rotherhithe where the earliest mention is made, 1616. A Mr. Henry Million, a Clothier of Coventry, made a Will in 1657 (Inf.Soc.Genealogists 24:Apr:86). It is of additional interest to note that the names of Thomas and Mary Million appear in the Boxley P.R. (KAO P 40 1/1) between 1677–1686; and, later, a John and Mary Million in the All Saints', Maidstone PR (bapt.). The name Million does not appear in the Wagner collection of Huguenot pedigrees which suggests that, unlike the Dupins, they were not immigrants.

[19] Among the partners listed in this document (Bib.22) are (i) The Corporation of White Writing, and Printing Paper in England (in other words the COMPANY): (ii) Nicholas Dupin Esq., the Patentee; and (iii) both Mr. Henry Million snr. and jnr.

items, two of which have been mentioned already. Brief comments on some of the other more important items are given below:–

Items 2   Further comment.
& 3   In spite of the fact that Dupin and his colleagues may have had great difficulty in obtaining French craftsmen earlier, a situation now aggravated by war, it is thought that his insistence on obtaining Dutch White paper makers from *Holland* may have been inspired by other motives. For instance, not only were the French becoming aware of the fact that the Dutch were making great advances in the manufacture of White paper but, by 1690, Dupin had unquestionably become informed of this also; and, possibly, aided by Huguenot refugees known to him and who had settled in Holland he was anxious to introduce these improvements into his own mill (cf. the case of Daniel Roussillon).[20]

As will be seen later others in England had already gained information of the existence of the "Engine", possibly before Dupin had, and since there is no evidence that the French had any practical knowledge of this at that time (not in use in France until 1741 and even after this it was a mixture of the Old and New Technologies), Dupin would have been looking to Holland and *not* France for this information. He was certainly in possession of an Engine by this date (see below) but needed the skills to work it.

Item 4   For an Artist in Paper–Mold–making brought over to Ireland.

The question of mould construction and the changes that were to take place in this will be discussed as a separate issue in this chapter, in particular a possible explanation for the noticeably wavy chainwire marks in his Dublin mill papers.[21] Although paper had been made in Ireland since 1590, the main reason for Dupin wishing to import a mould maker may have been that he was unable to obtain the superior skills he needed from local sources.

Item 10   For 43 Hammers made in London, and the materials thereunto Belonging, and one Mortar and a Sharp made also in London and brought up by Land and Sea to Dublin.
Item 11   For an Engine to beat stuff for the Paper brought from London to Dublin.
Item 35   For several sorts of Brass Wyer to work in the Engine, to make Molds and Strainers for the Mortars.

These three items will be taken collectively. First, a distinction is made here between a Mortar with Hammers (a Sharp is a corruption of "Shaft", OED) and an Engine for beating the stuff. Likewise item 35 makes a distinction between wire required for three different purposes, one in all probability for the Chess in the Engine; one for mould–making; and one quite specifically for the strainers in the mortar thereby distinguishing it from the "Engine".

The interpretation placed on these items is (a) the disparity between the number of hammers and the one mortar is seen as Dupin importing one trough for the Irish carpenters to model others on, but not relying on them for the hammers which may have required materials and special skills in their construction not available locally; and (b) quite separate from the mortar Dupin had imported one of the Dutch "Engines". Whether the latter had been made in London or imported from Holland is not clear, but the logical inference is that coming from London it must have been used already somewhere in England and before 1690.

Despite the fact that the Zaan mills in Holland, where the Engine had originated, never employed the fermentation process for their rags, when the Hollander was first introduced elsewhere, it was the practice to start with for the paper maker to ferment the rags as before, wash and dismember them in the traditional mortar (hence a requirement for the strainers in these, these usually being hair sieves but may have required additional protection or support from the wire specified); and then to give the stuff

---

[20] See this chapter note 7.
[21] Pollard, M. Bib.19 Plates I and II.

its final treatment in the Engine. Dupin's double installation would, therefore, have been compatible with this practice; but there is one unresolved question relating to this proposal.

The inventory indicates that his Engine must have been equipped with a chess. The chess in the Hollander Washer/Beater is used for removing dirty water when the rags are being washed and to be able to do this the rags must still be in discrete form otherwise the chess would very quickly become blocked.[22] In other words if the rags had been partially prepared in the mortar, he could not have used the chess in the Engine, indeed the rags would have already been washed once.

An answer to this may be that Dupin preferred to base his stuff preparation on the Old Technology though at the same time planned to experiment with the New, but not rely on it. For instance, strong rags may have been processed one way, using fermentation; and weaker rags by the other.[23] As will be seen in the next chapter the new methods required very different skills from those needed for the traditional process and the Dutch paper makers of the Zaanland had had long experience in this field, whereas Dupin did not possess this. In spite of importing Dutch paper makers he clearly could not have risked the success of his venture on them alone.

The point to note in all this is that there is positive evidence here of an Engine being employed in a COMPANY mill in 1690 even though it may have been only a primitive version of one. Further confirmation that the "Engine" was a Hollander is to be found in *Item 14* which refers to "several sorts of Iron Works" including the "Engine Wheels" as distinct from other ironware such as Plates for the bottom of the Mortars; Rings for "Sharps". The mortar shaft was connected direct to the Waterwheel, whereas the transmission for the Engine would have involved a train of toothed gear–wheels with iron rims.

Item 15   For a considerable number of coals for the Drying–Loft to dry Paper.

This is an interesting sidelight on drying practice; most mills of the time would have relied on air–drying the paper, but here the coals are unequivocally linked to drying paper. Possibly because of the humid nature of the Irish climate Dupin felt that the use of heat was a necessary insurance against failure to dry his paper. No other contemporary examples of this are known and it is nearly 100 years to the next reference, which seems to have been the use of auxiliary heating in the Drying House at Sauchie, Stirlingshire. Thereafter, 1795, it appears as a regular item in paper mill insurance policies.[24]

Item 16   This item is concerned with wood (Deal–Boards) for various uses including cisterns, gutters and, what is interesting, "Chests to hold the beaten stuff". The word Stuff Chest is still in use to–day and this is the first known example of the use of this term in the literature on papermaking.

Item 17   For several 100 yards of wrought white–Cloath, for several sorts of felts to put between every sheet of paper when it is in making.

It is assumed that the wrought white cloth referred to here was a woven woollen cloth. The subject of hand–felts will be discussed more fully later in this chapter. It is only necessary to note here that Dupin specified "white" for his cloth.

[22] See Chap.VI Plate 13 for the positioning of the Chess and Chap.VI p.230 for description.
[23] For further elaboration see Chap.VI 219 and Chap.VIII pp.359/360.
[24] Thomson, A.G. Bib.44 49.

Item 24 For several sorts of French, Dutch and English Moulds to make several sorts of Paper.

This item is interpreted as referring to moulds of different dimensions to meet orders for papers made in sizes peculiar to the countries named. In other words to make papers that would match imported products and satisfy customers who had used these.

Item 28 For Copper Pistolets and Pipes to make fire in the Vaults (Vats) and to convey the Smoak.

It is not known when pistolets were first used; Dard Hunter suggested during the 17th C.[25] Though they may not have been used universally in Dupin's time, he evidently considered them necessary for making White paper.

The pistolet (or pot hole) in old vats was a copper brazier inserted into an aperture in the side of the vat in order to warm the stuff. Whereas its function was partly for the benefit of the vatman, its principal use was to make the stuff easier to work on the mould. The viscosity of water is halved between room temperature, 15°C., and body temperature, 37°C., and it would therefore separate from the stuff much more rapidly during the sheetmaking process when warmed.

Item 29 This refers to various vessels for holding liquids; but amongst the uses listed is one for "basons to fling water to wash the mortars and hammers". To anyone who has worked in a paper mill this demonstrates how little things have changed. The 20th C. beaterman would use his handbowl, as it was known, to fling water against the sides of his hollander or the roll to wash off stuff still clinging to them after emptying.[26]

Item 30 For Crippings (corruption of Scrip, obsolete, meaning small pieces) of Gloves and Calfs Pates, and other things to Size the Paper.

These are merely other materials used as a source of gelatine for preparing size.[27]

Item 36 For a Loom and Tackling to weave the Brass Wyer.

This reference to a "Loom" and to "weaving" should *not* be interpreted as a method for producing woven wirecloth. It refers here to a method of fabricating a Laid cover for a mould or whatever other use a Laid wire construction might have been used for, as in the Chess for instance. (This subject is discussed in more detail below.)

Most of the other items in this inventory are concerned with the supply of various materials either for papermaking, construction or administration (such as account books, minute books and so on). Apart from the interesting light this document throws on the requirements of the Dublin mill, which incidentally was a two-vat mill, it also gives the impression of being a very businesslike record which, in turn, gives a favourable picture of COMPANY administration which, if matched by their other mills, must have had its impact on the more receptive paper makers in other sections of the industry.[28] Undoubtedly, albeit at a much

[25] Hunter, Dard Bib.37 173.
[26] Whether or not the handbowl had the function in Dupin's time as it had later, certainly by the 20th C. its main function was to allow the beaterman to inspect the state of the stuff that he was beating. Using a pair of handbowls he would take a handful of stuff from the beater, place it in one handbowl, dilute it to nearly the consistency used in the vat and when mixed pour it gently from one bowl to another to judge its length and the absence of unwanted strings, knots or clumps.
[27] (See Chap.I p.40).
[28] These comments must be seen in the context of both the short and the long term effects of the COMPANY'S performance during the first half of the 1690's, their most successful period, on other sectors of the White paper industry and to

(continued...)

later date, the success of operations at Turkey mill owed a great deal to the tight control that the two Whatmans maintained in their business affairs. (In this context it has to be remembered that literacy amongst domestic paper makers may have been rare in 17th/early 18th Cs.; hence the absence of records of their activities.)

Before leaving the subject of this inventory Dupin rounds it off with a number of comments on local circumstances that favoured this investment.

"Ireland is a proper Place for the said undertaking, the Water and Air being good, Raggs plenty and Cheap, being sold in Dublin for 5 l.(£5) per tunn, in London 10 l.(£10)

Rents of Mills, Houses, and Store–Rooms being cheap. Working Mens Wages being easie, because Provisions and Lodging cheap; Sizeing–stuff plenty, and cheap to Size Paper.

Paper in Ireland yields 20 l. per cent more than in England, there being a great Duty on all Paper Transported thither"

In concluding this section on the general influence of the COMPANY'S operations on the contemporary paper industry, mention may be made of the fact that in its embryonic form, in the 1680's, the skirmishing referred to in Chapter I that went on in the field of Patents must also have had a decidedly quickening effect on other sections of the industry and anyone else who may either have obtained or were applying for Patents. The Patents in question are discussed separately below. Beyond stating the obvious fact that the COMPANY must have had a beneficial effect on the domestic paper industry in the long term and brought many refinements to the process and were perhaps responsible for introducing the first tangible Engine to this country, it is difficult to attribute any specific innovation to any one of its members. However, there were two developments in which Dupin figured prominently and in this sense his contribution can be regarded as being more specific. One of these concerns the methods used for constructing the papermaking mould; and the other his attempts to develop the linen industry of this country. In neither case does he, personally, seem to have achieved any success. Nevertheless his efforts, certainly in the case of improvements to mould construction, eventually bore fruit.

Improved Methods of constructing the Papermaking Mould

Among the documents relating to Dupin's activities there are two statements that make an interesting conjunction. One of these is the item, No.36, in the Dublin mill inventory which refers to "a Loom and Tackling to weave the Brass Wyer"; and the other is a claim made by him to the Privy Council in 1694, when he was trying to set up a paper mill in Scotland, that "He had arrived at the art of making all sorts of fine paper moulds, as good or better than any made beyond seas and at a far cheaper rate, insomuch that one man may make and *furnish* more moulds in one week than any other workman of other nations can furnish in two

---

[28](...continued)

distinguish these from the state of the COMPANY in 1697 as portrayed in a contemporary report (MSS House of Lords X New Series 1712–14, 160) describing them as technically ignorant, using poor quality rags, with several mills idle and beset with other misfortunes. At this time the market was being flooded again with imports (see Chap.I p.20) and the COMPANY under the terms of its charter was the most vulnerable part of an industry going through bad times.

months' time".[29] Even if one allows for a considerable margin to cover exaggeration in this claim, it is unlikely that he would have made it at all unless there was some substance in it. It is also rather more specific than the average Patent claim of the period.

Only the bare essentials of mould construction will be covered here.[30] As described in Chapter I[31] the mould is made up of a rectangular wooden frame reinforced and made rigid by a series of wooden ribs running parallel to the short sides and spaced, typically, about 25–30mm apart. To complete the mould in those days a Laid Wire Cover was constructed on top of the Ribs and was then sewn to them with fine wire (see Plate 9).

In more recent times the Laid cover has been fabricated separately and then placed on and sewn to the mould after; but in Dupin's day covers were constructed *in situ*.[32] There appear to have been many different ways of making Laid mould covers[33] and we have no means of knowing exactly what method Dupin's mould-maker used, although Dupin himself was probably familiar with one of two common methods used in France, both technically the same but one working from the top (back edge) of the mould downwards as illustrated in the 1698 engraving of a French mould (see Plate 5) and the other, as illustrated here, from the bottom (the front edge) upwards.[34] Because many of the later improved methods worked from the bottom upwards, for convenience, Desmarest's description of cover fabrication[35] will be followed here.

As illustrated the mould was fixed in an inclined position with the long sides horizontal. Along the upper surface of the lowest member (the front edge) pegs were fixed in holes in line with each rib. To each of these pegs a *pair* of fine wires, the chainwires, were fixed with a bobbin on the other end of each. A Laid wire (much thicker and more rigid than the chainwires) was placed at the bottom (i.e. parallel to the long edge) and lying *in between* the twin wires of each pair of chainwires.

Having positioned the Laid wire, the mould-maker would then twist each pair of chainwires to lock the Laid wire in position. After completing the twists *for each pair* of chainwires the mould-maker then placed another Laid wire parallel to the first, between the chainwires once again, and then repeated the twisting operation. The twists determined the spacing between each Laid wire and sometimes, if wider spacing was needed, more than one twist was made between each Laid wire. And so the process was repeated until the mould face was

[29]   Pollard, M. Bib.19 231.

[30]   A more detailed account is given in Balston, J.N. Bib.76.

[31]   PLATE V and Chap.I p.43.

[32]   According to E.G. Loeber this may not always have been the case. Certainly early Spanish moulds may have been put together differently.

[33]   For an extensive account of these see Loeber, E.G. Bib.45 Chap.VI.

[34]   Loeber, E.G. (Bib.45 21) claims that normal French practice was to work downwards, but to judge from contemporary literature this may not have been the case. Certainly the 1698 engraving showing the downward method was used unaltered by Le Francois de Lalande in 1761 with no intimation that a method working upwards was practised (Bib.23). And yet, our PLATE 9 was used in Diderot's "Encyclopédie", the Plates being engraved in 1767 and later borrowed by Desmarest (Bib.21) in 1788. The fact that these two illustrations were used so close in date and both evidently regarded as standard practice coupled with the fact that Lalande did not trouble to amend his nor Desmarest comment on the newness of his suggests that both methods had been used in France from an early date. Moreover, neither of them mention the use of a "loom", probably devised by Dupin and certainly used in the U.K. in the elder Whatman's time.

[35]   Desmarest, N. Bib.21 498–500.

Plate 9 181

THE MOULD MAKER

(Top) The Mould Shop (Bottom) Fabricating the Cover

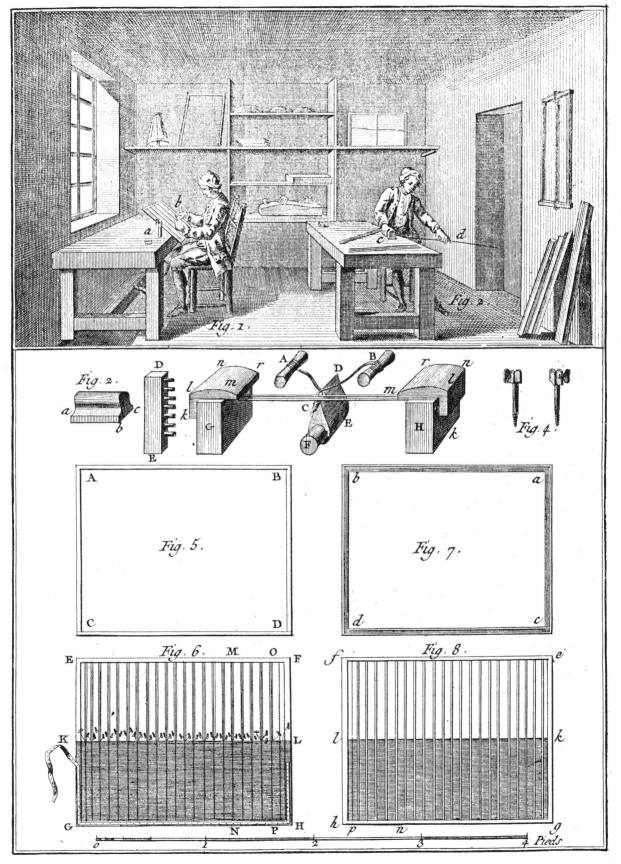

Engraved for Diderot's *Encyclopédie* in 1767

completely covered by Laid wires lying parallel to the long sides and spaced and locked in position by twisted chainwires *placed above and following the lines of the Ribs underneath*.[36]

In this method of fabricating covers (as part of the process of making the moulds and *"furnishing"* them), obviously the most time–consuming operation would have been the manipulation and twisting of each pair of chainwires for every Laid wire. It could, for example, amount to more than 5000 twisting operations for an ordinary Foolscap mould (and, of course, more than this for finer and larger moulds). If Dupin then was looking for dramatic savings (a thing he was *very* keen on) in the time needed to construct a mould ("more moulds in one week than any other workman.......can furnish in two months' time"), undoubtedly he would have sought first and foremost an alternative method for twisting the chainwires.

Apparatuses for twisting all the chainwires *simultaneously* as each Laid wire was placed in position are known to have been in use during the 18th C. though none of them can be dated precisely before Elliot's Patent of 1793.[37] In modern times this apparatus has been termed (incorrectly in common parlance) a "loom"; incorrect though it may be, this usage evidently has a much longer history than one might imagine e.g. the reference in Dupin's inventory "for a loom and tackling to weave the Brass Wyer".[38] It may be taken as certain that this did *not* refer to a paper loom for making woven wirecloth.[39]

Dupin's claim that his mould–maker could make and *furnish* moulds much faster than others suggests strongly that he was using a mechanical device or "loom" to achieve this performance. Whether the loom referred to in the inventory was an apparatus of this sort or not, the fact remains that by the mid–18th C. Whatman's mould–maker (and others) were capable of fabricating *extremely* fine and *regular* laid covers for moulds. For example, one of his laid covers for a Crown size mould would have involved over 25,000 chainwire twists and such is the regularity of the wirework it is inconceivable that this could have been achieved without the use of a mechanical device.

[36] Needless to say there were many variations of this; sometimes the chainwires were placed in between the rib spacings. In Antique Laid moulds this leads to the illusion of double chainwire marks when one of these is, in fact, a rib mark and not another chainwire mark.

[37] Joseph Mosely Elliot's Patent No. 1959.

[38] According to the OED there are two of several very different meanings of the word "Loom" which could apply in this connection; (a) An implement or tool of any kind; and (b) a machine in which yarn or thread is woven into a fabric by the crossing of threads called respectively the warp and weft. In Dupin's inventory the now obsolete form (a) was, as events showed, the one intended. (See also Note 39 below).

[39] In the course of work carried out by the author for his study of "The Development of early Wove Papers" (Bib.76) it emerged that the history of the Loom weaving of wire to produce woven wirecloth is a singularly obscure subject. Early references in the literature to "weaving" wire almost invariably refer to the kind of "Loom" mentioned in the text above, namely, to a mechanical device for twisting chainwires in order to bind laid wires.
     That wire had been woven on a simple handframe much earlier than this is not questioned; but the state of the metallurgy of brass at the end of the 17th C.; the method of smelting the ores from which the metals for the alloy were extracted; impurities in the metals themselves, particularly zinc, were such that it would have been virtually impossible for the wire produced at that time to have withstood the mechanical distortion of weaving on a proper loom.
     Rapid advances were made in the technology of copper and zinc extraction during the first half of the 18th C. and although woven wirecloth of a fine quality had become available by the 1750's (albeit still a scarce commodity), it seems very doubtful from the author's research that either a loom of this sort or wire of the right quality would have been available for such a casual use as Dupin's in 1690. In any case, even if a proper loom had been available, it is difficult to imagine what Dupin would have used it for. Hair sieves were normally used in the mortars; and, if as we believe, he installed a Hollander, the "Chess" would have been constructed in the manner of a Laid wire cover.

However, from the wording, the device referred to in Dupin's inventory was clearly some sort of apparatus that *already existed* and had, perhaps, been used formerly to make certain kinds of wire structure, but had not as yet been applied to the fabrication of mould covers; either this or that the method was in the process of being developed. Whichever was the case the notion receives some support from the irregular nature of the chainwire marks in some of the papers made in his Dublin mill. These suggest that his mould–maker was trying out a new method of constructing laid covers and had experienced teething troubles, which one would expect.[40] This state of affairs would also account for the fact that Dupin's claim was not made until some four years later. Summing up, it looks as if Dupin and his mould–maker were either the inventors of this kind of "Loom" or else the first to introduce it into the British Isles.

Nicholas Dupin's interest in the British Linen Industry

Dupin's other contribution to papermaking, it might be argued, lay in his interest in promoting the British Linen industry. Miss Pollard[41] has drawn attention to the fact that on three separate occasions, in England, Ireland and Scotland (to which may be added Jersey and Guernsey) Dupin had either set up or attempted to set up or been otherwise involved in both papermaking and linen manufactures. She has pointed out that the dual interest may have been coincidental; but, on the other hand, the inference is that such an interest may have originated from Dupin's realisation that one of the weak points in the British White paper industry was the absence of a thriving domestic source of flax for the linen industry and, in due time, for the supply of rags from such a source. The question is, does this notion bear closer examination ?

Whatever the real influences may have been that changed the course and the status of the British Linen industry, one has to remember that, though the projects were short–lived and that Dupin ran into considerable opposition, it is a fact that he initiated these ventures *parallel to* his White paper companies; and it is also a fact, as numerous petitions of the period indicate, that linen rags for papermaking were in short supply.[42] Indeed, this must have been one of the first things that he noticed when he came to England; good quality linen rags were essential for White paper manufacture and he had come from a country where rags were always surplus to requirements.

---

[40] Dupin's improvement can only have been a first step towards what was to come later, namely, a device for producing "twisted" twists between all sets of Chain–wires simultaneously; the twisted twist was clearly preferred in the 18th C. It is conceivable, however, that an alternative technique may have been tried initially either by him or others claiming improved methods of making Laid mould covers.
Loeber (Bib.45 21 and fig.47a Ex.2) illustrates another method which, he believed, had been used in early times; this was cross–twisting, the chainwires merely crossing between each laid wire. This technique could have been applied to all sets of wires at once and accelerated by, say, the use of some form of heddle rod to create natural and artificial sheds for inserting the next laid wires. Use of such a method might account for the irregular wiremarks referred to in the text above.

[41] Pollard, M. Bib.19 227/8.

[42] It is of interest to note that Burnaby's Patent for improved paper (1675) preceded Dupin's by 11 years; and that he also applied for a Patent connected with the manufacture of "fine linen" (1687) three years before Dupin's undertaking to introduce the French method of bleaching and manufacture of fine white linen in partnership with Mr. Million, the latter formerly being closely associated with Burnaby. It is possible that Henry Million may have been a descendant of the Henry Million, a Clothier of Coventry (see this chap. note 18) and thus had an interest in textiles; this might account for Million's association with Dupin. But what prompted Burnaby's Petition ? Does one see le Gaultier behind this ?

England at this time was heavily dependent on continental sources for its linen, France being its principal supplier for fine linen. With England constantly at war, first against the Dutch, another important source, and then followed by the prohibition of French imports between 1678-1685 and shortly after by a prolonged war with France, the English paper industry could be seen to be in a very vulnerable position with regard to its *future* supply of rags. Whether one can ascribe such altruistic motives to Dupin's interest in linen manufacture, as suggested here, or not is a debatable point. He had, after all, been a refugee, a fact that must have coloured his attitude to the question of goods imported from France. At the end of his Dublin paper mill inventory, for example, he states that the "Undertaking.....will be of great advantage to the Kingdom, by Employing their Poor and *keeping the Money from sending to France, and other Foreign Parts*". But to judge from his multifarious activities, it seems more probable that his intentions were really typical of the entrepreneur, namely, to have as many irons in the fire as possible in case any one of them should fail.[43]

If as a by-product of these policies Dupin's aim was ultimately to increase the supply of raw material for papermaking and he would have had more than 20 years to appreciate this deficiency, then, and this is the important point, his interest would have had to have been a long-term one. The cultivation of flax was by nature slow; the production of linen, particularly bleached (for White paper), a laborious process;[44] and the journey from textile to "rags" an even longer business, a matter of decades even generations.[45] *The "rag" state was an essential requirement in those days for papermaking.*

Mr. Million does, however, preface his account of the papermaking process with the remark that "Fine paper may be made of anything from flax and hemp dressed clear from the Bun (stem or stalk), but it is chiefly made of linen rags". But new fibre or new cloth, on the one hand, is very difficult to beat without producing excessively "wet" stuff[46] which in turn is difficult to handle at the vat though it might have been marginally easier with stuff prepared in the Mortars. (In modern times and with more efficient machinery "New Pieces", as they were known, were used sparingly in paper furnishes on account of this). And on the other hand doubt must inevitably be cast on the practicability of Mr. Million's claim that *"Fine"* paper could be made from flax waste because for one thing it would not have been in a bleached state. That there was a continuing interest in the latter is shown by the fact that the Dublin Society offered a premium in 1758 for the "best Writing or Printing paper made of the waste of flax".[47] Though there is some contemporary evidence to show that brown or coloured papers could be made successfully from material such as this,[48] it must have been a foregone conclusion, if for no other reasons than those of dirt and the presence of shive,

---

[43] In addition to all his paper and linen enterprises Dupin also had interests in a company for working mines and minerals in Scotland (Coleman, D.C. Bib.15 61). And undeterred by the failures of his earlier ventures he was petitioning for a Patent in 1700 to run a ballast office in Dublin (Pollard, M. Bib.19 227).

[44] See App.V. pp.200 ff.

[45] See App.V. p.204.

[46] See App.V. note 91.

[47] Pollard, M. Bib.19 228

[48] Scott, W.E. Bib.43 Vol.III 71. There is a reference to a Patent application by Thomas Neale (1692) which was concerned with making brown and coloured papers "without using coarse or fine rags or linen cloth, but out of a material of which store may be had in England and Ireland". Neale's petition was unsuccessful. There is another reference also (JCHI. IV [1796]526 10:Nov:1747) to Francis Joy of Randalstown, County Antrim, using the refuse of flax and tow for making paper in 1747 (presumably the brown paper that he made at his "third" mill).

that there would have been no successful outcome to the Society's offer (certainly none have come to light). To reinforce this point, it is well worth reading the younger Whatman's comments in a very similar case when he was presented with a sample of Wild Cotton by the Society of Arts in 1774.[49] Briefly, he points out that vegetable substances "*in their first state are too gross and full of soil*" to be used without expensive pre–treatment. (It was to be another half century before processes were available and established in the factory for boiling and bleaching materials like this with the aid of chemicals economically). Whatman, in his reply, stresses the fact that the best materials for papermaking in his day (and with his equipment) were "Linnen and Ropes, *after* they are unfit for the purpose for which they were made"; moreover these were cheaper than other materials.

Reverting to the subject of the supply of the rags themselves, it has been said that the quantities of linen in use in England during the 17th C. were very large[50] so that the endemic shortage was clearly due to other factors such as (a) the actual amounts surviving to reach the "rag" stage; and (b) the difficulty of collecting discarded material efficiently. In the letter referred to above Whatman endorses this view that the Public could have been more careful in saving their rags – "in most families of opulence, where the largest quantities of the *best* rags are made, the fewest are saved, as I am afraid they are generally thrown into the fire from an inattention to, and a contempt of, their worth".

The answer to the question posed earlier is that Dupin's twin interests cannot be conveniently or logically linked as a single enterprise in the short term for supplying raw materials directly to an industry that was starved of them. But it is still possible, in view of the strikingly parallel nature of these interests, that he may have been thinking of the future. In the event all of his linen ventures were short–lived; the Irish Corporation failed in 1692; the Scottish enterprise ran into difficulties because of entrenched opposition to it; and the English Company, in spite of difficulties encountered by an earlier Patent granted to Charles Howard, fared rather better. All the same it had ceased manufacture, and probably trading as well, by 1698.[51] Despite all this Dupin's efforts may have provided a stimulus during a critical period in the history of the British Linen industry, because shortly afterwards the situation changed dramatically. In this wider sense it is conceivable that later generations of British paper makers, including Harris and Whatman, might have derived some benefit from his actions.[52]

---

[49] Whatman's reply is too long to quote here in full. It does, however, make most instructive reading and is printed in its entirety in Balston, T. Bib.1 36/37.

[50] A clear distinction must be made mentally in this context between the quantity of linen textiles in use and the quite disproportionately smaller quantities of rags subsequently derived from them. In spite of the wars and the prohibition of French imports referred to in the text and despite the effects of ever–increasing rates of Duty levied on imported linen, especially after 1690, linen continued to arrive in quantity from abroad by devious routes and sometimes falsely labelled as a type of cloth which carried a much lower rate of Duty. It has been estimated that in 1719, for instance, about 33% of the linen entering this country was being smuggled in from France and Holland, the countries hardest hit by this imposition (Harte, N.B. Bib.65(a) 84/85). By this time the Irish linen industry was getting into its stride. So, apropos of potential supplies of rags for the paper industry, the effect of the wars and the duties need not necessarily have led to any diminution in their quantity for this particular period.

[51] Scott, W.E. Bib.43 Vol.III 90ff.

[52] In spite of many earlier attempts to rectify this deficiency the various linen industries within the British Isles remained undeveloped until the 18th C. The market had hitherto been dominated by imports from Europe; in fact, linen was a major import and second only to groceries in value (Harte, N.B.Bib.65(a) 74/75).
The principal factor that led to a change was the introduction of higher rates of Duty imposed, as it happened, in an entirely irrational manner and for political rather than any mercantilist reasons.

(continued...)

In fairness to Dupin it might be said in conclusion that *we*, today, are seeing the whole of the linen textile/rag situation in retrospect. Dupin, obviously, viewed it without the benefit of the information that is available to us. He was confronted with an acute shortage of good white linen rags and he took whatever steps that lay within his power to correct this deficiency. He had come from a country where shortages of this kind did not exist.

The indications are that the COMPANY contributed positively to the progress of the British paper industry not only in assisting in advances made at that time in process technology, but also in bringing a new broom with them which led to a raising of standards throughout the process; better management of materials; improved equipment; possibly better methods of constructing mills; and efficient administration. If other members of the COMPANY resembled Dupin in any way, his energy and drive, then their impact on the locality must have been significant, if only in the long term. Moreover men like these would have been quick to exploit new ideas emanating from domestic sources. Examination of the Dublin mill inventory shows that there, at least, Dupin was drawing on Dutch sources for advancing his capability and that this must have included acquiring operating experience in the use of the Hollander Engine. He, himself, appears to have contributed to improvements in the method of constructing covers for papermaking moulds; and among his other activities he may have done something to stimulate the linen industry in the British Isles and thereby increase, indirectly, the supply of rags for the next generation, though on the face of it this does sound doubtful. He did, however, make strenuous efforts to preserve for better *utilisation* the limited quantities of good linen rags at the nation's disposal, probably one of the lasting benefits that the monopoly brought to the domestic paper industry. It will be recalled that the opponents of the COMPANY had maintained that any shortcomings in the manufacture and supply of White paper in the Kingdom was not due to lack of skills but to the fact that "Materials proportionable to the quantity required could not be had here to make a sufficient supply". The effect of the monopoly must have concentrated the minds of the paper makers who made this statement; the answer lay in a more effective method of saving and collecting rags and better management of this resource when they possessed it.

[52](...continued)

After previous attempts to foster a linen industry in Ireland (including the schemes of Strafford and Ormonde, and Dupin), linen manufacture took off in a surprising manner between 1705–1750 in the north with the export of plain linen cloth, for instance, rising from 500,000 yards to 11,000,000 (Gill, C. Bib.38 Chap.III). The reasons he gives for this are complex and are discussed further in App.V pp.190–191.

This expansion owed a lot to the 1696 Act which granted duty–free access to the English market, which Harte (ibid. 92) has described as the then largest Free Trade area in Europe and the fastest growing in the 18th C. Duty–free access was not granted to Scottish linens until after the Act of Union in 1707, so that their development was behind that of Ireland; but, jointly, low labour costs and duty–free access gave them great advantages over the English Linen industry initially. As a result of a series of further complex measures and the introduction of a system of bounties, mainly during the earlier half of the 18th C., English flax production and, more important, the manufacture of linen goods from imported flax and yarn underwent a very remarkable expansion between ca.1740–1790 (Harte, N.B. ibid. 103–108). During this period foreign imports rose to a peak in 1750 and then declined.

In spite of this major development of a domestic linen industry, the British paper industry remained chronically short of linen rags during the 18th C. In fact the import of rags rose twenty–fold during this period to meet an estimated four-fold increase in production (Coleman, D.C. Bib.15 Chap.IV). All the same, the author has made a very approximate calculation from Professor Coleman's figures to show that between 1750–1800 ~80% of the total raw material used was supplied from U.K. sources and nearer 90% for the 1730's (for the basis of these calculations see Chap.III n.78).

Other Sources of Influence on Process Technology

1. *The Papermaking Patents*

As noted in Chapter I the latter part of the 17th C. was characterised by a flood of Patents for various sorts of inventions. In an article entitled "Paper making in England, 1682–1714" Rhys Jenkins has described some of these.[53] He has suggested that many of these Patents were grants for monopolies conditional on setting up manufactures in this country not hitherto carried on rather than Inventions *per se*. An instance of this may be seen in the affair of the COMPANY and their Charter. In their opening CASE the COMPANY claimed that though James II had "granted divers Letters–Patent to several Persons, for their respective Inventions, of making White–Writing and Printing–Paper......He, by the advice of his Council, united the separate Interests, and Incorporated them, by the name of the Governor and Company of White–Paper–Makers; and granted them the sole Power of making White–Writing and Printing Paper for Fourteen Years". But one is seeing here that in this Charter, to avoid a conflict that "threatned the Ruin of the Whole", a number of individual Patents lost their identity and were merged into the operations of one undertaking, a point considered again later. Whereas some of these Patents, and other contemporary ones belonging to their rivals such as those granted to Eustace Burnaby or assigned to Lady Theodosia Ivy, may have received protection on the grounds that they were a "new manufacture never practised in any of our kingdoms or dominions", is it legitimate, as Jenkins' comment suggests, to assume that none of them contained any novelty in their claims ?

The applications for these Patents were not accompanied by Specifications, as became customary in the latter part of the 18th C., so that it is well–nigh impossible to assess their significance on this basis. One has to try instead to determine their element of novelty, if any, by indirect means. Disregarding for the moment the validity of the claims, one might group these Patents under three headings:–

(i)   New inventions never practised either at home or abroad.

(ii)   Fundamentally new methods or processes that had been developed abroad and were now being imported into this country for the first time.

(iii)   The importation of refinements of processes already practised in this country.

Using the method suggested above the Patents relating to the manufacture of White paper are shown in Table V, divided into the three groups. The grouping has been made on a purely arbitrary basis because we have no real means of knowing the validity and substance of the claims. However, it has been said that Hagar's Patent was much sought after and for this reason it may well have been Hagar's own invention and not an imported idea. Hence the reason for placing it in Group I. Just what this Patent embraced is a matter for speculation and the subject will be examined separately.

---

[53]   Jenkins, Rhys Bib.34.

TABLE V – LATE 17TH CENTURY PAPERMAKING PATENTS

	DATE	PATENT No.	PATENTEE	CLAIM
GROUP I	1682	222a	George Hagar (originally a Dyer)	A new and extraordinary way of making paper by sizing all sortes and kindes of white, blue, purple, and other coloured papers and pastboards whatsoever *in the mortar*, whereby the sizing is totally intermixed and incorporated in the masse, whereas in the way now practized the sizing is received but superficially, conducing to the bettering and making the said commodities more dureable and usefull.
GROUP II	1682	220	Nathaniel Bladen (Inner Temple)	Hath attained to the art and knowledge of an engine, method and mill, whereby hempe, flax, lynnen, cotton, cordage, silke, woollen, and all sorted of materiall, whereof all manner pastboard and of paper for writing, printing, and for all other sorts of uses hath beene, or may be, made, are prepared, and wrought, into paper and pastboard, much speedier and cheaper than by the milles now used.
	1684	242	Christopher Jackson (Rither, County of York. Gentleman)	By his great industry and expense in improving... writing and printing paper, he hath made great progresse therein, and amongst severall other improvements hath invented a mill or engine, either for wind or water, which dissolveth, whiteneth, and grindeth raggs, and prepareth all other materialls whereof paper and pastboard hath been... made in farr less tyme than the mills hitherto in use doe, being a new invention never practiced in this kingdom.
	1691	271	John Tyzacke of Wapping	A way by an engine to be worked by one or more men... applicable for pounding and making raggs fit for paper.
	1695		Peter Oliver	An engine for beautifying of all manner of linen, cloath, calicoes etc., paper, pastboard by glazing, slicking and smoothing of the same much better and finer than now is used or done.
GROUP III	1675	178	Eustace Burnaby Esquire	The art and skill of making all sorts of white paper for the use of writing and printing, being a new manufacture never practised in any of our kingdoms or dominions.
	1685	246	John Briscoe (a Salter)	With great paines, study, and charge, in many experiments [he] att last hath invented and found out the true and proper art and way of making English paper for writing, printing, and other uses, both as good and serviceable in all respects, and especially as white, as any French or Dutch paper (which hath been the great defect of all other pretenders and undertakers, who have hitherto had patents for making paper here)... etc.
	1686	249	Nicholas Dupin Adam de Cardonnel Elias de Gruchy James de May Robert Shales	The art of making all sorts of writeing and printing paper, and to imprint our (James II) armes upon such paper.

There were a number of other contemporary Patents and Petitions connected with papermaking which have not been included in this Table either because they are not relevant to White paper manufacture or were never granted.[54] They have been mentioned to show that the Table opposite represents only a small selection of the many Patent applications of this period. This may be contrasted with the fact that no further papermaking Patents were issued after 1695 until 1747; and even then only three between 1747–1790.[55]

In Group II there are two Patents that clearly refer to the Hollander Engine and the conversion of rags into papermaking stuff; a third one, Tizak's, appears to be of lesser interest than the others; for one thing it is dated 1691, by which time the Engine was already being used by the COMPANY; and, again, it is not at all clear whether it refers to the new Engine or, more likely, to an improved method of operating the mortars, perhaps using tidal power. Opinion on the other two seems to vary considerably,[56] mainly dismissive or disbelieving in tone. But there are a number of features relating to them which demand that we should consider them more seriously. Firstly, it has been shown earlier in this chapter that the COMPANY had installed an Engine in their Dublin mill in 1690 and all the evidence points to it having been the new Dutch beating engine. Furthermore, the inference to be made from the mill inventory is that it was an item already available and, in all probability, in use in England. Somehow then one has to explain how this came about. Secondly, inadequate though the specifications may be, there is something in both Bladen's and Jackson's Patents that indicate the claims are connected with this type of new Engine. Both, for instance, stress the point that rags may be prepared for papermaking "much speedier and cheaper than by mills now used" or words equivalent to that; and, as will be seen in the next chapter and also in Appendix V, it is unlikely, given the linen rags in use at that time, that this could have been achieved using hammers and mortars. Moreover, Jackson claims that his mill not only "dissolveth" (breaks) the rags, but "whiteneth" them (washing using the chess) and "grindeth" them (beating). Lastly, there is the position of Nathaniel Bladen in this situation. Although Jackson was granted a Patent for his "Invention", one seems to hear nothing further about him or his Patent, possibly because Bladen's preceded his by two years or that he might have been

[54] For example, they refer to commodities like Blue paper; or various others for which the Petitions were unsuccessful like le Gaultier's (1691) for making White paper (see Chap.I); Neale's (1692), already referred to (this chap. note 48); and Hutton's (1692) connected with a mill or engine driven by water or wind to work 80 stampers or more at once etc. And yet another category where it is uncertain whether a Patent, in the sense used above, was granted or whether it was just a privilege conferred by the Crown, an example being the case of the immigrant paper maker Denis Manes, who had been authorized to use the English Royal Arms as a watermark in his papers shortly after his arrival in this country, ca.1683/4 (Shorter, A. Bib.12 159). In Manes' case there is an example of a bit of arm–twisting by the early forerunners of the COMPANY. Cardonnel, Dupin and Gruchy petitioned for similar privileges from James II a year or so later, in 1685, "to improve the art of making all sorts of writing and printing paper, and to imprint our (James II) armes upon such paper" while Manes had been imprisoned in Caen for 11 months after trying to obtain French paper makers for Cardonnel et al. When Manes was released he was forced, on his return to England, to sign over his privileges to the others (Hazen, A.T. Bib.5 328 note 12).

[55] Shorter, A. Bib.12 61 note 4.

[56] Shorter, A. (Bib.12 62 note 16) is a little non–committal about Bladen's claim, stating that it (the Engine) may have been known to and adapted by him as early as 1682 (slightly more forthcoming in Bib.9.23). Cameron, W.J. (Bib.18 4) makes a highly ambiguous remark that neither Bladen's nor Jackson's Patents were essential to the technique of papermaking. Coleman, D.C. (Bib.15 63) asks the question, did the English Patents cover such a device as this (the Hollander Engine)? and comes to the conclusion that there is no adequate evidence that the Hollander was introduced into England through the Patents or at this time.

out of touch with the mainstream of papermaking in the south of England.[57] Bladen, however, remained in the centre of things and *there must have been a reason for this*.

In point of fact Bladen's position in relation to the opposing factions in White paper manufacture is not clear. Bladen, like Jackson, was a gentleman and also a lawyer of the Inner Temple. He does not appear to have had any practical connection with papermaking and it may be for this reason that he has been regarded as nothing more than a dilettante in this respect. But, possibly in the manner suggested in the case of Eustace Burnaby, Bladen may have come into possession of the particulars of the Hollander Engine in return for services to an immigrant or someone in a similar position; or he might even have met Johann Becher in London or read his book (published in 1682). By whatever means he came by this information, the fact is that the paper makers were interested in his Patent. This in itself does not necessarily imply that the claims were particularly significant; it will be recalled that many Patents in name were (a) flimsy in their claims; and (b) used purely as a basis for raising capital for a Joint Stock Company.[58] The COMPANY obviously used any material it could get hold of for just this purpose. In their CASE (1689) it was asserted that the Charter of 1686 had brought together all the best letters Patent and they appear to have been under the illusion that they had acquired the rights to use Hagar's, Bladen's and even Burnaby's Patent of 1675, these being merged with Briscoe's (1685) and that of Dupin and his associates (1686) which included the right to imprint arms[59] on their paper, a privilege they had appropriated from Denis Manes.[60]

These claims were disputed vigorously in 1690. Hazen has shown conclusively[61] that Lady Theodosia Ivy had acquired both Burnaby's (which meant le Gaultier's expertise) and Bladen's Patents ca. 1682, very soon after the latter had been granted; and she still owned them. This is an example of a paper maker's genuine interest in the contents of a Patent as opposed to using it as a device for floating a Joint Stock Company. Since Burnaby, through the agency of le Gaultier, had produced good White paper, it is reasonable to place Bladen's Patent in the same realisable category. However, Lady Theodosia disappeared from the papermaking scene soon after she had made her objections in 1690 and no evidence has survived to indicate that she ever owned a mill with an Engine in it, *whereas it is a fact that the COMPANY did*. The situation is complicated in that there are references in the literature to Bladen being associated with Dupin and others at some stage prior to 1689, although his name does *not* appear in the full list of Petitioners for the Charter in 1686[62] nor in the first list of Officers and Assistants;[63] whereas Cameron claims that it does.[64] Whether a member of the COMPANY or not and whether they had the right to use his Patent, in real terms there

---

[57]   Shorter, A. Bib.12 49 note 109.

[58]   See Chap.I p.8.

[59]   Cameron, W.J. Bib.18 4.

[60]   See this chap. note 54.

[61]   Hazen, A.T. (Bib.5 332) quotes from a clause in the private Act of 1690 "This Act shall not prejudice any right or interest which Dame Theodosia Ivy alias Brian hath.....by vertue of any conveyance or assignment made unto her by Nathaniel Blaydon Esq." followed by a second quotation from the debate about the Act in the Commons (15:Apr:1690) relating to a Petition from Lady Theodosia "that about 8 years since she purchased several patents of Eustace Burnaby and Nathaniel Bladen Esq., the first that were ever granted for white paper and they are not yet expired".

[62]   Overend, G.H. Bib.66 203.

[63]   loc.cit 204.

[64]   Cameron, W.J. Bib.18 4.

is no doubt that they installed the new Engine in one or more of their mills. A possible explanation for this may lie in Lady Theodosia's and Bladen's inability to translate his Patent into practice. It has been emphasised more than once that the Dutch Engine was something totally new in papermaking process technology and would, therefore, have required prior training and operating experience for it to be effective (see Chapter VI). Hence one sees Dupin importing "Five Dutch White–Paper–Makers out of Holland", the inventors of and the only country to possess these Engines at that time.

Summing this up one might say that the source of influence on the paper industry of this country for this change in the process stemmed originally from Bladen's Patent of 1682, but only became a practical reality through the efforts of Dupin and his colleagues. It is not known how Bladen became aware of this innovation or whether, prior to 1690, action had been taken by Lady Theodosia, Bladen or others to import or construct Engines in the London area. What is certain is that by 1690 the new Engine had arrived here, though probably in a small and primitive form.

Apart from Tyzack's Patent, mentioned previously as being rather late and unenlightening, a Patent for glazing paper granted to Peter Oliver has been included in Group II. Quite what innovation this referred to is a matter for speculation. Traditionally paper had been smoothed with a slicking stone, usually polished flint or agate, that was rubbed over the surface of the sized sheet, sometimes with the addition of a little fat. Later, probably in the 17th C., the "glazing" process was extended by increasing the size of the stone and facilitating its movement using a water powered shaft to raise and lower it, although it was still moved and guided manually.[65] At some point, however, two other methods came into use (a) the glazing wheel; and (b) the use of a pair of heavy wooden nip rolls. The latter were in use early in the 18th C. and both may have been known in the late 17th C. so Oliver's patent could refer to one of these. It is not thought that Whatman would have resorted to any of these processes when finishing his Writing papers; it is likely that he would have relied much more on obtaining a relatively smooth surface by using the Exchange process to reduce the basic grain of the paper and then pressed the sized sheets in a screw press in the Salle. Slicking tended to leave striations on the paper surface and Oliver's claims do refer to "slicking" as well as to "glazing"; the glazing wheel would have produced a buffed rather than a glazed finish; and, finally, wooden rolls, if Whatman had ever used them, would have had *no lasting effect* on the surface finish. All the same one cannot be sure whether he had experimented with any of these methods or not. The so–called "glazing" of paper had its main applications in other directions e.g. in papers used for marbling, wall papers (possibly), Press papers[66] and the like

[65] Duhamel de Monceau, M. Description des Arts et Métiers (1762) "Art du Cartier" XXIX Travail du Lisseur and Planche II.

[66] The subject of Press papers was raised in Chap.II n.88. Contemporary with the other Patents discussed here was another connected with Press Papers (and thus not included in the Table) which arouses interest partly because of its claims and partly because it must have been of papermaking interest rather than one for Company flotation. Robert Fuller, a Baysmaker, was granted a Patent in 1684 (No.238) for "the art and mistery for making of paper and pastboard in whole sheets without piecing for hott and cold pressing of cloath, which will be of great advantage to the woollen manufacture and never practised in England". This "invention" probably refers to the use of a larger mould than used hitherto to make sheets that would cover narrow (three quarter) loom widths of cloth. Certainly by 1693 Colombier had been experimenting with the use of these larger moulds whose manipulation was assisted by pulleys. Narrow loom widths were 30 inches and sheets of Colombier dimensions were 34½ inches wide. This idea for making larger sheets of paper could have stimulated Whatman's interest in this subject at a later date. (q.v.Development of Antiquarian. Balston,T. Bib.1 28–34; App.IV)

and sometimes may have employed additives like starch or the use of heat (ironing) to obtain an effect. (The surface characteristics of paper is a complicated subject which the author has examined more fully elsewhere).[67]

Comments have already been made earlier about the Patents listed in Group III of the Table. Although it has been argued that the Ancient Paper Makers, if not other English paper makers, could make tolerable quality White paper, it was also pointed out that due to the shortage of good white linen rags in this country, and the totally inadequate method of collecting them, domestic paper makers could not always afford to be too fussy about rag-sorting and the consequent incidence of dirt (shive etc.) which can be seen in some of their not so white papers. In France, where there was an abundance of rags and where the industry was carefully regulated, the quality of White paper was bound to have been more *consistent* than our own. So it is not surprising that Patents for making what might be considered as Whiter, or cleaner, paper abounded. This is just one example of a refinement that justified the existence of these Group III Patents. Burnaby's, the earliest of these, must have been based on Peter le Gaultier's experience of papermaking in France.

That Burnaby was not a practising paper maker himself, and therefore not fully conversant with all the refinements, is more or less confirmed by Briscoe's Patent granted 10 years later, where he claimed that his papers were "especially as white, as any French or Dutch paper *(which hath been the great defect of all other pretenders and undertakers, who have hitherto had patents for making paper here)*". This is an obvious dig at Burnaby's claims; or rather at the papers being made ten years later by Lady Theodosia who, as seen, had acquired Burnaby's Patent in 1682. The quality may well have declined by then, because Burnaby's "own" papers stand up very well in comparison to the COMPANY'S products.[68]

One could go on through the process identifying other stages where similar improvements no doubt came within the claims of the patentees, in the beating of the rags; better quality moulds and covers coupled possibly with more durable watermark wire profiles (where used); improved hand felts, a subject raised later in this chapter; improvements in the control and quality of the sizing process; and in the general finish of the paper. One reads these raising of standards and improved housekeeping into Burnaby's and Briscoe's Patents, the latter being what one might term a Patent of Improvement to-day on the former together with a few additional items purloined from others (Cameron has suggested, for example, that Briscoe had wheedled Hagar's secret out of him).[69]

The last Patent in this group, Dupin et alia, can be seen purely as an instrument for furthering their Petition to James II for Letters Patent granting them monopolistic powers in the manufacture of White paper. So any influence that may have come from this source would not have been technical but instead reflected Dupin's dynamism in getting the COMPANY into action and putting the various claims, and ideas borrowed from others, into practice.

---

[67] Bib.76
[68] See App.V.pp.262–263.
[69] Bib.18 6.

In this brief review of the Patents listed in the Table, one has to concede that in nearly all cases they had some genuine substance in their claims, from whatever source these may have been derived, and were much more than empty devices for raising money. They definitely contributed to an advance in papermaking technology in this country and the ideas clearly found their way through the system in time for paper makers of Whatman's time, if not earlier, to apply.

2. *Hagar's Patent for Sizing in the Mortar (No.222a of 1682)*

Hagar's claim for sizing all sorts of paper "in the mortar, whereby the sizing is totally intermixed and incorporated in the masse, whereas in the way now practized the sizing is received but superficially" is an almost perfect description of what has been called in modern times Internal sizing or Engine sizing.

Sizing is a method of restricting the pore size of the absorbent fibre matrix comprising the waterleaf sheet of paper in order to control the penetration of aqueous media, such as ink or watercolour, when applied to its surface.

A wide range of materials is used to-day to achieve this end (and indeed partial sizing may be induced by beating stuff to a high degree of wetness;[70] but, of course, with the danger of not being able to make a good sheet at the vat because the drainage of the water becomes excessively slow). The method currently in use then would have been the after-process described by Mr. Million and which had been employed in Europe for centuries, namely, that of immersing the paper in a hot solution of gelatine and alum[71] In some ways this process might be regarded as the re-creation of a sheet of parchment (albeit an imitation one) from which the collagen of the gelatine had been extracted in the course of preparing the size.

Owing to its viscous nature, and also to the dimensions of the very large gelatine molecules, the size does not always penetrate the finer interstices of the fibre matrix. This usually manifests itself when the surface of a sized sheet of paper is disturbed as, for instance, by the erasure of an ink line; when this spot is written over again the ink will spread or "feather" because the sizing in the interior of the paper, more particularly that of the fine capillary structure, is inadequate. To overcome this deficiency methods were devised in more recent times for introducing at an earlier stage of the papermaking process more mobile solutions than the gelatine sol, and capable of penetrating the finer capillary structure, these containing suitable water-repellent substances that could be precipitated onto the fibre *in situ* and thus impart a degree of sizing to these otherwise inaccessible regions. This was known as *Internal Sizing*.

[70] For a description of the "wetness" of stuff and its effects see App.V n.91.

[71] See Chap.I p.40.
   Some paper historians have suggested, though no sources given, that alum was not added to the gelatine until the end of the 17th C. This assertion is questionable in view of Mr. Million's quite specific references to alum in the preparation of the size. There is no hint in his account that this was in any way a recent innovation. Moreover gelatine is very easily washed out of paper, if it has not been "fixed" (or cross-linked) by the use of alum. Even Evelyn's account (1678) of his visit to Byfleet paper mill refers to the sizing process as dipping the paper "in alum Water" (Bib.30 Vol.II 338).

Reverting to Hagar's Patent, it is uncertain whether his claims refer either to substances introduced in the mortars to achieve a level of internal sizing to be followed by the normal gelatine sizing after-process; or to a method of total sizing in the mortar with the aim of eliminating the gelatine sizing process altogether; in other words replacing it with *Engine Sizing*. Gelatine could not have been used for Engine sizing (a) because to be usable it had to be in the sol form and thus hot; and (b) even if it had been possible to heat it in the mortar, its use would have led to excessive foaming.

There are several things then to consider at this point. First, no matter whether Hagar's aim was internal or engine sizing, one has to look for some substance that could be used as a sizing agent either together with or as an alternative to gelatine. What could this have been? and what prompted this invention ?

Second, Hagar's claims refer to the sizing of all sorts of paper including White and it is most unlikely that any substance would have been available to him in those days, which, if used on its own, could have given White paper the durability normally conferred on it by gelatine. Where other papers might have got by with a new sizing agent that did not impart durability, *durability was an essential requirement for White paper in earlier times.*[72] So one asks the question, what had he in mind ? If, as seems to have been the case, his Patent was sought after by the White paper makers, then durability would have been a factor that was important to them.

Third, one has to consider what Hagar's objective was. If it was to introduce an engine sizing stage in order to replace the gelatine sizing process, then on these grounds alone this is to be regarded as an imaginative concept, something quite new and one that may not have been achieved in reality until well over 100 years later; but whether and how he might have achieved this in 1682 is another matter and is considered briefly below. But there is an alternative to this which, seen in retrospect, is more realistic, namely, to supplement gelatine sizing, which for one reason or another might have become noticeably deficient and required remedying, with internal sizing. The claims made in the Patent do not, however, reflect this notion; all one can say is that at some point before or just after the beginning of the 19th C. paper makers had found it necessary to introduce a degree of internal sizing into the process to supplement the standard gelatine sizing.

Summarizing these points (i) one is looking for an alternative or supplementary sizing agent; (ii) what sort of market was this new method of sizing aimed at ? was the requirement a durable paper ? (iii) was Hagar's objective engine or internal sizing ? Are there any clues to this ?

To answer these questions there is very little to go on and what evidence there is leads to no firm conclusions. Hagar was by trade a dyer and would therefore have been familiar with the

---

[72] The durability of paper is not an essential requirement for most modern documents; if necessary, they can be reprinted, photocopied or reproduced from micro-film with the greatest of ease. In contrast to this the books, ledgers and registers of earlier ages would have been subjected to repeated handling, often over decades, and where parchment was not used, paper had to withstand this usage. Over and above its property to bear ink gelatine sizing would have given waterleaf paper the added strength (several hundred per cent) and toughness to resist wear and tear, which no other substance available then could have conferred on it.

effect of alum on various substances. This suggests, but only suggests, that he might have stumbled on the precipitating effect that alum has on soap; at a later date soap and alum were used as an internal sizing agent, but how far back this dates we do not know. This is a complicated subject and is dealt with in greater detail in Appendix V.[73] It can be said here, very briefly, that the treatment of rags with alkali e.g. boiling them under pressure with caustic soda, a process that was in use by the 1830's, removed the greasy impurities from the fibres. It was a logical step, therefore, to compensate the loss of the sizing effect imparted by these fatty impurities by replacing them in a controlled manner with an internal sizing agent such as, for example, soap precipitated onto the fibre by alum. In fact this method was being considered by paper makers *before* the alkali boil was used in the paper mill. Moreover, it is quite possible that it may even have been tried out during the latter part of the 18th C. If so, then one has to seek some other reason for the introduction of this technique. The need for it might have arisen from something like the early use of the steel pen nib which came into use in the late 18th C. (although not as a manufactured product until the 1820's). By this time paper was being used more and more for purposes like engineering drawings, cartography and ordnance survey, town planning etc., where the precision of the drawings may have required more frequent erasure. The idea that Hagar might have discovered this method of internal sizing cannot therefore be ruled out, albeit only as a possibility. Both soap and alum would have been available to him; they could be used in White paper without altering its appearance; and the substances used could have been added in the mortar.

Against this Hagar's Patent suggests an engine rather than an internal sizing process. There is a further piece of evidence that indicates that some other substance might have been used. When Evelyn visited Byfleet mill in Surrey in 1678, they were making *coarse* White paper (which points to it being a printing grade) and he recorded that "They put some gum in the water in which they macerate the raggs"; at the same time his description of the process as a whole implies that, whether this "gum" was a sizing agent or not, a sizing after–process was used as well – "[they] dips it in alum water", this following the drying of the waterleaf paper.[74] William Sutton was the tenant of this mill in 1675 until mid–1690 when he leased it to the COMPANY.[75] At an as yet undetermined date he was also associated with Hagar and his Patent, probably ca.1682.[76] Whether one can link this fact to Evelyn's description or not, one cannot say; but in this "gum" one might well be seeing Hagar's additive or a precursor of it.

Evelyn's description is obviously that of a layman visitor and not a technologist's. As a result one is left guessing as to what he may have meant by "gum" and, later, "alum Water". Gum is not a very specific term; in the early part of the 17th C. gums embraced such things as rosins, turpentines and pitches, all of which at that time would have been unsuitable for use in paper, especially White paper. In this instance it might have referred to a mucilage such as starch paste; or since neither Evelyn nor Hagar mention the word "starch" something like gum arabic, known in the 17th C. but too expensive to have been used in papermaking, though there may have been a cheaper alternative, but quite what is not clear. Both starch and gum arabic would have been soluble in water, but neither of them would have been

[73]   See App.V pp.251–260.
[74]   Evelyn, John Bib.30 338 Aug.24 1678.
[75]   Crocker, Alan "The Paper Mills of Surrey". (Surrey History Vol.IV No.I 1989/90. 55)
[76]   See Chap.I notes 34 and 36.

precipitated by alum. This is an important point because, unless the water soluble additive is precipitated in some way, it will merely pass out of the system again and drain away with the water in the sheet–making process. Dr. Gascoigne has kindly pointed out to the author[77] that as much as 73% of raw starch added to the beater may be retained in the paper. So the addition of a starch mucilage is a possibility; but the idea of some other "gum" remains a mystery. Starch had, of course, been used as a sizing agent from very early times, but usually applied dry and rubbed into the pores of the paper. This applied more to papers made by the Arabs and it has been generally held that it was abandoned by European paper makers, presumably soon after the introduction of gelatine sizing. Whether it was used from time to time to obtain perhaps a special glazed effect in paper, applying it as a coating, it is impossible to say.[78]

That there may have been alternatives to the use of soap and alum and starch as internal sizing agents remains a possibility but, if they had been beneficial, they would have survived to a much later date, say the 19th C., when their use might have been recorded in the literature; but this does not seem to have happened. Casein, a substance derived from milk, was used later as a sizing agent and this can be precipitated onto the fibre with alum; but to be effective it has to be in a concentrated form, a condition unlikely to have been found in the 17th C. Oriental paper makers also made use of various mucilages, but in the vat. These were made up from root extracts, sometimes mixed with starch, the function of the extracts being more for the purpose of dispersing the very long fibres and making the stuff easier to work on the mould than for their sizing effect; but Hagar is not likely to have used this type of agent.

From what is known at present one cannot be more precise about the nature of Hagar's patent other than presuming it employed some agent to confer internal sizing and at the same time preserved the durability of the paper. This is indeed one of his claims, his method being conducive "to bettering and making the said commodities more *dureable* and usefull". On the other hand he may also have had in mind a form of engine sizing where the sheet strength was of less importance e.g. in wrappers or blue paper. Starch added to the mortars would have gone some way towards fulfilling both of these requirements, but without gelatine the durability of the ultimate paper would have suffered. Starch would have given all of these papers an added stiffness which may have been the "bettering" that he claimed, a property that other paper makers, like the COMPANY, sought to acquire.

If gelatine sizing was not excluded from Hagar's method, one could resort to the suggestion that he discovered the internal sizing effects of soap and alum; but what prompted the need for this innovation ? Good reasons can be put forward as to why internal sizing may have become necessary towards the end of the 18th C.; but there appear to be no obvious reasons for anyone to have become especially aware of poor sizing in the interior of the sheet at this time. The internal sizing may indeed have been deficient, but what could have brought it to the paper maker's attention ? and why should Hagar's contemporaries have been so interested in this property ?

---

[77] Dr. John Gascoigne of Messrs. Cross & Bevan drew my attention to Radley's work on "Starch and its derivatives" (1940).

[78] As is well known starch was widely used for stiffening textiles for various purposes. As a result of this, and despite the rag fermentation process, one will almost certainly find traces of starch residues in many early papers, so that it is impossible to say with any certainty that starch is present as an additive or as a residue.

On the basis of the above, starch appears to be the most plausible explanation of Hagar's additive, in which case it is unlikely that his invention had any lasting influence on the industry and had become obsolete long before Whatman's day. Nevertheless Hagar's Patent was not only unusual but very positive in its claims as well as being original and imaginative in conception. Used for engine sizing the cheaper sorts of paper it could have had valuable cost–cutting benefits; but to have had starch mucilages lying around the paper mill and residues of it in the plant would inevitably have led to undesirable fungal growths and breakaways of dirt getting into the paper. Gelatine had its problems but it could be kept out of the stuff preparation and sheetmaking processes.

3. *The Papermaking Hand Felt*

In order to understand developments that were taking place (probably) in the second half of the 17th C. in the characteristics of the hand felt, it is important to know what the hand felt is, what functions it has in the process and what effects it has on the final sheet of paper.

The period referred to above has been qualified here by the adverb "probably" for the simple reason that very little is known about the early history of "felts". But, as will be seen later in this section, there is evidence of interest in an improved form of felt by some English paper makers during the 1670's; and by the beginning of the 18th C. changes were taking place in the surface of papers, which can be attributed directly to changes in the construction of the hand felt and which must have taken place in the British Isles from ca.1670 onwards; but since these changes originated on the Continent one has no idea how far back they were introduced. Judging from the scant interest shown in "felts" in early accounts of the process, it looks as if the improvement of the European felt was not very much earlier; or, at least, its general use.

The hand felt plays a very important role in the Western Sheetmaking process (the Oriental method is quite different and does not require the use of a felt). It also plays a fundamental part in determining the surface characteristics of a sheet of handmade paper and its quality is, therefore, clearly an important consideration in the manufacture of Writing paper. General considerations relating to the hand felt will be considered later. In the meantime the felts that would have been used for making Writing paper are described below.

The hand felt is a piece of *woven* woollen fabric somewhat similar to a blanket and is slightly larger than the sheet of paper with which it will come into contact. Apart from being made of wool it is not related in any other way to true Felt, the material used for making hats, for instance. It has two functions in the papermaking process. First, it acts as a temporary support for the newly formed sheet of paper in its transference from the papermaking mould; and, second, it serves as a drainage medium in the subsequent dewatering of the sheet in the press.

It will be recalled from the description of the couching operation[79] that after a short interval for draining the sheet, with the mould leaning against the ass, the coucher swings the mould across in front of himself until it comes to rest in a vertical position with one of its long

---

[79] See Chap.I p.36.

edges resting along the right hand edge of a felt that is stretched out, horizontally, on the wooden felt block below him. Holding the upper edge in his left hand he lowers the mould with an anti-clockwise rotating action until the wet sheet of paper (still on the mould face) is in contact with and pressed against the felt. Without pausing he continues the rotating action by lifting the right hand edge of the mould. The back-pressure of this couching action forces the sheet off the face of the mould thereby transferring it on to the more permeable surface presented by the felt.

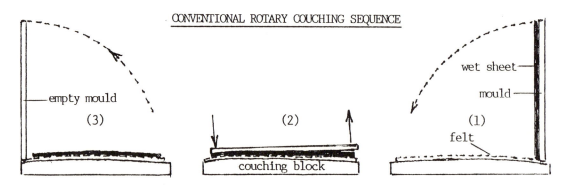

CONVENTIONAL ROTARY COUCHING SEQUENCE

empty mould

(3)

(2)

couching block

wet sheet

mould

(1)

felt

To judge from CELIA FIENNES' description (and possibly EVELYN's also) Flat Couching may have been practised at the mills in question. (see LOEBER,E.G. Bib.45 PLATE 16).

The empty mould is then returned to the vatman and the coucher pitches another felt so that it lies *on top* of the sheet that he has just couched. By repeating this process again and again he builds up a pile of wet sheets *interleaved by felts* to a depth that is convenient for pressing. The size of this pile, which is known as a "Post", will depend on the kind of paper being made. This illustrates the first of the felts' two functions referred to above.

After the couching operation the post, resting on its block, is dragged away to be placed in the nearby press where, after suitable adjustment, the pressure is applied and *water is squeezed out of the less permeable paper into the more porous felt.* These remnants of the "free" water[80] pass from the centre to the edges of the post and then run down its sides and away to a drain. This illustrates the second of the felts' two functions.

After this second operation the largely dewatered post is taken out of the press and passed over to the third member of the vat crew, the layer, who separates the felts from the sheets, returning the felts to the "felt board" for the coucher to use again and laying the pressed and consolidated sheets of paper on top of one another to form a "pack".

The felt then is primarily an instrument of the hand sheet-making process; and any other effects it may have on the paper are only incidental to this though none the less important, for the felt literally leaves its "mark" on the surface of the paper. This manifests itself in two ways. First of all, *a macro-effect*: the weave of the cloth is impressed onto the wet sheet

---

[80] For an explanation of the term "free" water see App.V p.216.

giving the latter a roughness of surface known as the "grain" of the paper.[81] Second, what might be termed *a micro-effect*: the woollen fibres, unless steps are taken to correct this, can penetrate and their profiles become imprinted on the surface of the sheet too. In this section interest is centred principally on these two effects in relation to the papermaking of the period; and to a lesser extent with the hand felt itself.

The Macro-effect

It is self-evident that for paper that was to be written on, the smoothest surface possible was aimed for in the finished sheet. Once paper has been allowed to dry and bonding takes place[82] the grain "sets" and once set this could not have been removed with the equipment available to the paper maker in those days. So, to achieve a smoother surface, treatment was necessary while the paper was still in its wet state. As a first step this took the form of pack-pressing, an operation that has been described in Chapter I, based on Mr. Million's account.[83] This was a repeat of the earlier pressing process except that instead of the sheets being interleaved with the felts (the Post), the now more consolidated paper enters the press as a single pack without felts, that is the surface of one damp sheet of paper being pressed directly against another. The pressure is applied more carefully, so as not to rupture the sheet, and increased gradually as further dewatering takes place. The effect on the surface of the paper is to reduce and soften the "grain", but it does *not* eliminate it. This process was described by Mr. Million without any suggestion in his account that it was in any way remarkable or a recent innovation, so that one might take it that it was a process already practised by manufacturers of White writing paper.

There were two avenues open for making further improvements to the smoothness of the paper surface. One of these appears to have been developed by Matthieu Johannot of Annonay and undoubtedly introduced into this country by Andrew Johannot at Eynsford mill in Kent.[84] This consisted of repeating the pack-pressing process again and, if necessary, again but parting the paper (pack-parting) after each pressing operation and reassembling the pack so that each sheet presented a new surface to its neighbour, the Exchange process. This process was clearly known to Whatman.

The other method which may have been used with or without the Exchange process was the practice of using old felts, ones that had worn smooth, for the thinner sorts of paper. Using this technique it was possible to reduce the grain to a level where it was less noticeable than the ridges produced by the apertures between the laid wires of the mould cover. But there

---

[81] This subject is discussed in greater detail in the author's work on the Development of Wove paper, Bib.76.
[82] For more information on the bonding that takes place during sheet formation and the drying of paper see App.V., the section on the cellulose/water relationship and sheet formation. Despite Le Francois de Lalande's claims (Bib.23 Art.79) that "Les feutres sont bien refoulés pour qu'ils ne fassent point d'impression sur le papier" the underlying weave still left its mark.
[83] Chap.I p.38.
[84] See Chap.IV p.148.

Plate 10 – Felt Hair Marks

1703 Document (approx. 3 x) KAO P.241 12/5
(Kind permission of the Kent County Council and the West Kent Archives Office)

were limitations to this approach;[85] nevertheless there is some evidence that it was practised.[86]

The Micro−effect

Although pack−pressing was an effective method of eliminating the major protuberances caused by the weave of the felt on the wet paper, and the Exchange process a way of reducing these even further, they were quite ineffective in dealing with the micro−imperfections. To overcome the effect of the fine surface marks caused by the felt hairs certain refinements were necessary in the make−up of the felt. The fully developed hand felt, unlike a blanket, was constructed with the nap on one side shorter than the nap on the other. Using this modification the sheet of paper was now couched onto the side with the shorter nap so that, in its wettest and most vulnerable state, the effect of the wool hairs would have been minimal. When the coucher pitched the next felt, the side with the long nap would come to rest on the upper surface of the sheet that had just been couched and would thus have provided a passage between the body of the felt and the paper for water to escape laterally during pressing later on. In 1788 Desmarest[87] described the effect of the incorrect use of this kind of felt "Si l'on changeoit les feutres de disposition, et que l'on couchât les feuilles de papier sur *le côté qui est garni de long poils*, non seulement elles ne s'appliqueroient pas exactement sur le feutre, mais encores les poils longs et roides ou perceroient les feuilles ou produiroient des bouteilles qui en altéreroient le tissu".

The obvious inference to be made from these descriptions of the finer characteristics of the hand felt is that at some point in the history of the industry paper makers had sought and found a means of rectifying a defect they had either noticed themselves or which had been drawn to their attention by some user or other. The occurrence of these marks in early papers was not due to the coucher using one of these 2−sided felts the wrong way round accidentally as happened sometimes later on, but rather that their disappearance from the surface of papers represents *an evolution of the hand felt* which led to improvements in the quality of the paper. That this was the case is demonstrated by the fact that this micro−defect may be observed on *both* sides of the paper in early documents.

The result of using an unmodified felt, or blanket, is to produce a "crazed" effect on the surface of the finished sheet of paper. In severe cases this can be seen easily with the naked eye; the sheet has the appearance of finely wrinkled skin and a closer inspection shows that the surface is made up of a mass of fine wool hair impressions (see Plate 10). In other cases the effect may be slight to very slight and one comes across the occasional example in

---

[85]   It might be thought from this that the obvious answer to this problem would have been to reduce the prominence of the weave or, where possible, to use smooth worn felts. But it must be remembered that one of the primary functions of the felt was to facilitate, through the openness of its weave, the dewatering process during pressing; and also that an old felt would not only have become increasingly clogged with fibre but have lost much of its resilience, an important feature in its capacity to assist the dewatering process. So there were limits to which this practice could be extended.

[86]   That this method was used (by some at least) is demonstrated in a passage from Le Francois de Lalande. Having considered various kinds of cloth and ways of treating it, he goes on to say "d'autres s'employent les feutres neufs que pour faire du papier bulle (generally lower grade, whited−browns etc.), et après qu'ils ont été lavés deux ou trois fois les font servir au papier fin". (Bib.23 Art.80).

[87]   Desmarest, N. Bib.21 500. Le Francois de Lalande, J.J.(Bib.23 Art.80 last para) also mentions this subject, but in his case the description is less specific.

TABLE VI

Incidence of Felt Hair Marks in a sample of papers (697 pieces) used between 1694–1732 and all taken from one source, a continuous series of parish documents (Bills) belonging to All Saints', Maidstone, Kent. (KAO P 241 12/4–12/14).

		(1)	(2)	(3)	(4)	(1 + 2)	(3 + 4)
Years	Sample	Not Visible	Very Slight	Slight	Severe	Not Noticeable	Blemished
1694–99	7	14%			86%	14%	86%
1701–04	115	29%	5%	11%	55%	34%	66%
1705–07	91	45%	3%	14%	38%	48%	52%
1708–09	79	68%	11%	8%	13%	79%	21%
1710–12	99	65%	14%	7%	14%	79%	21%
1713–16	36	67%	19%	3%	11%	86%	14%
1724–26	83	78%	13%	4%	5%	91%	9%
1727–29	38	66%	18%	3%	13%	84%	16%
1730–32	149	76%	13%	5.5%	5.5%	89%	11%

April 1981   J.N. Balston

For actual incidence of the marks see Appendix V, pp.262–263. The Table above shows the results of this examination expressed as a percentage.

It will be clear, particularly from columns (1+2) and (3+4), that a significant change had evidently taken place in the overall quality of papermaking felts during or round about this period.

The papers came from various sources, France, Holland and almost certainly some from the British Isles (including one from Ireland).

With one or two exceptions all the paper was White.

modern papers where the odd felt has been used the wrong way round and the fault has escaped the eye of the sorter. This lapse could apply to papers made by reputable makers in the 18th and 19th Cs. Although common in wrappers or whited–browns cases of severe crazing are found in sizeable batches of paper made well on into the 19th C., papers that in some cases might be mistaken for White in quality. Usually papers like these are accompanied by other defects such as dirt and iron spots and can thus be safely classified as *inferior* "White".[88] Obviously paper makers like these were not particularly concerned with the kind of material they used for "felts" and it might have been any blanket–like material they could lay their hand on.[89] It should also be noted that the vermicular shaped felt hair marks should not be confused with fine wrinkles that occur sometimes in old papers, particularly near the edges of the paper; the latter are usually caused by uneven contraction of the paper during drying, e.g. paper that may have been moistened for printing and possibly dried under conditions where restraints may have existed in different parts of the sheet caused by the irregular distribution and migration of moisture.

As mentioned in the opening paragraphs of this section virtually nothing is known about the early history of the hand felt or just when the improved type was first introduced. Reference will be made later to what little has been discovered about this subject from documents. An alternative approach is to examine the paper itself. The author is unaware of any systematic work that may have been done in this direction. It would, inevitably, be a slow business accumulating evidence, co–ordinating it and ensuring that the documents used for this purpose were securely dated. This work, it seems, has yet to be done.

A limited step to remedy this situation has been made here by examining a small (pilot) sample of papers belonging to the period under consideration (see Table VI opposite). Though the result may be regarded as a pointer, there are many imponderables in an examination of this kind and it cannot be emphasized strongly enough that not too much should be read into these findings at this juncture. That changes, in the form of a general drift, took place between, say, 1650 and 1750 is indisputable; but, in the particular, these changes may have made more progress at a given date in one area compared to another and perhaps applied more to one kind of paper than another. In addition, as seen, the criteria for defining White paper were clearly flexible at this time. If one was to consider a much longer period, one might have to take into account other exogenous factors such as coating paper in earlier periods for use with metal points; the effect of the printing process on the surface; and at any time up to the last decades of the 18th C. the rubbing or burnishing of the surface of paper to smooth it, all of these might have reduced, obscured or eliminated the felt hair marks.

---

[88] One cannot always be certain of this. For example, between approx. 1807–1811 there are about 30 drawings and watercolours by John Sell Cotman (all executed on wove paper) where crazing varies between very severe to noticeable. In the normal way these papers would not have been regarded as "first" class. On the other hand the incidence of dirt is not necessarily high in these specimens (as it might have been in whited–browns) and it is just conceivable in this case that the paper maker (unknown) may have been trying to achieve a special surface for the artist. On balance this is not thought to be the correct explanation for this; if it had been the case then one might have expected this kind of paper to have been more widely used than it was. A more probable reason is that it was made in a local mill where the quality standards were low. (It may be pointed out that there are other examples of papers of this period with crazing, usually laid, used by Cotman and other artists, which are definitely inferior in quality. So even in the 19th C. by no means all paper makers were using the improved type of felt).

[89] It has been said that cases have been known where old curtains were used as "felts".

The bulk of the sample examined here came from a continuous sequence of bills submitted to the parish church of All Saints', Maidstone between 1694 and 1732 (the date at which the sampling stopped). Just under 700 pieces of paper were examined for various characteristics, among them the degree of "crazing" shown in Table VI (details of other features noted will be found in Appendix V). The samples were graded empirically between blemished and unblemished surfaces and it can be seen that a marked shift to the unblemished took place during the first decade of the 18th C. The sample contained a proportion of torn pieces of paper and it is thus possible that some of them may have come from the same sheet, though against this one has to take account of the fact that the bills were submitted by many different people. The paper used for these bills came from Holland, France, Genoa, Ireland and the rest, presumably, from England.

Unfortunately, the origin of most of the pieces could not be determined, even though some of them had watermarks and countermarks. Where it was possible to identify the country of origin, the results have been grouped in Table VII opposite. These have been listed as "blemished" or "unblemished" and by date and country. To this list has been added a few further examples of countermarked papers, where the marks might have represented Kent paper makers; and, finally, there is a group in which the countermarks could not be identified at all but which occurred more than once.

From this Table it will be seen that in the first group none of the Dutch papers were blemished, although it must be said that in this particular case the samples date from 1705 (for an earlier sample of Dutch papers see paragraph below). The French papers were blemished to begin with, one later sample being unblemished.[90] The Genoese papers were still blemished as late as 1718. If any of the "GG", "H" or "RA" countermarks are regarded as those of Kent paper makers, then it is significant that they do not exhibit crazing at this comparatively early date (see also paragraph below).

Another separate examination included examples of manuscripts bound into book form and written on papers made by Eustace Burnaby, the COMPANY and others which were almost certainly Dutch in origin.[91] Burnaby's paper showed slight crazing on one side of the sheet only and thus falls within the "blemished" category. The COMPANY'S paper is variable, some of it falling as with Burnaby's just within the blemished category and others entirely "unblemished", no crazing at all. In another book of bound manuscripts[92] the paper must also have been made by Eustace Burnaby (though using a different countermark); these papers were entirely unblemished. The whole of this group belongs to the last decades of the 17th C. The sample also included a number of White Printing papers made at the COMPANY'S Dublin mill.[93]

These results, together with a collection of random observations made on papers used for various drawings by French and Dutch artists, all support the view that this was a period of transition between the unmodified woollen cloth and the improved hand felt. The indications are from this evidence that this transition was under way in England during the last decade of the 17th C., if not a little earlier.

---

[90] Crazing seems to have been more widespread and persisted much later in medium quality French papers than in British examples being found as late as the 1850's.

[91] See App.V pp.262,263 & Fig.13.

[92] Ibid. The date of this second book is uncertain; it could have been earlier or later than the first. The "EB" countermark in this case must have been Burnaby's, the paper belonging to the 1675–1680s and not paper made for Elliston and Basket whose "EB" countermarks are quite different in style and would have been found in paper made in the 1690–1700s. See Extension to Fig.13 and footnote.

[93] Miss Mary Pollard has very kindly examined for me some of the papers made by Dupin at his Dublin mill. Her assessment of four separate works dating between 1692–1695 was that the papers varied from slight crazing to more marked. Another sample sent by her to me, d.o.d. 1696, varied from not visible to very slight. One has to qualify these results by saying that some, if not all, of these documents were on White printing paper, where the requirement for quality was clearly less stringent.

TABLE VII – INCIDENCE OF FELT HAIR MARKS IN SELECTED PAPERS

Country of Origin or Mark	Countermark No. App. V, Fig. 13	Blemished	Unblemished
France		1702 1703 1704	1724
Holland			1705 1706 1706 1707 1724 1731/2 1732 1732 1732
Genoa		1718	

" G G "	2		1705 1706 1710
" H "	1		1702 1705 1715
" R A "	22		1712

" G F "	6	1702 1703	
" IT / TI " ?	5	1702 1705	
" L L "	8	1699	
" F " (dagger)	11	1705	
S " G G "	3		1707 1707 1707
" M C "	16		1707
" G C "	15	1715	
" S P " (harp)	9	1705	

It is possible that these improvements took place in stages; for instance, the first of these may have been a move away from the rough–haired felt or "haircloth" to one in which the nap had been cropped perhaps on both sides to varying lengths to give different degrees of crazing (or the effects might have been due to different degrees of wear). The final stage, in which one side was cropped and the other left with a measure of roughness, must have been reached by trial and error. To get a truer picture of this transition and where it originated a great deal more systematic work needs to be done.

Turning now to descriptions of Felts in the literature, there is very little to go on in any period before (probably) the mid–19th C. or perhaps even later than this. Two notable exceptions are the accounts given by Desmarest and Le Francois de Lalande; Desmarest's account is the most specific and the one preferred by the modern Hand Felt Designer.[94] The gist of Lalande's description is much the same as Desmarest's; but of greater importance in this context it may be nearer in date to the date when the transition to the modified form took place. One cannot be certain of this, but on the face of it nearer to 1700 than to 1761.[95] Even so early accounts make no mention of these modifications despite the fact that the improvements were patently manifest in the paper itself before the end of the 17th C.[96]

One or two contemporary references to felts are nevertheless instructive. Generally speaking the references in the 17th C. in the British Isles are to "felts", "flannel", "haircloth" and "hair rugs";[97] so any deviation from this is likely to be of interest. The interest is heightened when it is remembered that Wool was Britain's premier manufacturing industry, accounting for over

---

[94] Desmarest, N. Bib.21 500. I am indebted to Mr. N.W. Taylor, Chief Designer to Messrs. Porritts and Spencer, Bury, Lancashire for this view of the two accounts (Letter 30:Oct:1975). The other account is Le Francois de Lalande, J.J.Bib.23 Art.79.80.

[95] Ostensibly Lalande's description dates from 1761; however, as his account succeeded that of M. Desbillettes read before the Academy in 1706 (but now lost) and was originally commissioned by them towards the end of the 17th C. (see Gachet, Henri Bib.24) and although Lalande insists that he replaced Desbillettes' description completely, he may well have incorporated information on the make–up of the felt from the earlier account.
There are instances in Lalande's work where he mentions the fact that he has brought his information and his Plates up–to–date (as, for instance, in the case of the Hollander Beater, whilst still retaining the account and illustrations of the Old Technology). In the case of "Felts" he makes no mention of "recent improvements" when, in fact, there is unequivocal evidence that the improved felts were already in use early in the 18th C. It would be strange indeed if these facts had not been common knowledge long before 1761 and possibly just known to M. Desbillettes. Lalande more or less confirms this view when he wrote, "Cependant dans la pratique ordinaire on ne fait pas grand attention à la qualité des feutres; les uns prennent du gros drap, d'autres espèce de pluche.....; il y en a aussi qui les font tondre pour qu'il n'y ait pas de grands poils". This suggests an experimental phase long since passed and that his description is thus based on an earlier rather than on a later view.

[96] Imberdis, S.J. (Bib.26) writing in 1693 describes the felt as a rough haircloth.
Mr. Henry Million giving his account in 1699 also tells us nothing about the felt beyond the fact that the sheet of paper is couched upon a Felt laid on a plank; and since his account remained almost unaltered for the next 75 years, one learns nothing more from the numerous repetitions of this by later encyclopaedists.
Savary des Bruslons, J. (Bib.25) writing in 1723 is also unaware of the changes; to him "Feutre ou Flôtre....un morceau de reveche ou autre étoffe de laine écruë".
Because M. Desbillettes was commissioned specifically to write about papermaking, it is possible that he might have known more about felts than the others; but as seen above Lalande, who may have based his account on Desbillettes', is not as informed as Desmarest.

[97] Evelyn, J. (Bib.30) refers to "flannel" in 1678 : Thomson, A.G. (Bib.44 46,66,67) gives references to "Haircloth" in 1683 and 1714 in Scotland. Mr. Henry Million refers to a "felt": Bagford, J. (Bib.22) Included in a list of items for Auction at the Coffee House, Birchin Lane, near Cornhill held on 25:Oct:1695 are "Woollen and Hair Rugs for Papermakers, Cloathworkers, Sadlers and Pouch Makers".
There are also less specific references e.g. Dupin's "several 100 yards of wrought white Cloath" (1690) : and Celia Fiennes references (1697) to "coarse woollen" and "white woollen".

50% of all exports, and one finds, unexpectedly, *some Paper Makers wishing to import a specimen of a coarse woollen cloth*. A Minute in the Calendar of Treasury Books for *1672/5*[98] reads "Those persons who have undertaken to set up manufacture of paper in this Kingdom may be permitted to import one piece of coarse woollen cloth to make others by". The obvious inference from this statement is that the material in question cannot have been an ordinary piece of blanket material or haircloth, which the paper makers could have obtained almost anywhere in the country.[99]

Somebody in 1672, whether English or immigrant paper makers, had become aware of a couching technique used perhaps by the French or the Dutch, which resulted in a better quality paper than they were capable of producing in this country. As the Minute refers specifically to "coarse woollen cloth" and not to a tanned material, for instance, there must have been something about the weave or else the nap, that they wished to copy, some refinement of the blanket–like material that they already used. Since the weave in those days would almost certainly have been plain (with greater twisting of the warp to give strength, leaving the weft slacker for cushioning and absorption) it is difficult to imagine that such a cloth would not have been available and in use here already. It seems reasonable, then, to assume that the interest lay in the Nap rather than the Weave. Although the literature is silent on this subject, examination of contemporary papers (witness pilot examination) tends to bear out this assumption.

The other contemporary descriptions point to a more discriminating and understanding attitude towards the function of the felt than a mere reference to it. For instance, in his description of couching at Byfleet mill, Surrey, Evelyn refers in 1678[100] to the felt's water absorbing role during pressing: "this [the wet sheet on the mould] they dextrously turning, shake out like a pancake on a smooth board between two pieces of *flannel*, then presse it between a great presse, the flannel *sucking out the moisture*". Shorter has suggested that the paper maker at Byfleet (William Sutton) might have been one of those paper makers who sought permission to import the special woollen cloth referred to above.

Another contemporary account, which is of interest, is that of Celia Fiennes when she visited Barton mill in Canterbury in 1697.[101] This is instructive because it emphasises a distinction made at this mill between those felts used for Brown and those used for White paper. It is also of interest in the present context to note that this distinction was made in 1697 at a mill in *Kent*, which though an ancient one can only be regarded as provincial and one of the less progressive: "they were making brown paper when I saw it; the mill is set agoing by the water and at the same time it pounded the raggs to mortar for the paper, and it beate oatmeale and hemp and ground bread together that is at the same tyme" (quite a mixture). It is worth quoting in full Celia Fiennes' description of the couching process, which runs as follows:–

"then they turn the frame [mould] down on a piece of *coarse woollen* just of the size of the paper and so give a knock to it and it falls off, on which they clap another such a piece of *woollen cloth* which is ready for the next frame of paper and until they have a large heape [post] which by a board on the bottom move to a press, and so lay a board

[98] BIV 768 indexed under "paper" and not "wool".
[99] Further Notes on the Provenance of the Hand Felt will be found in App.V.
[100] Evelyn, J. Bib.30 Vol.II 338 Aug.24 1678.
[101] Fiennes, Celia. Bib.31 124.

on the top and so let down a great screw and weight on it, which they force together into such a narrow compass as they know so many sheet of paper will be reduced, and this presses out all the thinner part and leaves the paper so firme as it may be taken up sheete by sheete, and laid together to be thoroughly dryed by the wind; they told me *White paper was made in the same manner only they must have white woollen to put between...*"

It will be remembered that Dupin, in the 1690 Inventory for his Dublin mill, also specified "several 100 yards of wrought *white* Cloath"; but unlike Barton mill he was setting up his mill to make White paper.

It might be asked why "white woollen" or "white Cloath" ? Whether a paper mill in those days was geared to making White paper or whether it housed a corn and paper mill in the same building (as at Barton mill), the paper maker would always have had a proportion of his output in the form of "dirty" papers, wrappers, littress, whited–browns and Brown paper. Even at George Gill's Turkey mill, Harris recorded that "the Brown and White Brown Paper which they make here is chiefly from Old Ropes and Sails etc." In the case of a mixed corn and paper mill the problem created by dirt would have been even more acute and it would have been compounded in this instance by the use of mixed furnishes in the paper mill itself, colours or coloured threads not to mention other dirt lodging in corners of chests, vats and pipes and then breaking away later to spoil clean stuff and *contaminate the felts as well*. So, on these grounds alone, there would have been a case for using separate felts for making White paper as distinct from the dirtier sorts. This requirement might also have embraced the need to use the improved two–sided felts in the one case and any sort of woven cloth in the other.

But there was another aspect to this question. The furnish for Brown paper would have frequently included materials from ships, such as hempen ropes containing tar and old sailcloth that had been tanned with horse grease and tar and coloured with red or yellow ochre.[102] These materials would have stained the felts and rendered them unsuitable for the subsequent manufacture of White paper. Someone like George Gill might have fared somewhat better, as he would probably have obtained his sails from the Naval Dockyard at Chatham, where the sails at least may have been white.[103]

From the above it can be seen that there are pointers in contemporary records supporting the visible evidence that there were some paper makers, even ones like those at Barton mill, who took a special interest in the quality of their felts. Beyond these instances there is nothing to indicate how widespread the application of the improvements were initially.[104] All one can say is that, later in the century, the blemishes caused to the surface of the paper by wool hairs disappear completely from the best qualities of paper, so that practice appears to have matched the theory set out by Lalande and Desmarest. But in paper mills geared more to the production of Brown or mixed papers including some White and situated perhaps in

---

[102]   Steel, Bib.32 85. The use of tar together with ochres might account for the term "brown" paper.

[103]   Steel, Bib.32 loc.cit. "The tanning of sails in the royal navy has been tried, but is not approved of"; but all cables and cordage, however, had to be tarred "with good Stockholm tar, without mixture of any other, except about one third part, which may be of Russia tar". (1794).

[104]   An inventory for Ivy mill, Loose, Kent (1732) makes a distinction between two kinds of felts, but these probably relate to size rather than quality: 26 Fulling Felts for Press Paper Moulds : 77 Shop Paper Felts for Shop Paper Moulds. (Clapperton, R.H. Bib.33 144).

provincial areas where customers were not over-critical, the "crazing" of the paper's surface persisted well on into the 19th C.

The question might be asked, who made these improved felts ? Were they supplied to paper mills from a local source or from a central one ? For Notes on this subject see Appendix V under "The Provenance of the papermaking Hand Felt in Britain".

In this Chapter attention has been directed towards a number of technical advances in the papermaking process that had taken place during the last decades of the 17th C. and were being applied progressively in British paper mills, probably to begin with through the agency of immigrant paper makers and, by the early 18th C., by the domestic side of the industry. All of these undoubtedly would have helped improve the quality of British White paper *vis-à-vis* its continental counterpart. It is also clear from the quality of his papers that Whatman had assimilated these improvements in his operations at Turkey mill. But the fact remains that, in spite of these advances, British White paper still remained uncompetitive in the home market during the early decades of the 18th C. Protective measures had been increased steadily from the introduction of the New Duties and despite widespread evasion would in the long term have a beneficial effect on the domestic industry. But in its execution Protection may have been less effective in promoting White paper manufacture in 1733 than it became later.

It looks very much then as if these economic benefits, so much needed by the domestic industry, were really of more help to Whatman *after* he had launched his papermaking venture than in the period leading up to it; and, indeed, even after he had launched himself as a Paper Maker in 1740. The expansion of the industry in the Maidstone district had reached its peak soon after the New Duties, 1712, and showed little further growth for the next 30–50 years. Protection provided George Gill and William Harris with moral support rather than economic benefit occasioning no more than a passive response in contrast to William Gill and William Quelch who had reacted positively, too positively in Gill's case, to this stimulus; but taken overall the result had not been successful in promoting the economics of White paper manufacture in the area. It seems more likely that the New Duties reflected the aspirations of the paper makers at the end of the 17th C. who, with their improved technology, could see a future for the industry in this country, but who needed some sort of assurance that these advances would not be lost once again. It provided the industry with new prospects for the opportunists such as William Gill and William Quelch; but it was unquestionably advances in Technology that weighted the scales in favour of Whatman's investment rather than the economic climate.

The question may be asked then, was there any other technical agency that might have led to a breakthrough for a new generation of White paper makers ?

Chapter VI

THE ENGINE OR HOLLANDER BEATER : ADVANCES IN PAPERMAKING TECHNOLOGY (2)

The *pièce de résistance* in the technological armoury of the papermaking of this period was undoubtedly the Engine or Hollander Beater. In its own way it had just as revolutionary an impact on the process as the paper machine was to have approximately a century and a half later.

There is a tendency, perhaps, for people to concentrate their attention on the sheet–making process, and subsequent operations, at the expense of the prior process of preparing the stuff. This attitude is understandable in these days of tailor–made and more or less homogeneous pulps; but as any paper maker familiar with the use of rags would know, success in making a sheet of paper may be completely jeopardized, if the stuff has been prepared incorrectly. Moreover, as mentioned earlier,[1] to have prepared stuff correctly from rags either in the older process, using hammers and mortars, or in the new one, using the Engine or Hollander (at any time in its history before the introduction of modern instrumentation) required a skill and experience scarcely less than that needed to make the actual sheet of paper. Thus a fundamental change in the method of preparing papermaking stuff such as the transition from a hammering process to the brushing, bruising and cutting action of the Hollander roll obviously needs most careful consideration. It would not have been just a case of installing a new contrivance, but one of learning how to adapt it, on the one hand, mechanically to the source of power available to the paper maker; and, on the other, how to meet the needs of the vatman. To put it mildly it cannot have been an easy task and the real purpose of this chapter is to illustrate the very complicated nature of this innovation, too often just brushed off as a simple pulping operation.[2]

At present absolutely nothing seems to be known about the very early development of the Engine or Hollander (the term "Hollander" does not appear to have come into common use before the 19th C.). In Holland, from the time of its first documentary mention in the Zaanland (a district to the North West of Amsterdam) in July 1673, it was known as the "Maalbak" which may be roughly translated as a "grinding trough".[3] In the British Isles it

---

[1] See Chapter 1 p.13.

[2] It is not disputed here that a combination of rotten rags and ropes and some sort of unskilled grinding operation might not have produced a pulp from which paper of a kind could have been made; but in this book we are concerned with the production of high quality paper and, in particular, with the growth of this industry in the British Isles. Indeed, when one comes to some of the papers made by Whatman, particularly during his experiments in developing Wove paper (only just over 20 years after building his Hollingbourne mill), one finds that they are of superb quality and clearly great skill was needed in the preparation of the stuff used to make them. Although great skill and experience must have been required to manipulate the hammers and mortars of the old process, and there are many fine papers to bear witness of this, the skills needed to operate the Hollander Rag–breaker and Beater, with their far greater input of energy, must have been that much more considerable.

[3] I am indebted to Mr. Henk Voorn for this information: Bib.28 letter 28:Aug:1981 PC.811.469.

seems to have been known from the time of its introduction as an "Engine", a term that has continued in use right up to the 20th C. It is clear, however, from the first references to it in Holland, in 1673, that even at that time it was already a sophisticated machine and one which, quite obviously, cannot have been thought out at one sitting. In fact this new Engine was constructed and operated on principles without any precedent in the paper industry; and it is difficult to know where to find an archetype in any other industry from which it might have been developed, a subject which will be examined again.

In order to appreciate the significance of the transition from the Mortar to the Hollander it will be necessary to examine some of the mechanical principles on which these different processes are based. But before this can be done, it is essential to have some idea of what the rag–breaking and beating operations are trying to achieve. The starting point in this instance is the rag and the end point the sheet of paper. The problem confronting the paper maker then is how to get the rag into a state from which it can be converted into the uniform, cohering matrix of fibrous material that makes up the sheet.

For example, if one takes a quantity of rags that have been cut up into small pieces, soaks them in water, drains the water away and then allows the mass to dry, one will end up with the same separate pieces of rag that one started off with. On the other hand, if one takes a quantity of beaten stuff (prepared from the same rags) and drains the water from this, even in this wet state the fibrous matrix will show a degree of cohesion (as one finds, for instance, when a sheet of paper is transferred from the papermaking mould to the felt during the couching operation); and, at a later stage, when the mass is dry, considerable energy is needed, if an attempt is made to disintegrate it again. Obviously, something has taken place in the pulping process to create this difference in behaviour. In the case of cellulose, which is almost the sole component of the flax and hemp fibres, this transformation is not simply a question of subdivision and fibre entanglement but is due to the effects of *a complex relationship between cellulose and water.*[4]

To return to the paper makers' problem of preparing the rag in an appropriate form for use in the vat, a distinction has to be made between two phases of this operation, breaking and beating. The paper maker's first task is to dismember the textile or "break" the rag, as it is known. If he attempted to "beat" a mass of rags cut up into pieces of varying size, different in thickness and strength and some containing other features like "hems" etc., the treatment of the fibre would be so uneven that some of it would disintegrate at an early stage and be lost down the drain as "fines"; whereas other pieces would have been scarcely touched, leaving knots and strings and unbeaten lumps of rag in the stuff going forward to the vat. So clearly the first stage he has to undertake is to separate the threads out from the woven fabric

---

[4] In order not to confuse the discussion in the text regarding the impact of the introduction of the Hollander on the paper industry of this period, the kind of rags used for the making of White paper in British paper mills of the 17th and 18th Cs.; the fibres of which they were composed; and the significance of the relationship of water in the conversion of these rags into paper are subjects that are discussed separately in Appendix V. To appreciate the full significance of the transition between the two methods of preparing the stuff, these sections in Appendix V should be read and digested by the reader at this point.

Plate 11 213

HAMMERS & MORTARS
(1698)
(Ground Plan of Beater Floor)

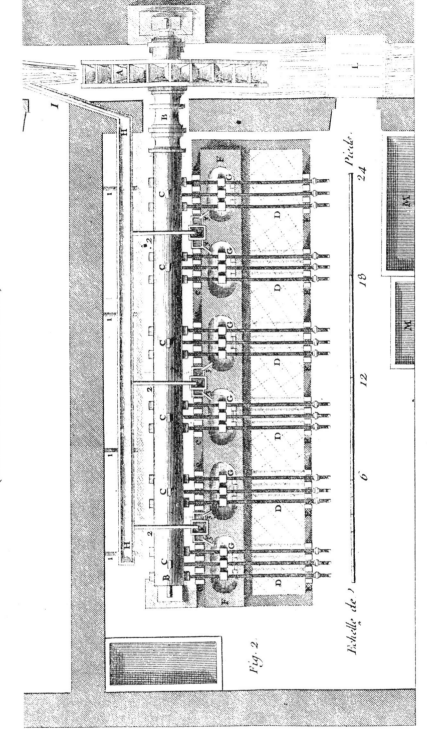

Note
The illustration shows the waterwheel right; and to the left of it, first, three rag–breakers each with three Hammers; to the left again two beaters with three Hammers; and, finally, extreme left, one *Pile à affleurer* with wooden mallets.

(Elevation of Beater Floor : and Figures illustrating Equipment)

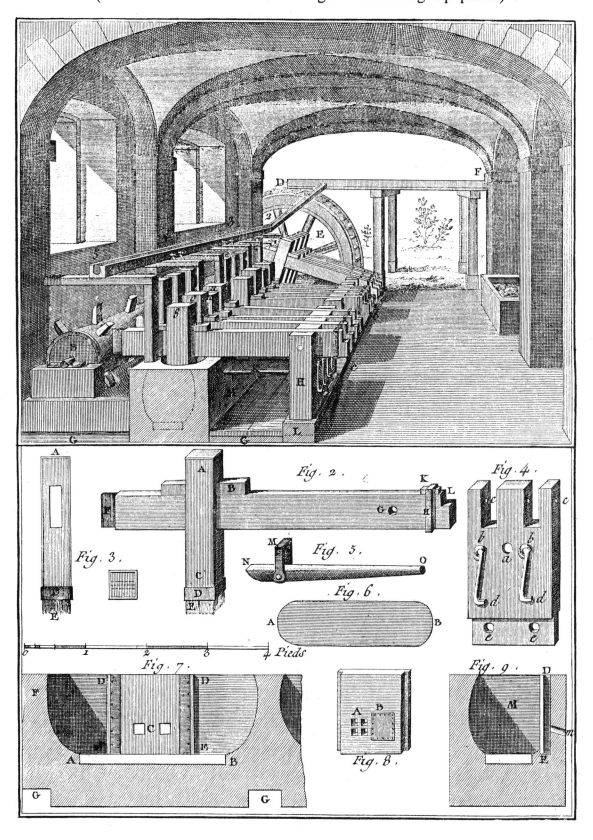

Figure 2 above illustrates the mallet (AC) with its nails (E) and attached to its shaft which pivots at (G) and is raised at (F) by the cam on the main shaft. The shaft can be kept in the upright position by means of hooks illustrated in Figure 4 and at the pivotal end of the shafts (upper half of Plate).

The Hair Sieve Unit is illustrated in Figure 8 and slots into the outlets (C) shown in the cross–section of the trough, Figure 7.

without, as far as this is possible, "beating" the rag at the same time.[5] This is known as the rag–breaking process.

It has been said that in rag–breaking lies the art of papermaking; by comparison beating is relatively simple. Once stuff has been spoilt in the breaker, it is spoilt for ever; nothing can retrieve a ruined furnish. The traditional method of stuff preparation thus employed two distinct stages with an optional third, the latter as experience was gained becoming incorporated in the second of these, "breaking" and "beating" and, finally, brushing it out or homogenizing it in readiness for use in the vat.

For the purpose of comparing the two principal beating processes in use during this period, the hammers and the mortars and the Hollander, a generalized account will suffice.

HAMMERS & MORTARS

The design of the mortars and stampers, the number of troughs and hammers etc., undoubtedly varied widely from place to place; all the same the equipment and methods described in Le Francois de Lalande's "Art de faire le Papier",[6] to which the reader is referred for further detail, may be regarded as typical for this comparison.

One of the illustrations of the earlier process, Plate 11, dates from 1698;[7] and the other, Plate 12, from 1767.[8] They both show the prime mover, the waterwheel at the far end, driving a long wooden shaft fitted with cams spaced at certain fixed intervals along and around the shaft. The function of these cams was to raise the hammers (shown to the right of the shaft) at different times so that they fell under their own weight into oval troughs below (illustrated in the ground plan). These troughs contained the rags or stuff as the case might have been. In the example cited by Le Francois de Lalande the troughs were approximately 1 x 0.5 m. cross section at the top tapering to about 0.6 x 0.2 m. at the base, some 0.5 m. below, giving very approximately a cubic capacity of ~0.15 cu.m. per trough.

In his example the sets of hammers in the three troughs nearest the waterwheel were headed with nails that had a cutting edge; these troughs were used to break the rags which, it will be recalled, would almost certainly have been subjected to a prior fermentation process to assist in reducing the materials into their ultimate fibres during the beating stage, a step that would have been difficult to accomplish without this. The sets of hammers operating in each trough not only rose and fell through slightly different distances, but they were also slightly different in width.[9] As they operated at different times, so the rags in the trough would have been forced from side to side as well as being pounded with the middle of the three hammers driving the rags against a horsehair sieve slotted into the side of the trough and having an outlet through it, thus expelling dirty water down the drain. The whole system was continually

[5] As will be seen in the Rag Section of Appendix V, some beating effect will take place during the first two or three minutes of treating the rag in the breaking operation; but this should not be confused with the effects of the beating process proper.
[6] Bib.23 Art.34–51.
[7] Le Francois de Lalande, J.J. Bib.23 Plate IV middle section. (1698). (For the top section of this Plate see Note 8 below).
[8] Diderot, Denis "Encyclopédie" Paper Section Pl.V.; used also by Desmarest Bib.21. (Substantially same as 1698 Plate IV in Bib.23).
[9] Le Francois de Lalande, J.J. Bib.23 Art.41.

supplied with filtered water from the sides of each trough; and because the rags at this stage had only been teased apart there was little danger of losing fibre down the drain with the dirty water. The rag–breaking process might have taken anything from 6–12 hours to complete; and, in this case, would have made use of 3 troughs with a total cubic capacity of ~0.45 cu.m. Measured quantities of rags were used, but they were not all filled in at once in order to avoid choking up the trough.

The 3 rag–breaking troughs were adjacent to 2 beating troughs which worked in exactly the same way except that the hammer heads were furnished with blunt, wedge–shaped nails that pounded (or beat) the stuff as it would have become by this time; and there would have been no sieves either. Because the stuff would have been more dense now than in the earlier more bulky rag state only 2 beating troughs were needed to follow the 3 breaking troughs. The beating operation might have lasted from 12–24 hours depending on the nature of the rags and other circumstances.

The last trough, *la pile à affleurer*, was provided with wooden mallets, no nails, for the final homogenizing of the stuff. Just as equipment would have varied from place to place, so procedure would also have done. Sometimes it seems that when the beaterman judged that his broken rags or stuff had reached the right state, he would transfer them by means of bowls to the next set of troughs. In other cases, as cited by Mr. Million for instance,[10] the stuff was emptied out of the troughs and put into bins, with a sloping bottom, to allow the water to drain away; this "first stuff" (later known as half–stuff) was sometimes allowed to stand for as much as a week to mellow "more or less according to the weather". As the water drained away from these bins, so the volume of the half–stuff would have shrunk so that it was usually necessary to add further half–stuff from another batch to bulk it up again.

It can be seen from the foregoing that this method of preparing stuff was a laborious low productivity process. The system needed constant adjustment, particularly the hair sieves which became blocked. It was slow (taking anything up to 36 hours for rag furnishes); low energy input (requiring a prior rag fermentation process); inefficient (each hammer beating about 40 times per minute); and a wasteful process (stuff constantly spilling over the edges of the troughs) requiring great skill and experience to work it successfully. To judge from contemporary comment it produced, as one would have expected, a long–fibred wet stock.

THE HOLLANDER

Before attempting to compare the Hollander Engine with the traditional Hammers and Mortars process, it may be helpful to those readers who are not familiar with what this Engine looks like to give a brief description of it, and van Zyl's example (Plate 13) will serve to illustrate this.[11]

---

[10] Bib.20 2:June:1699.

[11] For the purpose of illustrating a contemporary Hollander washer/beater the author has slightly modified, and in the process indicated the principal components of this Engine, J. van Zyl's Plate IV taken from his book entitled "Theatrum Machinarum Universale, of Groot Algemeen Moolen–Boek, behelzende de Beschryving en Afbeeldingen van allerhande soorten van Moolens". Amsterdam (1734).

Plate 13 217

"THEATRUM MACHINARUM UNIVERSALE" J. VAN ZYL PLATE IV
(Amsterdam 1734)

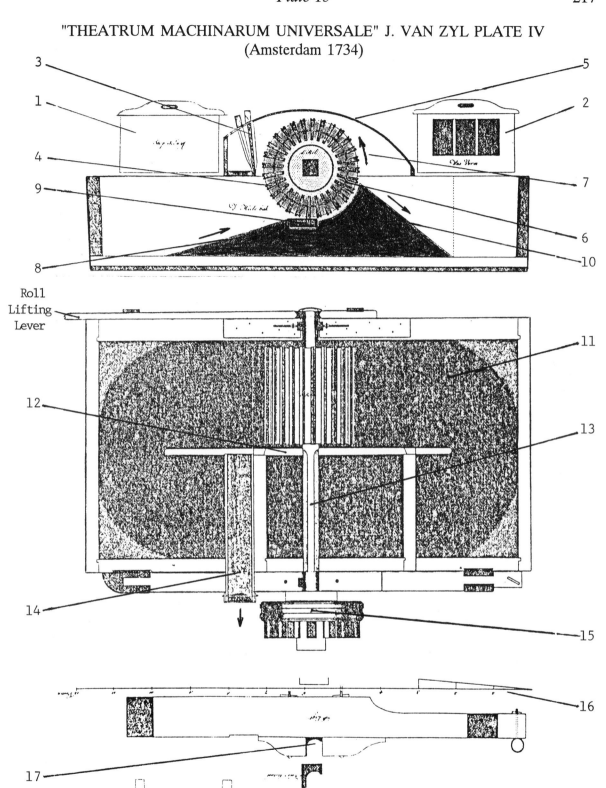

1. Tap Board or solid Splashboard.
2. The Chess or Splash Frame with wire Screens.
3. Slots for the Tap Board and Chess.
4. The Roll.
5. The Roll Cover.
6. The Fly–bar Retaining Ring.
7. Direction of Roll rotation.
8. Contoured approach to Roll.
9. The Bed–Plate.
10. The Backfall.

11. The Trough.
12. The Mid–feather.
13. The Shaft.
14. Outlet for dirty water from the Chess.
15. Coupling for the Drive.

16. Scale in (Dutch) Feet.
17. Roll Shaft Bearing.

The central section of this Plate shows the Hollander (without its roll cover) seen in plan. This shows a more or less oval–shaped trough, supported by a rectangular frame, approx. 60 cm. deep (at its deepest point) and nearly 3.7 m. long (that is if the dimensions given in van Zyl's Plate are to be believed). The vessel is split vertically part way down the centre by a partition known as the mid–feather, thus creating two troughs, one on either side of it, whose cross–section (as well as the ends of the vessel) are roughly a flat–bottomed U–shape. At right angles to the mid–feather and supported by bearings on the two outer sides of the vessel is a shaft, one end of which may be coupled to the drive. This shaft carries a cylindrical roll (approx. 76 cm. in diameter and width) which revolves in the trough furthest from the drive. The dimensions given above will be referred to again.

The surface of the roll is fitted with axially oriented bars with spaces in between them; an illustration of an end–on cross–section of the roll and two troughs may been seen in Fig.12 [App.V]; the side–view is shown in the top section of van Zyl's Plate with the roll cover in position. When coupled to the drive the roll rotates in its trough (the direction is indicated); and it may be lowered so that its bars come into contact with other bars fixed to a bed–plate underneath it. The trough contains either the rags or the stuff suspended in water and the rotary motion of the roll draws the rags or stuff into the very confined space between the bars of the roll and the bed–plate, dismembering the rags or grinding the fibres as they pass between. The design of the trough ensures that the contents are circulated so that in the end they come back to the roll again and undergo further attrition. This process, which may last for one or several hours, will reduce the rags to threads (breaking) and the threads to fibres (beating). In short, one has here the "Maalbak" or grinding trough.

Having given a general description, this must now be placed in some sort of historical context before proceeding with a comparison with the earlier process. It will have been noticed that the date of van Zyl's book is 1734 so that one might legitimately assume that the Plate represents a near relative of a Hollander that may have been installed in Whatman's mill at Hollingbourne in 1733. But of this one cannot be certain since there is no information on the kind of Hollanders that were being installed in England at that time nor any other reliable information on the design itself until one comes to Le Francois de Lalande's description in 1761. Earlier accounts or illustrations have been considered in some quarters as being too generalised or too unreliable to depend on; this has been denied by others.[12] However, as will be seen later, the dimensions and design as illustrated in van Zyl's Plate do appear to conform to the type of Hollander that one comes across later, albeit some of the dimensions are rather different; but all the main features are there and it is arguable that one could have constructed one from such a drawing. But so far as the history of the Hollander is concerned its date, if contemporary with the date of publication, is roughly 60 years after the first documentary reference to the Maalbak, 1673.[13] Moreover, as mentioned, this evidence shows

---

[12] An example of this is Sturm's "Vollständiger Mühlen–Baukunst" (1718), although this does provide us with evidence that the floor of the beater trough was contoured by this date. To preserve the secrecy of their invention it was claimed that the Dutch deliberately obscured the more important details in their illustrations and gave incorrect dimensions. Certainly Natrus, Polly and van Vuuren's "Groot Volkomen Moolenboek" (1734/6) is not helpful, although E.J. Labarre (Bib.36 59 note 2) considers that they have been maligned. However, their Plate XVIII is not nearly as informative as J. van Zijl's Plate IV (as illustrated here).

[13] I am greatly indebted to Mr. Henk Voorn for a very helpful and informative letter on this subject, a letter that will be referred to again in a later footnote (Bib.28 PC.811.469 28:Aug:1981). The first mention in Dutch Archives refers to a

(continued...)

that even at this date one is already dealing with a sophisticated piece of equipment. The origin of this Engine must therefore date from well before this and since there is no prior reference to it, its invention and development still remain a mystery. All that can be said is that to the best of our knowledge it makes its first appearance in the Zaanland where most, if not all, of the paper mills were not only wind–powered but, to judge from the construction of these mills, they had never employed the fermentation process for the preparation of their rags, two significant features.

Several points arise from this for consideration; first, why wind–power ? and, second, why the Zaanland ? and, third, what have these to do with the use of the Hollander ? The Dutch, from the very nature of their country, had been compelled from early times to look for alternative sources of power to the conventional waterwheel; and, as Voorn has pointed out,[14] political circumstances had also forced many of their paper makers into regions where they just had to devise new methods. He instances Du Bois' wind–powered and horse–powered paper mills erected in Alkmaar in 1586, followed shortly by van Aelst's tidal–powered paper mill at Zwijndrecht; and, further, it is known that a number of wind–powered paper mills were established in the Zaanland from 1616 onwards. The flat open country of the Zaanland not only favoured wind–power as a source of energy but, arising from this, it is claimed that windmills are capable of generating much more horsepower than watermills, a very important factor when it comes to the method of reducing rags to papermaking stuff.

The fact that the first mention of the Maalbak or the "wrijver" anywhere is in the Zaanland suggests that it may have been invented and developed there between 1616 and 1673 or possibly 1660, if one interprets the comments on the 13 years of papermaking at Maarten Sevenhuysen's mill in a way that implies the use of some form of Hollander there during these years.[15] Whatever the case may be by 1673 it is clear that the Zaanland paper makers were manufacturing both cartridge and White writing papers, both requiring strong rag furnishes. One can well imagine then the special features of this situation coming together in this period to produce a successful innovation, one that was to have a momentous impact on the future of papermaking. White paper, for which the Zaanland paper makers were justly famous, was made from strong linen rags which require by whatever means employed a considerable input of energy to reduce them to the fibrous state. This process hitherto comprised of a biochemical alias fermentation treatment to assist in the disintegration of the

---

[13](...continued)

     comment about the payment of workers in Maarten Sevenhuysen's paper mill, where the latter had been making very good blue, grey and white cartridge paper, as well as good White writing paper, for the past 13 years and whose mill was now equipped with "metal" (bronze) beater bars and "metal" plates, which enabled them to make White papers. The inference here is that hitherto they had employed fly–bars made of iron and that their replacement by bronze bars would have reduced the risk of contamination. (The so–called "metal" referred to here was apparently an alloy of copper and tin with a little silver added). The workers went on to say that they knew of other paper makers who were trying to obtain exclusive rights to make White papers with "metal on metal". These comments were recorded in July 1673. Later in the same year Gerrit Pieters van de Ley made just such a Patent Application "for making a kind of paper, invented by them, better than the French". Although the Patent Application is lost, the reply from the States of Holland, who turned down the application, shows that his application involved the use of a metal "wrijver" (or rubber) alias a beater. Mr. Voorn interprets this term "wrijver" as possibly referring to a fly–bar shaped to give more of a rubbing and bruising effect than a cutting action. This subject is referred to again in footnote 23, this chapter.

[14]   Voorn, Henk Bib.48.

[15]   See this chapter note 13.

Plate 14

THE EDGERUNNER
(19th C.)

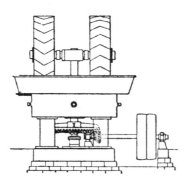

(Reproduced here by kind permission of Messrs. Cross & Bevan)

THE ROERBAK

(J. van Zyl "Theatrum Machinarum Universale" Amsterdam 1734)

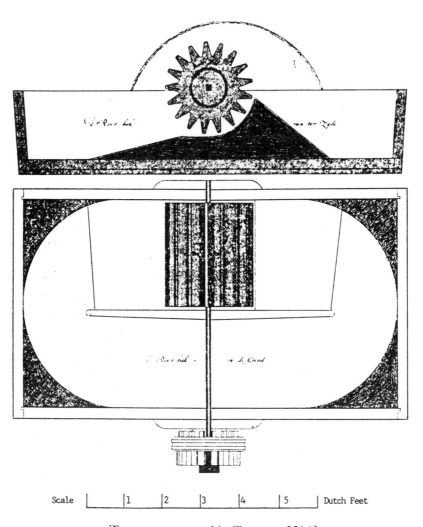

Scale |⎯⎯⎯|⎯⎯⎯|1⎯⎯⎯|2⎯⎯⎯|3⎯⎯⎯|4⎯⎯⎯|5⎯⎯⎯| Dutch Feet

[For comment see this Chapter n.23(a)]

fibre coupled with low energy attrition by the stampers was replaced here by high energy attrition arising from a combination of the Hollander roll and the use of wind–power.[16]

One can only speculate on the possible reasons for the conception of this entirely new method of reducing rags to a fibrous state, a development for which there appears to be absolutely no precedent. Voorn has suggested[17] that coupling the vertical driving shaft of a windmill satisfactorily to the horizontal arrangement of a stamping apparatus would have been a very difficult obstacle to overcome. In short, because of this, the first Zaanland paper makers would have sought other methods of preparing stuff. In these circumstances it seems unlikely that these early paper makers would have attempted to make White paper and may, therefore, have started by manufacturing Brown papers, or their equivalent, using weak materials that could be reduced to pulp without the aid of fermentation and using unconventional equipment such as the Edgerunner and the Kappery for this purpose.[18]

The edgerunner consists of two grindstones revolving vertically on their outer end surfaces in a trough (Plate 14) and was used for grinding more or less rotten materials into pulp for inferior papers. (More recently, 19th C., it was used, for instance, to repulp certain classes of "broke" for re–use in low grade papers).[19] The Kappery on the other hand consisted of stampers operated on much the same principle as the hammers and mortars, but on a smaller scale, the head of these stampers being equipped with knives; their rising and falling movement was used for cutting up old ropes. The reason for mentioning these two pieces of equipment is that both of them are to be found in the Schoolmeester, the only surviving wind–powered paper mill now left in the Zaanland.[20] The edgerunner in particular could have been the source of the concept of grinding rags rather than hammering them, a method that awaited development in some other way.

In its developed form the Dutch used what they called a half–trough (for the preparation of half–stuff), a full–trough (for beating) and a stirring trough (the Roerbak). The last of these (illustrated, Plate 14) was simply a trough with a wooden paddle with no bed–plate and was used primarily for keeping stuff stirred and diluted in readiness for the vat. Apparently, it was never used outside Holland;[21] but, according to Loeber,[22] it was used by dye–millers and it is just conceivable, though there is no evidence for this, that this contrivance was used at an earlier date and that its horizontally rotating roll with its paddles might have suggested the idea of a metal barred roll to the paper makers. From ideas such as these (though how far back some of these contrivances date is a matter of guesswork) it is possible to visualize

---

[16] For discussion of this subject see App.V pp.196–198.
[17] Voorn, Henk (as before Bib.28 PC.811.469 28:Aug:1981).
[18] I am indebted to the late Mr. E.G. Loeber of Hilversum for this suggestion (letter 18:Oct:1981).
[19] Cross, C.F. & Bevan, E.J. "A Text–Book of Paper–Making" Spon (1900) 147.
[20] The Schoolmeester contains much machinery built in the traditional pattern, but just how far back some of these machines date is a matter of guesswork. Certainly the Edgerunner and the Kappery have a very long history (E.G. Leober Letter 18:Oct:1981).
[21] Voorn, Henk Bib.51 9.
[22] Loeber, E.G. Letter 18:Oct:1981. It must be emphasised that it is not known how ancient this use by the dyers was but possibly as far back as the late 16th/early 17th Cs.(?).

some sort of link graduating from the edgerunner, used for low grade materials, to the Maalbak, for use with stronger rags.[23]

Beyond these very broad based suggestions there is nothing to indicate the stages through which the Hollander may have passed in the course of its evolution from some ancestral form early in the 17th C. to the 18th C. model portrayed in van Zyl's Plate, the latter being in a form that one would recognize easily in comparison with those that were used in the 19th and 20th Cs. But there were, obviously, a lot of features in its design that had been either introduced or were improved between its first appearance and van Zyl's model. These features have yet to be discussed but in the course of its evolution might have included, for example, the number and shape of the fly-bars; the materials from which they were made and how they were fixed to the roll; the nature and development of the bed-plate and its positioning; the contouring of the trough; the form of the roll cover; the introduction of the chess; and, perhaps the most important of all for paper makers in the British Isles, the overall design and size of the Engine in relation to the energy available at the site to make it work efficiently. *Any one or more of these features might have contributed to the distinction, postulated in Chapter V, between the Hollander used by the COMPANY in the 1690's and those installed by Peter Archer and Whatman nearly 40 years later.*

[23] With regard to the ideas suggested in the text above (and associated footnotes) and possible alternatives to these, the following points may be worth mentioning here:–

(a) van Zyl's Plate of a "Roerbak" (illustrated above) is probably dated ca. 1734 and shows a trough contoured in a similar manner to his beater trough. However, if a Roerbak had served as a source for the idea of using a barred roll for the paper makers' ancestral model of the Maalbak, then one has to bear in mind that this may have taken place some 100 years earlier and that the dye-millers might not have used or indeed needed a contoured trough to prepare their dyes. In other words the barred roll and the contoured trough features might have been derived from quite separate sources (see also [c]).

(b) In footnote 13 reference is made to Voorn's interpretation of the word "wrijver" as used by the States of Holland in their rejection of Gerrit Pieters van der Ley's patent application of 1673. He suggests that this term implying the "rubbing of metal on metal" may have referred to some special characteristic of the fly-bars that bruised rather than cut the fibres. There is no particular reason to cast any doubt on this interpretation in a broad sense. It is perfectly true to say that blunt bars will tend to produce more development of the fibres during beating than sharp bars; but there are a lot of other features that play a very important part in achieving this state of affairs such as the consistency of the stuff in the beater as well as the total thickness of the bars (see App.V pp.226–227). In addition to this we do not know to what extent the bed-plate of the Maalbak had been developed at this time, for example, whether it consisted of a single stout bar, several bars or, indeed, whether it might not have been a grinding surface, something like a millstone. Certainly by van Zyl's time we can see that a primitive form of bed-plate was in use, but the bars (if present) are not very clearly indicated.

(c) Another early "Engine" that has yet to be identified and described is the "Potcher" (pron: poacher). At some point around the middle of the 19th C. the term "potcher" makes its appearance in the literature on papermaking (first mention found so far is in the Eighth Edition of the Encylopaedia Britannica [1858]) where it is referred to as an improvement in the bleaching process. It was, in fact, a Hollander type of engine that was used for comminuting or washing rags and its use continued well on into the 20th C. The point of mentioning this is to ask, why was the term potcher applied to this engine ? and from what usage was it derived ? The OED has no earlier reference to this word on their files than the 1877 papermaking sense that they cite; neither has Labarre (Bib.36) anything further to say on it. For an earlier use of this word we have to go back to the 16th C. but quite what it referred to is uncertain other than the fact that it was a leasable entity probably connected with the woollen industry. Henry VIII leased 5 mills in the Maidstone area to William Sheldon (Exch:Dep.41 & 42 Eliz.11) listed as 2 Wheat, 1 Malt, 2 Fulling (total 5) and 2 Potchers. Mr. R.J. Spain has kindly drawn my attention to the fact that the English Dialect dictionary does have the word "Potch" to beat clothes in washing with a wooden instrument; "Poach" to drive backwards and forwards.....a wooden instrument resembling a dolly used in washing; "Pote" to push or strike heavily. It has been suggested that these words might have been applied particularly to some stage in the processing of wool or woollen cloth and that in its Maidstone context it might have referred to a discrete object used in fulling mills. (Extensive enquiries made to authorities on the history of the woollen industry have so far failed to produce any knowledge of this word or likely engine). The question that this poses for us is whether there was some sort of engine in use ca.1600-1650 with a rotating roll in a trough that was called a potcher and which might have served as a source for the paper makers' Maalbak ?

If we accept van Zyl's model as an example of a Hollander in a reasonably efficient and workable form, the first that we have an actual picture of, then this can be used as a contemporary basis for a comparison of the new method of preparing stuff with the traditional stamping process.

THE NEW AND DISTINCTIVE FEATURES OF THE HOLLANDER

Returning to this comparison of the beating methods one has to bear in mind that not only is a new contrivance for reducing rags to the fibrous state represented here but one that worked on entirely different principles to the traditional stampers; one might almost compare this difference to that between the horse drawn vehicle and the motor car, both will get you somewhere but each of them operates within a totally different technical and working environment. It is an understatement of the first order to say that there must have been a lot of problems that had to be overcome before the Hollander became a practical proposition.

The Transmission of Power

One of the first problems that the paper maker would have encountered would have been that of power transmission. To be effective the Hollander roll has to rotate at a considerable speed. Gearing, therefore, had to be introduced between the waterwheel, which in Le Francois de Lalande's example turned at approximately 12 revolutions per minute, and the beater roll shaft which, again in his example, made ca.138 r.p.m. His ratio seems to have been fairly typical, although his estimation of the speed of the Dutch wind-powered models does seem to be unusually slow.[24]

But the problem clearly did not end there. In the old method the single shaft was capable of working whole batches of hammers and mortars; but in the new one the paper maker would have had to decide whether the water power available to him enabled him to drive one or more Engines; and it would also have determined the size of the Engine or Engines, their arrangement, the weight of the roll and the energy needed to circulate the troughs full of stuff. *These would all have been unknown quantities to uninitiated British paper makers;* the Dutch, after all, would have discovered all this in the course of evolving their Maalbak.

The Zaanland paper makers not only had the advantage over other paper makers in having considerable reserves of power compared to the watermills,[25] but the transmission of this

---

[24] Le Francois de Lalande, J.J. Bib.23 Art.53. Other examples include John Farey's figures in Rees' Paper Section (Bib.50 1813) which range from 120–150 r.p.m.; the early 19th C. Breakers and Beaters at Springfield mill (possibly modified since) 152–156 r.p.m. Mr. R.J. Spain (letter Jan:1982) has informed me that the two water-powered engines at Hayle mill turned at 200–220 r.p.m. It is somewhat surprising, therefore, to find Lalande estimating the speed of the Dutch wind-powered models as ranging from only 49–78 r.p.m. (Bib.23 Art.61 end). If this was correct, then possibly slow rotations of this order may have resulted in more of a grinding than a cutting action, but at the same time a much slower rate of beating.

[25] The margin for this reserve of power is for the time being an unresolved question. E.G. Loeber (letter 31:May:1982) cites Ir. F. Stokhuyzen (former President of the Dutch Mill Association) book 'Molens' (p.106) where it is claimed that the Benthuizer mill with a sail span of 25.8 m. at 16 r.p.m. generated 55 h.p. and at 25 r.p.m. 110 h.p. and even higher. Mr. R.J. Spain, quite frankly unable to believe this, checked Derry & Williams "A Short History of Technology" and found that they had calculated that a Dutch windmill with a sail span of ca.30 m. generated 10 h.p. in a 32 km.p.hr. wind. It

(continued...)

power to the breakers and beaters grouped round the base of the main windmill shaft could be made with the minimum of complication. Elsewhere it is more than likely that many different systems were employed and that local circumstances would have played an important part in determining the capacity and number of engines that could be used, a factor that was of considerable importance in the effect it was to have on the future distribution and success, or otherwise, of many British paper mills. Lalande's description and illustrations[26] give some idea of the kind of problems all this would have created for the owner of a watermill. An example of this type of installation is illustrated Plate 23 and Fig.12 (App.V). The latter has been cited here because, although slightly later in date, it represents a viable installation, whereas the former illustrates an "ideal" mill which, in fact, never worked in practice,[27] a glaring example of mis-matching energy demand and supply.

To judge from the evidence available at present[28] the introduction of the Hollander into British mills seems to have been a more cautious one than the French. Dupin (1690), used a combination of mortars and an Engine and this practice seems to have been followed at Wansford mill, Northamptonshire (1725), Bramshott, Hampshire (1725); Astley Brook, Worcestershire (1735); Hay mill, Herefordshire (1740); and Catteshall mill, Surrey (1745).[29] There were other mills where no mortars are mentioned and the word "Engines", in the plural, is used; for instance, Thomas Watkins of Longford mill, Middlesex (1713) who procured both workmen and Engines from abroad;[30] Peter Archer with two Engines in his new-built mill at Chartham, Kent (1732/3); one Engine only is mentioned at Brandon mill, Warwickshire (1741); two Engine houses at Wolvercote, Oxfordshire (1743); "Engines" at Colthrop, Berkshire (1744); and an Engine at Stoke Holy Cross, Norfolk (1744). Thus, at most, it would seem that transmission of power would have been made to a pair of Engines unlike the five illustrated for a Dutch wind-powered mill[31] and the two batches of six at Montargis.[32] This suggests that in British mills the gearing and transmission systems were simpler and that the use of fewer Engines was prompted by the lower power of the waterwheel. This may possibly have been a reason why the Hollander seems to have achieved more success in Britain than in France at this time. If one is to believe Lalande, the Hollander was not introduced into France until ca.1740, whereas one can see from the above that by this date the installations in Britain were quite numerous, certainly more numerous than exemplified above.

[25](...continued)
was added, however, that the power output does not increase in direct proportion to the speed of the wind, but increases more rapidly. Stokhuyzen, unfortunately, does not give the wind velocity in his example, but gives average wind speeds over a year for the Netherlands as <14.4 km.p.hr. for 3754 hours; 21.6 km.p.hr. for 1771 hr.; 28.8 km.hr. for 1332 hr.; and up to 43.2 km.p.hr. for 1339 hr. The Dutch used a 4-sail windmill and it is possible that at the top range of windspeeds their windmills may have generated considerable horsepower figures. Even so 10 h.p. is distinctly higher than the 1-5 h.p. generated by the average waterwheel.

[26]   Le Francois de Lalande, J.J. Bib.23 Art. 52–57 and Plates V & VI.

[27]   Lalande's great plan of the mill at Montargis (Bib.23 Pl.III) shows 12 Hollanders, but he admits in Art.66 that only 6 out of the 12 were able to work at any one time, simply because there was insufficient water power to drive more than this number and one wonders whether even these 6 were ever effective. It has been said that this "ideal" mill never managed to produce a sheet of paper.

[28]   Shorter, A. Bib.9 40.

[29]   Inf. Catteshall, Crocker, A & G (Surrey Arch. Soc Research Vol.8 1981.6)

[30]   Shorter, A. Bib.12 65 note 62.

[31]   Le Francois de Lalande, J.J. Bib.23 Plates VII & VIII.

[32]   ibid. Pl.III.

Design Features of the Hollander

The main components of the Hollander have been described earlier in this chapter where it was assumed that the model installed by Whatman at Hollingbourne in 1733 may have resembled in its general design the one illustrated by van Zyl in 1734; but there are a number of details in this that can only be guessed at. One of the most important of these, of which the first mention is in the younger Whatman's notes on the new Engine at Hollingbourne mill (1771),[33] was the angling of the axis of the bed–plate in relation to the axis of the roll. The fact that Whatman noted the actual difference in their alignment suggests that by this date, at least, the angling was intentional, though barely effective ($< 2°$). The bed–plate shown in Plate II accompanying the Paper Section of Rees' "Cyclopaedia"[34] indicates that a more realistic angle had been adopted by 1813 ($3°$).

The Angling of the Bed–Plate

The Hollander Roll was set immediately above a fixed grinding surface or barred bed–plate and to work effectively the axis of the bars in this bed–plate have to be angled in relation to the axis of the fly–bars. Parallel fly– and bed–plate bars lead to very high shearing forces at the point of contact causing the roll to jump unnecessarily, increasing wear and the danger of loosening a bar and wasting driving power. Modern practice stipulated that angling should fall between a minimum of $3°$ and an absolute maximum of $43°$.

If the early wind–powered Dutch Maalbaks did in fact rotate at much slower speeds than the later versions of the Hollander, then it is possible that the absence of angling may not have been too serious a problem. In fact this, in theory, is another factor that would have reduced the cutting action of the beater on fibres. But there is absolutely no indication as to when angling was first introduced and whether it was done accidentally or intentionally but on a purely empirical basis. Neither Le Francois de Lalande (1761) nor Desmarest (1788) mention this subject, although Desmarest does refer to a "scissor" action[35] in his description of a bed–plate, but he does not specify any angling of its axis; he merely redescribes Lalande's reversible bed–plate (a bed–plate in which the bars on one side of the working surface were inclined slightly in one direction and those on the other edge in the opposite one so that when one set became blunt and worn the bed–plate could be removed and turned round, facing in the other direction).[36] Whatman (1771) evidently accepted as a matter of course that the alignment of the bed–plate bars differed from that of the fly–bars, though only by a small margin. This suggests that, although the angling may have been normal practice by then, the extent to which it was taken may have been arbitrary and that Hollanders in some mills may have performed more effectively than those in others.[37]

---

[33] See App.V p.231.

[34] Bib.50

[35] Desmarest, N. Bib.21 583 under "Platine".

[36] Le Francois de Lalande, J.J. Bib.23 Art.58 and Pl.6γ.

[37] Further comments on the angling of the bed–plate, the degree to which it was offset known as the "cutting angle" and different methods of achieving this are referred to in App.V. n.119.

The Beater Roll and the Fly–bars

It seems certain that for the whole of this period, and indeed in some cases up to the 20th C., the beater roll was made of wood and, obviously, had to be carefully balanced for rotating at high speeds; this must have been quite a feat. Lalande, for instance, gives a figure for the weight of the roll and shaft of the Montargis beaters as lying between 1400–1500 kg. The Dutch models, by that time, were apparently smaller than the French ones and were probably favoured by the English also simply because they would have required less energy to drive them. Lalande does mention, however, that in France they had tried hollow rolls, but had rejected them because they were too light and, probably, because they jumped seriously when breaking up clumps of rags.[38] The figures below (if the scale of early engravings is to be believed) give some idea of the relative sizes of the troughs and rolls of beaters between 1734 and the early 19th C. It will be noted that the figures for van Zyl's beater roll contradict the statement that the Dutch rolls were smaller than the French in this particular instance. (Further data will be found later in this chapter and in App.V).

DATE	MODEL	TROUGH		ROLL	
		Width	Length	Diameter	Width
1734	van Zyl	1.67m	3.36m	0.76m	0.76m
1761	Le Francois de Lalande[39]	1.52m	3.15m	0.61m	0.68m
1771	Whatman, the Younger	1.32m	3.13m	0.61m	0.69m
1813	Springfield	1.68m	3.97m	0.66m	0.76m

These figures must be regarded only as approximate; and, again, the 1813 date given for the Springfield mill engines is based on an assumption that these were the same Engines as those referred to in John Farey's 1813 account in their general dimensions though since modified in various details, e.g. in the barring.

The position of the roll could be varied, vertically, in relation to the fixed bed–plate underneath it; rotation would have started with the roll in the raised position (for rag–breaking or beating probably not more than ~3.5 cm. above the bed–plate); and this would have been lowered gradually by the beaterman according to his requirements until it brushed the bed–plate bars. In the early beaters this movement of the roll position was achieved by using a lever in the Dutch models (see App.V Plate 13) and by a jack in the French. The lever or jack ran along the outside of the trough adjoining the roll and was kept in position by wedges. By the end of the 18th C.[40] the roll position was adjusted by means of a more precise system

---

[38] Le Francois de Lalande, J.J. Bib.23 Art.56 also mentions that a solid iron roll had been made for Voujot mill near Dijon, but the results of this experiment were not available to him by the time he published his work.

[39] The dimensions for Lalande's beater roll are based here on his Plate V and the scale indicated there. The figures he gives in the Text (Bib.23 Art.55) do not agree with these; the width of his roll given here is only 23 inches (0.585 m.) compared to a bed–plate of 30 inches (0.762 m.) probably with a working width less than this and nearer to the roll width (0.685 m.) given above. The 23 inches seems to have been a mistake.

[40] Mentioned by Johnson, B.jnr. "The Paper Maker's Guide or the Art of Papermaking" publ. by the author and sold at Ludgate Hill, London (1794)

using a screw operated lighter bar.[41] This improvement is mentioned because it was one of
the advances made in obtaining better control over the beating operation through the greater
refinement of roll position adjustment, something which the earlier users of the Hollander
clearly lacked.[42] To the mechanically minded, and the point is noted by Lalande,[43] the
raising and lowering of the roll will be seen to pivot about the driven end of the roll shaft;
and thus the aperture between the roll and bed-plate would have tapered from the outside to
the inside.

With regard to the barring of the roll and bed-plate here again considerable changes seem to
have taken place as experience was gained from the use of the Hollander. Initially, it would
seem, the beater was furnished with "Iron Knives" and that the comments relating to Maarten
Sevenhuysen's Maalbaks in 1673, and the basis for Gerrit Pieters van der Ley's Patent
Application, were to do with the substitution of these for bronze in order to make White
paper. Presumably one of the reasons for this change was that iron knives tended to rust and
either contaminated the paper or wore out too quickly (it would not have been an easy matter
to change fly-bars). Certainly, the Zaanland paper makers were very much aware of the need
to control contamination, because they also took stringent measures to filter and purify the
water used in making these papers.[44] Voorn has also suggested that the use of bronze bars
may have been aimed at reducing the cutting action and replacing it with a more bruising
action which would result from blunter and differently shaped bars. It will be noticed, for
instance, that by van Zyl's time the fly-bars in his beater were grooved, a feature that might
have been more difficult to achieve with iron bars.

As the use of the Hollander became more widespread so the materials used for the bars varied
also. In Lalande's account[45] the fly-bars are described as being made of iron and the bed-
plate bars of iron or "Red Copper" to which rather less tin had been added to reduce
brittleness. The Dutch, it appears, used steel bars for their rag breakers and a mixture of
"brass and copper" for their beaters (it is assumed here that this meant bronze and a hardened
brass alloy probably somewhat similar to Lalande's "red copper"). The British seem to have
favoured steel, certainly for the fly-bars;[46] the bed-plate bars may, however, have been
made of a softer material. From all accounts it was generally recognized that wear on both
sets of bars could be reduced, if one of them was made of a softer material than the other
and, since the bed-plate bars were more accessible for changing or sharpening, it was these
that were usually made of a softer or a different metal.[47]

Not only were experiments made with the materials used for the beater bars but also in their
arrangement and shape. The first reference to the Maalbak (1673) mentions "knives" and by
van Zyl's time (1734) it can be seen that the fly-bars are now grooved and at the same time

---

[41] Illustrated in Plate II for the Paper Section of Rees "Cyclopaedia" Bib.50. Also in Balston, T. Bib.74.152.
[42] This point is discussed further in the author's work Bib.76.
[43] Le Francois de Lalande, J.J. Bib.23 Art.59.
[44] Voorn, Henk Bib.28 Letter 28:Aug:1981 PC.811.469
[45] Le Francois de Lalande, J.J. Bib.23 Art.55 & 58.
[46] See App.V n.111, 112.
[47] For instance the fly-bars of the 20th C. versions of the "Springfield" Hollanders (referred to earlier) were made of steel
and the bed-plate bars of gunmetal, a type of bronze. In more modern beaters, where stainless steel was used, very often
both fly- and bed-plate bars were made of the same material, but may have differed in their degree of hardness.

set at equidistant intervals all round the roll. Unfortunately, the bed–plate bars are not shown, so one cannot tell whether it was a grooved grinding surface or actual bars set in a plate. Apart from the reversible bed–plate, mentioned above, neither Lalande (1761) nor Desmarest (1788) show any advance on this arrangement; and yet, when one comes to Whatman's new Engine at Hollingbourne (1771), we have reached what was effectively modern Hollander design, but the inference to be drawn from his notes[48] on the novelty of this model is not a clear one. One learns from these that he could not treat his rags in this Engine in the same way as "Mr. Willmott" was doing (at Shoreham or Sundridge ?); but this, he concluded, was due to the sharpness of his bars rather than implying that it was in any way connected with the overall design of the Engine. Since one is seeing here the *first documentary evidence* of a Hollander with a number of features never illustrated before, there is no telling how far back these innovations might have been introduced. For instance, the cross–section of the fly–bars is quite different from that of the earlier grooved ones and in some ways might be regarded as a reversion to the original "knives". The bars are now arranged in clumps (Whatman's term is "tiers") of 4 bars with a significant gap between each clump (known as the roll cell space) which Whatman increased in depth, improving the performance of the beater; one might regard the last as a piece of evidence supporting the idea that clumped fly–bars were something relatively new in beater design. In addition, he has shown two arrangements of the bed–plate bars, which have been interpreted here (this being based on what appears to have been accepted practice by 1813)[49] as 17 bars for the beater and 8 for the rag–washer, the difference to give a greater teasing action to open up the rags in the breaker and more triturating surface for the beater. The technical aspects of these innovations will be discussed later, but the point of raising the subject of Whatman's beater here is to show that one could get a very misleading picture of the development of the Hollander, if one were to base ideas of this on Lalande's and Desmarest's accounts and in the case of the latter this was being repeated in the literature right up to the second decade of the 19th C. when we know now from Whatman's drawings, B. Johnson jnr.'s references and John Farey's accounts that so far as beater design in Britain was concerned this was far from being the truth. In fact it compels one to speculate on what kind of innovations had been introduced into the original installations at Old Mill, Hollingbourne and Turkey Mill and whether, when one comes down to details of design, they really did resemble van Zyl's model.

Other design features include the number of fly–bars used and the method of fixing them to the roll. The Dutch method of using a fly–bar retaining ring at each end of the roll, and with the bars set deeply into the roll itself, seems to have been the preferred method of fixing the bars; Lalande admitted that the French method[50] was less stable. It will be appreciated that, if one of the bars were dislodged and came loose at high speed, the effect could be lethal. Hence the imperative conditions when setting up the Engine that the roll be accurately positioned in relation to the bed–plate, properly balanced and the bars securely fixed.

At first sight there seems to be a big difference between the earlier and the later Hollanders in the number of fly–bars used. In terms of separate bars this is so. Van Zyl and Natrus, Polly and van Wuuren (Lalande and Desmarest follow them) illustrate 28 grooved fly–bars;

[48] See App.V p.228.
[49] Rees, Abraham Bib.50 11th page col.2 of the Paper Section.
[50] Le Francois de Lalande, J.J. Bib.23 Art.55.

Whatman and Rees show 60 separate fly–bars (Rees 40 bars in the rag–washer). But it might be argued that the 60 separate bars had evolved directly from the 28 grooved bars as a result of increasing the depth of the groove until it became in effect two bars. Finally, it was mentioned above that the Younger Whatman's new Hollander was furnished with exceptionally sharp fly–bars resembling knives and this undoubtedly caused him problems and a need to adjust his method of beating. This practice, however, was not followed and within 20 years it had become customary to use blunt bars again.[51]

The Working Area and Circulation

In this comparison the primary working parts of the Engine have been examined, but there were other features in the overall design that had to be developed before the Hollander could perform efficiently as a machine for processing rags. If the trough was filled with a mixture of water and rags and the roll rotated, then, theoretically, the rags would have been circulated by the motion of the roll so as to pass through the aperture between the roll and the bed–plate and thus, in time, be ground into pulp. With a very slowly revolving roll, like the edgerunner, one might have been able to do this at an unacceptably inefficient rate of production. But with the higher speeds obtainable in the wind–powered and water–powered engines, it would have been necessary to cover the area occupied by the roll in order to prevent stuff being thrown out by centrifugal action; even the design of this cover is an important feature, because stuff can become lodged underneath it, if it is incorrectly constructed.

Having taken the obvious step of covering the roll a more important design feature would have been discovered in experiments with the archetype as a result of trying to get the roll to circulate either the rags or the stuff as the case may have been round the trough. Initially, but still in rag form, circulation in a primitive edgerunner type of Engine would have been possible but very inefficient; but as the rags were progressively reduced to fibre so the circulation would have slowed down and eventually have come to a stop. By van Zyl's time[52] the paper makers had devised a method to overcome this difficulty by using a specially contoured trough, the design of which appears to have remained substantially the same up to modern times. It will be seen from the illustrations that the floor of the beater trough is inclined gently upwards as it approaches the gap between the fly– and bed–plate bars. The rapidly rotating roll then carries the material forward with it through a narrow space between the roll and the concentrically contoured trough to a point just below the upper edge of the vessel, a point which is considerably above the level of the stuff as it approaches the roll. It is the kinetic energy of this mass of stuff as it emerges from this narrow channel and flows down the steeply contoured slope of the trough, known as the backfall, that forces the material round the mid–feather and on until it approaches the roll once again. The actual design of this contouring is more complex than the description given above might suggest and, as before, it is likely that it went through many different modifications before a reasonably satisfactory solution was found, namely, one that avoided dead spaces in the trough, improved the rate of circulation and reduced streaming and energy consumption. Some of these points will be considered again below.

---

[51] See App.V pp.231–233.
[52] Even Sturm's 1718 illustration (Vollständige Mühlenbaukunst), hopelessly inadequate as it may be, shows that an element of contouring existed by this date and thus, presumably, earlier than this.

The Chess

In the description given above it was stated that after passing through the narrow space between the roll and concentrically shaped trough, *the stuff* emerges at the crest of the backfall and then moves forward and down the slope. However, at an earlier stage in the process before the rag has been dismembered (i.e. the initial phase of rag–breaking) a proportion of the material, mostly water, is carried on round with the roll until centrifugal force separates the two and the material is flung against the roll cover and eventually falls back into the trough again. At some unknown point this characteristic was turned to advantage by the paper maker who discovered that it could be used as a method of washing the rags. As van Zyl's Plate shows this had been put into practice by his time and so one can take it for granted that it would have been known to Harris and Whatman (and, indeed, Christopher Jackson's Patent confirms that it was known by 1684).

The top section of Plate 13 shows a solid board on the left known as the tap or splash board and on the right a similar sized frame for holding a screen of laid wire construction, sometimes backed with cloth in early models. This screen was known as the "Chess" (the anglicised form of the French "chassis de chapiteau" or "Kas" described by Lalande).[53] Either of these could be inserted into a slot in the roll cover; sometimes there were 2 slots, one for each of them. When not used for washing the material carried round with the roll would be flung against the solid tap board, fall back again into the trough and re–circulate under the roll. When rag–washing was required either the tap board was removed and the chess inserted in its place or, if there were two in place, the tap board was removed so that the dirty water, flung against it, could pass through the screen and out down the drain. While washing was in progress the trough was replenished with clean filtered water. (This rag–washing process will be examined again below).

The purpose of this extended (but by no means comprehensive) description of the Hollander is three–fold.[54] First, it is intended to show that the Engine operates on entirely different mechanical principles from the Hammers and Mortars and that it could never have evolved from these. Second, it will be appreciated that the conception of this method, apparently without precedent, and the evolution of the Engine from some unknown ancestral form to one that was viable in a manufacturing process and reasonably efficient, much more so than the traditional method, called for considerable powers of inventiveness from the paper makers who developed it in the first place and acute observation and resourcefulness in those who mastered it and continued to improve it, particularly when one remembers that it was not a piece of equipment that one could study in slow motion. And third, this description should help the reader understand, in the pages that follow, how rag–breaking and beating is achieved with this Engine and what advantages or disadvantages it might have had compared to the older process, an understanding that will be increased by consulting the parallel consideration given to this subject in Appendix V, in particular the notes on the nature of the flax fibre, its extraction and the resultant linen textile and rag.

[53] Le Francois de Lalande, J.J. Bib.23 see under "Tables des Matières" p.141.
[54] More extensive accounts may be found in Le Francois de Lalande, J.J. Bib.23 Art.52–72; and in App.V pp.225 ff.

The Uniqueness of the Hollander

The fact has emerged from this account of the Engine, that an enterprising British paper maker of the last decades of the 17th C., and equally in the early part of the 18th, would have been confronted with a very sophisticated piece of machinery to master, had he chosen to make use of it, without having the advantage that Dutch paper makers would inevitably have had in growing up with it as it developed in the country of its origin. It is true that Nicholas Dupin appears to have had the help of the five Dutch White–paper–makers in making a start, but not everyone would have had this facility and there is no evidence that an initiative of this nature met with instant success. In fact Dupin and the COMPANY disappeared from the papermaking scene before the end of the 17th C. without having achieved any significant advance in improving the economic performance of their manufacture. And, indeed, as seen in Chapter IV, even 23 years later Thomas Watkins, who had imported raw materials and workmen from abroad likewise does not appear to have made Engines work any more effectively or to his advantage since he was bankrupted in 1723[55]. The fact is, it would have been an impossible task for a paper maker to have made successful use of this new Engine without some form of initiation; importing foreign workmen does not appear to have been a successful substitute for this either.

The Hollander might be described as an "all or nothing" kind of engine which a paper maker has to adapt to what in any case and however achieved is an operation requiring great skill. In the old process the beaterman had to deal with a relatively slow and inflexible method where the hammers pounded the rags at ca. 40 times a minute, *an operation that he could see.* Whereas in the new and totally different process he may have had to cope with running, perhaps, more than one Engine at the same time fitted with rolls over a ton in weight and rotating at high speeds, producing somewhere between 20,000 and 90,000 cuts per minute; and, more important, controlling an operation that *he could not observe* at first hand. Having mentioned the critical nature of rag–breaking it can be seen that in the new method a lot of damage, irretrievable in its consequences, could have been done in a very short space of time by anyone inexperienced in handling the new Engine.

Apart from the difficulties arising from the purely mechanical aspects of the new method it will be appreciated by those readers who have digested the significance of the relationship between water and cellulose in the sheet–making operation in this context (see Appendix V) that it would have taken time and painstaking observation to adapt this new process to suit the needs of the vatman. In contrast to a relatively unskilled grinding or chopping operation when using low grade materials, the breaking and beating of strong rags was not just a question of subdividing the materials by a process of attrition, but rather one of carefully conserving it while washing and dismembering the textile using the tearing action of a fast moving roll in place of nails on the end of a mallet. Likewise, for the operation that followed, a shearing process would have replaced a hammering one to develop both the plasticity of the separated fibres and their specific surface in order to enhance their physical and chemical relationship with water and, through this, inter–fibre bonding. To ensure success in achieving these ends, a correctly beaten and homogeneous stuff, would have involved all the features

---

[55] See Chap.IV note 107.

described earlier, namely, the correct lowering procedure of the roll and, in turn, the accurate adjustment of the roll to the bed–plate; the design and performance of the fly– and bed–plate bars; wear and tear; the maintenance of good circulation and appropriate consistencies, quite a lot to swallow all in one go; all hurdles to be overcome by the uninitiated, a daunting task that goes some way in countering the accusations sometimes levelled at the industry for its seemingly slow progress in the 18th C. compared to that of other industries.

The Hollander in Use

In its developed form the Hollander performed four functions:–

(i)   Washing the Rags.
(ii)   Breaking or dismembering the textiles into their component threads.
(iii)   Beating the fibre, developing plasticity and specific surface.
(iv)   Homogenizing the stuff.

As John Farey pointed out[56] in 1813, it was possible for small paper mills with limited water supplies to make do with only one Engine, which served for both breaking and beating the rags. In the early stages some mills may have used a single Engine in conjunction with hammers and mortars, particularly those where the output of energy from the water was too low to process strong rags in the Engine. The real advantages, however, of the new method accrued from the use of two or more Engines, one of them for (i) and (ii) above; and the others for (iii) and (iv).

The use of two Engines for these different purposes will lead ultimately to an imbalance of output. Rag breaking, though carried out at a lower consistency, is a quicker operation than beating. Table VIII opposite gives an indication of the order of quantities and times needed for the work (and compares the old and the new methods). But there were so many variables in this situation that, in the absence of any records, it is impossible to generalize on what sort of arrangements may have prevailed in paper mills of this period. For instance, the higher consistencies used in beating stuff had to be made up by the addition of further quantities of half–stuff, that had been drained and held for this purpose after the completion of rag-washing and breaking, to a normal engine of half–stuff. The Table shows, according to Lalande's figures, that 55 kg. of rags would have been filled in to the rag–breaker and 72.5 kg. required for the subsequent beating operation. The drainage and handling of the extra half–stuff for this purpose would have taken time to accomplish, an unknown variable. Another unknown factor is whether all half–stuff was drained or only a proportion, providing a reserve needed to make up engines for beating. Likewise, depending on the nature of the rags and the end requirements of the vathouse, beating times on the one hand could also have varied considerably to accommodate variations in the quality of the rag,[57] the type of end-product[58] and possible fluctuations in the energy transmitted from the waterwheel; and, on the other hand, although not considered good practice,[59] to avoid waiting time some beatermen would put the roll down in the rag–washer after washing and breaking had been

---

[56] Rees, Abraham Bib.50.
[57] In general the thicker the paper the weaker the rag. (See also App.V pp.226–227; p.232).
[58] For certain thick papers short fibres are often preferable to the long more heavily beaten fibres used in Writing papers.
[59] Le Francois de Lalande, J.J. Bib.23 Art.66.

TABLE VIII – HAMMERS & MORTARS v THE HOLLANDER

The Table below gives a very approximate idea of the times and quantities referred to by Le Francois de Lalande and Rees to illustrate the order of magnitude involved.

Operations : Quantities : Sources	Hammers & Mortars	Sources	Hollander
RAG-BREAKING Le Francois de Lalande Art.50 Abraham Rees (incl. washing)	6–12 hrs.	Art.63 Art.64	4–6 hrs. 28 Bars (not grooved) 3–4 hrs. 40 bars (not grooved)
BEATING Le Francois de Lalande Art.51 Abraham Rees	12–24 hrs.	Art.63 Art.64	6–7 hrs. 28 Bars (grooved) 4–5 hrs. 60 bars (not grooved & higher r.p.m.)
CAPACITY (very approx:). Le Francois de Lalande Art.37 (3 troughs)	0.45 cu.m.	Pl.VIII Dutch Model	1.51 cu.m. (working capacity)[1]
RAG QUANTITIES (assumed to be air–dry) Le Francois de Lalande Art.49 (3 troughs)	34–41 kg.[2]	Art.64	(Montargis) 55.0 kg. (breakers) 72.5 kg. (beaters)
CONSISTENCIES (based on the above data) (2 troughs)	8–9% 11–13%		3.7% (breakers) 4.8% (beaters)[1]

NOTES

1. It has been assumed here, purely for convenience, that the average working depth of the trough in the Dutch model was 0.43 m. compared to the full depth shown in Pl.VIII 0.56 m. In other words about 77% of the trough capacity was in use. It may, of course, have been more or less than this.
2. Also assumed here that Lalande's figures (Art.49) refer to 11.3–13.6 kg. per trough.

completed and start beating the half-stuff there until it was ready to be transferred to an empty beater. The permutations in production scheduling are so numerous under these conditions that installations and production procedures could either have varied widely from mill to mill; or, because it was simpler to use standard transmission systems and because the cost of water power did not have the same implications as those we face to-day from power derived from fossil fuels, idle beating capacity may not have been an important factor. Unless he had another beater that he could draw on (not indicated), it looks as though the younger Whatman's installation at Old Mill (1771), Hollingbourne, was made up in the ratio of two rag-washers to one beater and one wonders from this whether this was the normal pattern and, indeed, how far back the Whatmans and others may not have used such an arrangement. Without knowing what factors there may have been that may have lessened this disparity, a few simple calculations will quickly show that an installation of this nature will, theoretically, soon lead to an imbalance.[60]

Though the physical and chemical principles underlying the stuff preparation and sheet-making processes remained unchanged, the new machinery of the Hollander clearly demanded the development of new techniques in achieving similar ends to those resulting from the use of hammers and mortars. Once again, until one reaches Lalande's account there are no sources to tell us how and when these were evolved. It is not easy for us to-day, after centuries of experience in the use of these Engines, to appreciate the magnitude of the effect that these radical changes must have had on the contemporary paper maker, to whom beating and sheet-making were an art rather than a science. Since he was unable to observe directly what he was doing, it must have been a case of "suck it and see" on a much larger scale than he would have been used to, a matter of risking hundredweights of rags per engine (120–160 livres) compared to pounds per trough (25–30 livres) and with an expensive commodity in short supply at that. *The experiments must have demanded powers of acute observation and very difficult decisions as to what to do next,* if the results were unsatisfactory. Without going into too many technicalities but for a better understanding of this situation a few practical aspects of the Hollander in use are given below and others will be found in the section dealing with the younger Whatman's new Engine at Hollingbourne in Appendix V. Just how many of these things were learnt and mastered by the early users of the Hollander must remain a matter of guesswork.[61]

Beginning with the rag-breaking operation, the washing process must take place while the rags are still in a discrete form otherwise the chess would quickly become blocked with fibre; in other words washing would start soon after filling in. It is probably safe to assume that practice at the time of the Old Mill installation (1733) would have been much the same as that which Lalande described for Montargis (ca.1740),[62] namely, that the rags were first washed and then broken. This point has been made because in modern practice, using the same type of equipment,[63] the views of experienced beatermen differed with regard to the degree of rag-breaking that was applied before washing. Some, for example, filled their rags into a trough full of water with the roll in the raised position and, once the rags had been

---

[60] The subject of imbalance is discussed in more detail in App.V pp.242–243.

[61] Loeber (Bib.45 38) refers to the existence of miniature moulds (ca. 12×18cm) in the 18th C. which may have been used to test the stuff during the last stages of beating (details of location etc., not given).

[62] Le Francois de Lalande, J.J. Bib.23 Art.63.

[63] In the more modern 20th C. versions of the Hollander the chess was replaced by a drum-washer.

thoroughly wetted and clumps of them dispersed by the roll, washing would begin i.e. the tap board would be replaced by the chess and water added to the trough to compensate for that removed. Others believed in lowering the roll early on for a period to "open up" the rags a little and release dirt held in the interstices into the washing water, the material still being in discrete form.

Two further points on washing procedure emerge from this. Firstly, Lalande mentions in his account the use of a cloth filter to back the laid wire screen used in the chess. It is not clear whether this was merely used in case of the wire screen failing mechanically or because, for some reason or other, the latter was not always effective as a screen; or whether, due to an inability to control the roll lowering procedure accurately (see below) or due to the presence of a proportion of weak rags in the furnish, an unacceptable level of fines was produced which would pass through a wire screen and would therefore need something further to trap them. A cloth filter does not, however, sound a very practicable feature to operate in these circumstances; maybe it was a relic of the times when fermentation was practised in conjunction with the use of the Engine.

Secondly, what is meant by precise roll lowering procedure ? The principles underlying and the effects of roll lowering are treated further in Appendix V;[64] here the concern is more with the contemporary mechanics of this operation and what sort of control the beaterman might have lacked in this critical stage of stock preparation. There is a hint of ambiguity in Lalande's account of this.[65] In referring to the graduated wedges ("un coin..... divisé sur la longueur") used by the beaterman to immobilize the roll lifting gear, he states that regulating the roll position is a matter of feeling one's way ("avec lequel [the wedge] il s'agit de *sonder* le cylindre, c'est à dire d'en régler la hauteur"). "Sonder" has two meanings that could apply here, to feel one's way or to sound in the sense of probing. In one sense this can be interpreted as the beaterman adjusting the position of his wedge gradually as a result of experience; and, in another sense, it could be taken as a reference to the use of a sounding stick to gauge the proximity of the roll to the bed–plate. The modern beaterman often placed one end of a sounding stick against his ear and the other on the end of the bed–plate block which projected through the wall of the beater vessel; he could thus listen to the sound coming through the stick which increased as the two sets of bars approached one another.[66] With the more modern screw operated lighter the beaterman could lower his roll gradually until he judged that the two sets of bars were just brushing. He could then raise the roll by a measured number of turns of this screw and thus start his roll lowering procedure from a fixed position in relation to the bed–plate; lowering his roll a round at a time he knew where he was. Control of roll lowering is of vital importance to the success of the rag–breaking operation. How the early 18th C. beaterman achieved this control is uncertain; was it in most cases a hit or miss affair ?

---

[64] App.V. n. 97.

[65] Le Francois de Lalande, J.J. Bib.23 Art.58.

[66] In a letter (22:Mar:89) Mr. A.E. Balston kindly informed me that another method used for sensing the roll position during lowering was to place the foot on the protruding lug of the bed–plate. It was claimed to be a more sensitive method detecting the slightest of vibrations and, in addition, enabled the beaterman to use his hands for adjusting the roll lifting gear.

In an assessment of both the rag–breaking and beating processes it is important to have an understanding of what actually takes place at the meeting point of the fly– and bed–plate bars. The action that takes place there increases the plasticity of the fibres and develops their surface; but how is this achieved and what factors affect this process ? To answer these questions attention is focused here on the concept of "fibrages", material that becomes entrained across the working edges of the fly–bars and the bed–plate bars, and their formation (see Fig. 5).[67]

Figure 5 – FIGURE ILLUSTRATING FIBRAGES

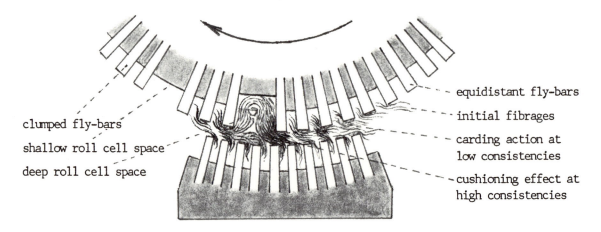

The illustration above is purely diagrammatic. For instance, it will be seen that equidistant barring is shown in the right hand sector of the roll and clumped barring on the left. An example of shallow and deep roll cell space is also given; and the shape and thickness of the bars must again be seen as figurative only.

---

[67] Once again this subject is treated more extensively in App.V pp.226–227; p.232..

Fibres suspended in the beater trough start forming a fringe across the leading edges and working surfaces of the fly–bars as the bars approach the bed–plate, where other fibres are similarly drawn in across the rear edges and onto the corresponding working surfaces of the bed–plate bars. Depending on several different factors such as the consistency of the stuff, the proximity of two sets of bars to one another, the size of the roll cell spaces and the rate of circulation in the trough, so beating of the fibres will be variously affected.

In general the innermost fibres of these fibrages, those against the actual bar edges, will be cut and the outermost torn and stretched; but much will depend on the sharpness of these edges, as the younger Whatman was to discover in 1771 at Hollingbourne Old Mill. Again, at low consistencies the fibrages will be sparse and this leads to a carding action that is particularly suited to the rag–breaking operation.[68] Conversely, at high consistencies, more usual when *beating* half–stuff, the cushioning effect of thick fibrages tends to reduce fibre cutting and increase the plasticizing and surface development effects of beating. If the roll cell spaces are too small or the rate of circulation in the trough too slow, then fibrage formation will be reduced and, as a consequence, the beating effect. The size of fibrages will also be affected by the fibre length. Thus they will diminish as fibre shortening takes place; the fibrage becomes so attenuated that no further cutting action can take place until the roll is let down further and the clearance between the bars reduced. The fly–bars in effect have a selective action in that they work more on the longer fibres, the shorter ones tending to slip through untouched.

Once a fly–bar moves to a position above the bed–plate no further stuff can enter the narrow passage that follows, stuff that could enlarge the fibrages already formed as they move through the gap. This is where the roll cell spaces play an important part in that they carry surplus stuff into this beater roll/bed–plate gap which, as a result of a circulating effect within the cell, helps increase the thickness of the fibrage on the leading edges of the bars; and in like manner, it has been claimed, the leading edge of a fly–bar following a wide roll cell space gathers more stuff on to it than it does when following a narrow one. Hence, deepening the roll cell space, as Whatman did to his new beater roll in 1772, "made the Stuff turn in the Engine Faster and cleared the Stuff better from Knotts".[69]

It will be seen from the above that quite apart from the state of the beating tackle itself, the performance of the Hollander will depend enormously on controlling both the position of the roll and the consistency of the stuff accurately; and the latter would have depended in turn on the accuracy with which the quantities of rags were measured out, by weight, and their moisture content (an important variable in terms of weight).

All these considerations would not, of course, have been known in this form to the 18th C. beaterman. But, with experience, he undoubtedly learnt how to achieve a certain flexibility within the limits of his Engine. That he was aware of variations in performance is evident from Lalande's comments, for instance, on the reversible bed–plate; beating tackle will obviously show wear with time and become less effective and so adjustments would have been necessary periodically, which a competent beaterman would have sensed. In addition,

---

[68]   App.V pp.220 ff.
[69]   App.V p.228.

one might ask what could have prompted the younger Whatman to deepen the roll cell spaces of his new beater roll at Hollingbourne ? He must have been confident that this course of action would have a beneficial effect, because once the wood had been removed it would have been an expensive course of action to try to put it back. So in spite of not having the benefit of modern technical experience, it is clear that *the 18th C. paper maker must have been very sensitively attuned to the behaviour of his new Engines.*

Hitherto attention has been confined to features of the Hollander's performance that the paper maker could not observe directly. In the case of another variable, affecting beating times significantly, the circulation characteristics of the Engine and its contents would have been something that he could have seen and noted. The two most important factors in this respect were the effectiveness of the contouring of the trough and the consistency of the material in it. In the first case one is faced with keeping the stuff moving properly and, associated with this problem, mitigating the effects of streaming. Apart from adequately graded contouring, circulation times will also vary between the inner streams nearest to the mid–feather and the outermost, both of which tend to move more slowly, even in modern beaters, than the centre stream. This was, of course, not only a matter of contouring but one of common or garden hydraulics and the factors that affect the flow of liquids (and the solids suspended in them) through a confined space. Streaming tends to lead to unevenly beaten stuff unless the streams are deliberately interrupted and diverted from their course. In addition, poor trough design will lead to partially beaten stuff becoming lodged in dead spaces and tending to spoil the uniformity of the finished stuff with knots and strings. That all this was familiar to the early beaterman is clear from Lalande's direction to stir the stuff frequently with a wooden paddle, "il est fort essential de spatuler souvent".[70] Just to give an idea of the order of circulating times the following example may be instanced from typical rag furnishes broken and beaten in the 19th C. Springfield Engines:–

Preparative Stage		*Time once round the trough**	
Rag–Breakers		65–90	sec.
Beaters	very early stage	450	sec.
	nearly ready	140–170	sec.
	ready	65–70	sec.

* Times all fastest in the centre

These figures also demonstrate the relatively rapid circulation of rags in the breaker where low consistencies were used and the very slow initial circulation times in the beater gradually accelerating (a matter of hours) to the same sort of pace as the rag–breaker as the fibre shortens. If, as is thought, lower consistencies were used in the 18th C. beaters, then circulation would have been much more rapid and accompanied by fibre cutting, particularly with sharp tackle.

[70] Le Francois de Lalande, J.J. Bib.23 Art.65.

Advantages and Disadvantages of the Hollander

Having considered the hurdles that the early user of the Hollander would have had to overcome in learning to adapt this new method and totally different engine to his process, one might wonder what made him pursue this difficult path. The fact that he did and that the new Engine replaced the traditional process is indicative of the exceptional advantages that the new method had to offer. What were these ? and were there any serious disadvantages ?

Although it is not possible to make too specific comments on the performance of the early Hollanders, one can say that their introduction must have led rapidly to an enormous increase in productivity. If the time needed to ferment rags, as practised in the old process, is taken into account, then the differences in overall stock preparation times is not just a matter of, say, 36 as opposed to 10 hours, with quantities doubled as well (see Table VIII), but a difference of several days, even weeks. This striking increase in productivity would have given the paper maker another advantage in allowing him to increase the number of vats in his mill in relation to his beating equipment.

The new process was also capable of developing sufficient energy to separate the linen thread into its ultimate fibres without the assistance of biochemical degradation, enabling the paper maker to dispense with the fermentation process. Apart from relieving him of what must have been a very messy, smelly and objectionable process, it would have given him additional working space within his mill buildings.

Over and above these obvious advantages the new Engine offered a much more efficient method of washing the rags; and, further, Lalande claimed that the Hollanders turned out more homogeneous stuff than the hammers and mortars, with the Dutch producing more even and consistent papers than the French.[71] (With regard to British papers, see below under disadvantages).

In spite of these benefits the introduction of the new Engine would have created a number of problems for the first users in this country to overcome. For example, devising a suitable transmission system and matching the energy demands of the new installation to the potential of the site. Having solved these he would have been faced next with operational difficulties, the safety of using the heavy high speed barred rolls; the precision with which the beaterman could adjust the roll position; the most suitable consistencies to use for his products and the sharpness of his tackle; how best to schedule the throughput of his beater floor to meet the requirements of his vathouse and so on. There were no doubt many other minor practical problems that he would have had to learn how to manage. For instance, how to start up his beaters full of stuff from a standstill position because of a breakdown somewhere or water shortage. This would have placed an exceptionally heavy load on the transmission system, possibly too much for the prime mover to cope with. No clutch would have been in use at that time to disengage the drive.[72]

---

[71] Le Francois de Lalande, J.J. Bib.23 Art.69 (Possibly because national pride got the better of him in Art.127–130 he claims that whereas Dutch papers may be more "beau" than the French they have numerous shortcomings in other respects, some related to their beating).

[72] See also App.V pp.239–242.

Added to the above, if the power supply was not really man enough for the job, the paper maker might have been forced into using lower consistencies than he would have wished, which in turn could have led to excessive fibre cutting, a problem unlikely to have troubled the Zaanland paper makers. British paper makers, with their newly found improvement, may also have been tempted to force the pace too much by putting the roll down too hard too early, also leading to fibre cutting. That there is evidence for this is to be found in a comparison, made in an anonymous memorandum that was produced for the Society of Arts in the mid–1750's,[73] between the disadvantages of English paper and the qualities of contemporary French paper.

Here it was claimed that in French papers the "Knotts in the Rags are crushed by the Hammers", while in English papers "The Knotts in the Rags are drawn through the Engine, and not broke; consequently remain in the paper, and, if taken out, make a hole" (this "taking out" would have been done when the paper was being sorted and finished). The fact that we do not see this defect in the best papers that have survived might point to superior beating control; on the other hand there is nothing to say that defective paper was not removed when sorting in the Salle. (The introduction of the Knotter or Strainer early in the 19th C. must have been greatly welcomed). Apart from the possibility of the paper makers trying to the beat the stuff in too much of a hurry,"knotts" and strings could also have resulted from a roll that jumped unnecessarily (parallel fly- and bed–plate bars being one cause of this) or from stuff caught up anywhere in the dead spaces of the beater trough.

The 1755 memorandum lists another defect that was observed in (some) English papers, namely, that "English Rags, being cut by the Engines, make the fibres so short, tho' coarse, that the more size is required to bind them together, to render them firm and serviceable, and makes the Paper of a harder nature". This was a point that Poggi, in his letter to the younger Whatman,[74] also made some 35 years later, where he complained about the shortness of the fibres due to beating with a Cylinder; and, indeed, French Plate Papers continued to be preferred to English ones until very late in the 18th C.[75] Poggi claimed that too much fibre cutting in the beater coupled with too heavy pressing produced too inflexible a paper for absorbing ink from the delicate parts of an engraved copper plate. This was no doubt a contributory factor; but probably the main cause of this was what the author of the Memorandum had diagnosed, namely, that rapid beating with cutting would produce a "free" stuff (absorbent) that took up more gelatine size than the usual moderately wet beaten stuff

[73] Royal Soc.Arts Guard Books Vol.III No.43 (ca.1755–6) printed in full, Balston, T. Bib.1 35. n.1.
[74] Poggi, A.C. de Bib.39. (see also note 75 below).
[75] Certainly for engraving, and this may have included printing, English White papers had a long battle with their French equivalents for a great part of the 18th C. before they gained supremacy, or at least superseded the French papers. For instance, this was the whole tenor of the Society of Arts Memorandum. As a further and later example of this Mr. Andrew Cook (Map Department of the India Office Library and Records) kindly drew my attention to the fact that as late as 1781 the distinguished Map Maker, Major James Rennell, Surveyor General of Bengal, preferred French paper to British for his Bengal Atlas (1781 Edition) although English paper of more than adequate quality would have been available to him at that time (Cook, Andrew S. India Office Library & Records Report 1976.25). Then, later still in the 1790's, Poggi in his letter to Whatman wrote "There is certainly a great difference in favour of the French paper, yet, when I consider the progress you have already made towards perfection, I am fully persuaded that with your perseverance you will obtain what is still wanting, to accomplish a general fabrication of paper in this country....." the latter referring to Whatman's experiments to produce a Plate paper to match the French.

used for writing paper. This would have produced a much more hard sized and inflexible paper.[76]

For most classes of paper then the Hollander offered very great advantages over the older process in terms of increased productivity and space within the mill and opportunities for greater cleanliness; and with a better understanding of the different factors that affect beating there was no reason why these advantages should not have extended to all classes of paper especially after papermaking entered the chemical era. It must be said that in removing the flax residues the fermentation process, as with the later introduction of the alkali boil, would have produced a more supple and tender fibre than one beaten without it; the Memorandum does make the observation that the English fibres were "coarse". As the 18th C. progressed and the number of engraved works increased, the ability to manufacture a good quality Plate paper would clearly have been an important consideration for those paper makers who customarily served the top sectors of the White paper market. So it would seem that for perhaps three-quarters of a century British paper makers using the Hollander would have been handicapped in this respect. However, with this exception the advantages of the Hollander completely outweighed any disadvantages it may have had *provided one had an adequate source of energy*. But in terms of mechanical efficiency it could be described as a "sledgehammer to crack a nut" type of process, a huge input of energy directed at a very small quantity of fibre at any given time. So long as water or wind-power was used this was not as an important consideration as it was to become later, when other sources of energy were employed. Nevertheless it was an Engine that lasted as long as strong fibres, like flax and cotton, continued to be used in papermaking. Whatever its drawbacks in terms of energy consumption may have been, it was a major step forward in the papermaking technology of 18th C. Britain and eventually became the pathway that led to modern methods of stock preparation, introduced in the 19th C. for new materials, such as woodpulp, but hinted at in the 18th.[77]

The practical aspects of an installation on the River Len[78]

In Chapter III, for all intents and purposes, a cast-iron case was made out for supposing that the elder Whatman had incorporated one or possibly two Engines in his *new* mill at Hollingbourne in 1733. It was also observed there that he chose a site intentionally which, in Spain's view was a *very* superior one. Spain has written[79] "throughout the centuries the mill-dam with the farm road on top has been successively built up, until by the turn of the

[76] In his second paragraph the author of the Memorandum wrote "The Paper, being hardened by excessive Sizeing, its elasticity is taken off, which prevents its sucking out the Ink from the Plate, and occasions the Print to be more feeble and Pale". Poggi likewise, though attributing it more to "cutting it with the Cylinder" (Hollander), wrote "thus comes that we lose that emptiness or spongy quality which is so necessary in order that the paper should attain in all its parts all over, that infinite pliableness which is the cause of its entering the incisions made on the copper, and absorb the Ink etc." In the event Plate papers became a speciality item in the early part of the 19th C. and were produced only by certain mills. For the finest results resort was often made to "India" proof paper, an absorbent paper imported from China from the mid-18th C. onwards.

[77] Le Francois de Lalande, J.J. Bib.23 Art.71 & Pl.IX fig.1 anticipating the advent of the conical refiner.

[78] I would like to acknowledge at this point my indebtedness to Mr. R.J. Spain for information that he has given me with this section (Nov.1981 and Jan.1982).

[79] Spain, R.J. Bib.8 60.

last century it was providing for *the most powerful mill* the Len valley has ever seen".[80] In view of the fact that as a flour mill (converted after 1850) it drove six pairs of stones, he has calculated that the wheel at this mill was capable of generating at least 30 h.p. Earlier than this, at some point between 1800-1848, it had become a five-vat paper mill, equivalent in size to Turkey Mill at its peak in the 18th C.[81] Here again the demand for horsepower must have been considerable, if not the same as for the flour mill.

However, in this context it has to be remembered that the use of wrought and cast-iron in the construction of waterwheels in the last decades of the 18th C., together with other improvements in the design of the system, greatly increased their power and efficiency.[82] Consequently, if one takes into account that the mill-dam may have been lower in 1733 and that the waterwheel would have been less efficient at that date, the elder Whatman would not have been able to generate quite the same level of horsepower that the site provided later in its history.

Most waterwheels on the River Len were overshot by the end of the 16th C. (some possibly well before this); and certain mills, like Otham[83] had two Waterwheels as early as 1529, each capable of generating 3-5 h.p. (Otham was less than two miles downstream from Whatman's mill). In Spain's view, Old Mill, Hollingbourne, by virtue of its great pond would have been a superior mill in 1733 with a mill wheel more powerful than Otham. In fact it could have had two waterwheels, although judging from the site today it probably managed with one. He goes on to say that by 1752 Maidstone Church mill,[84] based on the number of stones at work there, would have been capable of generating ~15-20 h.p.; and, it will be recalled, before 1716 Turkey Mill had three waterwheels each producing ~4 h.p. From all these considerations it would seem safe to assume that the elder Whatman had 10-15 h.p. at his disposal for his mill at Hollingbourne, double this, if he had made use of two wheels (Mr. Spain's assumption). This would have been more than sufficient power for him to have worked at least one Hollander; and, if one takes into account that the Zaanland windmills may not have generated much more than 10-15 h.p. at average wind speeds and that, according to Jean Schenk's engraving of a Dutch wind-powered paper mill,[85] this drove no fewer than

---

[80] For a further account of the site, as it is to-day, with sketch maps and photographs see Preface to Appendices I & II pp.xii ff.

[81] See App.I the Synopsis of the History of Old Mill, Hollingbourne.

[82] Spain considers that waterwheels had, in general, improved in efficiency from late mediaeval times to the latter half of the 18th C. But from approximately 1760-1770 progress was accelerated by both John Rennie and John Smeaton, who were in the process of introducing improved designs based on cast-iron construction, giving advantages in both weight and strength. Murdock was another pioneer in this field. Though it took several decades for these innovations to become generally accepted in practice, it is noteworthy in this context that Smeaton designed a waterwheel for the younger Whatman's Loose paper mill in 1787 (Library Roy.Soc. Smeaton Colln. Box I/1 Dwg.No.47), although it was never constructed; but it was by no means his first waterwheel for a paper mill. Rennie, in the same year, also started work for Whatman (Balston, T. Bib.1 101/3), which to judge from the surviving invoices (P.S.M) appears to have been connected with improvements to the transmission system.

These more powerful waterwheels (and even more the case where steam power was used in their place) together with a greater understanding of the engineering principles involved in the working of the Hollander would have led to improved design and greater output per Engine early in the 19th C.

[83] Spain, R.J. Bib.8 72.

[84] Spain, R.J. Bib.8 96/7.

[85] Reproduced in Le Francois de Lalande, J.J. Bib.23 Plates VII & VIII.

five Engines, then Whatman could have installed at least two Engines, a rag–breaker and a beater, if he had wanted to.[86]

The nature and size of the installation at Old Mill

Having described the Engine, its development and the potential of the site at Hollingbourne, can one come to any conclusions regarding the installation at Old Mill ?

(a)   The whole conception of Whatman's investment, the aftermath at Turkey Mill and the repercussions of this (Chap.VII) strongly suggests that there must have been a technical breakthrough that led to these events. Are there any clues as to what this might have been ?

(b)   The fact that Whatman and Harris went out of their way to secure a site for an unusually powerful waterwheel implies that previous installations in this country may have been under–powered with all the consequences that this would entail both with respect to mechanical efficiency and the ability to treat strong rags in a way that suited the vathouse requirements. Alternatively, though amounting to much the same thing, the size and weight of the roll of the earlier Engines may have been too small to work effectively on strong rag stock and as a consequence they planned to use a larger Engine more in line with van Zyl's which in turn would require greater water-power.

Recognition of either of these shortcomings lends further support to the notion that Harris had trained in Holland and seen at first hand the effectiveness of wind–power in relation to the size of the Engine. (If this had been the only consideration, there would have been less need to postulate such a visit; but the correct use of the Engine, its adaptation to water–power for breaking and beating rags, was a far from simple matter requiring practical experience to achieve this end).

(c)   As a corollary of the above one assumes that Harris had mastered the new procedure but that its requirements in terms of water–power had yet to be determined. Hence the suggestion that the Old Mill venture was primarily experimental in character.

---

[86]   Although the situation is not strictly comparable, information supplied by Mr. Alfred Spain (formerly Engineer to Messrs. Barcham Green at Hayle mill on the River Loose) can be used as a yardstick to gauge the horsepower requirement of a small beater.

The waterwheel at Hayle mill generated some 12 h.p. which was sufficient to drive two small beaters and work the ancillary machinery used in the vathouse (20th C.). The rolls in these beaters (different in size) were of hollow cast–iron construction and lighter than Lalande's solid construction roll, weighing approx. 610 kg. and 765 kg. against 1400–1500 kg. The rolls at Hayle mill rotated at 200–220 r.p.m. and the beaters were used to produce strong wet stock at high consistencies. Based on this information Mr. Spain believed that, provided consistencies were lower and the roll not set too close to the bed–plate, 10–15 h.p. would have been sufficient power to have worked the heavier beater roll cited by Lalande. Allowing for the fact that the Dutch model, described by Lalande, was smaller than the French one; and, further, that the power out–put of the average waterwheel might have been lower than that of a windmill, it would seem that the 10–15 h.p. suggested for the Old Mill waterwheel would have been enough to work a pair of Engines, confirming the assumptions made in the text.

(d)   The impression gained from the lay–out of the Old Mill beater floor in 1771[87] is that the annular arrangement of the Engines had perhaps been there from the time the mill had been built. Lalande illustrates similar arrangements typical of 1740 or before and there is no hint in Whatman's notes that anything other than the new Engine had been "put up" in 1771. It is not necessary, however, to assume that three Engines had been installed in 1733, but that this system, conforming to Dutch practice, was convenient for expansion. In these circumstances to balance the swimming wheel two Engines diametrically opposite one another would have been more suitable than one on its own.

(e)   There is nothing to indicate how many vats Old Mill had initially. The installation of a new Engine in 1771 might indicate that it was being converted from one to a two–vat mill. Apart from one anomalous figure the Insurance premiums between 1733–1770 remain unaltered, but this had doubled by 1774 and increased 10–15–fold on the original sum by 1791.[88] On this basis it is legitimate to assume that it was a one–vat mill when first commissioned.

(f)   A one–vat mill would have been capable of producing eight reams of foolscap at, say, 18 lb. per ream, a total of 144 lb. (or 5 reams at 30 lb. totalling 150 lb.) in a 12–hour day. A single washer/beater could, in theory, process 160 lb. in 10 hours (see Table VIII) which accords with Peter Archer's two Engines for two vats at Chartham. But in view of the imbalance of the breaking/beating operation a two–Engine facility would have been much more satisfactory operationally and for power transmission, another reason for seeking a site that would provide sufficient energy.

(g)   It becomes increasingly speculative to go much further than this, but to judge from the reputation Whatman's papers acquired later one might assume that the criticisms listed in the Society of Arts Memorandum of 1755 did not apply to them and that both at Hollingbourne and Turkey mill there was sufficient power to maintain high consistencies in their Engines leading to good fibrages which together with less impetuous roll–lowering would result in reduced fibre cutting and the survival of knots and strings.

(h)   The considerations listed above have centred principally on the advantages that would accrue from having adequate water power to service equipment that was more efficient at treating strong rags and capable of handling higher consistencies than had perhaps been possible with earlier installations in this country. But if one looks at the features that are to be found in the 1771 model, more numerous, sharper, bevelled and clumped bars (advances not reflected in Lalande or Desmarest's accounts nor in Husslage's reconstructions) one wonders whether there were not other features in the Old Mill Engines that contributed to a technical breakthrough.[89] Certainly, the success of this venture points to a more refined model, capable of better and more

---

[87] See the younger Whatman's drawing App.V PLATE 23.
[88] See Synopsis of the History of Old Mill, Hollingbourne, App.I.
[89] See App.V p.230.

precise control, than Dupin's mark, coupled with a thorough mastery of the new procedure; further consideration is given to this subject in Chapter VIII.

Turkey Mill v Old Mill, Hollingbourne

The circumstances that led Richard Harris to move to and ultimately acquire Turkey mill have already been examined.[90] Apart from its greater size were there any other factors that might have persuaded Harris to take this step ?

It is obvious from their continuing close relationship that there had been no difference of opinion between himself and Whatman that might have prompted him to leave a mill that had been purposely built for him. But by any standards Turkey mill was an exceptional mill for its time and the two of them must have laid their sights on it at an early date. Their plans to build Old Mill were evidently well advanced before Gill's bankruptcy; but, although Turkey mill was open to bids from 1731 onwards, they would not have been in a position to take this up since they had not yet had an opportunity to master the New Technology in a mill of their own. Once this had been achieved then it would have been a logical step to have moved to premises that clearly had a greater potential for them. On reflection the financing of this is unlikely to have been a major deterrent because in the event Harris ended by working both mills; the technical aspects of this situation clearly dominated the issue. However, as a tenant (1736–1738) he was not in a position to pull down and reconstruct the mill, but it would have enabled him to assess its qualities and plan accordingly. As intimated earlier, one senses that the whole episode had a purposeful direction in it.

One of the reasons put forward for their choice of the Hollingbourne site was the exceptional waterpower available there. Harris soon discovered that he had overestimated his horsepower requirements. Turkey mill would have offered him three waterwheels[91] which in Spain's view, operated independently, each generating 4 h.p. On the basis of one washer/beater providing for one vat, it could be argued that three of these would serve the three vats worked there in George Gill's time. But with better management, lower horsepower requirements and other improvements Harris would almost certainly have been able to go further than this and get three *pairs* of Engines geared to these wheels. That this was more than a possibility is shown by the fact that at some point before the elder Whatman's death (1759) Turkey mill had become a five–vat mill[92] and this expansion could have taken place in 1738/9 when the mill was rebuilt. But would this increased beating capacity have been sufficient reason by itself for Harris to make this move ?

Taking this last point, when Harris discovered that he had horsepower surplus to his requirements, it could be argued that, had he wanted to, he could have enlarged the beating facility at Old Mill without having to move. Turkey mill obviously had other advantages to offer.

---

[90]   Chap.IV p.169.
[91]   Harris, John Bib.4 191. Referring to the River Len at Turkey mill he wrote "Here it turns three over–shot wheels, of about 8 feet in diameter, which moves the whole work; the Water–Boards are about 2 feet and a half long, and the trough delivers a stream of water six inches deep".
[92]   Balston, T. Bib.1 13.

For one thing Harris would have had more space around him to expand his other facilities and one of the first things that he enlarged very considerably, when rebuilding the mill, was the Drying Loft,[93] a clear indication of his intention to increase production at the mill. Hollingbourne Old Mill, although it eventually became a five-vat mill, was situated in a narrow, steep-sided gorge which did not lend itself readily to expansion either in terms of building or for manpower and accommodation.[94] For one thing the mill site was remote and whereas labour for a one-vat mill might not have been too difficult to obtain there, a three-fold expansion of the whole mill (possibly five-fold) would have been another matter.

In addition to the problem of obtaining labour, there was also the question of transport and shipping. The proximity of Turkey mill to Maidstone, where both of these services were on hand, was another obvious point in favour of a move when the object behind it was to scale up operations by a factor of at least three.

Finally, there was the question of a clean water supply for preparing rags and for making White paper. Though it was customary to filter water by tying flannel bags over the water pipe outlets that fed into the Engines[95] and though rag-washing may have been more effective in the Hollander than in the stampers, it was still considered necessary, as it was in the 20th C., to have clean water for making the best qualities of paper and in those times this can only have come from springs.[96] In theory, Old Mill had similar sources of spring water

[93]   Balston, T. Bib.1 11 and Plate 2(b).

[94]   See Preface to Appendices I & II. Map 6.

[95]   Le Francois de Lalande, J.J. Bib.23 Art.26 in describing the old stamping process refers to settling tanks, piles of rags to keep back fine sand and straining bags for the removal of impurities in the water.

[96]   It is worth recording at this point some of the references that were made at this time to the subject of clean spring water in relation to the manufacture of White paper. George Gill's view has already been quoted earlier in Chapter III p.128. The advent of the Hollander washer made no difference to this requirement and clear water for White paper was still rated as of paramount importance in 1764 when the younger Whatman, on behalf of the Master Paper Makers of Great Britain, delivered to the Commissioners a Memorial (B.M.Add.MSS.38203 f.316) concerned with remedying serious anomalies in the method of levying Excise. One of the proposals included in its argument was that "it would be too hard on those Mills that make only Second (quality) Paper, as some, by reason of their situation and want of Spring Water, cannot possibly make Fine.....". As the sentence goes on to mention "Engines", it can be seen that even after the introduction of the New Technology the quality of water was a significant factor in the successful manufacture of White paper.

It is noteworthy also that, when the younger Whatman decided to increase his manufacturing capacity by acquiring Upper mill, Loose, in 1774/5, an important feature of this choice may have been the abundant supply of "Spring" water there. Spain, R.J. Bib.10 54 believed that its mill-pond was fed entirely from springs. But a recent pronouncement (1989) claims that the "strong springs" feeding this pond may in fact originate from the River Loose reaching it via an underground course from a sink-hole further upstream (see Map 3). On present evidence it has not been possible to determine whether this alternative channel resulted from recent activities e.g. blasting at the Boughton Monchelsea ragstone quarries further up the valley or even the result of a channel excavated in the 19th C. between Leg o' Mutton pond and Upper mill pond, i.e. in either case after Whatman's occupation of the mill; or to a much earlier geological fault in which case one would expect the water to have reached the pond thoroughly filtered and, effectively, as clean "spring" water. Other, genuine springs undoubtedly contributed to this supply also (local opinion disputes the sink-hole theory or at least minimizes its contribution).

In passing it may be noted that it was at this time (1774) that Clement Taylor jnr. took up the lease of Hollingbourne Old Mill following Whatman's occupation of it (1770-74) and one wonders what lay behind the latter's decision to leave one mill in favour of another.

Whatman certainly maintained an interest in spring water later than this. In 1785 when he drew up his proposals for allowing Mr. (James) Taylor to remain at Poll mill (Balston, T. Bib.1 79), after requiring him to keep the mill and its equipment in good order, he specifically adds further instructions regarding the Spring Water rights and pipes.

To judge from the increase in the number of mills making White paper as the 18th C. progressed and the enormous diversity of sites that they occupied, one wonders just how essential spring water was to them. However, when William

(continued...)

to those used by George Gill at Turkey mill, though possibly not so easily accessible to or sufficiently developed for the newly-built mill at that time as the well established supplies at Turkey mill. It may not have been a determining factor for Harris' move, but at least he knew that the clean water that he needed was there.

It was fortunate for Harris, and subsequently for Whatman also, that the opportunity for acquiring Turkey mill arose at just the right time.

[96](...continued)
> Balston took his courage in his hands and built a large paper mill in the middle of a field in 1805/6 (powered by steam) he chose the site for its copious supplies of spring water (Spring Field) and to this day the quality of the water there is still of paramount importance though many different kinds of water are used to match the wide variety of products still produced there. Certainly for those classes of paper, which were once covered by the term "White" paper, spring water was used for their manufacture right up to the mid-20th C.

In concluding this chapter it may be said that its purpose has been three–fold. First, although the differences between the traditional stamping process and the new method of stock preparation employing the Hollander may be well known to the majority of readers, at the risk of labouring the point the aim here has been to treat this subject in some detail in order to emphasize the magnitude of this change.

It has been pointed out that the breaking and beating of rags is not just a question of attrition, but one of separating out the fibres from the textile and then plasticizing and developing their surface to promote inter–fibre bonding. This can be achieved by both processes, but the paths by which this is accomplished are totally different. Consequently, the change involved learning and mastering the use of very heavy and high speed machinery in an operation requiring great skill and adapting this to suit the requirements of the vathouse. It may sound ridiculous but, whereas to some extent the beaterman could see what was going on in the troughs, in the new method neither he nor the master paper maker could poke their heads underneath the beater roll cover (or even lift it off) in order to see what was going on. It really was an act of faith on the part of these pioneering paper makers to make an installation of this kind, particularly as much larger quantities were involved in the case of every engine processed compared to those used in the trough.

Seen in retrospect and with a greater understanding of the underlying principles of this process, one perhaps sees the magnitude of this development more forcibly to–day than the contemporary paper maker might have done. One senses that in that age he would have been more conditioned than we are to–day in "having a go" at it. Contemporary accounts, like Lalande's and Desmarest's, give no sign of any trepidation on the part of the paper makers.

Second, to support the assertion made above, regarding the magnitude of this change from one process to the other, details of the evolution of the design and the practical aspects of operating the new Engine have been examined in order to demonstrate the much greater complexity of the new method, emphasizing the importance of establishing the most suitable system for the transmission of power from the waterwheel and the most effective ratio between energy supply and demand; maintenance of good circulation within the Engine; precise control of the roll position; and the use of the appropriate consistencies and arrangement of the barring in order to produce the correct type of fibrages for the preparative stage in hand.

And, with all this in mind, it was shown that the advantages of the new method far outweighed any of the difficulties which British paper makers clearly encountered when they first introduced the Hollander into their mills. They achieved outstanding increases in productivity and the ability to dispense with the messy rag fermentation process, providing themselves with more space within their mills to expand into; and, at the same time, gaining a more efficient rag–washing process together with producing, in theory, more uniform stuff. However, it has also been shown that in the course of adopting the new method many paper makers obviously ran into difficulties such as an insufficient supply of energy resulting in the practice of using low consistencies, impetuous roll lowering procedure and excessive fibre cutting with consequent deficiencies in the quality of the paper. Even where paper makers may have circumvented these shortcomings, for the period between the abandonment of the biochemical processing of rags and the advent of the "chemical era", they now had to contend with the presence of unremoved impurities surviving from the flax, that is as long as they continued to use linen rags, and this tended to produce coarse fibred stock.

Third, after considering the technical features of the Hollander itself, the practical aspects of an installation on the River Len in 1733 were examined and the energy generated at various mills along it, in particular the potential of the Hollingbourne site in relation to the use and requirements of an Engine there. An attempt has been made to determine the nature and size of Whatman's facility at Old Mill and the conclusion was reached that it heralded a technical breakthrough, probably in the form of a better ratio between the energy required and that supplied; or, alternatively, the use of a heavier and more effective installation than formerly used in Britain, also an energy consideration coupled perhaps with other improvements in the arrangement and design of the bars. As a result of demonstrating the complexity of this new process it must be patently self–evident to all and sundry, with or without knowledge of papermaking, that an essential ingredient of the ability to make this breakthrough was a thorough mastery of the new procedure, and not the result of a casual acquaintance with it.

The impression gained from this assessment was that (a) it confirmed the experimental nature of this investment; and (b) it showed that Whatman and Harris must have overestimated their energy requirements for this venture. Rather than develop the Old Mill site, which had several shortcomings in terms of space for expansion and remoteness for satisfactory logistics, they turned their attention to Turkey mill which had, as it happened, an adequate supply of energy and other advantages to offer in the form of space, more readily available labour, shipping and more proven supplies of spring water.

Finally, having outlined some of the difficulties and complexities of the new method of preparing stuff for the vat the reader should now be in a position to appreciate more readily the problem (for which a solution has been proposed earlier) of accounting for Harris', and subsequently Whatman's, acquisition and mastery of the new technique. The Hollander had been introduced into the British Isles some 40 years earlier, but the impact of this seems to have been less dramatic and with fewer installations than one might have expected. Something had happened in this case to change the course of events and one reverts inevitably to the suggestion that Richard Harris had acquired the art in Holland (where else ?) and had seen at first hand the essential features needed for a successful application of this method in his own country.

Chapter VII

THE STATUS OF THE ELDER JAMES WHATMAN
AS A PAPER MAKER
AND HIS INFLUENCE ON PAPERMAKING IN KENT

Having described the elements of the New Technology, the problems that it would create for the paper makers adopting it and the general state of the domestic White paper industry in the early decades of the 18th C., with particular emphasis on papermaking in Kent, the time has come to bring all these strands together to try to determine whether progress in the industry during the latter part of the century was haphazard in character or whether there was an underlying pattern in this evolution and, if so, what factors influenced this. Paper historians have tended to latch onto a statement of Thomas Balston's:–[1]

"Till the outbreak of war with Spain in 1739 little good white paper was being made in England and stationers and publishers relied almost entirely on importations from the Continent, but during the war importation was much impeded by enemy action, and by its end in 1748 the English manufacturers, with Whatman among them, had so much increased and improved their output that they permanently secured the market."

There is little doubt that these years were important in encouraging the growth of the domestic industry, but were the effects of this war really responsible for increasing and improving output and securing the market place for the English paper maker ? Doubt has already been expressed on several occasions in this book on the validity of this conclusion.

The almost complete absence of documentary references to installations and other improvements relating to the New Technology makes it essential to scrutinize very carefully such circumstantial evidence as is available in order to present a credible alternative to Thomas Balston's claims. Examination of this situation for reasons to be given later will be confined mainly to the period 1740–1800. It will not escape the reader's notice that the starting date for this was the year when the elder Whatman took over Turkey mill and made his official début as a paper maker.

The analysis of the data covering this period is a complicated exercise and to simplify matters as far as possible this chapter has been divided into eight parts followed by a summary. Parts I–V together with the summary will provide an adequate picture for the *general reader*. Parts VI–VIII include for the *specialist reader* thumbnail sketches of some 42 paper mills with important evidence and new material to complete the picture of papermaking in Kent up to and sometimes beyond 1800. To pave the way for this it is a *sine qua non* that the position the elder Whatman occupies in this picture should be considered first.

---

[1] Balston, T. Bib.1 12

CHAPTER VII

PART I

THE STATUS OF THE ELDER JAMES WHATMAN AS A PAPER MAKER

It is worth quoting at this point certain excerpts from the opening passage of Thomas Balston's Introduction to his book "James Whatman, Father and Son".[2]

> "All paper historians from Richard Herring (1855) to Dard Hunter (1947) have noted the pre-eminence of a James Whatman in the great revival of English paper making in the eighteenth century, but none of them has been able to give more than a few facts or figures to substantiate this claim and most of them were unaware that there were two James Whatmans, father and son".

He goes on to quote from Wardrop who had said that of the father nothing was known of his activities; but, as a result of his own research, it could now be definitely stated that:–

> "James Whatman I, though still elusive as a human being, established one of the greatest, if not the greatest, paper factories in the United Kingdom, and was also the first maker, and probably the inventor, of wove, the kind of paper which is now in almost universal use."

And at the beginning of Chapter IV of this book he went on to add:

> "There are good reasons.......for thinking that James Whatman I was a man of exceptional ability and no less enterprising than his more famous son to whom all credit for the pre-eminence of Whatman papers has hitherto been given. It has, however, proved impossible to find any direct evidence of the father's education and character".

One can see from these excerpts, and many other examples could be cited right up to and including some in this century, that the figure of the elder Whatman had for all intents and purposes disappeared from the historical scene, but that within the last thirty years he has been largely re-instated, recognized, at least, as a paper maker "no less enterprising than his more famous son". We shall have to come back later and see whether this is really a fair assessment of his contribution to British papermaking. In the meantime, in spite of Thomas Balston's work, the mystery surrounding his involvement and rapid success in papermaking had remained. Interest in this question was heightened further by more detailed examination of his later achievement such as the development of Wove paper and these prompted one to ask whence had he, a tanner, acquired expertise of this order in another trade ? A solution to this problem has already been discussed in some detail in Chapter III: e.g. his early association with the papermaking Harris family, the nodal position he occupied as a supplier to the local paper industry, his investment in a new and obviously very special paper mill of his own and many other contributory factors. If we take all this and consider it in conjunction with what has been revealed in the preceding chapters of this book about the technical progress of the White paper industry in this country during the half century prior to 1740 and the bringing together of the various strands by Harris and Whatman during the 1730's, it must surely have become increasingly obvious that one is witnessing in these events what must represent the most important technological watershed in the history of British papermaking prior to the 19th C. and, at the same time, demonstrates that Whatman played a key role in

---

[2] Balston, T. Bib.1 ix.

this advance. Even so a watershed could be defined in its simplest form merely as a line separating one set of practices from another, when in fact the claim made here goes much further than this. The progress achieved could, for instance, have lapsed with the death of Richard Harris. In the event there was much more to come.

The Status of the elder Whatman

What Thomas Balston had to say about the status of the elder Whatman and his assessment leaves us with an extremely shadowy figure. One discovers that he married, gained control of Turkey Mill; his paper was used by important persons; he made the first wove paper in Europe; he made money and had a very large paper mill. But we learn virtually nothing about his background nor whether there was any sort of projection of his achievement on the industry. He remains as a result an isolated figure.

In this book, though documentary evidence is for the most part missing, it has been possible to construct a credible background for Whatman's formative years and explain how he acquired an intimate knowledge of papermaking during this time. This can now be coupled with Thomas Balston's findings and henceforward one has to recognize that it is a *fact*, and no longer a supposition, that from 1740 onwards Whatman went from strength to strength, financially, in the quality of his products and in reputation. Though others have argued that the factors that led to his success resulted (a) from progressive amendments in the past to the rates of Duty starting to have a protective effect on domestic output;[3] and (b) the interruption of imports caused by the War of the Austrian Succession,[4] to take advantage of this situation it cannot be over-emphasised that Whatman had to be *technically equipped and ready* to employ his more productive methods by 1740 to enable him to compete successfully in the market place and not fail as other paper makers had done. All this could not have been accomplished overnight.

Though imports of White paper had fallen substantially,[5] they were still very significant, particularly those from Holland where the excellence of their papers and the long established application of the New Technology with its higher rate of productivity put them in a very strong position *vis-à-vis* British papers. Imports were not prevented, only impeded, by the War and clearly Protection was not yet enough by itself; to have succeeded Whatman would have needed all the weapons at the disposal of the Dutch paper makers to overcome the in-built prejudices of the London Stationers, who favoured foreign papers. So it can be said that, even on this basis, a very important phase in the history of British papermaking was in the process of unfolding; and, in retrospect, one can see that the New Technology, in its broadest sense, in the hands of Whatman was already playing a vital role in releasing the White paper manufacture of this country from the fetters that had for so long restricted its progress. Unless this is accepted, how else can we explain the prosperous nature of this provincial paper maker's business and the quality of his papers ? To sustain him in this invasion of the home market he had none of the experience or entrepreneurial flair of a cosmopolitan figure like Nicholas Dupin. He had to rely instead on something much more substantial.

[3] See Chapter IV pp.159/160.
[4] Balston, T. Bib.1 12.
[5] Coleman, D.C. Bib.15 94 (Table IV), 95.

Although a new paper mill and the New Technology had been at Whatman's disposal as early as 1733 it is unlikely that he could have exploited these assets successfully without the help and experience of Richard Harris.[6] He and Harris had knit the improvements in technology together in a way that no other paper makers of the period could match. It was really the joint efforts of these two men that laid the solid foundation on which Whatman's reputation was subsequently built. And yet, as events after 1740 demonstrate, Whatman manifestly had the capability to carry this work forward and extend it into new fields. He could not possibly have "established one of the greatest, if not the greatest, paper factories in the United Kingdom" without a technical competence of his own. So that at no time can he be regarded as a passive partner to Harris. The economic climate of the 1740's certainly helped his work forward, but success sprung, initially at least, from an ability to execute the tasks set him, and to implement these meant gaining the entrée to an intractable market.

It seems safe to assume that he was helped in this respect by James Brooke, the London Stationer and Bookseller who, it will be recalled, had been custodian to both William Gill senior and junior and one time owner of Turkey Mill. As a central figure in this situation he had obviously seen the merits of Harris' and Whatman's methods which, in the end, must have persuaded him to sell the mill to the former of these two.[7] Now that the business had passed into Whatman's hands it would clearly have been to the benefit of both that Brooke should continue to act for him; that it is a perfectly legitimate assumption to make is upheld by the longstanding relationship that followed between Brooke's protégé, William Gill jnr., and the Whatmans. It is also possible that it may have been partly, or even wholly, due to the good offices of Brooke that Walsh knew where to turn for his paper in 1740.[8]

But, according to Thomas Balston, the elder Whatman appears to have gained his reputation in the early stages of his career more because of the quality of his Writing papers than from paper used for printing. He cites examples of Whatman papers found among the State Papers (Domestic) from at least 1747, as well as papers in other public offices and in the great households;[9] and, indeed, we find his Writing papers *being used in America* as early as 1753.[10] To set the seal on all this Professor Hazen made the observation that the Whatman laid papers of this period were the best on the market.[11] As to printing, Thomas Balston pointed out that "few books were then being printed on first–class papers", nevertheless he does give some examples of ones that were printed on Whatman paper, especially those published in the 1750's.[12] In retrospect it can be seen that he had made for himself a position in the market place from which he and his son never looked back.

It is worth mentioning in the context of the above that, among others, Robert Dodsley, the publisher, must also have been attracted at this time by the excellence of Whatman's papers and that it was through him that Baskerville obtained the paper needed to bring his opus

---

[6]   See Chap.V p.172.
[7]   See Chapter IV p.169.
[8]   See Chapter III p.104.
[9]   Bib.1 13.
[10] For further details see App.V pp.281 ff. and note 2 citing Gravell, T.L. Bib.16 Letter 17:Dec:1980.
[11] Hazen, Allen T. "A Bibliography of the Strawberry Hill Press" (Yale, 1952).
[12] It is hoped that with the introduction of ESTC more examples may come to light (the computerised Eighteenth–century Short Title Catalogue).

P. Sandby 1794

Plate 15 – View of the Whatman Mills and Vinters from the Roebuck Fields

(Private Collection)

magnum, the intended Virgil, to fruition in 1757.[13] Baskerville's requirement, first specified in 1754, was for "a very fine Writing Royal Paper" to match his newly perfected type, his more accurately constructed press and the improvements he had made in the colour and firmness of his ink. In the event Whatman developed papers specially for this purpose, including the first specimens of Wove paper.[14] That the initiative for this technical innovation came from the paper maker and not the other way round, from the printer, is supported, to give one example, by Dryden Leach's use of this new paper (quite independent of either Dodsley or Baskerville) when printing Edward Capell's "Prolusions" in October 1759 for the publisher Tonson. This more developed and improved specimen of wove paper bore the single line "W" with loop type of countermark used by the elder Whatman and was made on a similar sized mould, possibly slightly modified in construction, to the one used to make the uncountermarked paper for Baskerville's 1759 4° "Paradise Regained".

All these indicators, his prosperity, his success and reputation in the market place, taken in conjunction with the great size of his paper mill (a factor often overlooked), his mastery of the New Technology and the confidence he clearly had in his products, demonstrable through his extensive use of countermarks,[15] point to him as a person of some considerable standing in the paper trade. And, if one adds to all this the preparative work that went into his investment and venture with Richard Harris before 1740, then one must not only accept Thomas Balston's statement that "there are good reasons.....for thinking that James Whatman I was a man of exceptional ability", but, inevitably, one begins to question whether his verdict "that he was no less enterprising than his more famous son" is in fact a fair appraisal of his status.

The younger Whatman, as Thomas Balston demonstrated, had many claims to fame; he was a very able person in more ways than one and in some respects at least this must reflect the abilities and position of his parents. It was no mean achievement, for instance, for the young James to have been appointed High Sheriff of Kent at the age of 26. Moreover, right up to the end of his career he acted very much as a spokesman (together with Joseph Portal) for the paper industry in matters connected with Excise and the like. He had a considerable reputation as a paper maker during his lifetime, his papers were in great demand and his business expanded and prospered, his products becoming a symbol of excellence. There are

---

[13] It is not known whether Whatman ever met either Baskerville or Dodsley. Professor Hazen in his paper "Baskerville and James Whatman" (Studies in Bibliography, the Bibliographical Society, Univ. of Virginia Vol.V 1952/3) claimed that "the association between Whatman and Baskerville has to be traced through William Shenstone and Dodsley, but it is nevertheless exactly demonstrable". (The role of Shenstone, landscape gardener and poet, does not seem to have been relevant in this particular case).

[14] Balston, J.N. Bib.76

[15] Examples of early Whatman countermarks have been given in various parts of this book e.g. an "IW" mark of 1740 (see Chap.III); and the single line "IW"s, "JW"s and "W"s with loop (see App.V Section on Solitary "W" countermarks and Balston, T. Bib.1 App.V). Whatman is known to have used most of these forms, including his cypher (Plate 26), between 1740– 50. All the same the number of examples recorded appear to remain small and, indeed, the *only certain* single line "W" marks with loop occurring before 1759 have been found in American documents. The author drew attention to this fact in a letter published in the June 1986 issue of "Paper Conservation News" No.38 (Publ. by The Institute of Paper Conservation) and pointed out that during this decade (1740–50) Turkey Mill must have produced at least 10,000,000 sheets of paper and that it was difficult to believe that the great bulk of this could have been lost or remained unidentified. (There was a nil response to this communication.)

many other facets of his life which show that he was a progressive and cultured man whose interests extended far beyond the boundaries of Kent.[16]

That he was a man of distinction in his own right is beyond doubt; but he had the undeniable advantage of starting from a very favourable position, the solid foundations laid down by his father and Richard Harris who together had had the task of mastering the New Technology and other improvements in papermaking, building up a great manufacturing business and his father establishing an unassailable position in the market place as well as extending the technology of papermaking.[17] Some achievement, but was this all ? Did the elder Whatman exert any demonstrable influence on his contemporaries ? It can be said at once that there is no documentary evidence to show that he did. But, if we examine the progress of the paper industry in Kent beyond the point where we left it in Chapter IV, we can undoubtedly infer from the events that took place after this that his influence extended beyond that of laying the foundations for the success of his son.

[16] Socially he was indeed a "child of his time" employing Humphry Repton with his red book to redesign Vinters Park; he commissioned Paul Sandby, the grandfather of English watercolour painting of whom Gainsborough had said "the only man of genius who has painted real views of nature in this country", to paint Turkey Mill with Vinters in the background (PLATE XV); his second wife, Susanna (Bosanquet d.o. Jacob, a Director of the East India Company), now noted for her enchanting "Housekeeping Book", had her portrait painted by Romney; he bought a number of pictures at Christie's in 1776 and inherited from his first father-in-law a remarkable collection of paintings including a famous van Dyck, Salvator Rosa, Tintoretto, Carlo Dolci, Reynold's portrait of Laurence Sterne, Hobbema and a Wright of Derby. He also knew many of the distinguished people of his time.

[17] The following might be seen as a corollary to this. In their relations with the paper industry it would be wrong to assume that either of the Whatmans were in any way arrogant or supercilious. The younger Whatman represented the interests of the trade as a whole and his correspondence always appears thoughtful and courteous. From the other side it is equally clear that they were regarded as exceptionally gifted paper makers. One might take as an unsolicited example of this the Society of Arts' approach to the younger Whatman in 1774 regarding the possible substitution of wild cotton for linen rags (for details see Balston, T. Bib.1 36/7); in a sense it was a measure of his status. This point is made here because it is also noteworthy that neither of the Whatmans ever took part in the Society of Arts' deliberations or competitions for improving the qualities of various papers. Coleman (Bib.47 364/5) has commented on this abstention and, in fact, questions the effectiveness of the Society's premiums on the development of the English paper industry, concluding that it was probably very limited. One might read into all this that both of the Whatmans must have been aware that they were a long way ahead of the others. In short, they were self-sufficient and evidently considered that they would have been wasting their time taking part in these rather dubious projects.

PART II

*FACTORS INFLUENCING THE MANUFACTURE OF WHITE PAPER
IN ENGLAND AFTER 1740*

Between 1740–1800 the number of paper mills of all types in England and Wales doubled in number.[18] Much the same picture holds for Kent, the number rising from ca. 23 to 45; and countywise Kent was still at the head of the Table. But compared to an extended West of London Region (70+ mile radius), where the figure was some 123 mills, they were completely outnumbered by a factor of ~2.73.[19] In terms of White mills, however, this disparity is considerably reduced with Kent having 33/35 White mills compared to a re-assessed total for the West of London Region of ca. 60–70 giving a ratio of ~1 : 1.76–2.06, that is Kent v the *whole* of the West of London Region embracing 11 counties.[20] It can be seen from this that from "close to being, if not actually, the most important White papermaking county in England"[21] Kent had by 1800 become beyond doubt the most important centre for this manufacture in the United Kingdom with over 70 vats compared to the West's 93.[22] These figures, it must be understood, at best are *very approximate* (mostly 1957 data) but at least indicate the order of magnitude; they are discussed in greater detail later and compared in 3 Tables (IX, X and XI).

As already indicated this growth, initially, was slow, an increase of about 30 mills in England and Wales in the first 15 years of this period; and only 6–7 new mills in Kent up to 1755, out of which probably fewer than 2–3 made White paper of sorts at that time.[23] The pattern of this expansion will be examined in parts IV–VIII of this chapter. The points to note at this juncture are (a) that for a considerable period after 1740 the expansion of the industry as a whole was by no means a sudden one; and (b) although later in the century paper manufacture

[18]   Shorter, A. Bib.9 76.

[19]   It is difficult to arrive at an exact figure for the number of mills in a county at a given date and even the choice of a date can easily affect the interpretation of the resulting figures, a number of mills would have ceased working and others about to begin. Add to this the fact that in many cases it would be difficult to classify the mills productwise, particularly as by the end of the 18th C. the range of paper products had widened extensively. The figures given in the text must be seen in the light of all this and only be regarded as an approximate indicator of growth. By 1800 Kent had ca.45 mills and the extended West of London Region ca.123. Other areas where there had been a notable growth of paper mills (all types) include the West of England, Devonshire with 30; Gloucestershire ca.17 and Shropshire 14. Further north one has Yorkshire with 38 and Lancashire with 21. However, not many of these were White mills. The date 1800 has been chosen because it marks the near peak of waterpowered handmade paper mills. In 1738 it was claimed that there were 338 vats operating in England & Wales and in 1800 there were probably something like 650 vats (the estimate excludes Scotland & Ireland. Shorter, A. Bib.9 104 gives a figure of 760 vats in the U.K. for 1805).

[20]   Both the Kent figures and the West of London Region's are based on a re-assessment, the basis of which will be discussed later in this chapter.

[21]   See Chapter I p.27.

[22]   The main basis for this comparison is Shorter, A. Bib.12 App.J. The ratio shown here is 1:1.4. It is quite possible, therefore, that the number of vats in the West of London Region may have been higher than indicated by Shorter i.e. for White mills. An added difficulty in making this comparison is that by the end of the 18th C. the number of vats per mill was increasing very rapidly.

[23]   Chap.III p.115.

in Kent was almost exclusively concerned with White papers this is only partially reflected in the growth for this early period.

Apropos of the above the demand for all sorts of paper increased approximately four–fold between 1740–1800, the demand for White paper increasing roughly in the same ratio.[24] In very general terms, then, for the initial period (1740–1755) the indications are that this increase must have been met mostly by either an increase in size of existing mills; taking up the slack in existing capacity and/or up–grading from brown to white; or through increased productivity, probably a combination of all these.[25] The factors that affected this situation, and in particular the growth of White paper manufacture in Kent, are decidedly much more difficult to disentangle from one another, in terms of rating their respective influence, after 1740 than they were before. Some of these are examined below, mainly with a view to trying to isolate, if possible, the effects of the New Technology in this situation.[26]

The two sides to the equation in this set of circumstances were made up on the one hand, for the purchaser by market forces including the prevailing political climate, the demand for paper, the price of papers on offer, their quality and availability; and on the other, for the supplier whether foreign or domestic, by production costs linked to existing fiscal obligations and coupled with the technical resources and competence of the paper makers concerned and their ability to deliver the goods. Since all of these quantities were subject to considerable variation as the century progressed, so a shift in emphasis on one or more of them would have affected the balance between imports and domestic products and thus, in turn, influenced the direction and character of the British paper industry; and because the country was more or less self–sufficient in supplies of Brown paper at this time, one is in effect talking here about the fortunes of the White paper industry.

For example, it has been said that while this country was still dependent on importing the best qualities of White paper, as was the case for the first decades of this period, War could have been a crucial element affecting the supplies of these papers to the domestic market. So that one might expect the War of the Austrian Succession, 1740–48, to have imposed a certain degree of Hobson's choice on the Stationers and Printers who normally used French or Dutch paper, thus favouring the domestic supplier, even if he could not compete in price or quality. Thomas Balston's much quoted reference to this has already been cited at the beginning of this chapter. This was undoubtedly an important contributory factor to Whatman's rapid achievement of success; but it was clearly not the only one and had it not been for assistance from other agencies he might have ended as a bankrupt once the war was over; the same

---

[24] Chap.III p.114.

[25] For the 15 years following 1740 the number of paper mills in England & Wales increased by 30 approximately on a figure of 278, namely, equivalent to ca.10%. Using Coleman's curves for output (Bib.15 fig.2 opp.p.90) for England & Wales during this period, there was a rise of approximately 1700 tons on a figure of 2800 tons for 1740, equivalent to 60%. An increase of output of this order, taking into account the small number of new mills and the limitations imposed on their production through the use of water power, can only be explained by attributing it mainly to the mills already in production. In an indirect way this conclusion is lent further support by his figures for Rag imports for this period (loc.cit). Though his curve for these fluctuates considerably during this period, the general upward trend is greater than the 84% indicated (i.e. between ca.650 tons for 1740 and 1200 tons for 1755), probably something nearer to 140% increase. As suggested earlier, it seems likely that imported rags were destined mainly for White paper production and that the quantities of these would be more closely related to the output of White paper than to the total paper output (see Chap.III note 78).

[26] For a full account of the *economic* factors see Coleman, D.C. Bib.15 Chapters IV & V.

circumstances could have arisen, and probably did, equally in the case of other manufacturers of White paper in Kent, leading to failure or, at least, increasing their difficulties.[27]

Another, and probably more important element in this equation, certainly in the long term, was the question of Protection. After a further tightening up of the protective barriers in 1743, to reduce evasion of Duty on imported papers, Coleman considers that the wide margin that existed between Customs and Excise rates led to the paper industry growing up for the greater part of the 18th C. "as an extremely sheltered industrial child".[28] He goes on later to say:‐

> "Be it by accident or intent.....heed seems to have been paid to the notion that 'Wise Nations' were 'fond of encouraging Manufactures in their infancy' (Sir Theodore Janssen). In the short run the home consumer paid for this policy by paying more for his paper. Perhaps the slowness of the industry's growth for most of the century may be in part due to this brake upon demand. Yet an industry was developed, albeit a high cost industry reared in an atmosphere of duties and surrounded by a deal of conservatism. But it did exist and might well not have done without protection".[29]

Whether one can agree entirely with this view is something that will be reviewed later. Without any doubt the protection afforded by Customs was a major plus to the domestic producer in our equation. Nevertheless it can be said in passing that for most of the 18th C. the industry was tied to a very limited supply of energy from a low efficiency waterwheel, which unlike windpower, prevented it from expanding into much larger, and potentially more economic, units. In contrast to the plus afforded by protection there were a number of important minuses so far as home production was concerned. Up till 1781 Coleman considers that the rate of Excise was low enough not to hinder the progress of the domestic industry; but after 1781 the gap between Customs and Excise was narrowed. Customs had had an increasingly deterrent effect on imports ever since 1714. The regulations had been tightened up in 1725 and again in 1743. This had been followed by further increases of 5% in 1747, 1759, 1779 and 1782; these had a really punitive effect on imports.[30] But the underlying aim of all these increases was directed more towards raising revenue to pay for War than any motive for saving the paper industry from extinction. In parallel, after 1781, the rates of Excise became progressively more oppressive. The effect of this is exemplified in the younger Whatman's production expenditure, Excise comprising 4% of this in 1780 and 22% by 1785 and it did not stop there; between 1770–1800 the output of paper "rather less than doubled whilst the yield of the duty multiplied over eleven‐fold".[31] But for the early period when the rate of Excise had been relatively low, it was applied inequitably and penalised the "Fair Trader" and the manufacturer of the better classes of paper. They were entitled to a Drawback on the Excise paid for papers exported, and certain other special cases, but through inefficiencies in the administration they were unable to obtain it, causing "a very material injury to the Manufacture" particularly when faced with competition from the Dutch "who already undersell us". So despite the beneficial effects of Protection in the period immediately

---

[27] Though possibly due to a variety of different causes, paper maker bankruptcies in Kent during this period include (a) Richard Archer at Dartford No.2 in 1740; (b) Andrew Johannot at Eynsford in 1746; (c) William Stevens at Sittingbourne in 1749; (d) Herbert and Slater at Chartham in 1757; (e) the failure of John Sanders at Old Mill, Hollingbourne, in 1745 and his bankruptcy in 1748.

[28] Bib.15 142.

[29] Coleman, D.C. Bib.15 145.

[30] Coleman, D.C. Bib.15 127.

[31] Coleman, D.C. Bib.15 141/2.

after 1740 the Excise picture was not an entirely rosy one for the White paper makers of this country.[32]

Other important minuses include the cost of raw materials and wages. Coleman quotes two sets of figures for these, one of them based on the younger Whatman's Ledger (1780's) and an earlier set based on Keferstein ca.1765,[33] which he feels may be regarded as not untypical. They at least show that the order of expenditure on these two items was considerable; rags in Whatman's case amounting to 47.5% and that is out of a total that

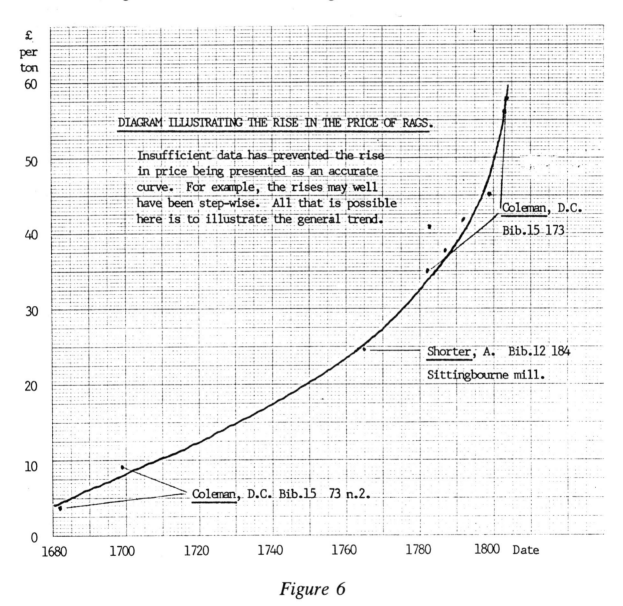

DIAGRAM ILLUSTRATING THE RISE IN THE PRICE OF RAGS.

Insufficient data has prevented the rise in price being presented as an accurate curve. For example, the rises may well have been step-wise. All that is possible here is to illustrate the general trend.

Coleman, D.C. Bib.15 173

Shorter, A. Bib.12 184
Sittingbourne mill.

Coleman, D.C. Bib.15 73 n.2.

Figure 6

[32] B.M. Add. MSS 38203 f.316 quoted in full, Balston, T. Bib.1 App.III 149 A Memorial delivered by the younger Whatman in 1764 to the Commissioners of the Excise on behalf of the paper makers of Great Britain. Balston (ibid.70) has calculated that the younger Whatman was paying between 8–10% of the Excise on Class I & II papers (the best) collected from the whole of the English paper industry. (cf. this chapter pp.273/4 and n.73).

[33] Coleman, D.C. Bib.15 169 using the Whatman Ledger, P.S.M.; and G.C. Keferstein "Unterricht eines Papiermachers an seine Söhne" Leipzig 1766.

includes 21.5% Excise, other raw materials amounting to 11.5%. In Keferstein's case the figures were somewhat lower with 38% arising from rags, 12% from other raw materials and 7% Excise. (He claims also that even the old ropes used for Brown paper accounted for ca.35% of the selling price).[34] Unfortunately, very few figures seem to have been unearthed for the cost of rags. The few that are available have been plotted to give the curve shown in fig.6.

The figures are too few to enable one to draw precise conclusions from this curve. Whatever the basic reason a shifting supply and demand situation would have caused rag prices to fluctuate. Thus, if War led to a shortage of imported paper supplies (in 1743, for instance, only 14 reams of White paper were imported from France with whom we had been at war for 3 years) the price of rags probably rose sharply to meet a consequent increase in domestic production (even though in this case the potential for importing rags from Germany may have remained unaffected by the conflict). Or, again, when domestic White papers were struggling initially to gain a foothold in the market, the demand for rags may have been less than when they had established a firm position. In other words the probability is that the curve was flatter than shown here up to, say, 1740;[35] rose more steeply for a period after this date and even more steeply in the 1760's as the manufacture of domestic White paper gathered momentum.[36] The curve as it stands may well represent then less drastic changes in rag prices than actually took place at certain intervals. Even so this smoother curve shows rises of nearly 26% between 1740–55; 86% by 1780 and 180% by 1800. As rags formed ca.40–50% of White paper production costs, these rises can only be regarded as severe minuses for the domestic producer; so that it was, perhaps, just as well that Customs afforded him protection against a situation that was really outside his control. It will be recalled that during this period there was no shortage of linen textiles in the country. Despite every effort to overcome the paper maker's problem, no efficient system was devised for the collection of rags. Even the younger Whatman, who must have been a very efficient paper maker, made the plea to the Society of Arts in 1774 that they "would do our Manufacture an essential service if, by Advertisements or any other means, they could Induce the Publick to be more careful in saving their Rags".[37]

It seems that it is not until the last decades of the 18th C. that any figures have survived for the wages of individual paper mill employees in this country. That industrial wages rose during the 18th C. is a recognized fact, but on present evidence it is not possible to quantify this rise as a Paper mill cost for the whole of the period between 1740–1800. Indeed it is not known precisely how many people were employed in any given mill. Fortunately, at the top end of the trade some statistics based on the younger Whatman's accounts provide us with a

---

[34] Coleman, D.C. Bib.15 170 note 2.

[35] cf. the valuation of rags in Robert Archer's Inventory for 1737 at £6 per ton. The indications are that he was making White paper at Sittingbourne mill, but whether the rags were top quality is not known; but, if the quality was good, then this figure would support a stepwise upward trend in the curve, rising perhaps sharply during the War of the Austrian Succession. (See Chap.IV n.25).

[36] In Chap.III n.78 it was suggested that the quantities of imported rags during these periods were more closely related to White paper production than to the total output of paper. Although one is dealing with 2 different measurements, cost and quantity, if one plots Coleman's figures for Rag Imports (Bib.15 fig.2 opp.p.90) using a linear scale, the steep rises in rag imports for the periods 1740–52 and the 1760's with intervening platforms do, though it may be pure coincidence, correspond with the steps suggested above for the more likely shape of cost of rags curve.

[37] Letter quoted in full, Balston, T. Bib.1 36/7; see also this book Chap.V p.185.

general indication of what these costs may have been for the trade as a whole; at least they are unlikely to have exceeded these figures. Wages appear as a lump sum in his accounts, but from the remarkable constancy of the figures for two lengthy periods one might legitimately assume that both the numbers of his workforce and their wages remained unaltered for the duration of each of these terms. Thomas Balston has given figures for the wage bills at Turkey mill between 1762–1766 and 1780–1787 as well as the wages of Upper mill, Loose for the second period.[38] For the first period the figures range from £980–£1,049, averaging £1,015; and for the second they average £1,253 for a period of seven years (excluding 1781 when the wage bill for some reason was out of line with the others at £1,081) for Turkey mill; and averaging ca. £224 for Upper mill, Loose, over eight years. The latter figure, as Thomas Balston pointed out, is almost exactly one fifth of the Turkey mill figure and therefore following the ratio of 1 : 5 vats. In other words we have here a unit figure for a high class one–vat mill. To be seen in conjunction with the above it may also be said that there is no evidence, particularly given the limitations in water power, of any enlargement of Turkey mill or its workforce to account for the different levels in Whatman's wage bills for these two periods.

It may be taken then that the above figures represent a rise in workmen's wages of ca. 27% over a period of 20 years (1767–1780). Whether this was gradual or not and whether it was representative of the White paper industry as a whole can only be guessed at. But this figure may be compared with general industrial wages which appear to have risen by ca. 25% during the latter part of the 1770's after a period of some 45–50 years of comparative stability.[39] It could be argued then that for the initial period after 1740 the domestic White paper industry was not faced with a rapidly rising wage bill; but in terms of being a minus factor in the equation it still had to face a much higher wage bill than the French paper maker, quite possibly as much as three times greater.[40] At a later stage the industry had to cope with further troubles. It is not known exactly when its workforce began agitating for higher wages. There had been occasions earlier when a paper maker found it difficult to hire labour at almost any price; but at some point in the 18th C. a journeyman's union came into being that could now exert positive pressure on employers, particularly those in White mills. Some claim quite an early date for this, but there is no evidence within the paper trade for combinations of workmen acting against their employers before the 1780's, e.g. near Manchester and in Kent, where paper mill employees' wages were higher than elsewhere in England; that was ca.1790.[41] But there are indications that the pressures were already in being in that some employers were attempting to recruit cheaper Scottish and Irish labour in the 1780's. The trouble could easily have started much earlier if the English paper makers had not consented to pay much higher rates than the French.[42] In France combinations of

[38] Balston, T. Bib.1 67.

[39] Wilson, C. & Parker, G. "An introduction to the Sources of European Economic History. 1500–1800" (London, 1977) British Isles 5.5. Two curves are illustrated; one for prices at levels considerably above the level of industrial wages. Though prices fluctuated between 1740– 1760 the average of these remained more or less level for this period. Likewise wages, after a rise ca.1730, also remained as a plateau until ca.1777 when the level rose abruptly by 25%.

[40] Coleman, D.C. Bib.15 143–4.

[41] Coleman, D.C. Bib.15 262/3.

[42] That this situation dates back a long way is seen in "Angliae Tutamen" (1695) whose anonymous author wrote "White, Blue, and Brown–Papers, made here in England, Ireland and Scotland, shall be examin'd next. This good Fortune we in England have had to improve wonderfully in this Art, and though we cannot reach the French Perfection, yet we come

(continued...)

journeymen or "compagnonnages" had been active since the 17th C. and in spite of repeated legislation against them there were many instances of strikes there, increasingly so in the 18th C.[43] and, indeed, the invention of the paper machine by Nicholas–Louis Robert conceived in 1796 might have been considerably delayed had it not been provoked by this industrial unrest.[44]

Taken as a whole, then, the wage element in the equation, probably lying somewhere between 10–15% of production costs and considerably above French wage levels (noteworthy as they continued to use the Old Technology with its lower productivity and larger workforce much later than in England), must be rated as a significant minus despite there being no major increase until the 1770's by which time the domestic White paper industry was reasonably well established and better able to cope with this situation, that is *vis–à–vis* competition from the Continent; a significant debit item but not anything like as damaging as the rise in the cost of raw materials.

With regard to the effect of paper mill costs as a whole, a lot would have depended on the alterations that took place in various mills as they up–graded their product range, adopted the New Technology and expanded. Richard Harris and the elder Whatman had undertaken all of this before 1740. Even so one finds that during the period 1763–1766 the younger Whatman's "maintenance" costs rose from £566 to £1,035; and, if the total expenditure for Turkey and Upper mill, Loose, for the period 1780–1787 is broken down, the separate costs are:[45]

	Average
Rags	49.9%
Other Raw Materials : Gelatine, Alum, Smalts, Coals	9.6%
Wages	13.3%
Sundries : Insurance, various services & goods, timber etc..	8.5%
Excise after, but not including 1780.	18.7%

	100%

One must conclude then that as paper mills were converted to the New Technology and White paper manufacture, or were constructed as new mills for this purpose, the capital costs in addition to the rises in production costs could well have accumulated into a formidable minus in the equation for the aspiring manufacturer.

In the foregoing pages the political and economic circumstances that influenced the development of the domestic White paper industry for the period immediately after 1740 and

[42](...continued)
  pretty near it, and make much finer Paper than ever, which in this our Exigency, I mean the Prohibition of Commerce with France, is of very great Service to us; but *our Hands are dearer that are employ'd*, we cannot work so cheap as the French, because we must have Beef, Pudding and strong Drink, our people can't live upon Onions, Turnips, and small Soupes.....". Even so food prices were considerably higher in England than wages and few could have afforded the "roast–beef of Old England" referred to here.

[43] Coleman, Bib.15 259–261.

[44] Coleman, Bib.15 180 ff. giving many sources of information.

[45] Balston, T. Bib.1 Chap.X deals with the Mill Ledger for 1780–1787 and Whatman's Expenses are summarised in Table G p.71. The figures given above are averages of the figures taken from this Table.

for later periods in the 18th C. have been examined separately and briefly, mainly with the object of trying to arrive at a picture of events whereby it might be possible to determine what sort of impact the New Technology, as distinct from these other factors, may have had on its progress. It is clear from what has been discussed here that some elements in this situation would have had more effect than others depending on the period in question so that their progression within the industry would not have been a simple straight line function of the rates of Duty or wages or whatever. If one reverts to the "equation", although it would be difficult if not impossible to quantify the effect of its components on the development that took place, an attempt at least can be made to allocate a measure of the extent of their importance as the century progressed.

Taking the market side of the equation, it is a fact that the demand for White paper in the British Isles increased steadily between 1740–1780 (more rapidly after 1780); the factors influencing this have already been considered.[46] It is also a fact that imports of White paper fell away rapidly after 1740 and, with the exception of special items like Plate paper, had dropped to negligible levels before the end of the century (~2%); in addition, the situation had so changed that we were not only manufacturing nearly all the White paper needed for home consumption (~85% by the mid–1740's : and ~96–97% by the 1770's), but we were exporting not insignificant quantities from the 1770's onwards (albeit it is clear that small quantities of English papers were being used in the American colonies, and possibly in the East as well, as early as the 1750's), a considerable turn around. The price of these papers was, according to Coleman, artificially high due to factors on the other side of the equation. With the exception of Plate papers[47] the quality of British papers appears to have satisfied the market, presumably matching for the most part the White papers that had previously been imported; in fact in some cases, such as Whatman's paper, they were considered superior.[48] Finally, with regard to availability, there does not seem to have been any shortfall in the supply of paper to the market at any time during this period. The increasing demand appears to have been met mostly from domestic sources and in ever–dwindling quantities from abroad. In short the market appears to have got the paper it wanted at a price.

But it is the production side of the equation that is of particular interest to us and the elements that made up this were the imposition of Duty on imports, a two–edged weapon; Excise on home production, a minus; capital outlay and production costs, a deterrent; methods of reducing the latter and of improving quality; and, in turn, reputation. The main contenders for this production between 1740 and 1800 were the Dutch, the French (imports from Italy do not appear to have been a significant quantity at this time) and home production. Holland was the home of the New Technology and had employed it for the best part of 80 years before 1740. They held a deeply entrenched position in our market place and we had nothing to teach them at that stage. In other words it can *only* have been the effect of protective Duties that eliminated them from the home scene,[49] but not from other markets such as

---

[46] See Chap.III pp.114/115.
[47] See Chap.VI n.75, 76.
[48] This Chap. p.254.
[49] Coleman, D.C. Bib.15 96 demonstrates that the Dutch were feeling the draught as early as 1742, quoting a comment made by a firm of importers to this effect. "We are pretty much out of Business and entirely discouraged out of the Paper Trade, which is brought here to a very low Ebb and will decrease more and more by reason of the great quantities made in England which Manufactory encreases every Day". Because of their high cost "the great quantities" would not have

(continued...)

Ireland, America and the East. As the Memorial presented by the younger Whatman to the Commissioners of Excise in 1764 pointed out ".....the Manufacture [that is of White paper], which of the great increase of it in England now depends very much upon the exportation of the Commodity. And the rivalship of the Dutch (who already undersell us) makes it necessary that we should afford ours at a Foreign Market as cheap as possible".[50] As noted earlier the primary subject of this petition related to the current inequities of the Excise system, but it also illustrates by implication that although Duty had progressively removed the Dutch from the home market, the domestic producer would still have had to do something about his costs (if he had not already done so) to compete successfully in foreign markets on equal terms. Possibly the French might have been able to retain a position in the English market place on account of their very low wages and abundant supplies of rags had it not been for the effects of war. It is an indisputable fact, however, that the home market place was eventually emptied for the domestic producer by the effects of Duty and, intermittently, by War.

In theory this leaves us with a situation where the domestic producer of White paper could have remained *in statu quo*, employing the Old Technology with its wasteful and costly techniques and sheltering under the protection of the Duties for as long as this lasted. By means of simple linear expansion of facilities the paper makers could have met the increasing demand. But the fact is that some of them did not remain in this state and by the end of the century the White paper industry as a whole had reached a dominating position in price, volume and quality not only at home but abroad. Duty in itself could not have brought about this revolution; it merely kept the rivals out. Moreover, unless they had had exceptional powers of prevision the paper makers could not have foreseen the potentially crippling increases in their costs that were to take place later, particularly in rags, wages and Excise. These may have forced the stragglers to take action; but there were others who joined the van long before these events took place. How was this change brought about then ? Apart from Duty which prevented access to the market from outside, all the other elements on this side of the equation bar one were minuses in the system. *The indisputable answer to this question lay therefore in the policy of adopting the New Technology*. Nothing else in the circumstances could have mitigated the industry's rising costs or even have kept its head above water (The application of steam power and mechanisation were still a half century away.) The fact that the domestic industry expanded and was profitable proves this point, confirmed by the event that most if not all the paper mills had been equipped with Hollanders by the end of the century.

These changes clearly did not happen all at once. The salient features of the New Technology were set out and examined in Chapters V and VI; these, it will be recalled, included more careful management of materials; the advantages of using the new Engine with its ability to wash and beat rags at a far greater rate, with less waste and fewer personnel employed in the rag preparation process than in the Old Technology; improved methods of constructing papermaking moulds, another cost saving; the use of a new type of hand–felt to reduce surface defects; and to match the quality of the best imported papers there also had to be a general raising of standards in sizing, sorting and finishing the paper. Against these

[49](...continued)
   ousted the Dutch from the strong position in the London Market; the effective element was the swingeing rate of Duty payable on such imports.
[50]   B.M.Add.MSS 38203 f.316 quoted in full Bib.1. App.III 149.

improvements one has to set the time taken to learn the new skills, slow at first but as more and more paper mill workers became familiar with the new techniques so the process of expansion would have become easier and spread more rapidly. Another major deterrent in this development would have been the very considerable capital expenditure that faced the individual Master Paper Makers for new equipment and the reconstruction or the building of new mills to accommodate it all. (The day was approaching when this set–up would be replaced by partnerships and more complicated financial arrangements).[51] Added to these difficulties would have been the problem in some cases of obtaining adequate water power to work the new equipment efficiently; by the 1780's improved waterwheels were being developed, but apart from one or two of the more progressive paper makers making use of them before 1790, it was to be several decades before these became generally accepted, by which time steam power had come on the scene.[52] This, however, all lay in the future and there were a lot of formidable obstacles to overcome before this stage was reached.

In these last pages the economic factors that could and did affect the course of the industry's progress for the rest of the century have been examined and set out either as unfavourable or as favourable agencies. It is an historical fact that by 1800 the paper makers had responded to change successfully. How did this take place ?

---

[51] Coleman, D.C. Bib.15 Chap.IV "Organization & Finance" discusses this problem as it emerged at the beginning of the 19th C., "to place the manufacture in larger hands" as Richard Mackenzie Bacon, one of the first paper makers to buy a paper machine, put it in a letter written to William Balston in 1813.

[52] The classic example of this was William Balston's Beater floor at Springfield Mill constructed in 1806 and driven entirely by Steam Power. In a White mill of this class a clean atmosphere is of paramount importance. High winds penetrating draughty buildings can dislodge dirt and dust from roofs and rafters spoiling clean stuff and paper. William soon discovered that he was "very much annoyed by the smoke from the chimney of the boiler"; James Watt's original chimney rose vertically from the mill buildings. After consulting Watt the smoke was carried away through an underground channel to a new chimney built on higher ground 500 feet away (Balston, T. Bib.74 p.48). This arrangement was to last another 150 years.

PART III

HOW DID THE INDUSTRY REACT TO THESE INFLUENCES ?

In adapting itself to the new methods progress after 1740 would inevitably have been irregular, studded with failures and slow to begin with but gathering momentum later. This is the general *pattern one might expect to find*, not so much a manifestation of conservatism as one of overcoming considerable practical difficulties. But seen in the light of the question asked at the beginning of this chapter, was progress as haphazard as the above might suggest? Or is it possible to discern a more purposeful sequence of events that led ultimately to the achievement referred to in Thomas Balston's statement, namely, that English manufacturers "so much increased and improved their output that they permanently secured the market?"

To find an answer to this question one should, ideally, examine the growth of the White paper industry between 1740–1800 for the whole of the country. Information on this scale is not only very limited but on the grounds of cost alone is not a practical proposition for the time being.[53] (The activities of the recently formed British Association of Paper Historians may, it is hoped, rectify this deficiency in due course). But quite apart from this a lot also depends on how one defines "WHITE" paper and whether more or less mills should be included in a given list. One has to remember that a great many so–called White mills may have been little more than ramshackle and squalid collections of buildings very far from the sort of factories that the mind might conjure up in the 20th C.[54] Finally, as previously indicated,[55] in compiling lists, the first evidence we have of a mill's existence cannot necessarily be taken as the date when it started making paper; sometimes the only evidence available is of a paper maker taking an apprentice on a given date. So there is no knowing, unless other documents confirm this, just how much earlier a given mill may not have been operating. The general lists presented below of White mills for this period of the 18th C. (with the exception of Kent) are based mainly on 1957 data and can only be seen as a broad guide to the industry's growth (see Table IX).

A word of explanation is required for the three Tables that follow. The first of these (Table IX) is a list of White mills set out Region by Region in order to show (a) the growth in the number of White paper mills between 1740–1800; (b) to demonstrate that the main concentration of White mills was still centred round London in 1800; and (c) to compare the strength of this manufacture in Kent v an extended West of London Region, not all of whose mills necessarily depended on the London market. The basis for this comparison is outlined in notes underneath.

---

[53] See FOREWORD on limited data; and this chapter (n.356) on rising cost of searches.
[54] Even in the 20th C. "White" mills could still be found with their quota of hens nesting in the rag store, but if one adds to this the horsed transport of the 18th C., the stables which would have formed part of many mills, the mud; primitive, if any, sanitary arrangements; the offal arising from the size preparation plant etc.; leaky roofs and generally damp premises, it is not difficult to imagine the sort of conditions that might have prevailed in some of the lesser paper mills.
[55] See especially Chapter II Table IV note 3.

TABLE IX – THE NUMBER OF WHITE PAPER MILLS IN SELECTED AREAS OF THE UNITED KINGDOM IN 1740 AND 1800 COMPARED

REGION	COUNTY	1740 List in Chapter I expanded	1800 Shorter, A. Bib.12. App.D	Column IV re-assessed	%age increase due to re-assessment	No. of Mills producing countermarked paper by 1800
West of London	Bedfordshire	–	–	–	–	–
	Berkshire	3 + 1 ?	5	8		5
	Buckinghamshire	7 + 2 ?	11	12 + 6 ?		8 + 1 ?
	Cambridgeshire	–	1	1		–
	Hampshire	3 + 3 ?	10	11		7
	Hertfordshire	1 ?	6 + 1 ?	7 + 1 ?		6 + 1 ?
	Middlesex	3	(2)	none after 1777		–
	Northamptonshire	2 ?	3	6 + 2 ?		3 + 2 ?
	Oxfordshire	2	4	6		3
	Surrey	2 + 3 ?	5	8 + 2 ?		7
	Sussex	1 + ?	2	2 + 1 ?		2 + 1 ?
	Total	20 + 13 ?	47 + 1 ?	61 + 12 ?	25–46%	41 + 5 ?
West of England	Devonshire		7	10		
	Somerset		3	3 + 1 ?		
	Gloucestershire		9	9 + 2 ?		
	Herefordshire		1	1		
	Worcestershire		2	2		
	Total		22	25 + 3 ?	14–17%	
Midlands	Shropshire		3			
	Staffordshire		–			
	Derbyshire		2			
	Nottinghamshire		–			
	Total		5			
North of England	Lancashire		2 + 1 ?			
	Yorkshire		6			
	Westmorland		2			
	Cumberland		–			
	Durham		3 +			
	Northumberland		2			
	Total		15+ + 1 ?			

Scotland   Considerable increase in the last two decades of the 18th C.
Ireland   Increased but still significant imports of White paper from England
Wales   Negligible

	KENT	13 + 2 ?	28 + 2 ?	33–35 +	17–18%	30

1. Only the two principal Regions, KENT (shown at bottom) and the WEST OF LONDON (top) are compared fully for 1740 and 1800. The White mills, as listed in Shorter, A. Bib.12 App.D., are shown for the three other Regions merely to illustrate that their numbers are small by comparison with the two main Regions; only the West of England Region has been re-assessed (column V) for comparison with the re-assessments of these two. (See 2 below).

2. Shorter's App. D lists only those White mills (column IV in Table above) for which there was at that time (1957) more or less positive evidence of White paper manufacture there and clearly his list does not represent the total number any longer. Since 1957 a number of additional countermarks have been discovered and can be attributed to paper makers working at mills not listed in his Appendix. The fifth column represents a re-assessment of his App.D. taking into consideration the new countermarks as well as a best guess regarding the mills' status based on the Master Paper Makers who may have worked there or insured the mill in the tenure of A.N.Other.

In the case of Kent the evidence is firmer than, say, for the West of London Region simply because it has been possible to examine more local records. The West of London Region, therefore, can be seen only as a best guesstimate in the circumstances, but it is not thought that the totals are likely to be significantly higher. The re-assessment for the West of England Region is even more uncertain, but was carried out in order to see whether it revealed as significant a growth as those Regions nearest to London. In the 19th C., of course, the distribution was to change dramatically; but for our purpose it may be taken that during the 18th C. the main concentration of White paper manufacture was still centred round London.

The other two Tables X and XI take the comparison of the two main regions a stage further. An attempt has been made in these to estimate the date when it is thought the mills in question may have been modernised effectively and had adopted the New Technology. As explained previously there is virtually no evidence of installations on which to base the up-grading of these mills, so one has to fall back on other pointers for this such as those outlined below. For the West of London Region this is a matter, for the time being, of pure guesstimation; and in the case of Kent, as will be seen later in this chapter, the arguments supporting modernisation are rather stronger. The reasoning that lies behind these estimations is based on the following guidelines:-

Bracketing dates to work within 1740-1800

1. It has been claimed on the one hand that virtually every paper mill in England had been equipped with a Hollander by 1800, some mills much earlier than others.[56] Going to the other extreme we have seen that certain mills had employed primitive or underpowered Engines as early as the 1690's.[57] Further installations, believed to be similar, followed in the early part of the 18th C.[58] The notion that an early model could well have been used at the COMPANY'S No.2 Dartford mill in the 1690's[59] has led to the proposal that, since it would thus have been known to both the Archer and Quelch families, its employment may have been extended under the former to Sittingbourne and, later, Chartham mills; and under the latter first to Basted mill, Wrotham, in 1716 and then, just conceivably, to Gurney's mill, Loose, in 1728/9. From this it can be seen that installations of one kind or another had become widespread (though thinly) in the United Kingdom before 1740, to be found in mills as far apart as Dublin and Worcestershire in the West, Northamptonshire in the Midlands as well as in several mills round London. Clearly these Engines would have been known to other paper makers in the same districts.[60] It could be argued then that the process of "modernisation" was already under way many years *before* 1740. Even so it is equally clear that for a number of reasons already discussed such as the rudimentary nature of some of these Engines, inadequate water power or the inefficient transmission of this; and, perhaps more important than these in the early stages, lack of experience and the proper skills to operate them coupled with the capital expenditure required for their installation resulted in a slow and hesitant introduction of the New Technology, a state of affairs that was still ineffective in producing the best qualities of White paper on a competitive basis.

   Set against this a convincing case has been made out for (a) Whatman and Harris incorporating an improved model of a Hollander, adequately powered, at Old Mill, Hollingbourne, in 1733;[61] and (b) that this had led to a technical breakthrough to be followed by a much larger installation at Turkey mill, which had come into operation in 1740.[62] Whereas this development could not reasonably be claimed to have influenced anything beyond the Kent Region's industry except marginally, it nevertheless heralded a most important stage in the modernisation of the papermaking process in the United Kingdom. So the 1730's or, more realistically, 1740 may be regarded as the earlier of the bracketing dates for the introduction of effective modernisation, although due consideration is given in the re-assessments shown in the Tables to the possible influence of earlier installations.

2. Working within these date limits further clues to the status or possible date for the modernisation of a mill may be gained from the following (the examples cited in the relevant footnotes refer to the West of London Region; Kent will be dealt with separately):

---

56 Shorter, A. Bib.12 App.G. 402 cites the use of hammers still in operation as late as 1776 at Moretonhampstead, Devonshire. In some of the more out of the way mills this practice may have persisted even later than this.

57 Chap.V p.191.

58 Discussed in Chap.VI p.224.

59 For all these proposals see Chap.IV.

60 Thomson, A.G. Bib.44 41 refers to the Hollander being used in Scotland as early as 1721 but in a Barley mill and not for rags (reminiscent of the "Potcher" mentioned in Chap.VI n.23c.). No positive evidence of its use in paper mills before 1789.

61 Chap.IV pp.134/135.

62 Chap.VI pp.244/245.

TABLE X – DATES SUGGESTED FOR THE ADOPTION OF THE NEW TECHNOLOGY BY WHITE PAPER MILLS IN AN EXTENDED WEST OF LONDON REGION

COUNTY	MILL[1]	suggested[2] date of up-dating	1st[3] mill date	1740–55	1755–65	1765–75	1775–85	1785–95	1800	COUNTERMARKS[4]
BERKSHIRE	Sutton Courtenay	1770's	1631			- - -	————			HOLYOAK
	East Hagbourne	1760's	1690		- - -	————				SLADE
	Cookham	1772	1658			————				VENABLES
	Sheffield Mill	?	1687		- - - - - -	? -	- - - -	- - - -		
	West Mills	1779	1743				————			
	Tile Mill	late 1780's	1710					- - ———		HOOKE
	Bagnor	1763	1743		- - - -	————				WICKWAR
	Colthrop	1744	1744	————						
BUCKINGHAMSHIRE	Long Wick)	1766	1719			————				WILLIAMS
	Saunderton)	1780's	1769			————		- - ———		WILLIAMS
	Chesham	1768	1768			————				MOWDAY
	Blackwell Hall	1765	1765			————				STREET
	Chesham Bois	1767	1767			————				
	Chenies	1770's	1741			- - ———				DODD
	Ball's Mill	1779	1717			————				
	Rye Mill	1788	1788				————			EDMONDS
	Lower Marsh	1750–60's	1724	- - ———						BATES
	Lower Marsh	1756–60's	1740		- - - ———					GOODWIN
	Loudwater No.3	1780–90's	1638					- - ———		
	Overshots	1766	1766			————				(BATES ?)
	Hedge	1760's	1690		- - - - -	- - - -	- - - -			
	Glory	1790's ?	1690					? - -		
	Taplow	(never)								
	Horton	1786	1635		? - -	- -		? ———		
	and others	late								
CAMBRIDGESHIRE	Sawston	1760	1753		————					
HAMPSHIRE	Hurstbourne Priors	1790's	1729					- - ———		ALLEE
	Laverstoke (3)	1740–50's	1712–18	? - - -	————					PORTAL
	King's Mill, Alton	1759	1759		————					KING
	Barford	1757	1739	? ————						
	Frogmill	1780's	1663				- - ———			
	Up Mill	1770's	1690			- - - ———				GATER
	Romsey (1)	1770	1715			————				SHARP
	Romsey (2)	1780's	1759				- - ———			SKEATS et al.
	Romsey (3)	1770	1770			————				SHARP et al.
HERTFORDSHIRE	Hatfield	1745?–81	1663	? - - -	- - - - -	- - - -	- - ———			VALLANCE
	Two Waters	1763	1763		————					
	Pickford	1800	1775						————	(VALLANCE?)
	Apsley	1778	1778				————			APSLEY MILL
	Nash	1770	1769		————					BLACKWELL
	Sarratt	1770's	1776			- - - ———				STEVENS
	Mill End	1770's	1773			————				MUNN jnr.
	Hamper	1776	1776				————			LEPARD
NORTHAMPTONSHIRE	Wansford	1725	1704	————						HAYES et al.
	Perry Mills (2)	1757–90's	1719		? - ———	- -		- - ———		HAMERTON
	Cotton Mill	1782	1782				————			HALL?
	Boughton	1790's	1717					- - ———		(HAYES?)
	Rush Mill	1769	1763			————				HAYES
OXFORDSHIRE	North Newington	1790's	1756					- - - ———		
	Hazleford	1790's	1792					- - - ———		SELLERS
	Upton	1741–80's	1741	- - - - -	- - ?		- - - ———			
	Eynsham	1761	1682		? ————					FAICHEN
	Wolvercote	1743	1672	————						(Several)
	Henley	1790's	1791					————		
SURREY	Carshalton (1)	1746	1744	————						CURTEIS
	Carshalton (2)	1770	1770			———				PATCH
	Ewell	1766 ?	1732			————		————	(1797)	JUBB
	Chilworth (1)	1793 ?	1704				? - - - -	- -		BALL
	Chilworth (2)	1755 ?	1704		————					HUGHES
	Catteshall	1765 ?	1661	? - -	- - - ?	————				CHANDLER et al.
	Sickle	1769	1736	? - - - -	- ———					SIMMONS
	Albury	1790	1790					————		BALL
	Eashing	1764 ?	1658		————					
SUSSEX	Isfield	1800?	1789						? ———	MOLINEUX et al.
	Iping (1)	after 1744	1725	- - -	- - - -	- - ?	- - ———			BIGG
	Iping (2)	1777	1777				————			BIGG

Total up-datings → 6+4? 10+4? 20 11 12+2? 2 incl. 2 ??

1. Although col. 2 above refers to mills indicated in TABLE IX, the totals are not necessarily the same because in this Table some of them like Laverstoke (3) have been grouped together whereas the Romsey mills are shown individually because managed separately. Others like Sheffield made White and Brown and like Taplow may never have been modernised though White paper may have been made there; yet others were described as "best" and "old" mills.

2. For discussion of datings in col.3 see Text p.269 [2], 271, and notes 63-69.

3. Dates in col.4 as per Shorter Bib. 12 with minor amendments from other sources.

4. The countermarks in this column are shown merely to indicate that White countermarked paper was made there by the end of the 18th C. and in no way represent a succession of marks that may have been used from a much earlier date.

(a) evidence relating to the installation or use of an Engine.[63]

(b) Reference to a new or newly–built mill within the date bracket.[64]

(c) As an extension of (b) a mill known to have been destroyed by fire within this period; unlikely to have reverted to rag fermentation.[65]

(d) A mill known to have been converted from another use after the 1740/50's.[66]

(e) The acquisition or occupation of another mill by a paper maker known to have been using a Hollander in his own mill; he either converted it or moved because he knew it had been modernised earlier.[67]

(f) The rise in the ratable value of a mill, coupled perhaps with other factors such as being insured by a London Stationer; local tradition etc.[68]

(g) In the absence of other clues one might have to base assumptions on the documented arrival at a given mill of a paper maker known to have made White countermarked paper, albeit at a later date perhaps.[69]

[63] *Colthrop* (Berks) 1744 (Bib.9 40, 57; see also Note 3): *Wansford* (Northants) 1725, almost certainly up–dated later: *Wolvercote* (Oxon) by 1743: *Catteshall* (Surrey) recorded as having Engine and Mortars 1745 but up–dating probably ca. 1765 with mill reorganisation (Crocker).

Queries; *Laverstoke* (Hants) assumed that important mills like this under progressive paper makers such as Henry Portal and after 1747, Joseph, must have modernised at an early date. *Hatfield* (Herts) if the John Archer there from 1726 was Peter jnr.'s brother, an installation could have been made during his tenure (bur.1764) (see also Note 69 below and App.IV pp.144–145). *Perry* mills (Northants) same paper maker as at Wansford in 1737. *Eynsham* (Oxon) nr. Wolvercote and also supplier to O.U.P. may have been influenced. *Sickle* mill (Surrey) near Bramshott (a Brown mill but with an early installation, 1725, Engine and mortars) was insured by James Simmons (1769) soon after appearance there in 1758. *Up* mill (Hants) Rousillon had employed a Dutch paper maker late 17th C. possibly a primitive Engine, but may not have been fully modernised until Gater, 1771.

[64] *West Mills* (Berks) rebuilt 1779 (a John Quelch had been there, 1748, and if same as John of Dartford No.2 [1698–1700] may have installed early Engine. William Sims who followed him moved to St. Mary Cray, Kent, 1771, which had been modernised by that date so presumably he had experience of using Engines). *Chesham Bois* (Bucks) new–built 1767: *Sawston* (Cambs) second mill new–built 1760 (one of these mills adapted to fine paper in 1768). Four mills (Herts) *Apsley* 1778; *Nash* 1769; *Hamper* 1776; *Two Waters* 1763. *Upton* (Oxon) very considerably repaired 1741. *Chilworth No.2* (Surrey) reference to "new mill" 1755. A spate of new mills or conversions in Hertfordshire during 1750's, most of them probably Brown, *Scots Bridge* 1755; *Solesbridge* 1757; *Loudwater* 1758; but *Mill End* 1755 became a White mill.

[65] *Colthrop* (Berks see Note 1) was rebuilt after fire 1763; *Rush Mill* (Northants) burnt 1769; *Bagnor* (Berks) fire 1756, insured by Joseph Wells 1763.

[66] *Horton* (Bucks) reconverted to papermaking 1786; formerly under Thomas Pearson who departed ca. 1765 possibly because it was out–of–date ? (see this Chapter pp.335/6 and TABLE XV). *Carshalton No.2* (Surrey) converted and occupied by Patch family 1770 (inf.Crocker); *Albury* (Surrey) converted from corn in 1790 by Charles Ball.

[67] The occupant of Lower Marsh (1), John Bates (see Note 69 below) a White paper maker of distinction insured *Lower Marsh* (2) in 1756 and *Overshots* (both in Bucks) in 1766. Later, John Goodwin (occupant of Lower Marsh 2) insured *Balls* mill in 1779. Similarly, the Hayes family of Northants had an interest in *Perry* mills from 1737 (see Note 63); Francis Hayes of Rush mill (see Note 65) in *Boughton* 1797. *Barford* (Hants 1739–19th C.), another mill close to Bramshott, insured 1757; *Chilworth* (1) (Surrey) was leased to Charles Ball in 1793, but may have been up–dated earlier?

[68] *Cookham* (Berks) insured 1772 by Taylor of London et al. *Longwick* (Bucks) by Taylor et al. in 1766. *Eynsham* (Oxon see note 1) by a London Stationer in 1761 and presumably up–dated effectively by then. *Rye mill* (Bucks) had a London owner 1788. *Ewell mill* (Surrey) under Jubb family (1732–97) making high quality White paper. Hand–in–Hand Insurance Policy of 1766 shows mill greatly enlarged (inf. Crocker, who has suggested Wm. Jubb snr. may have been Wm."Tubb" of West Drayton, Mddsx. in 1726 and who had shown interest in Dernford, Cambs. but did not follow this up; see Bib.9.50).

[69] With some mills no clues have emerged yet to help one beyond the knowledge that at some point in their history they were occupied by paper makers who made countermarked White paper continuing usually well into the 19th C. In some cases it seems legitimate to assume that modernisation dated from at least the time of their arrival; or, if this was unusually early, that change took place with a change in family generations.

Examples in Berkshire are *Sutton Courtenay*, Benjamin Nind 1770; *Tile mill*, Hooke 1796. In Buckinghamshire *Chesham*, Mowday 1768; *Blackwell Hall*, the Street family, 1765; *Lower Marsh (1)*, John Bates had been there since 1724 so probably modernised with change in generation in 1750–60's; *Chenies* with a new generation of Dodds 1770s; *Hedge mill*, the Spicer family had been there since 1690 so probably up–dated in line with other mills in vicinity, 1760's. Hampshire, *Hurstbourne Priors*, Allee in 1791; *Frog mill*, John Smith 1786; the *Romsey mills* in line with William Sharp 1770. Hertfordshire, *Hatfield* (if not earlier, see Note 63), with Vallance 1781; *Pickford*, also Vallance 1800. Northants, *Cotton mill* 1782. Sussex, *Iping*, probably modernised when Bigg jnr. started a second mill in 1777.

(continued...)

TABLE XI – DATES SUGGESTED FOR THE ADOPTION OF THE NEW TECHNOLOGY BY PAPER MILLS (ALL TYPES)[1] IN KENT

DISTRICT	MILL	suggested date of up-dating	1st. mill date	1740–55	1755–65	1765–75	1775–85	1785–95	1800	COUNTERMARKS[2]
MAIDSTONE	Forstal 3	ca.1755 ?	17th C.	?						Uncertain
	Cobtree 3	ca.1755 ?	1717	?						Not until 19th C.
	Snodland	1755 ?	1755 ?	?						[Brown mill?]
	Millhall, Ditton 3	1745–55	17th C.	?						
	East Malling Upper	by 1763 ?	1763 ?							LARKING
	East Malling Middle	1760's ?	17th C.							[Brown mill]
	East Malling Lower	1780 ?	1780 ?							[Brown mill]
	Eyehorne	1762	1762							WILLIAMS
	Park mill	1800	1800							STROUD (1802)
	Old Mill 3	1733	1733							CRISPE & NEWMAN
	Otham	1745–50 ?	1715							EDMEADS & Co.
	Poll mill 3	1756–61 ?	1718							WHATMAN
	Turkey mill	1739	1680–							WHATMAN
	Padsole	1795	1795							HAYS & WISE
	Leg o' Mutton	1745 ?	1742/5	?						
	Upper mill	1755–70 ?	1726		?					WHATMAN
	Gurney's mill 3	1742–60 ?	1688							FRENCH
	Great Ivy	1747–62 ?	1685/6							EDMEADS & PINE
	Upper Tovil 3	1760–72 ?	1680–							CLEMENT TAYLOR
	Lower Tovil	1760–80 ?	1685/6							J PINE
	[Springfield]		[1806]							
	[Pratling Street]		[1804]							
	[Little Ivy]		[1808]							
	[Hayle mill]		[1810]							
	[Sandling]		[1819]							
WEST KENT	Dartford No.2	1741/2	1679							FINCH
	Dartford No.3	1741/2	1742							BUDGEN
	Hawley	1758/9	1758 ?							[Brown ?]
	Eynsford	1761 ?	17th C.		?					FLOYD & Co.
	Shoreham	1750/60 ?	17th C.							THOMAS WILMOTT
	Sundridge	1766	1766							CHARLES WILMOTT
	Foots Cray	ca.1769	1767–							STAINS
	Cray Valley 3	1742/7	1742							CRIPPS
	St. Mary Cray	1771 ?	1749 ?							LAY
	Bromley	1765 ?	1765 ?							
	Basted 3	1742/3	1716							I TAYLOR
	Hampton's 3	1743–1775	1740	?						BUTTANSHAW
	[Roughway]		[1807 ?]							
NORTH KENT	Sittingbourne	1752/56	17th C.	- -						LAY
EAST KENT	Buckland No. 1 Dover	1790's	16th C.							[Brown mill]
	Buckland No. 2 Dover	1770	ca.1770							KINGSFORD
	Crabble, Dover	1791	1791							[Brown mill]
	River Mill Dover (2)	1790's	1689 ?					?		[mixed : PHIPPS]
	Bushey Ruff Dover	1794/5	1791							[mixed low grade]
	Cheriton Folkestone	1780's	1771–							STACE
	Barton Canterbury	1750–90 ?	17th C.	?						[Brown by 1795]
	Chartham	1732/3	1732/3							PIKE
	Conyer Little Chart	1770's ?	1740 ?			?				[Brown mill]
	Ford Little Chart	1776	1776							MUNN
SOUTH KENT	Chafford Penshurst	1768 ?	1756 ?			?				STIDDOLPH
	Ockley Hawkhurst	by 1787 ?	1755 ?		?					[mixed ?]
	Hinksden	1787	1787							[mixed]
	[A.N.Other]		[19th C.]							

WHITE Up-datings per period → 8 + 5? 6 + 3? 9 4 + 1? 2 ? 2 → (40)

1. This Table unlike the previous one (p.270) covers not only all the mills active in Kent between 1740–1800 but, for information, shows in square brackets some of the more important mills that came into being between 1800–20, including William Balston's "Springfield" steam-powered mill with 10 vats; Barcham Green's Hayle mill that continued to make handmade paper until July 1987; Buttanshaw's "Roughway" which probably housed his papermachine in 1807 etc. Other lesser mills that appeared for short periods like George Dickinson's Spring Gardens paper mill (Dover) during the 1830's are not shown here. In the general summary (the line below the Table) known or almost certain Brown mills have been omitted so that a reasonable comparison can be made with a similar summary for the West of London Region. But, inevitably, there are a number of mills where the status of the products is not known e.g. where the quality of White paper, probably marginal at best, as suggested for Forstal and Ditton mills may have fluctuated according to prevailing circumstances e.g. Bushey Ruff, Ockley and Hinksden making a precise comparison difficult.
2. Countermarks (shown in the right-hand column), as in the previous Table, are merely indicators that countermarked papers were made at these mills. In some cases there had been a long succession of different ones used. Thirty mills in Kent produced countermarked papers as against ca.45 in the extended West of London Region.
3. In Parts V–VIII of this chapter a number of mills are shown to have been up-dated in more than one stage; and with others where the date is uncertain but with a higher probability for one rather than the other, the uncertainties reflected as queries. A decision had to be made where to place them in the line under the Table. Examples of the first are Hollingbourne Old mill (new Engine 1771); Poll, Gurney's and Upper mill, Loose. The second type falls into two groups (i) where up-dating may have been early or late e.g. Hamptons, the earlier being chosen here; others include Forstal, Cobtree and Milhall where probably only the lower grades of White were made. And (ii) where up-dating took place early but White paper not made until much later e.g. Cray Valley q.v. initially making Cartridge for 20–25 years. Though modernised in the 1740's it is not shown as part of the White total until 1765/75. Others include Otham and mills that may not have had sufficient power to treat strong rags with the Engine. Decisions are based on the best estimate given present evidence.

(h) A mill that was either converted or occupied by a paper maker whose former activities can be traced to employment in or apprenticeship at a mill where it is fairly certain that a Hollander, old or new type, had been in use.[70]

It has not always been easy to match the guidelines given earlier. In Note 65, for example, Bagnor mill is cited as being destroyed by fire in 1756, rebuilt and insured by Joseph Wells in 1763, indicating modernisation somewhere in between, when Churchill (Bib.3 41) claims a (very dubious) WICKWAR countermark d.o.d. 1754. (Wickwars were certainly there by the end of the century but not documented before ca.1790). Again, opinion is divided as to whether Frogmore mill was ever White in the 18th C. Another borderline case is Eashing mill, Surrey (1658–1889) occupied in the 18th C. by three Thomas Halls but not insured until 1779; Crocker (letter 27:June:89) claimed "they made good paper".[71]

The three Tables, and the notes associated with them, presented in the preceding pages give a general, but not a quantitative, picture of the development of White paper manufacture in the two most important centres in the United Kingdom between 1740–1800. The data is too uncertain to enable a precise comparison to be made. All that can be said is that the growth, proportionate to their size, was initially slow in both regions, but that it was more rapid in Kent than in the 11 counties to the West of London. In terms of numbers of new, or reverting to, White mills appearing between 1740–1800 Kent showed an increase of 20 + 2 ? and the West of London 34; but so far as the West of London Region is concerned these figures do not take into account the number of mills ceasing to operate during this period.[72]

---

[69](...continued)

Some mills may never have been modernised at all, e.g. *Coltnett* (Bucks) which closed down in 1772 (see Table XV); there were a number of other mills, especially in Middlesex, that faded out in the 18th C. With regard to all of these mills especially those producing countermarked papers at a relatively late date (e.g. Tile mill see above) one can either envisage a certain degree of modernisation, a primitive type of Engine, being introduced at a much earlier date and full and effective modernisation taking place much later. On the other hand some of these mills may have remained as "cottage industries" until a very late date (see Buckland No.1 mill, Kent, this Chap. p.339).

[70] Only one example is known to the author outside Kent; no doubt there are many others. The reference is to *Carshalton (1)*, Surrey, occupied by John Taylor, cousin of Clement Taylor snr., who had moved there from Wrotham, Kent in 1744 and rebuilt it in 1746 (see App.II p.62 [iii]).

[71] No Thomas Hall marks are known but "TH" countermarks have been found in documents dating from 1734/ca.1810, the latest of these in a drawing by John Crome, Norfolk, (NCM 739.281.876) and provisionally assigned to Thomas Hamerton (act.Lyng late 18th C.–1804). Crocker has found a very similar mark watermark dated 1795 also in a circle which *might* (his comment) have belonged to Thomas Harrison, Catteshall, Surrey (1794–1803) [Surrey.Arch.Soc.No.8 1981 9–10]. Other marks (Gravell Bib.68 666–669 d.o.d's 1734–1774) appear to be foreign.

[72] The constantly shifting basis for a comparison of this nature makes the calculations very difficult and, at best, very approximate. It has been reckoned that for the six intervals covered in the Tables the number of new or reconverted to White mills in the two regions was:-

REGION	1740–55	1755–65	1765–75	1775–85	1785–95	1800	TOTAL
Kent	+3	+3+1 ?	+6+1 ?	+4	+2	+2	20+2 ?
West of London	+8	+5	+10	+6	+3	+2	34

If the 20 + 2 ? mills for Kent are added to the 13 + 2 ? proposed for 1740 (Chap.I p.27) this totals at 33/35 White mills active in 1800 (see this Chap. p.257). The main difficulty in arriving at these figures for Kent is that whereas a number of Kent paper mills were originally converted to make White paper in the 17th C. during the embargo on French goods, they had evidently sunk to manufacturing shop and other inferior papers at the time when Harris (Bib.4 191) made his comments on the paper mills of the Maidstone district, ca.1716. As there appeared to be no change in their status by 1740 they do not form part of the total of White mills shown for that time. However, as will be seen later in this chapter several of these mills were reconverted later in the century to make White paper again; this did not necessarily coincide with the modernisation of a mill. Unfortunately, no similar data was available to the author for the West of London Region; but to compensate for this deficiency in our comparison of the two Regions it is known that at least 10 paper

(continued...)

Expressed as an accumulating percentage of the total number of mills (all kinds) active in these regions in 1740 the growth in the number of paper mills, new or converted, making White paper reads *very* approximately as follows:

REGION	*(Period) 1740–55*	*1755–65*	*1765–75*
Kent	13%	26%	65%
West of London	11%	19%	33%

remembering that the first period covers fifteen years, and the others ten.

Figures of this kind, though useful perhaps as a general indication, do not necessarily reflect (a) the quality of the White paper output; or (b) the quantity at all accurately. For instance, as late as the 1780's Thomas Balston has suggested that the younger Whatman *alone* may have been responsible for producing ~8% of the total output of Fine papers (Classes I & II) made in England & Wales; he has based this proposal on the percentage Excise paid by Whatman on the total Excise for Class I & II papers.[73] Again, if one had more precise figures for the number of White vats operating in the two Regions one would obviously get a more meaningful comparison. On present evidence the number of vats accentuates the dominance of Kent in White paper manufacture for this period.[74]

The suggested dates for the up–grading of mills are even more uncertain than the estimates for the numbers of new White mills, but even when making some allowances for inaccuracies it appears that the paper mills in Kent made quicker progress (even in actual as distinct from proportionate terms) in adopting the New Technology than the West of London Region considered as a whole; and by this is meant a genuine advance into the *effective* use of the improved processes. Although this evidence has its shortcomings it is considered sufficient to show that the industry in Kent provides one with a more than representative basis for a study of the technical and material progress of the industry between 1740–1800.

Having established earlier in this chapter that the New Technology acted as a very positive in contrast to a protective force in helping the British Paper Industry forward and having

---

[72](...continued)

mills had ceased operating in the West Region before 1780 as opposed to none in Kent. It is accepted that this is a makeshift basis for such a comparison, but may not be far out when making the percentage calculations shown in the text above. These are based on a figure of 23 mills of all types active in Kent in 1740 and ca.70 mills for the extended West of London Region.

[73] For more details of this claim (covering the years 1781–87, though primarily for 1785) see Balston T. Bib.1 69–70. Evidently his proposal must refer only to the very top TABLE I of papers subject to Excise; or to mixed TABLES I & II but containing a dominant proportion of those sizes that attracted the highest rates of Tax; large and extra large papers. The reason for making this comment is that Coleman (Bib.15 98 fig.3) shows that in 1785, for example, some 150,000 reams of Writing paper were taxed under the heading of Table I alone. In 1785 Whatman was working 6 vats and based on an assumption that these produced from 5–8 reams per day each, then for a 5–day week for 50 weeks in a year, he would not have produced more than 7500–12,000 reams per annum and 8% of the 150,000 reams is 12,000. This does not take into account the further ca.120,000 reams of Table II covering (obviously lower quality) Writing and Copper Plate Printing paper.

[74] See this Chap. p.257.

examined the general disposition of White paper manufacture in relation to the principal market one can now revert to the more immediate task of trying to discover whether the achievement of the elder Whatman influenced other sections of the industry; and, if so, how this was done. As the industry, certainly in the early part of this period i.e. during his lifetime, had little if any coherent structure, it seems unlikely that his influence extended beyond the Kent Region except in marginal cases (e.g. see later the move of John Taylor of Wrotham to Carshalton in Surrey). Even so Kent accounted for a very significant proportion of the nation's domestic White paper output.

PART IV

CHANGES IN THE PAPERMAKING SCENE IN KENT AFTER 1740

Prior to Whatman's emergence as a paper maker in 1740 the state of the Kent paper industry was investigated in order to determine whether any of its papermaking activities had influenced Harris and Whatman as they prepared their plans for their investment in Old Mill, Hollingbourne. By 1740 the empire of William Gill snr. had dissipated itself, ending with the acquisition of Turkey mill first by Harris and, after his death, by the elder Whatman. The rest of the Maidstone paper industry was in a state of stagnation, technologically at least; and it cannot be said that things were any better elsewhere in Kent.

Seen in retrospect, apart from Whatman, the only glimmer of light in this scene was the embryonic empire of William Quelch snr. As part of the second wave in the expansion of the Kent paper industry[75] one of the principal activators of this movement outside Maidstone had been William Quelch snr. It will be remembered that in 1716 he had moved out of the moribund Dartford No.1 paper mill to Basted where he converted a corn mill to papermaking; and very probably put in a primitive form of Engine there similar to the one he may have seen at Dartford. By 1728 he had extended his activities to Maidstone, occupying Gurney's mill vacated only the year before by Richard Harris' father, William snr. Here he was making paper on Whatman the Tanner's doorstep and, once again, he could conceivably have modified this mill and introduced a primitive Engine; the ratable value of this mill went up 52% in 1729, indicating some undetermined change in its status;[76] two further cottages were added in 1741 which might have represented another stage of this. William Quelch snr. was not one to let the grass grow under his feet.[77] In 1736 he added another dominion to his empire. He bought Dartford No.2 mill off Richard Archer and insured it; "William Quelch, paper maker of Wrotham[78] in the County of Kent insured his house and paper mill at Dartford in the tenure of Richard Archer".[79]

Viewed over-all the papermaking scene in Kent in 1740 had only one or two latent buds, buds that had not yet burgeoned fully into new growth; in fact several had already withered. Richard Archer was made bankrupt in that year; Peter Archer jnr., another rudiment in this growth, had died in 1737 leaving what amounted to a vacuum in his wake; old Andrew Johannot of Eynsford was dead and his son, evidently not in a very secure position, was made bankrupt in 1746; the Russells of Shoreham had passed out of the papermaking scene altogether and had been replaced in 1737 by William Wilmott, the first member of a family that was later to leave its mark on the manufacture of high quality paper but had not done so as yet. In the absence of any other progressive element in the Kent paper industry at this juncture its future might be seen as resting with the elder Whatman and the growing impetus

---

[75] See Chap.IV p.133.
[76] See Chap.IV n.58.
[77] See Chap.IV pp.145/7.
[78] Basted mill lay in the Nepicar Ward of the Parish of Wrotham (pron: "Rootam").
[79] SFIP 72367 of 6:Jan:1736. (Shorter failed to correct the dates of a number of policies at this time; this is almost certainly 1737).

of the Quelch Empire. Even so, if the Quelchs had in fact installed Engines at Basted in 1716, and in Loose in 1729, then it is self-evident that these had not been effective. It could be said that the ground had been prepared but clearly after a period of anything between 12–24 years experience of their use they had not placed the Quelch family in the forefront of the Kent papermaking industry. So by a process of elimination one can see without having to seek further evidence that the advance that the Kent industry was to make must have stemmed in general terms from Whatman's influence.[80] But how was this influence transmitted ?

There are three ways in which Whatman's influence could have been exerted. First, through the example of his person, his success and his status, subjects which have already been discussed in the first part of this chapter. This had clearly been impressed on his son who, fittingly, became the leading spokesman for the industry in this country in due course.

Second, through personal contact, though nothing is known of this except that one can infer that he must have been closely acquainted with his next-door neighbours, the Quelchs; and the tenants of his Hollingbourne mill. A point to remember in cases like these is that communication of new ideas and methods in a provincial area like Maidstone would have been not only through personal contacts but through the movement of employees and journeymen as well. Fig. 7 overleaf shows that the population of Maidstone during this period was in the region of 4,000, to which one might add another 2,000 souls at most in the surrounding papermaking district, giving an adult male population for the whole area of, say, 2,000. In such circumstances the dissemination of information would not have been difficult or slow.

Third, and undoubtedly the most important in this context, *one must turn to his principal memorial, Old Mill, Hollingbourne.* From this source Whatman's influence would have passed direct in a practical form to its occupants and it also served as a model for other "new" mills. It is the impact of the innovatory nature of this mill that will be considered now. (A Synopsis of its history will be found in Appendix I).

Due to the fact that the most important potential source of information is missing for this period, namely, the Hollingbourne ratebook, it is not known precisely how this mill was operated or by whom between December 1736 and December 1739. On the 27th December 1736 Whatman insured the mill etc. in the occupation of Richard Harris (in the previous Policy of 1734 it was Harris who had insured the mill). The next consecutive Policy (same date as the other) shows that Harris had "insured his stock in Trade in his papermills and storerooms all in one building (i.e. at Turkey mill) and not elsewhere". (This looks as if he stored and despatched his paper from Turkey mill whether it was made there or in Hollingbourne). No further policies have survived between this date and the 25th December 1739. From other evidence, his Will, we know that Harris had moved his dwelling place from Hollingbourne to Boxley sometime before August.1739, presumably soon after Turkey mill had become his in September 1738. We also know that, since Old Mill lay partly in the parish of Leeds village, he paid his Poor Rate dues for the Leeds portion of the property for the first

---

[80] In theory it would be possible to argue that the motivation and influence that affected the Kent paper industry might have come from outside the County, but in practice from where ? There is no evidence of a technical invasion from Holland and we have seen that the other main region, to the West of London, was certainly no further, if as, advanced as Kent in these developments. Moreover there is no sign of Kent being invaded from this direction either.

half of 1739, indeed as he had done since 1733. But whether he continued to work Old Mill himself; or whether Whatman worked it for him or let it to another; or whether it remained empty is not known. One would have expected him to work it until September 1738 at least; but after the acquisition of Turkey mill both Whatman and Harris must have been very fully occupied in the rebuilding of this mill. On balance it is highly probable that one of them continued to operate Old Mill, as the payment of the Poor Rate dues indicate, up to and including the first half of 1739.

Harris died and was buried in Loose on the 26th November 1739. Within weeks of this, if not earlier (because they paid the Leeds Poor Rate dues for the mill for the second half of 1739), Old Mill was insured by William Quelch of Loose and John Terry of Hollingbourne (Quelch's son–in–law) in the occupation of Terry on the 25th December 1739; that Terry was described as "of Hollingbourne" in this Policy points strongly to the notion that Terry had been working there earlier than the insurance date. This occupation proved to be *a very significant event for the future of papermaking in Kent.*

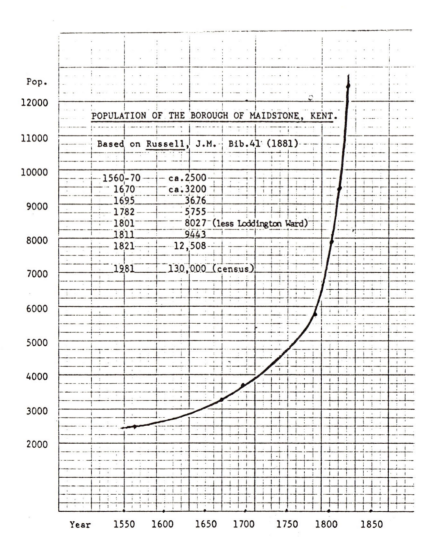

Figure 7

Before embarking on an examination of the effects of the new methods on the industry itself this is an appropriate point to mention another new course which these developments were to follow, an influence that will surface from time to time in later sections of this chapter.

It is self-evident that the advances that had been made by Whatman and Harris could only be put into practice by paper makers; and, at that, by paper makers learning from other paper makers how to make the New Technology effective. But, at the same time, the advantages that were evident to the paper makers Quelch snr. and John Terry, and those who followed them at Hollingbourne, must have become in time equally clear to James Brooke, a Stationer; and, as foreign supplies were progressively cut off either by War or Duty, so Brooke's fellow Stationers would have become increasingly interested in promoting or securing for themselves papermaking enterprises capable of exploiting the improved methods; and there is evidence to show that this was the case.[81]

There are few early instances of papermaker/Stationers; the majority remained primarily Stationers and just as in the case of Brooke's early efforts by no means all of them were successful in finding paper makers capable of serving their needs. In many cases they burnt their fingers meddling in a trade which they were not familiar with. The combination of paper maker and Stationer did not perish as a result of this; instead it became more common as the century progressed and particularly so in the 19th C. As this book's main concern is with the advances made in paper technology, and their application by paper makers, it is not the intention to explore this aspect further here, merely to note that Stationers in an indirect way played their part in changing the character of the British paper industry during the 18th C.

---

[81]   Coleman, D.C. Bib.15 164 cites an anonymous pamphlet "A general description of all Trades" (London, 1747) which specifically refers to the trend among Wholesale Stationers to acquire or monopolise the output of papermaking facilities.

PART V

THE EXPANSION OF THE QUELCH EMPIRE (AND ITS SATELLITES)

In the early part of the 18th C. it was fashionable for social occasions held in the evenings to have the candles lit in several candelabra simultaneously, instant illumination. This was achieved by threading slender strands of cotton steeped in saltpetre and other substances, virtually a gunpowder fuse, from one candle to another so that at the touch of a taper the whole assembly burst into light all at once. The rapid expansion of the Quelch empire and its satellites as a result of their occupation of Whatman's Hollingbourne mill might be likened to a display of this kind. The speed with which they responded to this experience tends to confirm the suggestion made earlier that *the Quelchs were already familiar with the workings of an Engine*, albeit of a more primitive kind. Equally, it supports the proposal made earlier regarding the special character of the Old Mill venture, namely that "one can be fairly sure that one is seeing here the introduction of a more advanced or more efficient model (of the Engine) than those used hitherto".[82] In the pages that follow, the expansion of the Quelch empire and its ramifications will be examined first; and then, at a later stage, the influence of Old Mill itself.

In this section it is proposed to deal with the movements of the William Quelchs and John Terry first and the other parts of this empire and the satellites later. To avoid too much detail in the text frequent reference will be made to the section in Appendix II dealing with the Quelch family and John Terry and to the Table illustrating their papermaking activities.[83]

John Terry had formerly been a journeyman whose papermaking ability was evidently held in very high regard by William Quelch snr. which in turn would account for him being installed in Hollingbourne Old Mill in preference to his son or any other papermaker. In the event Terry must have been there from an unknown date towards the end of 1739 until about mid–1741, just over 18 months.[84] Whether Whatman leased his mill to them on a friendly or strictly business basis will never be known. One would imagine that having lived next door to one another for the best part of 12 years Whatman was perhaps anxious to be of help to his neighbour; it certainly let the cat out of the bag. Later in that same year, 1741, William Quelch snr.,[85] aged 62 by then, and Terry moved to the Quelchs' Dartford No.2 mill. Richard Archer, the former occupant, had been bankrupted on 26th April 1740, so that the mill presumably had been empty for nearly a year, unless Quelch snr. continued to work it after Archer's demise.

---

[82] See Chap.IV pp.134/135.
[83] See App.II TABLE XXII & p.60.
[84] Quelch's first Policy for Old Mill was dated 25:Dec:1739 (details of what this covered will be found in the Synopsis, App.I). For some unknown reason Whatman took out a Policy on the 29:Dec:1740 followed within 10 days by Quelch's second Policy dated 8:Jan:1741 (corr:date, Shorter gives the uncorrected date). The next Policy for Old Mill was taken out by John Sanders on the 15:Oct:1741.
[85] The reason for proposing that this was William snr. will be found in App.II p.59 and Note 64.

As a result of Terry's experience at Hollingbourne the Quelchs had learnt, possibly by dispensing completely with rag fermentation which they may have continued to use with their primitive form of Hollanders, that they could now make more productive use of the space in their Dartford mill. The reason for suggesting this is because when they took out an insurance policy on the 2nd February 1742 (corr:date) it will be seen from this that they converted the old Dartford No.2 mill into two new mills (Shorter lists them as Dartford Nos. 2 & 3 from this date).[86] Although the No.2 mill may have had a primitive form of Engine dating back to the COMPANY'S days in the 17th C., the up-dating of this mill is shown in Table XI as ca.1742, this being the date when the application of the New Technology became effective.

It is conceivable that even though Quelch and Terry had converted these mills to the New Technology they may still have lacked, as was probably the case with some of their other mills, sufficient water power at that time to process the best qualities of linen rags and thus not have been able to make the top grades of countermarked Writing paper until a much later date in the mills' history, when perhaps they were able to make use of the more efficient waterwheels which had been developed by then. This comment is purely speculative; there are other equally valid reasons to explain why Quelch and Terry did not produce countermarked paper at that time. For instance, there would have been a much greater demand for common Printing paper than the best qualities of Writing, a market which Whatman may well have cornered. Moreover the use of countermarks was still rare in this country; it was to be another 20 years before they became at all common. So Quelch's paper could well have been good but unidentifiable until some point in the 1770's. The first Quelch countermarks belonging to this branch of the family are found in an English document dated 1780 and an American one of 1783, confirming this view, both obviously attributable to William jnr.[87]

In the meantime William Quelch jnr. continued to manage Gurney's mill in Loose. As noted the assessments made against the Quelchs rose in 1741 in respect of "two new houses" in Loose,[88] an investment that could well reflect further changes that had taken place in the mill. One cannot be certain of this, but one is faced with a choice between Quelch up-dating his mill at this juncture (in the circumstances a likely course of action) or leaving it to Henry French snr. (of whom more later) when he moved there in 1760 from Hollingbourne Old Mill,[89] a mill already using the New Technology and where he had been making paper for the last 11 years (and continued to do so). One has to ask the question then, would he with this experience have taken on a mill that had not yet been modernised ? Though there were fluctuations in the ratable value for this mill between the Quelch and French occupations,

[86] Shorter, A. Bib.12 181. William Quelch's Policy 90038 (2:Feb:1742 corr:date) insured two paper mills adjoining. Terry's Policy 90039 of the same date insured the utensils and stock in his paper mill called the West Mill. Shorter quotes a 1791 source referring to these mills as "one on each side of the water". The Dartford RB. is missing for these years, but when the entries resumed in 1756 it is clear that these two mills were assessed for £22 each as against the £40 which was the assessment made against Richard Archer for the one mill.

[87] See App.II n.63.

[88] Gurney's mill (like Upper mill q.v.) was assessed in both East Farleigh and Loose parishes. A rise in the ratable value in one parish did not necessarily correspond with a rise in the other. In 1741 the assessments against Quelch rose temporarily in East Farleigh from £20–£21, falling back again to £20 in 1742–49. The Loose assessments remained steady at £24 (annual) between 1740–50, but in 1741 and thereafter Quelch was assessed "for two new houses" at £4. The latter figure may have been consolidated into the mill figure after 1750 (cf. Chap.IV n.58).

[89] See App.I. Synop. Old Mill.

probably due to other factors,[90] there was no further substantial change until 1773, a date which may be regarded as being much too late for the modernisation under consideration here, more like a second stage in this case. On balance the 1741/2 date is favoured; but to allow for the alternative, namely, that the Frenchs up-dated the mill, Table XI shows a dotted line between 1741-1760.

William jnr.'s stay in Loose seems to have been ill-fated so far as his family were concerned, possibly losing at least one of his children there and then his wife, Ann, in 1745.[91] The latter event probably prompted his move to Dartford shortly after; an Insurance Policy of 1746 describes him as a paper maker of Dartford[92] and in the following year he insured Dartford No.3 mill in his own name.[93] His father would have been aged 68 by then, another contributory reason for the move. In the first of these two policies he continued to insure Gurney's mill and the millhouse in his name but in the tenure of a Stephen Scott. However, by 1753 it is evident that he must have parted with the mill altogether as it was then insured by Abraham Musgrove who occupied it between 1751-1758.

By this time the original core of the Quelch empire was getting on in years; John Terry died in 1766, though his widow (Quelch snr.'s daughter) continued to insure and operate Dartford No.2 for a number of years until their son-in-law, Thomas Budgen, took it over ca.1778 and it remained in Budgen hands until John was bankrupted in 1820. William Quelch snr. died in 1775, aged ca.96, followed two years later by William jnr., aged 73. Dartford No.3 was taken over by three members of the Finch family, one of whom was William jnr.'s godson. But by the late 1790's both mills were being worked by Thomas Budgen.[94]

Thus ended the Quelch side of this dynasty. As a family they had had a good run for their money and had been in papermaking, if connected with the other Quelchs, well back into the 17th C. Moreover they appear to have prospered and Dunkin (Bib.46) tells us that William jnr. died a relatively wealthy man. But it may be said that as one part of this empire was in decline the other was in the ascendancy and, seen in retrospect, the more celebrated of the two, at least in terms of producing identifiable papers. The example set by the Quelch branch at Dartford must have influenced other paper mills in the area as well as those that were either converted or new-built after their return there. Dartford was after all an historic papermaking centre that had gone very much into decline by the mid-18th C. and it was now about to witness a renaissance of White papermaking in the north-western part of Kent, as well as new growth albeit not as spectacular as that which had taken place in the Maidstone district earlier. But before considering this, an account of the other branch of the Quelch empire, namely, the activities of the Clement Taylor family, has prior claim.

---

[90]   In 1745 Stephen Scott took over from Quelch followed by Abraham Musgrove in 1750; it is in 1750 that the mill values start fluctuating, falling in E. Farleigh from £20-£15 but rising in Loose from £24 + £4 to £44, possibly due to some mutual adjustment between the two parishes. In 1755 there was a general rate rise in E. Farleigh, Gurney's going up from £15-£22-10 with Loose falling to £40 when Henry French took over in 1760. After 1763 the E. Farleigh rate fell to £20 and remained there until 1796, whereas the Loose value rose from a steady £40 to £60 in 1773, which may have been due to some enlargement of the mill rather than signifying a first stage of "modernisation".

[91]   See App.II TABLE XXII n.6.

[92]   SFIP 104723 27:Mar:1746.

[93]   SFIP 109027 21:July:1747.

[94]   Shorter, A. Bib.12 182.

Apart from the fact that Clement Taylor snr. had married Sarah, a daughter of William Quelch snr., ca.1740, it is not known how or why he became involved in papermaking.[95] He was probably born in Ightham,[96] a village about a mile north-west of Quelch's mill at Basted, in 1718 and may therefore have been apprenticed there later, although there is no documentary evidence to show this. Sarah's birthplace has not been found either and it can only be presumed that she was one of the last children of Quelch snr.'s first marriage. By 1742 (that is after Quelch snr. and Terry had moved to Dartford) Clement Taylor snr. insured Basted mill in his own occupation; the Taylor family were to retain it until 1802 when one of his least satisfactory sons, George, was bankrupted (see below).

Quelch's Basted mill became an important centre of influence in that area as well as the training ground for four of Clement Taylor's sons and for a number of satellite paper makers including, it is believed, John Taylor, a cousin of Clement snr. It is uncertain whether John Terry was trained there or not, but as with Clement Taylor snr., very probably. It is known for certain however that William Buttanshaw snr. was apprenticed there in 1723 and his case will be considered below together with others who may have been influenced directly or indirectly by the activities of this mill.

The idea has already been mooted that Quelch snr. had incorporated an early version of the Engine at Basted when he converted the mill. It seems most unlikely, therefore, that after Terry's experience at Old Mill the information he had gathered there on the New Technology would not have been passed on to Quelch's other son-in-law by 1742. There seems to be some evidence to support Quelch jnr.'s modernisation of Gurney's mill in 1741/2, so it is reasonable to expect Clement Taylor to have done the same at Basted at about the same time. In fact Table XI indicates this more positively than was the case for Gurney's, one of the reasons being that this had been a specifically Quelch mill and was thus not likely to have been neglected. Moreover at some point between 1742 and 1761 Clement Taylor must have become familiar with the workings of an improved model of the Engine in order for him to have installed and worked one when he up-dated Poll mill in Boxley (q.v.) in 1761, the evidence for which is certain.

Despite all this a doubt lingers in the mind as to whether they had sufficient water power at Basted to make full use of this new facility. However, at a much later date when James and John Taylor (son), succeeded to the mill, they do not appear to have found difficulty in making good quality countermarked paper there.[97] But there may have been good reasons

---

[95] The name Taylor is, of course, commonly found, but one wonders in this case whether there was any connection between these Ightham Taylors and the Thomas Taylor who had been occupant of Forstal mill in 1665 ? It would have been a gap of three generations.

[96] The uncertainty that surrounds this statement stems from the fact that no entry for his *baptism* has been found in the Igtham PR (neither microfiche nor original); nor has any family pedigree come to light yet. Nevertheless his family were closely associated with the district (see App.II TABLE XXIII) so one can only assume that he may have been born but not baptised there.

[97] Both "CT" and "CT & SON" and "J Taylor" (d.o.d. 1764) countermarks have been found in American documents of the 1760/70's (Gravell, T.L. Bib.68 140–142). Clement snr. died in 1776 so any more "C TAYLOR" marks after this date *probably* refer to Clement jnr. e.g. Gravell op. cit. 667 (d.o.d. 1789). John Taylor (son) only came of age in 1771 so the d.o.d. 1764 "J TAYLOR" mark must have originated from James. (This may give a clue to the origin of the "I TAYLOR" marks as distinct from "J TAYLOR" ?). Other early "J TAYLOR" marks have been found (author) in

(continued...)

for the Taylors not having done so before. Even as late as the 1830's when steam power had been introduced, and a paper machine, they still used water power to work their rag–breakers; and to do this they had to employ what was in effect the largest waterwheel in the county.[98] One also has to find some explanation for the mass exodus which the Clement Taylor family made later to the Maidstone area. It may quite simply have been a case of wishing to expand their business; and by 1760 there would have been prospects to look for in papermaking for four Taylor sons and the facilities for expansion at Basted were clearly limited. There would have been a premium to pay on mill sites nearer to London (since so many other industries depended on water power) so Maidstone, as had been the case earlier, was no doubt the most attractive proposition for widening their interests. But it could be argued equally that the Taylors had discovered that there were limitations within their paper mill as it existed then.

That both the Quelchs and Taylors had ambitions is known from the fact that Clement Taylor snr. had acquired a reputation, and an award from the Society of Arts in 1757, for making (unspecified) improvements to papers as part of a drive by the Society to encourage manufacturers to make Plate and other kinds of paper equal in quality to those produced by the French. Both Taylor and Quelch were approached again, later in the same year, by the Society to make papers from "silk" Rags and both were awarded bounties for their efforts in this unbelievable episode. The Society's Records also show that in 1759 Taylor[99] submitted "Four Rheams of large Drawing Paper.....vizt. No.1 of a Reddish Shade; No.2 of a Greenish Shade; No.3 of a Stone Colour and No.4 in the Rough".[100] This last piece of information, though interesting in another context,[101] is admittedly a detail, but it has been cited here

[97](...continued)

drawer 1/9 RIBA Drawings Colln. among a group of William Newton's (1730–98) No.5 and in a Thomas Hunt (1737–1808) *album* p.11v. In both instances there are also "J WHATMAN" marks with d.o.d.'s of 1770 and 1765.

[98] Bridge, W.E. "Some Historical Notes, Basted Mill" (Pamphlet 1948). The very early history of this mill has been omitted in this account.

[99] Society of Arts Minute 3:Feb:1759 (Information kindly supplied by Mr. D.G.C. Allan, Curator & Librarian, Roy. Soc. Arts).

[100] It would appear that two separate projects have been confused in a letter of John Stackhouse Styles (Stationer) preserved in Society of Arts Guard Book Vol.III p.31. In this Mr. Styles recalled an enquiry "out of the Country" for some Brown Academy Paper in 1755 and learnt from Mr. Highmore (presumably the Artist) that this was a product of France. It was usual in those days, especially for those trained in foreign Academies, to make drawings on coloured (demi–teint) papers, the colour acting as the middle tint. The Society of Arts objectives at this time was to encourage domestic production of various papers (Plate, Marbled etc.) equivalent to those made in France. Clement Taylor's coloured "drawing" papers were probably an answer to this enquiry, whereas Styles in his account makes them out to have been made "of Silk Rags alone". Styles was the moving spirit behind this very dubious project and was perhaps being over–enthusiastic here.

[101] This is the first use of the term Drawing Paper known to the author. Papers of one sort or another had, of course, been used for drawing on for centuries in Europe, but the term "Drawing Paper" implies a specific commodity manufactured in a paper mill. The artists' market at this time must have been minimal and the total quantities required covered by a single vat in a matter of a few weeks. Even if a paper mill had specialised in this product, one has the further problem of its distribution. Later in the 18th C. the growing demand for a special paper of this kind by Engineers, Cartographers, Architects, Townplanners etc. would have created a market that would have been large enough to have interested one or more paper mills. Evidence that this was the case may be seen in the classes of paper defined in the Excise Acts. Drawing Paper is not mentioned in the Acts of 1781, 1783 or 1787, but it is in the Act of 1794. Coloured (demi–teint) papers do not present the same problem since they were the stock in trade for many paper mills and used for a variety of purposes. The term "Academy Paper" does, however, imply that perhaps a large institution such as the French Royal Academy, where the demi–teint method of drawing was *de rigueur*, may have commissioned a paper mill to make these papers specially for them. In spite of enquiries made to the Cabinet d'Estampes at the Louvre and elsewhere on this subject by the author it was not possible to obtain an answer to this question. The British Royal Academy was not founded until 1768 and by this date British Artists had developed their own method of drawing, which seems to have

(continued...)

merely to indicate that what with Taylor's experiments with "silk paper" and then coloured papers, it looks as if Basted was not so much concerned with Fine papers as Seconds during Clement Taylor snr.'s régime there, a régime that ended in 1761 when he moved to Poll mill on the other side of the River Len to Whatman's Turkey mill.

In making this move it is likely that he left his eldest son, Clement jnr., in charge of Basted and that he was the "Clement Taylor" who took on an apprentice, William Appleton, in 1762. But the movements of Clement snr.'s sons over the next ten years can only be surmised. By 1772 Clement jnr. had moved into Upper Tovil mill at Maidstone and, in addition, took the lease of Whatman's Old Mill in Hollingbourne in 1774 (see below). So one might legitimately assume that during the latter part of the 1760's he was working with his father at Poll mill as "Clement Taylor & Son" and had got to know the lie of the land in the Maidstone district. This would have allowed James to have managed Basted. After Clement snr.'s death in 1776, John succeeded at Basted; James carried on with the help of George at Poll mill; and Clement jnr. continued to operate Upper Tovil and Old Mill. Thus one has the situation where the family element of the Quelch empire had now expanded their operations from two to six Kent mills in the 34 years since 1740, having made use of seven paper mills in the course of this.

The foregoing gives the general picture of the expansion at the centre of the Quelch empire; but before proceeding to its wider implications, the position is summarised below by brief comments on the mills concerned in this.

Basted Mill
(Wrotham)

Founded by Quelch snr. in 1716 incorporating very probably an early form of Hollander.
Possible training ground for John Terry, Clement Taylor snr. and, probably, his cousin, John Taylor (later Carshalton mill, Surrey).
William Buttanshaw apprenticed there in 1723 (see Satellites).
1728–32 managed by Quelch jnr.
1732–39 probably managed by John Terry.
1742 taken over by Clement Taylor snr.; and effective modernisation suggested 1742/3.
Served as a training ground for Clement jnr.; James; John and George Taylor.
Clement jnr. must have managed it for a short period after 1761; followed by James; John definitely succeeding there from 1776–1802, date of his death.
It was left to Charles Haddock and George Taylor. The latter was made bankrupt. The surviving assignees of George, Street and Fourdrinier, sold the Estate to Thomas Wildes in 1815 who, in turn, leased it to John Pine and William Thomas of Lower Tovil mill, Maidstone for 14 years (see App.III Synopsis Cobtree Mill note 1.).[102]
A paper machine was installed in 1836; and in 1839/40 the old mill was pulled down and Messrs. Monckton & Co. took over the new.

[101](...continued)
been almost entirely on White paper. Enquiries made to the Royal Academy on the subject of a special paper used for drawing on produced a negative result, not known. Chambers Encyclopaedia (1737) in referring to papers of the larger sizes does associate them with "merchants books and for drawing on". (This subject is examined in more detail in the author's Bib.76, a work which is subtitled "The Genesis of Modern Drawing Paper").

[102] A "BASTED MILL 1824" countermark has been found in a Constable Drawing of Brighton Pier (Victoria & Albert Museum R.289).

Gurney's Mill
(Loose)

Quelch snr. moved in there in 1728 after William Harris snr.'s departure.
A significant rise in the ratable value suggests the installation of an early form of Hollander there in 1729.
In 1732 joined by Quelch jnr. who took over the mill between 1741–45/6, modernising it in 1741/2, the last rise in the ratable value until 1773. Quelchs relinquished their interest in the mill by 1753. The later history of this mill will be dealt with when considering the French family at Old Mill (see this Chap. p.323).

Dartford No.2

Acquired by Quelch snr. from Richard Archer in 1736, but leaving him as tenant until bankrupted in 1740. Quelch snr. and Terry moved in, divided the old mill and modernised it into two new mills in 1741/2.
No.2 was held by Terry (d.1766); followed by his widow, Eleanor; and, later, their son–in–law, Thomas Budgen, who in the late 1790's took over both Nos. 2 & 3.
Succeeded by John Budgen, bankrupted in 1820.

Dartford No.3

See under No.2. Held by Quelch snr. from 1741/2–45/6, when Quelch jnr. took it over until his death in 1777. Three Finchs, one a godson of Quelch jnr., succeeded until the mill was ultimately taken over by Thomas Budgen (for details see *Shorter*, A. Bib.12 181/2).

Poll Mill
(Boxley)

After William Gill snr.'s final bankruptcy in 1731 Joseph Cordwell occupied the mill from 1732–56. He also managed Turkey mill from 1732–35. James Brooke cannot have been very impressed with his papermaking abilities otherwise he might well have kept him on there. It is highly improbable therefore that he did anything to modernise the process at Poll mill before 1736.
But it is possible that between 1736–56 or during the period of his successor, Abraham Fearon (a watchmaker from Soho), 1756–60, that an Engine of some description was introduced. A Bill of Sale[103] from Fearon to Clement Taylor snr., who succeeded there in 1761, refers to the presence of an "engine" or "engines" in the mill. Whoever it was that had installed them, Clement Taylor was not satisfied with the equipment and replaced it with the latest Engine at that date.[104] Hence the nature of the entry against Poll mill in Table XI.[105]
After Clement snr.'s death (1776) the lease passed to James Taylor.

---

[103] Balston, T. Bib.1 80/81. Some of the items mentioned in this Bill of Sale and in Whatman's proposals for settling the dispute (79) may be of interest. They include Moulds, Felts, Hand Bowles, Layboards, Press Boards and Planks; Mill Wheels, Engines, Presses, Vatts, Treble Lines, Stuff Chests, Cisterns, Pumps, Pump Standards, Brass Cocks, Pipes; and, in addition, stress was laid on keeping the Spring Water Pipes and Reservoir in good order.

[104] Balston, T. Bib.1 76. Reference to a conversation between George Taylor and the younger Whatman in which George had said that, if Whatman were to claim the latest Engine of which only the lighter and studs had been made with Lord Aylesford's timber, it would involve him in much hardship. Whatman discovered later that all the timber for this Engine had been specifically demanded and obtained from Lord Aylesford's Steward and did not belong to the Taylors.

[105] Shorter, A. Bib.12 65 n.61 cites a reference to the fact that Fine white linen rags were stolen from Joseph Cordwell's warehouse in Boxley the end of 1736. Apart from suggesting that this is evidence that Poll was a White mill, it might also indicate that around this date Cordwell had installed an early form of Engine to handle these materials more easily, having learnt perhaps of an installation at Gurney's mill or picked up a tip from Harris who had just moved into Turkey mill. This, however, is pure supposition; the conversion of what was in effect a traditional paper mill with troughs to one using an Engine cannot have been very extensive in view of Clement Taylor's subsequent actions there and the generally ruinous state of the mill. Alternatively, 1755 might be set as a date; the ratable value of Poll mill went up from £30 to £37–10 for that year, but then all four Boxley mills' Rates were adjusted at about that time (see App.III), Turkey mill's dropping from £65 to £34!

Although the interest here is in the modernisation of the paper industry in Kent, to place this in context it is necessary to digress from this briefly to consider the behaviour of the Taylor family. There was another and rather different side to these seemingly straightforward actions. It is evident that neither of the Whatmans (and the father it will be recalled did not die until 1759 and had just invented Wove paper) had a very high opinion of the mill which they considered to be in a ruinous state; or of Fearon of whom they had said that "he was inclined to quit". There were many applicants for the lease when Fearon decided to leave and it was let to Clement Taylor snr. by the third Lord Aylesford because Taylor had promised "to make great improvements" to the mill, a statement which does much to substantiate the opinion already expressed by the Whatmans. It was in the events that followed that some light is thrown on the equipment it contained.

To go back a generation there is nothing to indicate that there had been any ill–feeling in the relations between the elder Whatman and the Quelchs when they were in Loose. Indeed, if there had been, it is difficult to imagine Whatman granting the lease of Old Mill to them. Afterwards the Quelchs disappeared from the Maidstone scene to north west Kent where they seem to have been highly regarded as persons and paper makers at Dartford. The Clement Taylor family, however, constituted a rather different kettle of fish. It is difficult to know whether Clement snr. was just a little stupid or downright deceitful in his behaviour. The younger Whatman commenting on Clement snr.'s Will described it as "an extraordinary Composition of Knavery and Folly", leaving to his son, James, a Lease for Poll mill that did not exist as well as most of the fixtures in the mill that had been the property of Lord Aylesford.

All this emerged when the younger Whatman acquired the freehold of the property (including the mill and other land bordering on his Vinters estate) in 1785 from the fourth Lord Aylesford. He described the mill at this stage as a "shell of a building liable to great decay". To remedy this liability he sought new terms for the tenancy and out of this arose a long and bitter dispute between him and all the surviving members of the Taylor family, a saga which has been described in detail by Thomas Balston[106] and which ended in a court action and the eviction of the Taylors in 1787.

Two points of interest emerge. First, after Clement Taylor snr. took up the lease from Fearon he installed the latest kind of Engine. James, who prevaricated endlessly, claimed that his father had spent £7,000 on the mill and he some £3,000, considerable sums for those times and, if true, would represent a major reconstruction there. Second, James, equivocating again, claimed that his brother, John, had met one of the appraisers who had valued the fixtures between Lord Aylesford and Fearon and who could not recollect that anything more belonged to Lord Aylesford than a "screw" (probably a form of pump) and an "old engine trough". In actual fact a great deal more belonged to Lord Aylesford than this and the Bill of Sale referred to above does mention "engines"; but how effective they were or who installed them is not known except that one of the Aylesfords must have borne much of the expense.

---

[106] Balston, T. Bib.1 Chapter XI. This story makes extraordinary reading and is full of the evasive statements made and the deceitful tactics used by all the younger members of the Taylor family including threats of reprisals from Clement jnr. who was at that time occupying Old Mill, Hollingbourne. One wonders, had Whatman been able to foresee all this, whether he would ever have allowed Clement jnr. the lease of this mill (for details of this see text).

After the eviction of the Taylors Whatman took the mill under his own wing until 1794 when it was sold (together with Turkey and Upper mills) to Hollingworth and Balston as a two-vat mill[107] that remained in Hollingworths' hands until at least 1824. Whether it continued later as a paper mill (it was used by a bleacher for a time) is uncertain. In 1836 there was a flood in the river and a landslide that swept away two waterwheels (as well as part of Turkey mill). Shortly after this the mill was pulled down.[108]

Upper Tovil Mill
(Maidstone)

Continuing from the earlier account of this mill[109] Peter Musgrove jnr. carried on working Upper Tovil at times, in the occupation of minor paper makers (Gifford, Pilchard etc.)[110] until 1745 when a William Wilkins insured *his mill* in the tenure of William Musgrove and George Pitcher.[111] Nothing is known about the status of the mill at this point; it may have been a Brown mill or a mill making shop papers. The ratable value had fallen from £20 in 1723 to £18 when Wilkins took over. The fact that it had risen to £36 in 1763/5 cannot be regarded as a reliable indication that the mill had been modernised (the Maidstone RB. between 1742–62 is missing and the rise might have been due to a consolidation of a half-yearly rate?). By the time Wilkins had left the rate had risen to £39. If in fact it had been a Brown mill during this period it could have coped with a primitive form of Engine with or without the aid of mortars. William Musgrove who had been one of the occupants in 1745 moved to Eynsford in 1761 (see below).

However, the major change at Upper Tovil took place with the arrival of Clement Taylor jnr. in 1772 when the ratable value of the mill leapt from £39 to £83–10. At some point between then and 1797, when Clement Taylor was bankrupted, this mill became a five-vat mill (equal in size to Whatman's Turkey mill). Tradition has it that this took place almost entirely when the mill was new-built in 1772. The Upper Tovil entry in TABLE XI reflects this two-stage up-grading. Meanwhile Clement jnr. was expanding in other directions, both in the manufacture of White countermarked paper and in other activities.[112]

After Taylor's demise the mill, which ultimately was acquired by Albert E. Reed in 1896, passed to Edward and Clement Taylor Russell in 1797; and in 1799 to Joseph Ruse, all of

[107]   Balston, T. Bib.1 120.
[108]   The Original Papermakers' Recorder May 1903.
[109]   See Chap.II TABLES III & IV and Chap.IV p.152.
[110]   Spain, R.J. Bib.11 174/5.
[111]   Shorter, A. Bib.12 191. SFIP 103693 21:Oct:1745.
[112]   Clement Taylor jnr. was a member of an ambitious family who, to judge from his activities, could be described as something of a thruster and reactionary, offered himself as an Independent parliamentary candidate for Maidstone in opposition to the Hon. Charles Finch, brother of Lord Aylesford. In 1780 (that is five years before the Taylor family crossed swords with the younger Whatman), Taylor was returned and thanked the freemen of Maidstone for their noble stand which, he hoped, would convince the Finch party that they were determined to be "free".
In 1792 a very controversial Patent was granted to Clement and George Taylor for a rag bleaching process. The claims of this Patent were hotly disputed by Whatman and the rest of the paper trade. Whatman and others, including John Larking (of him more later), had already been experimenting in this field and claimed that a Mr. Willis, who had been engaged to do some work for Whatman, Curteis and Larking, had been seduced from us "by the offer of a sum of money and a share in their (the Taylors') Patent". In the event the paper trade ignored the Patent and the Taylors brought no action against them. (For full details see Balston, T. Bib.1 103 ff.).
In addition to his papermaking activities at Upper Tovil and Old Mill, a Taylor was clearly about to commit himself to a partnership with (William ?) Edmeads at Gurney's mill in 1797 (The Loose RB entries are 1797 Taylor & Edmeads £33; 1799 Russell & Co. £33. The relevant entry in the East Farleigh RB is reported by Spain, R.J. Bib.10 56 as "Taylor & Edmeads 1798, 1799" but in pencil underneath "M Russell & Edmeads"). It seems certain that this "Taylor" was Clement jnr. and that he fell out of this project because of his bankruptcy in that same year. His name also makes a brief appearance in the Land Tax Return of 1796 for East Malling; the reason for this is not clear. He also had a very short-lived interest in Padsole mill q.v. in 1797/8. See Shorter, A. Bib.7 [July] 58 for later occupants of this mill. (For his papermaking in Ireland see App.II p.61).

whom continued to produce countermarked paper. By 1805 "RUSE & TURNERS" countermarks appear, the former having gone into partnership with Richard and Thomas Turner. In 1816 the proprietors were Ruse, Turner and Welch. Richard Turner was still there in 1834 to be followed by the Allnutts in the 1850's.[113] (For later occupants see Shorter, A Bib.7 [July]58. The Mill was demolished in the 1980's; now a housing estate).

Old Mill
(Hollingbourne)

A synopsis of the entire history of this important mill as a *paper* mill will be found in Appendix I. To serve the needs of the text it has been divided up into a number of separate instalments. An account of John Terry's occupation of this mill (1739–41) has already been given earlier in this chapter (pp.280 ff.).

Other influential periods in its history are covered later in this chapter (pp.321 ff.). The section given below describes yet another chapter in its history, a further ramification of the Quelch Empire with Clement Taylor jnr. as tenant (1774–1793).

Before considering his occupation mention may be made of the fact that the younger Whatman re-occupied it between 1770–1774. Two curious features of this are (i) he is not entered as an Outdweller in the Hollingbourne ratebook; and (ii) he only insured his utensils and stock but not the mill itself. During these four years he installed a new Engine "put up July 1771" and a full account of this together with his drawings will be found in App.V pp.225–244.

The Taylors at Poll mill (opposite Turkey mill) may have got wind of this installation and, just as John Terry had done 35 years earlier, they wanted to know more about it. The fact is that Whatman vacated this mill in favour of Upper mill, Loose, which he acquired and rebuilt in 1774. Whether he left his new Engine in Old mill or moved it to Loose is not known, but an unexplained annual payment of £400 made by Clement Taylor (certainly between 1780–91)[114] to Whatman might indicate a charge for the use of the new Engine and to cover its cost. In Whatman's comments on this new Engine it is clear that he knew how Mr. Willmott washed and beat his rags so perhaps it is not particularly strange that he should allow a rival into his mill and not be especially anxious to conceal his latest improvements.

Clement jnr. continued to lease Old mill until 1793 when Whatman once more became proprietor.[115] During his tenancy the insurance premium for the mill rose from £1,400 in 1774 to £9,500 in 1791, the inference from this being that major alterations had taken place. It is known that sometime before the mill shut-down finally it had become a five-vat mill and this enlargement may have taken place during Clement jnr.'s tenancy either in part or whole. That a substantial enlargement had taken place is supported by the fact that Clement jnr. and subsequent proprietors found it necessary either to employ a manager (e.g. Daniel Newman from ca. 1791 with the Salmons possibly earlier than this) or sub-let it (e.g. Crispe

---

[113] The identification "TURNER" countermarks has its problems. Ruse and Turners' marks appear first in 1805; a "RUSE & TURNERS 1834" found by author in a Cotman drawing (The Sunken Road) at Norwich (NCM 227.235.951) shows the extent of its use. "TOVILL MILL 1813" found in a Turner drawing (T.B.CXVI–CXVIII group No.3) and a "TOVIL MILL 1815" in the Master Paper Makers' Correspondence (PSM) both of which have been attributed to Upper Tovil Mill (cf. Lower Tovil Mill marks see this Chap. TABLE XII n.17).
Other "TURNER" countermarks are mainly attributable to Chafford mill (Penshurst, Kent). These include, for example, "W TURNER 1815": "G & R T.....1813" (KAO P 173 5/2 Part II); "G & R TURNER 1824"; and "R TURNER CHAFFORD MILL" (d.o.d.1836). "G & R TURNER" marks are rare, but have been found in Cotman and Bonnington drawings. There was also an R. Turner of Aller mill, Devonshire, and Shorter, A.Bib.12 365 No.175 illustrates "T & F" (Turner & Fincher) d.o.d.1794 (Exeter City Library); Gravell, T.L. Bib.68 Nos.246/7 "F & T" marks; 252 "FINCHER & SONS" d.o.d.1825; and No.688 "J & R TURNER 1796" which he attributes to Aller mill (see this Chap. n.141).
[114] Balston, T. Bib.1 54.
[115] There is a conflict of evidence here which is discussed further in App.I Old Mill synop. periods 1793–5.

and Newman). Taylor had his hands full at this time with a lot of other commitments in politics, papermaking and industrial relations, the latter affecting both Whatman and especially Clement jnr., explaining his interest in Ireland.[116]

In Part V of this chapter it has been demonstrated how William Quelch snr. and his family generated a central core to an empire whose activities spread to three main centres from which, in 1740 and the years immediately following, the newly acquired knowledge affected either directly or more diffusely other paper makers in these districts. These centres were Basted mill; Dartford; and, to a very much lesser extent, Maidstone.

[116] Balston, T. Bib.1 117–9.

PART VI

THE SATELLITES : THE BASTED CENTRE : THE DARTFORD CENTRE

The term "satellite" was used earlier, for the sake of brevity, more in an umbrella sense than one of direct linkage though there were clearly cases of this. Even in the case of Quelch snr.'s *papermaking* sons–in–law, although highly probable, we cannot prove that they learnt their papermaking under Quelch's guidance. There is only one positive instance of this, William Buttanshaw's apprenticeship under Quelch snr. starting in 1723 at Basted mill. One has to assume then that news of any innovations introduced at a mill like this was disseminated and applied in other mills through indirect or unidentifiable agencies. It is a very necessary assumption when the difficulties described in the previous chapter are recalled, namely, *those a paper maker unfamiliar with the New Technology would have had to face when encountering the Engine for the first time*, not to mention the expenditure and problems involved in converting and equipping a mill for this purpose.

Apart then from direct experience as a member of a papermaking family who possessed an Engine of one kind or another; or serving an apprenticeship under a paper maker already using the New Technology, one must suppose that others acquired their knowledge from beatermen, or "engineers" as they came to be known, who moved from mill to mill; or millwrights; or other people who cannot be identified at this time but who definitely existed at a later date e.g. firms who specialised in the construction of Engines; but in the 1740's much of this would have lain in the future. Some mills, including some of those examined below, might already have been equipped with primitive models such as those postulated in the case of Quelch snr. In cases such as these the paper makers would have been quicker to pick up the improvements than others, but they would still have needed the kind of experience that Terry must have had at Hollingbourne Old Mill to have up–dated the process meaningfully.

So, apart from Buttanshaw, one can only surmise that the new methods spread from centres like these. In this case two have been singled out with which the Quelch Empire was particularly associated; other spheres where their influence may have been felt will be examined separately. It seems scarcely necessary to add the reminder that data is very scarce and very scattered so that in nearly all the examples considered below conclusions are at best tentative.

THE BASTED CENTRE[117]
(Map 4)

There were a number of paper mills, either in existence before Basted or which came into being after, that were close enough to have been influenced by what went on there; this is not to say that they were, but that they could have been, especially as some of them were in the doldrums at the beginning of the period 1740–1800. There was Shoreham mill on the River

---

[117] O.S. MR. TQ 607557.

SKETCH–MAP: LOCATION OF THE MILLS
AROUND THE BASTED AND DARTFORD CENTRES

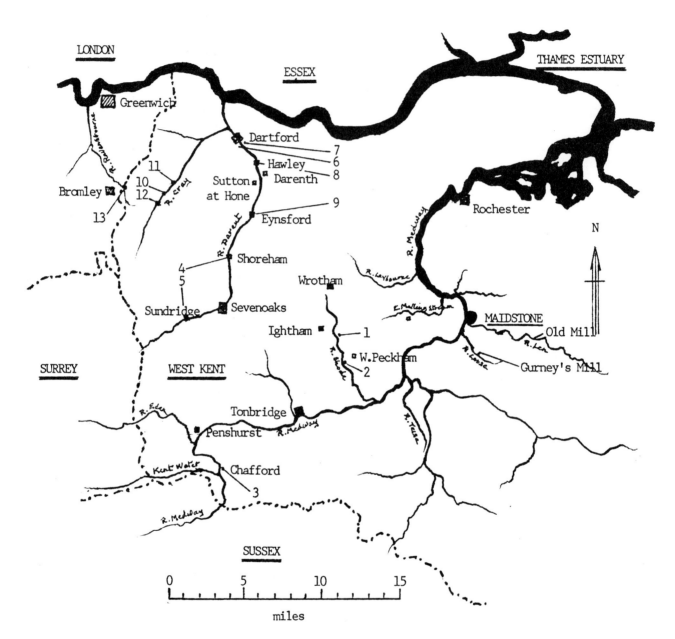

BASTED CENTRE

1. Basted mill, Wrotham.
2. Hamptons mill, West Peckham.
3. Chafford mill, Penshurst.

4. Shoreham mill, Shoreham.
5. Sundridge mill, Sundridge.

DARTFORD CENTRE

6. Dartford No.2 mill (West).
7. Dartford No.3 mill (East).
8. Hawley mill, Hawley.
9. Eynsford mill, Eynsford.

10. Cray Valley mill, St. Paul's Cray.
11. Foots Cray mill, Foots Cray.
12. St. Mary Cray mill, St. Mary Cray.
13. Bromley mill, Bromley.

Darent some 6.5 miles north–west of Basted, active from the late 17th C.; its dependent further up the Darent, Sundridge, about 8 miles due west and active from 1766; Hampton's mill at West Peckham about 2 miles downstream on the River Shode,[118] south of Basted, and in between and much later, Roughway;[119] much further south–west, about 11 miles from Basted; but otherwise isolated from other papermaking districts in Kent, Chafford mill;[120] and, finally, about 7.5 miles to the east, East Malling, though this was just as likely to have been influenced by the Maidstone district as Basted.

Hamptons Mill
(West Peckham)

There is documentary evidence to show that William Buttanshaw, papermaker, was building a drying loft at Hamptons mill in June 1740.[121] The West Peckham Church accounts confirm that William Buttanshaw's assessment for 1740 replaced a William Stidolph's which had lasted from at least 1719–1739. The proprietors of the mill were the Dalison family. Among the Deeds relating to the lease of the paper mill there is one for its renewal in 1759[122] in the preamble of which it states that the premises were "formerly in the occupation of William Stiddolph and late William Buttanshaw". No evidence has yet come to light to show that William Stiddolph of West Peckham was a paper maker[123] or that the mill was a paper mill before 1740.

William Buttanshaw (bapt. Wrotham 1715) must have been made free at Basted ca.1730 and decided to convert Hamptons mill to papermaking in 1740, possibly at the invitation of the proprietor.[124] If there had been an early model of an Engine at Basted, then it is reasonable to extend this idea to Buttanshaw's conversion of Hampton's; but 1740 is really too early to assume that a more advanced model had been installed there, seeing that this was probably not done at Basted mill till 1742/3 and thus unlikely to have been known to Buttanshaw. To lend some support to this is the fact that there is no mention of any other major building work in the Deed relating to the construction of a Drying loft.

The mill itself may have been assessed partly in the parish of West Peckham and partly in Shipbourne[125] on the opposite bank of the River Shode. The assessments in West Peckham are too low to represent the full value of a paper mill unless there was some other reason for this, namely, that the rate was borne by the Dalison family; the entries relating to Stidolph

[118] O.S. MR. TQ 618521.

[119] O.S. MR. TQ 615529.

[120] O.S. MR. TQ 517(5)405 Chafford Island.

[121] KAO U 522/E5/5. An Agreement between Thomas West of West Peckham, Carpenter, and William Buttanshaw of the parish of Wrotham, paper maker, regarding the erection 3:June:1740 of a drying loft 24 ft. wide and 70 ft. long. The construction, types of wood, tiles, nails, sand, lime etc. all specified. (I am indebted to Mr. M.J. Fuller for drawing my attention to this document).

[122] KAO U 522 T/13. The 1759 renewal of the lease refers to "the newly erected paper mill" supporting the view that this took place in 1740.

[123] William Stiddolph was a paper maker at Chafford mill, Penshurst, from 1762 at least, the son of Oliver Stidolph the paper maker who preceded him there. No connection has been discovered between them and the William Stiddolph at W. Peckham. The name Stiddolph, which dates back to the 14th C., if not earlier, is not uncommon in that part of Kent. Stiddolphs appear at Dartford in the 17th C.; Tonbridge, Thomas Stidolf, a dyer; Steddal/Stidolph millers and paper makers at Penshurst etc. (see Chafford below for further discussion).

[124] The River Medway was made navigable above Maidstone as far as Tonbridge in 1740/41 and the plans for this must have been known before this date. It is possible that this may have been a contributory reason for Buttanshaw's move to West Peckham.

[125] The only church accounts that have survived for Shipbourne for this period are disbursements only, no Assessments. (KAO P 334 12/1, which start at 1752).

and the Buttanshaws remain at £3 from 1719–1790, a figure that suggests a house rather than a mill.[126]

The Buttanshaw family held the lease of the mill from 1740–1835, when a John Buttanshaw relinquished it.[127] William snr. occupied the mill for 16 years, dying in 1756 of "a malignant fever"; his wife continued to run it until William jnr. insured it in his name in 1773; but he died the following year described as "a young man". His mother insured the mill again in February 1775 and another son, John, (bapt.1751), in August of the same year. Though another John Buttanshaw was buried in 1787, the John who was the occupant of the mill died in 1827 and was succeeded there by his eldest son, also John (bapt.1788). It was the latter who held the lease until 1835. "B" countermarks appear in local documents from 1775; more explicit ones in the 1780's; and in American documents in the 1790's.[128]

There is nothing to indicate when this mill was up-graded to the New Technology. It might be argued that because of the relatively short tenures of the two Williams modernisation might have been delayed until John snr. took over in 1775. However, since Basted mill was only a couple of miles away steps may have been taken earlier by William snr. in this direction. Could he have afforded it so soon after starting up the mill or, if he made papers from low quality materials, was there any need for it ? On the other hand it is known that the Buttanshaws employed a paper maker, James Crips (evidently from the locality), who had arrived there by the end of 1749, if not earlier.[129] There is nothing unusual in this except that Crips left to take over Cray Valley paper mill (St. Paul's Cray, NW.Kent q.v.) from Josias Johannot in 1753 and Table XI indicates that this mill had already been modernised by then. If so, the question arises, did Crips learn the New Technology at Hampton's ? or had he come from Basted after 1742/3 bringing with him the new method ? or had he learnt sufficient from the earlier model at Hampton's to enable him to manage a new model at Cray Valley ? The Table reflects this uncertainty so far as Hamptons was concerned. (Cray Valley will be discussed later in relation to the Dartford Centre).

The Buttanshaw family seem to have been infected with the same energy as the Quelch and Taylor families, more so as time went on. John Buttanshaw snr. was clearly a very progressive paper maker and was among the first to buy a Fourdrinier Paper Machine, in 1807.[130] It is not certain where he installed this. Some references in the literature state that this was at his West Peckham mill; but the 1816 Excise General List shows that he had two paper mills by this time, the other being Roughway, a mill still extant, that lay about half a mile upstream from Hamptons.[131] This venture seems to have been noteworthy in view of the fact that the Prospectus for the Fourdrinier machine, issued in 1813, was printed on Extra

---

[126] The West Peckham Church Accounts (KAO P 285 5/1) show much larger assessments e.g. from £8–£13 between 1719–93 against various occupants under the heading "more for the mill land".

[127] KAO U 522 T/13.

[128] 3 single line "B" marks found in surrounds of Dutch Lion, Britannia etc. in Ightham documents of 1775 and 1783. John Buttanshaw would have been Master Paper Maker by 1775. "J Buttanshaw" Wrotham Land Tax (Plaxtol Ward) for 1780 (KAO Q/RP1/431). Other marks commonly found are "J B" in concentric circles and "J Butt^w". See also Gravell, T.L. Bib.68 Nos.124/5.

[129] The W. Peckham Register of Baptisms (KAO P/285) has the entry for 19:Dec:1749 William s.o. James and Ann Crips, Papermaker. Although James' baptism has not been found there were a number of Crips families in W. Peckham, Shipbourne, Wrotham etc. So he might equally have learnt his papermaking at Basted or Hamptons, perhaps even going to W. Peckham with Buttanshaw in the first place. Buttanshaw baptisms, however, start earlier than Crips', in 1741. (A John Crips, carpenter, was in W. Peckham in 1751).

[130] Coleman, D.C. in his Table XV (197) reprints the Fourdrinier Committee's list (1837) of paper machines erected under licence and Buttanshaw's Licence was issued on the 1:July:1807, but does not specify where. Clapperton, R.H Bib.75 51, makes out that Buttanshaw installed a 60 inch width papermachine in 1809 at West Peckham.

[131] The Land Tax Returns show that Buttanshaw held various properties from 1780 in the Plaxtol Ward, Wrotham, where Roughway was situated (KAO Q RP1/431). But by 1807 these entries are reduced to a single one in which Widow Chilman was the proprietor and Buttanshaw the occupant; ditto 1813, no mention of a mill. The 1780 return does refer to "Long Mill" Proprietor Baldwin.

Large Thin Post made at Buttanshaw's mill, West Peckham. The document, to judge from the claims it makes for all the advantages the Fourdrinier machine brings to the paper maker, must have been printed on machine-made paper; listing greater strength, smoother surface etc. and the fact that the paper maker can start and stop when he pleases, no labour problems![132]

Chafford Mill
(Penshurst)

No direct connection is known between this paper mill and those in the Quelch empire. Being a paper mill completely isolated from others in Kent (and, indeed, from any in the neighbouring counties) it seems probable that the chief source of influence here would have come from Buttanshaw at West Peckham, about 10 miles to the north-east of it with the town of Tonbridge midway between. It is true, as mentioned above, the Medway had been made navigable as far as Tonbridge in 1740/41 and the improved communication with Maidstone that followed might be seen as another source of influence, although nearly twice as far away.

As a paper mill it had a life of at least 150 years, closing down between 1905-14,[133] but it is not known for certain when it first came into operation. The earliest evidence of its existence is an insurance policy taken out by Oliver Stidolph, paper maker, in 1756 for *a paper mill, fulling mill and a corn mill*.[134] The corn mill had been there in the 17th C. together with a malt mill.[135] There is no mention of a fulling mill until the early 18th C. when the site of these mills is described in the Penshurst Church accounts as on "Fulling Mill Island".[136] These show that in 1733 Thomas Steddal was the occupier of the fulling mill, succeeded by Oliver in 1734-1768. Although Oliver's policy of 1756 specifies three mills, the fulling mill appears to have become redundant after this date which might account for the Chafford Estate investing at that time in a more profitable venture, possibly at the Stiddolphs' suggestion. The fact that the paper mill came into being as a *separate entity* at a comparatively late date implies that it was designed to accommodate an Engine of sorts requiring a power transmission to suit. If it had been a paper mill with hammers and mortars then the fulling mill could have been adapted for use in the traditional process as earlier fulling mills had been before. But this would have been a most unlikely course of action in 1756.

But there is nothing to suggest what sort of Engine might have been employed here; much would have depended on the starting date of the mill, and whether it began its life as a Brown or White mill. If William Buttanshaw snr. had up-dated Hamptons before his death in 1756, then Oliver Stiddolph may have been influenced by this and built an up-to-date mill incorporating the New Technology, but this presupposes that Oliver had been trained somewhere in the more modern methods. It is a big assumption to make for a paper maker living in such an isolated area. In any case it is most unlikely that it would have been Oliver himself.

[132] Clapperton, R.H. Bib.55 App.I 255.
[133] The Original Papermakers Recorder for Nov.1905 reported the voluntary winding up of Turner & Co. (Chafford Mills) Ltd. But Shorter, A. Bib.9 174 gives a date of 1914 for the shut down of the mill; perhaps it was vats in one case, the machine in the other.
[134] Shorter, A. Bib.12 197 citing SFIP 152247 6:May:1756. Note that three types of mill are specified.
[135] KAO U 303 T 7-9 An Indenture Tripartite between Sir George Rivers Bart. et al. dated 1691 refers to "Meadow Land called Chafford Island" with Roger Rogers tenant of "the mill house and 2 mills, 1 wheat and 1 malt, commonly known as Chafford mills". The paper mill is marked on this same island in the O.S. 6 inch to the mile map, 1st Edition (1864/5) Sheet 60.
[136] KAO P 287 5/1 and 12/2 covering a period 1721-1782.

An acceptable solution to this problem, although it does not answer the question as to where the Stiddolphs learnt to use an Engine,[137] might be to suggest that a more modern Engine had been incorporated in this mill in 1756 but that it did not become fully effective in the sense that it could be used to treat strong rags for the manufacture of good quality White paper until some years later when more experience had been gained of its use. It is for this reason that a tentative date, ca.1768, has been proposed in Table XI for the modernisation of this mill. (If William Stiddolph had, in fact, acquired his knowledge of the New Technology from Hampton's then this date supports the view that the latter was modernised in William Buttanshaw snr.'s day i.e. at the earlier date. See Table XI note 3)

The case for this is that William Stiddolph had taken over the paper mill from his father by 1762,[138] when he took on an apprentice (evidence of his status), and further, the assessment against him rose significantly in 1768; and added to this, William was making White countermarked paper by the 1770's,[139] papers which he continued to make until the 1780's, and found in American documents.[140] He was bankrupted in 1785.

The history of the mill between Stiddolph's demise and William Turner's occupation, allegedly ca.1796/7, and even following this, is not crystal clear and is best covered in a footnote.[141] Briefly, it would appear that for a number of years the mill was in the hands of the Elgar family, mainly William Elgar, and because his countermarks continue to appear until 1802 at least and the first Turner mark discovered to date is not until 1805, Elgar's control of the mill evidently continued for some years after Turner had become the proprietor (1796/7).

[137] Reference Note 123, no obvious connection has been found between the Penshurst and the West Peckham Stiddolphs, the latter replaced at Hamptons by Buttanshaw (q.v.), the only common element being that both families operated watermills. Oliver Stiddolfe came from Edenbridge originally where William, his successor at Chafford, was born in 1734 (Oliver had two further children at Penshurst; and presumably he was related to Thomas Steddal, his predecessor there). None of this necessarily implies that the Penshurst and W. Peckham families were unconnected. If they were related and the latter had any influence with Buttanshaw, one might have seen the Chafford Stiddolphs gaining their experience in papermaking at Hamptons (not an essential proviso, but an aid). Oliver would have been too old to have trained there; in any case Hamptons had not been converted until he was nearing 40; but William is a much more promising candidate for this. [inf. Wm. Stiddolph bapt. Mrs. J. Stirk].

[138] Shorter, A. Bib.12 197.

[139] West Farleigh, Kent, document dated 1778 (KAO P 143 13/1).

[140] Gravell, T.L. Bib.68 No.648 d.o.d.1790.

[141] There are entries in the Church Accounts (KAO P 287 12/3, 12/4) of "late Stidolph" from 1782–91 indicating that he had ceased manufacture before his bankruptcy. In 1792 it is "late Thomas Elgar"; and then William Turner, the 19th C. proprietor, appears for the first time in 1796. A Joseph Turner is also mentioned about this time in the Ratebook (see further comment below). The Penshurst Land Tax Returns paint a different picture. They show that a Mr. Elgar was in Penshurst (himself) in 1780; later returns show him as the proprietor with other occupants up till 1797 with Mr. Turner (himself) appearing in 1797. William Elgar was concerned with the lease of a windmill in the manor of Ashurst on the other side of Chafford Park in 1787 (KAO U 302 T 7–9). The actual Tax documents for Penshurst bear "W Elgar" countermarks from 1794–1801. This fact together with the appearance of Elgar countermarks in many other documents from possibly as early as 1793–1802 points to the fact that not only did the Elgars have an interest in papermaking at this time but also in Chafford mill in particular. (East Malling Land Tax Returns, KAO Q/RP1/245, have an "E & C ?" mark for 1793; an "ELGAR & SON" for 1798; in other documents it is mainly "W ELGAR" up till "W ELGAR 1802" [Shorter, A. Bib.12 193]). It seems safe to assume that all these papers had been made at Chafford and that William Turner, whose first countermark seen so far is not till 1805, was under his direction until 1802 at least, a year in which unrest in the workforce reached a crisis point and when there was also an acute shortage of materials. As a Banker, Elgar no doubt decided it was time to get out. The conclusion is that William controlled the mill from 1793 (?) until 1802; and that Thomas Elgar may have operated it for a period between Stidolph and 1792.

It is not known where William Turner came from or whether he was related to the papermaking Turners of Aller mill, Devonshire, where by the 1780's Francis Fincher had gone into partnership with Joseph Turner. The fact that there was a Joseph Turner at Chafford may be pure coincidence. There is also mention of a William Turner at North Newington, Oxfordshire until 1796 (Shorter, A. Bib.12 225).

Where the Elgars came from and how they came to be involved in papermaking is not known. It has been said that Elgar & Co. were bankers in the Maidstone district[142] and, if they were one and the same as the Chafford Elgars, they perhaps decided that papermaking was an investment worth making. Seen in retrospect, however, the paper industry was going through a very difficult time towards the end of the 18th C. due to War, steep rises in the price of raw materials, in Excise and in wages. On the other hand the contemporary view would have been one of an expanding industry and one that was now experimenting with new processes and sources of power, which would no doubt have tempted a speculator. The Elgars were not the only ones; John Larking was doing much the same thing at East Malling, albeit over a much longer period; and there were several others at Hollingbourne (q.v.).

The later history of this mill is not really a function of this work, but mention may be made of the fact that the Turner family continued to run the mill well into the 19th C. and the "R TURNER" countermark was still being used up till 1905, although the mill had passed out of the family's hands by then and was in the possession of the Green family from Hayle mill, Loose.[143] It remained as a two-vat mill up till ca.1890, continuing with one vat into the 20th C. It also had a papermachine from 1873.

Shoreham Mill
(River Darent)
MR. TQ 520621

This mill raised a number of problems when its earlier history was examined[144] and for the next period the difficulties continue because, as before, no ratebooks have survived for Shoreham at all to help one with the history of the mill and its occupants.

The earlier problems centred round the Ancient Paper Maker, Alexander Russell, who (Shorter's assumption) had allegedly been at this mill in 1690 in spite of the fact that the first documentary evidence of his presence in the parish was not until 1692. Moreover, there are no means of telling whether he founded this paper mill or merely occupied one already in existence. In addition there were the unsolved problems relating to his origins and connections. Did he come from the Goudhurst area or Buckinghamshire ? and was he connected with Constant Russell, wife of John Hillyer the paper maker at Forstal mill, Boxley, and the Russells who followed him there for the next hundred years ? And how is one to explain the presence of Andrew Johannot as undertenant at Shoreham in 1716 ?[145] These are all unsolved questions that make the task of unravelling the later history of Shoreham and its possible relationship with the paper makers at Basted and in Maidstone more difficult.

Interest now centres on William Wilmott snr. who insured the paper mill in 1738.[146] Where did he come from ? and how did he come to take over this mill ? One can only guess at the answers to these questions. First, the demise of the Russells there; Alexander died in 1732 having handed the mill over to his son, John, in 1728.[147] But the latter died in 1736 and

[142] Shorter, A. Bib.12 193 states that Elgar & Co. were bankers in the Maidstone district. He also suggests (loc.cit) that they may have been involved at what is in effect Gurney's mill (his mill No.27); but there is no confirmation of this in either the East Farleigh or Loose Ratebooks. Another possibility is that these Elgars were Baptists. Russell, J.M (Bib.41 155) refers to a Thomas Elgar being present at a meeting at Bydews in Tovil in 1739; several of the papermaking Pines were present also and there may have been a link later between the two families, prompting the interest taken by Thomas and William Elgar in papermaking later in the century as well as explaining Shorter's reference to the Elgars' presence in the Loose/Tovil area (see also under Pine pp.315/317.

[143] Mr. Herbert Green was made Chairman and Managing Director there in 1898.

[144] For earlier references see Chap.II, Chap.IV and App.IV under Alexander Russell.

[145] Draft Conveyance for Shoreham paper mill (1716) KAO U 1007 E/128. See Chap.IV n.40 for details.

[146] SFIP 76249 23:Feb:1738 (corr:date).

[147] SFIP 44247 25:Mar:1728. Whether the Johannots were still there at this time is not known.

most of his family, including his widow, by 1745.[148] Second, we have the fact that William Wilmot married Jane Perch on 7:Nov:1737 at Shoreham and both are described in the register as "of this parish". Though there are no other indications of his presence there before this date, this at least suggests Wilmot's having been in the parish for some time, time enough one must assume for him to have learnt some of his papermaking there and become familiar with the mill. Third, if the Johannots were still undertenants of Shoreham mill as late as the 1730's, then the death of Andrew snr. in 1737 may have been a contributory factor to William taking over in 1738. But what William's origins were has not been discovered. There were no Wilmott families in any of the surrounding parishes; the only entries seen were two Wilmott widows buried in Sundridge in the 1720's, one described as from Bromley (Kent); and the other from Westminster.[149] Again, there is no record of his apprenticeship.[150] So one is at a total loss to explain how he became involved in this mill.

There is no doubt that William snr. was an energetic paper maker, the founder of a long dynasty of papermaking Wilmotts that lasted for 170 years and were specially known in the 19th C. for their first class drawing papers. William snr. clearly added the paper mill to the corn mill in nearby Sundridge in 1766 and installed William jnr. as paper maker there. Sundridge mill was taken over from the Wilmotts by T.H. Saunders some time after 1847 and closed in 1895; but Shoreham remained in Wilmott hands (George) until 1909, the mill ultimately shutting down in December 1925.[151]

Finally, what sort of mill did William take over at Shoreham in 1738 ? As Shoreham lay along an ancient and well-used route between Dartford, Wrotham/Ightham and Maidstone (though not turnpiked until after 1750) it is not difficult to imagine that news of developments at Dartford (1690s) and, later, at Basted (1716) reached Shoreham and resulted in the installation of an early form of Engine before William took over (though if the Johannots were still there this may not have been so). The point that matters about this supposition is that William could thus have gained some experience of its use prior to more comprehensive modernisation sometime after 1742. He would at least have been alive to any advances in this field. On the other hand was Shoreham mill in decline before he took it over ? As its early history is so uncertain a tentative 1750-60 has been proposed for the up-dating of this mill in Table XI. This would be in line with the extension of William snr.'s interest to Sundridge in 1766 where it is unthinkable that he would have installed his son in a mill with outmoded equipment.

The obvious inference from this last statement is that William snr. had already discovered the advantages of the new Engine and modernised his own mill before 1766. This is confirmed by the younger Whatman's comparison of his own experiments using the latest type of Engine at Hollingbourne in 1771 (only a few years later) with "Mr.Wilmott's" practice of beating rags. This comparison could have applied equally to William jnr. at Sundridge, a paper maker

---

[148] Shoreham Burials. 1736 John Russell : 1737 Elizabeth w.o. Alexander Russell : 1737 Sarah d.o. John & Elizabeth : 1741 Sarah, John's sister : Mary d.o. late John and Elizabeth : 1745 Elizabeth widow of John Russell. The only Russells not accounted for were a John & Elizabeth who were having a family in Shoreham from 1708 including a son, John, Bapt. 1711. These appear to have been quite separate from Alexander's children (see App.IV p.178).

[149] The surrounding parishes searched included Wrotham, Sevenoaks, Otford, Eynsford and Ightham. There were notable families of Wilmott in the Bethersden area, Clothiers in the 17th C.; and some in East Kent. A William was also baptised in Epsom in 1696 and another in Arundel in 1702, both probably too early for the Shoreham William.

[150] The Society of Genealogists Apprentices of Great Britain (1710-62) lists five William Wilmotts apprenticed between 1710-1717, but none of these is relevant. This list does show, however, that the name Wilmot (spelt variously) was widespread within the U.K..

[151] One wonders just to what extent this mill was modernised in the course of its history. It is reputed to have been the last vat mill to dispense with the old-fashioned pistolet for heating the vat, leaving it in use until late in the 19th C. (See Chap.V p.178 Item 28). This suggests that the mill may not have had a steam raising plant. It was the Layer's job to light a fire in an egg-shaped iron pot with a chimney and lay this apparatus under the vat on Sundays so that the vat was warm for Monday's work. There is no record of a papermachine ever having been installed there either.

who was an almost exact contemporary of Whatman's and who may have had more advanced beating equipment than his father.[152]

Having noted that Wilmott was situated about half–way (by road) along the Quelch/Clement Taylor axis, can one detect any signs that there were closer links than casual ones between the paper makers in these three mills or, indeed, with any other paper makers ? By the early 19th C. the Wilmotts obviously held an established position in the whole of this area and were on friendly terms with its paper makers.[153] Moving back in time, 1769, one of William snr.'s daughters, Sarah, married William Edmeads of Wrotham, the parents of William (b.1773) and Robert (b.1775) who were to figure in a number of partnerships with Clement Taylor jnr., the Russells and Thomas Pine at various mills in Maidstone towards the end of the century.[154] At the time of Sarah's marriage there is nothing to suggest that her husband, William Edmeads, was in any way involved in papermaking. Nevertheless, when considered cumulatively there is much to support the idea that there may have been closer links than casual between Basted and Shoreham that justify including this mill as a dependant or satellite of the Quelch empire for much of the 18th C.[155]

It has been assumed since Alexander Russell made White paper that William Wilmott snr. and his successor Thomas (1775), continued this tradition although we have no certain evidence of Wilmott countermarks in documents dated earlier than the 1780's; by the 1790's there is a profusion of them. These are divided between the later Wilmotts at Shoreham and those at Sundridge until ca.1812 when Charles Wilmott took over both mills. The spelling of the name is variable (perhaps intentionally ?). The earliest certain Wilmott countermark known to the author is Thomas' in paper made at Shoreham ca.1780; less certain double line block letter "W"s under a Crown appear in the Sundridge Land Tax Returns from 1780.[156]

---

[152] See App.V. pp.228, 233 & n.108.

[153] A printed document (formerly in the Maidstone Museum) concerns a General Meeting of Master Paper Makers of Kent held at the Star Inn, Maidstone, on 9:Apr:1812 and among those proposing a vote of thanks to the Chairman, William Balston, were Charles Wilmott, Budgen & Wilmott (Dartford), Charles Wilmott of Sundridge representing W. Turner & Sons (Chafford); George Wilmott at Shoreham representing John Fellows (Eynsford). (Pine & Thomas were present and thus represented Basted and Lower Tovil mills).

[154] See App.II pp.61–62.

[155] Much earlier there must have been some sort of Ancient Paper Maker affiliation between Shoreham and the Dartford/Basted axis, a relationship that persisted perhaps into William Wilmott's time (e.g. the Johannot connection). Throughout this period there were considerable colonies of Russells both in Wrotham and Ightham; Edmeads also in both parishes; Terrys were ubiquitous; and it may be noted that Anne Wilmott, another of William snr.'s daughters, married a Geoffrey Taylor of Sevenoaks in 1769 (see App.II pp.61–62). Again, there is a letter written by the younger Whatman in 1792 about Clement Taylor jnr.'s labour problems in which he specifically refers to Mr. William Wilmott (jnr.) as a "friend" of Taylor's (Balston, T. Bib.1 118). All in all considering how few mills are concerned here and their proximity, it is a fair assumption to make that there were closer than casual links though no direct Wilmott/Quelch/Clement Taylor connections have been discovered.

[156] Shoreham Land Tax Return for 1783 bears a "TW" mark (KAO Q/RP1/338 : 1780–82 have no countermarks). Another "TW" has been found in what was obviously an early attempt at making wove paper estimated between 1785–1790 (PSM). The first full named mark, "T Willmot 1794" is in the Springfield collection (PSM). Double line block letter "W" marks appear in the Sundridge Land Tax Returns from 1780–2 and 1787–91 (KAO Q/RP1/370); all of these "W"s are under a Crown and probably belonged to William jnr. (App.V n.195). No "W Wilmott" marks are known to the author. A "Wilmott 1794" mark is cited by Shorter (Bib.12 183) as possibly indicating the handing over of Sundridge mill to Charles in 1794 with a "C Wilmott 1795" to follow (although there is no evidence of this transfer in the Sundridge Land Tax Returns up to 1796 at least; the only entries before and after 1794 are Mr. Wilmott/himself). "C Wilmot 1832" appears in a Deed (KAO U 47/1 T 177) showing the extent of his marks. Finally, "H Willmott 1809–1812" marks have been found in the Susanna Whatman correspondence (PSM) and by Shorter (Paper–Maker and B.P.Tr.Jo. 1959 March p.46) in a context that identifies Henry with Shoreham; "HW" marks also occur.

Sundridge Mill

> The events at this mill have been largely covered under Shoreham. William Wilmott snr. insured it in his son's (William) tenure in 1766[157] and Charles succeeded him ca.1794/5. As mentioned Whatman's reference to the Wilmott's beating practice only five years later confirms that an Engine was used by them and by inference at both Shoreham and Sundridge.

It may be of interest to mention at this point a few extracts from the Original Papermakers Recorder (Nov.1905) recounting papermaking conditions at Shoreham mill in the 1840's. It worked two vats in summer double shift and three vats in the winter. Felts were rinsed in the river. The foreman, generally sizer or finisher, was required in addition to keep the books, get his hides or trotters as the case may be and when boiling them stay up all night (for which he received 1/–). He had two fires to look after, one for boiling the scrowls etc.; and one for heating the size bath. These duties were over and above those for sizing or finishing for three vats. The Engineer's job seems to have been even more arduous. Work began at midnight on Sunday. His job included helping press the posts from the vats up to breakfast time, when his mate would relieve him. But this did not relieve him from other work during the day. He had to fetch the rags from the rag house, dust and clean them, clean out the duster, press at one vat until 5 pm., staying on until midnight on Saturdays. The Engineers' duties did not finish there. They had to stay and keep watch until 6 am. (paid 2/6d. for that) and also call the hour under the foreman's window from 10 pm. to 4 am. (paid 1/– for this). In addition they were required to prepare their own bleach, soak papers and stir chests when they were being emptied.

Vatmen were paid about 6/6d. per day; Couchers 5/6d; Layers 3/8d. plus 4d. or 2/– per week beer money; and Engineers about 4/– per day.

The paper mills in East Malling were mentioned above as possibly falling within the orbit of Basted so far as modernisation was concerned; but in fact it is more likely that this influence came through a more direct route, namely, via the Harris' at Millhall mill, Ditton, and will therefore be considered later.

---

[157] Shorter, A. Bib.12 183 citing SFIP 230946 15:Feb:1766 (corn and paper mills).

THE DARTFORD CENTRE

Comparison of Table IV [Chapter II] and Table XI [this Chapter] shows that between 1740–1800 the number of paper mills (all types) in the Maidstone district increased from 14–20 and in the West Kent Region from 4–12, four of which have already been considered as coming within the orbit of Basted (though one of these is actually in the South Kent Region), which leaves a further six that may or may not have been influenced by the two Quelch mills at Dartford. Although the expansion in north–west Kent was greater proportionately than at Maidstone, the total was still less; vacant water mill sites would have been more difficult to find the nearer one approached the Capital, much more so than in provincial areas; even so the nearer to London the more desirable the site. As a consequence it is not so easy to demonstrate influence emanating from Dartford as the sole cause of a mill's advancement.

The mills in question can be conveniently examined in two groups, two of them lying upstream of Dartford on the River Darent, Hawley mill (almost certainly lower quality than White and perhaps wholly Brown but of interest in the present context) and Eynsford; the others being situated on the River Cray and one in Bromley.[158]

Hawley Mill
(River Darent)

Hawley lies about half–way between Dartford and Sutton–at–Hone to the south. The first evidence of it being a paper mill is a reference to Christopher Jarrett & Co., paper makers, taking on an apprentice in 1758.[159] The Sutton–at–Hone Ratebook[160] shows that a Mr. Jarrett had been there at a mill of sorts, from 1748 (the Ratebook does not go back further) assessed for the sizeable sum of £46. To judge from later information this may have been a leather dressing mill. (In 1800 the same property was insured as a paper mill and a leather mill).[161] Who comprised the "Company" in 1758 can only be surmised; but the ratebook shows that in 1759 the property was now assessed at £73, a rise of £27 (a sum that one might expect for a paper mill), in the names of Messrs. Jarrett and Archer; and by 1761 in William Archer's name alone.

Richard Archer snr. (formerly of Dartford No.2 mill [TABLE XXII] d.1746) had three sons that survived beyond infancy, John (1704–41) who had originally been apprenticed to a Stationer in London and who may have acted as a factor for his father;[162] Richard jnr. (1706–1773 and described as "of Sutton–at–Hone" when buried in Darenth) was having a family in Dartford from 1733 onwards and who, one assumes, worked for seven years in the paper mill before his father was made bankrupt in 1740. He then disappeared from the Dartford scene. Finally, there was William (1721–1781) who was having a family in Sutton–at–Hone from 1758.[163] William may have followed in his eldest brother's footsteps because when he was buried, like all the others, in Darenth, he was described as "of Southwark" and his brother, John, as "of St. Saviours". Whether Richard jnr. continued with a papermaking career after he left Dartford has not been discovered; but he may have worked in Mr. Jarrett's leather mill not more than a mile away from Sutton–at–Hone.

The interpretation placed on this is that a paper mill, probably not a White mill, was added to the leather mill in 1758, when the ratable value went up, and that William Archer made

---

158   Location uncertain but possibly on the River Ravensbourne.
159   Shorter, A. Bib.12 182.
160   KAO P 358 5/1.
161   SFIP 706977 20:Oct:1800.
162   See App.IV.
163   See App.IV.

up the "Company". One might surmise that William had been working in London up till this point and come across a worthwhile outlet for paper and, perhaps with the help of Richard jnr., persuaded Mr. Jarrett to extend his mill. On this basis one would expect that an Engine would have been incorporated in this addition; if the paper was not of a particularly high quality, the Engine would not have made any special or extra demands on the water power available. This accounts for the date 1758/9 in Table XI and the inspiration for installing this equipment, and perhaps for the enterprise itself, must have come from the mills at Dartford (less than two miles away), especially taking into account the former Archer connection with this mill.

William's venture, however, does not seem to have had any lasting success, because in 1773 the Ratebook entry is "late Mr. Archer" and the assessment is £27–10, just the amount it was raised in 1759. Possibly Richard jnr.'s death in 1773 might account for this demise, particularly if William was working in Southwark. A Mr. James Robson followed Archer and he was the Bermondsey proprietor who insured the leather and paper mills in the 19th C.

Eynsford Mill
(River Darent)
MR TQ 543661

This, one of the oldest mills in Kent, was the Johannot mill at the end of the 17th C. and has been referred to earlier.[164] Andrew Johannot snr. was not only the occupant of Eynsford but undertenant of Shoreham mill as well. It is possible that the Russells had recognized his superior papermaking skills and sublet their mill to him for this reason. But after Andrew snr.'s death in 1737 the impression is that the business went downhill with the succeeding generation. Andrew jnr. was bankrupted in 1746; Josias and Israel (if connected) had left their paper mills by the 1750's; and, although Shorter[165] has suggested that an Anthony Johannot may have continued at Eynsford for a while (there is no ratebook to confirm this), it looks at first sight as if the technology there had not kept up with the times.

By the 1770's the mill was in new hands, John Floyd's, a paper maker who later produced countermarked papers there. He may have been a natural successor to the mill possibly having trained there. (The name Floyd appears in the Parish Registers during the 1750's). Floyd was later partnered by John Fellows in 1789;[166] by 1804 John Fellows had become proprietor of the mill.[167] In the 1830's J. Arnold & Son took over the mill; later it was Arnold & Foster, a name retained after it had been taken over by Spicers. One of the best known products of this mill was a drawing paper known as "Unbleached Arnold".[168] The mill still under the name of Arnold & Foster, closed in 1952. It had always been a vat mill, mainly two–vat until after a fire there in 1906 when the number was increased to 5–8 vats. A papermachine was installed in 1898 and a second one in 1917, a distinct contrast to Shoreham mill.

With the Johannots holding a shaky position at Eynsford in the 1740's it seems doubtful that they would have gone to the expense of reconstructing their mill in these circumstances, unless this is what Andrew jnr. attempted to do and bankrupted himself in the process (see

[164]   See Chap.IV pp.147ff.

[165]   Shorter, A. Bib.12 182.

[166]   A John Fellows and his descendants were active at Soho or Wooburn mills (Buckinghamshire) from 1759–1803+ but whether they were connected with the Eynsford "Fellows" is not known. The Wooburn John was a malster, miller and paper maker and appears to have left there by 1761.

[167]   The Eynsford Land Tax Returns (KAO Q/RP1/130) show that up till 1803 the entry is Lord Romney/John Floyd £20; and in 1804 John Fellows/himself £20. The last Floyd countermark seen is for 1802. "Fellows" or "Fellows & Sons" continue until 1831 at least (PSM).

[168]   It is not known how far back this trade mark extended, but there is a drawing in the Fitzwilliam Museum (2676b) attributed to J.J. Cotman (by Alec Cotman) which bears a watermark motto "Warranted Not Bleached" in the paper. The drawing is undated, but probably 1840–60's.

also under Cray Valley mill below). It is true that, as in the case of Shoreham, the mill lay along the Dartford/Basted axis and at some point it could have acquired an early form of Engine. But the Johannots were undoubtedly experts in using the Old Technology and may have been reluctant to have made a change, at least during Andrew snr.'s time. White countermarked paper does not appear to have been produced there before the late 1780's; so, if the Johannots had not attempted to upgrade their mill, it must have been done in the interval between. If not by Floyd, was there any other candidate for this task ?

In 1761 William Musgrove was a paper maker at Eynsford having left Upper Tovil mill, Maidstone, sometime after 1745; with no ratebook for Maidstone 1747–62 one cannot tell precisely when.[169] As indicated (p.261) Upper Tovil may have been modernised partially during this period. In any case Musgrove must have been familiar with the changes that were taking place in Maidstone and thus brought know–how of the New Technology with him, but whether he was able to finance an installation is less certain. One must either postulate an installation made by the Johannots which he was able to exploit; or else modernisation had to wait until John Fellows took over in the 1770's. (It is conceivable that Lord Romney may have made the investment for either Musgrove or Floyd; as seen in the case of Lord Aylesford and Poll Mill (p.260). Engines were expensive pieces of equipment.) Table XI reflects this uncertainty as indeed the source of influence, Dartford or Maidstone ? The first (1780) Land Tax Return for Eynsford is on paper countermarked "W Quelch"; no identifiable paper from the mill itself has been found until the late 1780's.[170]

Turning now to the mills on the River Cray, Table XI indicates modernisation taking place in these mills in the following order: (i) Cray Valley 1742–7; (ii) Foots Cray ca.1767; (iii) St. Mary Cray in 1771; with Bromley ca.1765.

Cray Valley
(St. Paul's Cray)

Once again no parish accounts have survived. The first indication of a paper mill there is when Josias Johannot, son of Andrew snr. of Eynsford, insured his paper and corn mill in 1742.[171]

The uncertainty as to whether Josias added a paper mill to the corn mill or whether he took over a combination of the two creates a conundrum. The Policy describes the two mills as "under one roof" from which one might deduce that to adapt the power transmission to suit corn grinding and *effective beating with an Engine* must have presented difficulties. Although policies as late as 1778 still describe the premises as a paper mill and a corn mill, the one taken out by James Cripps in 1753[172] indicates that certainly by this date, as indeed it must have been in Josias' time, the functions had been separated since Cripps insured only the utensils and stock in *his paper mill*.

The events that took place there (see below) point to Josias introducing an alternative power transmission system between 1742–47 as a first step; and then, at some later stage, when Cripps undertook the manufacture of White countermarked paper, the two undertakings had become physically separated.[173] Initially, under Josias Johannot, it was clearly not a White

---

[169] Shorter, A. Bib.12 182, 191.

[170] See Chap.IV n.41.

[171] Shorter, A. Bib.12 183 SFIP 91499 (5:June:1742)

[172] SFIP 13825 (2:Nov:1753).

[173] SFIP 407111 (24:Dec:1778) was a Policy taken out by James Cripps snr. and jnr., paper makers and millers, for a paper mill *and* a corn mill.

mill, this view being based on the nature of his Patent granted in 1747[174] for making an improved form of cartridge paper using a formidable recipe.

The Patent Specification makes it quite clear that Josias was familiar with the Hollander Beater and quite a sizeable one, enough to hold a hundredweight of rags and similar to those described by Le Francois de Lalande as used at Montargis, ca.1740.[175]

The question is whether Josias equipped this mill with an up-to-date Engine or simply made use of an early form of Hollander similar to one that may have been employed by his family at Eynsford (q.v.). Being so close to Dartford he must have been aware of the changes taking place there, so it is unlikely with the state of the art at that time that he would have installed an out-dated model in his recently acquired mill; but this does not necessarily mean that the mill as a whole was fully up-dated then. The reason being that with a war in progress there would have been an undoubted demand for cartridge paper and, as a Stationer, Josias must have seen an opportunity for himself here (and not at Eynsford) and was backed in this venture by another Stationer, Robert Wilson, mortgagee for the mill.[176] Cartridge paper, however, was a "dirty" paper and provided that he had an Engine to prepare the stuff, there would have been no special need to refine modernisation beyond this point. One assumes that when James Cripps from West Peckham[177] took over this mill in 1753 he would have continued to make cartridge paper. Though the War of the Austrian Succession had ended, other military and naval activities continued with, for example, Clive's campaigns in India and the Seven Years War starting in 1756.

At some point in its history the Cripps must have up-graded this mill a stage further to make White paper. This second stage obviously took place while James snr. was still active because identifiable paper of theirs was being made certainly by the late 1770's[178] and one has to make some allowance for them to develop and market this paper.[179] Applying the above to Table XI it will be seen that this is shown as taking place between 1742-1747 (see note

---

[174] Patent No.625 granted in 1747 to Josias Johannot, Stationer, late of London for making cartridge paper that will not hold any fire by putting to an engine of stuff that holds about 1 cwt. of rags, 28 lb. of calcined salt, 7 lb. of copperas and 7 lb. of allom and *size it three times*.
Cartridges had made use of paper from some point in the 17th C. onwards, probably replacing parchment. It had to be a very tough product and beating with hammers and mortars would have suited this requirement. Sizing would have greatly increased the strength. It seems likely that Johannot's specification for triple sizing may have been made in order to compensate for the lower strength developed in the preparation of the stuff in an Engine, especially at that stage of its development.

[175] See Chap.VI Table VIII.

[176] Shorter, A. Bib.12 183. Wilson was replaced as mortgagee in 1745 by Robert Grosvenor & Sons, very old established Stationers in London. But this is not the last reference to these parties. Wilson was interested later in two other Kent mills, Otham in 1744; and Sittingbourne in 1756. Josias and Grosvenor were associated in another venture, this time at Deptford mill (London) in 1751. Josias was bankrupted in 1753 (Shorter, A. Bib.12 209). Another unusual feature was that Wilson was associated with an Alexander Mathison, paper maker, at Otham; and a Richard Mathison replaced Josias Johannot at Deptford in 1753 after the latter's bankruptcy. (See also under Otham & Sittingbourne mills; and to Stationers' interests this Chap. n.81).

[177] Under Hampton's mill, West Peckham, it was noted that James Crips, paper maker, made his appearance there in 1749 (see this Chap. p.294 & n.129). There are no other entries for him or his wife, Ann, after this apart from the burial of Joseph, an infant, in 1751. There were no Cripps families in St. Paul's Cray prior to 1753. James Cripps, paper maker, insured his paper mill there in 1753; was witness to the wedding of a Luke Munn there in 1755; and his wife, Ann, was buried there in 1760. It is reasonable to assume that both James were one and the same person.

[178] The St. Paul's Cray Land Tax Returns (KAO Q/RP1/96) for 1780, 1781 bear a "JC" with an oval surround countermark. The Norfolk Sessions Books for 1786-88 (Norfolk R.O. C/S1 14) contain "J CRIPPS" marks and this paper must have been made a year or two before use. Gravell, T.L. (Bib.68) illustrates 2 unidentified "JC" marks (i) d.o.d.1767 in a bell with Pro Patria; (ii) d.o.d.1773, "JC"/Britannia. Of these two the latter certainly resembles a Cripps mark. The manufacture of White paper may therefore have started there earlier, late 1760's ?

[179] James Cripps snr. was buried at St. Paul's Cray in 1795. A dated countermark of 1805 shows that Charles Cripps had succeeded James jnr. by that date (Gravell, T.L. Bib.68 No.167); Charles Cripps was still there in 1816 (EGL).

3 below Table). Full modernisation as a White mill must have taken place ca.1770 and this is shown in the 1765/1775 total.

In conclusion it may be said that although this mill was not linked directly in any known way to the Quelch Empire (indeed one might invoke here the Brooke/Stationers' source of inspiration with Josias, Wilson and Grosvenor all involved), it was clearly indebted in its early stages and *in practical terms* to the activities at Dartford and thus may be included among their "satellites".

Thomas Nash (third son of William at Frogmore, Herts, 1817–24) took over this mill in the early 1820's and had installed a paper machine there by 1828. The family continued to run the mill well into the second half of the 20th C. The mill closed down in the 1980's.[180]

Foots Cray Mill
(River Cray)

Once again there are no Ratebooks to help with the former history of this mill. There is little to go on beyond the information given by Shorter,[181] where the earliest mention of this mill is the bankruptcy of John Smither, paper maker, 1767. The obvious inference from this fact is that a paper mill must have been in existence there before this date. Taking this in conjunction with Shorter's next entry, namely, that two years later, in 1769, "a substantial *new–built* paper mill, late in the possession of John Smither" was for sale, suggests that this mill had been out–of–date during Smither's tenure and that it was unable to compete any longer with other mills in the area. 1769, therefore, has been taken as the date when this mill was effectively up–dated (see Table XI). There is nothing else to go on except that by the late 1770's White countermarked paper was being manufactured at this mill, then in the occupation of Hugh Bennett.[182] He was at Foots Cray from 1777 until after 1789[183] when he was replaced by Thomas Stains, there from 1792 until at least 1816, also making White countermarked papers.

In this case one can scarcely attribute modernisation to the influence of the Quelchs at Dartford. In a very general sense it might be said that the proprietor of the mill[184] became aware of the fact that his mill had become out–dated and had learnt of the innovations at Cray Valley which, in turn, were manifestly influenced by the developments at Dartford.

St. Mary Cray

The examination of the history and up–dating of this mill, as also for Bromley (which should be considered in conjunction, see below), is very dependent on the question as to whether one regards the John Quelch who appeared at West mill, Newbury, Berkshire,[185] in 1748 as the

[180] Thomas Nash was granted a Patent in 1844 for a new type of paper calender.

[181] Shorter, A. Bib.12 183.

[182] Hugh Bennett replaced William Wells described as a paper maker, dealer and chapman, who was made bankrupt in 1776 having been the occupant there from 1772, the first and seemingly not very successful one since the mill was rebuilt. It is not thought that he was in any way connected with the "William Wells", paper maker and step–father of William Jubb jnr. of Ewell mill, Surrey. The latter had assumed control of Ewell by 1763 at latest. His step–father would have been ca.67 in 1772 and in any case was buried in Ewell in 1785 (inf. Crocker, A.G.).
The author has found an "H Bennett" countermark in the 1780 Land Tax Return for Foots Cray (KAO Q/RP1/93), a poorly sized sheet. "HB" mark within a ring has also been found in the 1785 Eynsford Land Tax Return (KAO Q/RP1/130).

[183] Shorter, A. Bib.12 174 under Standon mill, Hertfordshire, provides evidence that a "Hugh Bennett" was at this mill from 1786–ca.1796. The Bennett family had been the occupants since 1752. Finerty, E.T. Bib.69 (April) 310/11, beyond confirming that Catherine Bennett was there in 1786, does not refer to Hugh at all.

[184] Curiously, there are no entries for H. Bennett in the Foots Cray Land Tax Returns for 1780–82. So the proprietor of this mill has not been identified. The name "Townsend" Esq. was noted; see under St. Mary Cray.

[185] Shorter, A. Bib.12 127.

same John Quelch who formerly occupied Dartford No.2 mill between 1698–1700[186] or as someone totally unrelated. The Dartford John Quelch was either William snr.'s brother or a relation; mention was also made that the origin of the Kent family was probably Oxfordshire or perhaps Berkshire.[187] If the same person (he would have been in his 70's cf. William snr.'s longevity) or closely related, it puts a different complexion on an approach to both St. Mary Cray and Bromley paper mills. It gives a rationale to the movements of a William Sims, paper maker, and the Demeza family at Bromley (q.v.). A William Sims, believed to be the same as the Sims who left West mill in the early 1770's, appeared at St. Mary Cray in 1771.[188] The Demeza family reversed this situation, as it were, some years later and it would be an extraordinary coincidence if the two were not linked. The relevance to Quelch is seen below.

· It is not known for how long there had been a paper mill at St. Mary Cray before Nicholas Townsend, paper maker, insured it in 1757.[189] 1757 is also the first time that Townsend appears in the St. Mary Cray ratebook; but the assessments against his name are perplexing and it is a matter of surmise whether one can read anything significant into them or not. The facts are that as early as 1749 a John White was assessed £20 for "the mill", but whether it was a paper mill then or not is not known. As there is no mention at any time in the later Insurance policies of the premises being described as "a corn and a paper mill", for instance, it might be legitimate to assume that it was a paper mill in White's time; the ratable value was of the same order as other small paper mills.

John White was followed by Widow White in 1754 and then by a Mr. Larshal;[190] and, ultimately, in 1756 Mr. Larshal with "Townsend" added in pencil. All this time the ratable value remained at £20. Thereafter, during Townsend's tenure, 1757–1770, the ratable value dropped to £8; and in 1771 the entry reads "late Nicholas Townsend, Mr. Simes (sic) £50".[191]

A suggested interpretation of these facts is that a paper mill, possibly making White paper, was active there in John White's time and that with the advent of Townsend (described as a paper maker) the character of the mill changed, perhaps making Brown or, like its neighbour Cray Valley, making cartridge paper.[192] West mill at Newbury may have been in a similar state, not having been modernised during John Quelch's and William Sims' occupation, especially so when one discovers that the mill was completely rebuilt in 1779 when William Demeza (from Bromley mill) became the occupant. In short it looks as if Sims had heard about the more modern methods of papermaking used by the Quelchs at Dartford through John Quelch at West Mill and made the move when the opportunity arose.[193] For this reason Table XI indicates Sims undertaking the up-dating of St. Mary Cray in 1771; it is obvious that some major change took place then from the ratable value. The foregoing is no doubt one of several different interpretations, but providing one accepts the proposal made concerning John Quelch, the assumptions are not unreasonable. In an indirect sense then the

[186] Shorter, A. Bib.12 181.

[187] See App.II (under Quelch).

[188] He insured the utensils and stock in his paper mill on the 28:Dec:1771 (SFIP 422657). The name "Sims" (spelt Simes in the PRs) does not appear in the St. Mary Cray PRs before 1771, so he must have come from elsewhere. He died of "old age", aged 79; was probably blind and was buried at St. Mary Cray 1:Mar:1786. His life span was, therefore, 1707–1786 in which case he would have been at least 35 when John Quelch was at West mill and must surely have known him.

[189] Shorter, A. Bib.12 183 SFIP 160271 (13:Dec:1757).

[190] In passing it may be noted that "Larshal" can be seen as an alternative form of "Archer", see App.IV n.45, 61.

[191] The author is indebted to Miss E. Silverthorne, Archivist for the Central Library, Bromley for making this search.

[192] Townsend might have had no other option but to make inferior papers using low grade materials if the mill had not been modernised during White's tenure.

[193] If in fact St. Mary Cray had been making cartridge paper earlier, the demand could well have fallen off by the 1770's, a period of peace.

fortunes of this mill can be seen as coming within the orbit of Quelch influence from Dartford.

The question as to whether Sims made White paper here is complicated by the fact that, though no examples of papers made by Sims have yet been identified,[194] a countermark believed to be Samuel Lay's[195] may have originated from St. Mary Cray early in the 1770's, pointing to the fact that the mill had become a White mill regardless as to whether Sims ever made paper there or not.

Other evidence shows that Samuel Lay was working at this mill by 1780, if not earlier, probably as an undertenant on account of Sims' blindness. Lay continued to run both St. Mary Cray and Sittingbourne until after 1800.[196] The 1816 Excise General List shows Martha Lay still at St. Mary Cray[197] and Edward Smith at Sittingbourne (given as Milton). Possible motives for Samuel Lay's move to St. Mary Cray will be considered under Sittingbourne mill.

St. Mary Cray continued as a papermachine mill until the 1960's under the Joynson family who must have installed a machine ca. 1830 with William Joynson patenting the first successful method of watermarking machine made paper, using the dandy roll for this purpose, in 1839. By the 1850's they were producing White sized paper in the web, employing a spar drum dryer (28 drums supporting 1000 ft. of paper) between the size bath and the cutter.

Bromley Mill

Nothing significantly new has been discovered in this case beyond those facts given by Shorter.[198] The first mention is an insurance policy of 1765 taken out by Solomon Demeza, paper maker, of Lambeth Street, Goodman's Fields, London; he insured the mill again in 1772. Shorter believed that William Demeza, paper and flock manufacturer of Leman Street, Goodman's Fields, succeeded Solomon at this mill in 1779 (certainly a Demeza was at the Bromley mill in 1785). In 1788 William was bankrupted and in the following year the mill was for sale.

One must see these events in conjunction with William Demeza appearing at West mill, Newbury, just after it had been rebuilt in 1779; in fact Shorter suggests that he had an

---

[194] Although "WS" countermarks are known, probably belonging to William Sharp (Romsey, Hampshire), no papers made by Sims have yet been identified.

[195] Gravell, T.L. Bib.68 has recorded "SL" countermarks in American documents dated 1758–63 (Nos.612,613) and there are no other English candidates for "SL". He has also identified an "S LAY/C" mark in an American document dated 1775 (No.483) and another "SL/C" in a 1791 document. It seems probable that the subscript "C" represents St. Mary Cray mill. There is other evidence to show that he was in St. Mary Cray by 1780 at least. The 1775 American document therefore points to him as having been at the mill *before* 1775.

[196] The St. Mary Cray Land Tax Returns (KAO Q/RP1/94) show that from 1780–82 Thomas Borrett (see later in this note) and William Eveling Esq. were the proprietors of property occupied by (a) Mary Townsend £10–8; and (b) Samuel Lay £2–12. William Sims was the occupant of other property (Joseph Snelling) assessed at 4/-. From 1780–90, by which time Lay is known to have been working the mill, Herman Behrens Esq. had replaced Borrett and Eveling, and Farrant replaced Townsend, with Lay continuing at £2–12. (Sims' name is entered ditto for some years after 1786) Samuel Lay died in 1803/4 and the 1804/5 return shows Mrs. Lay/herself at £2; and in 1812 Martha Lay/John Evans at 18/-. Whether these assessments referred to the paper mill or not, it is clear that Lay was in St. Mary Cray by 1780 and from the E.G.L. that Martha Lay was at the mill in 1816; the June 1818 Excise General Letter shows John Lay at St. Mary Cray.
It may be a coincidence but, it will be recalled, in 1716 John Borrett acquired Shoreham paper mill and the surrounding land (Chap.IV n.40).

[197] The 1816 EGL shows another paper mill at St. Mary Cray occupied by John Hall. (A John Hall also appears at Cotton mill, Ringstead, Northamptonshire, 1816 EGL.) This, however, was probably the John Hall described by Clapperton as having a mill at Horton Kirby (see this Chap. n.272).

[198] Shorter, A. Bib.12 184. Regarding the Demezas, a "Mr. Demeza" leased Westbrook mill, Surrey, in 1778; by 1790 it was in the hands of a Mrs. Demeza, paper maker, replaced by Smith & Knight in 1794 (inf.Crocker, A.G.)

interest in this. It is difficult to ignore then the conclusion that the Demezas must have met William Sims between 1771–79 and learnt about the state of the Newbury mill, clearly a site with a much greater potential for expanding their business, modernising and occupying it in 1779.

Whereas West mill (later "mills") continued to operate into the 19th C.,[199] Bromley mill does not appear to have survived, which makes one wonder if it had ever been a satisfactory watermill for papermaking; and, indeed, if ever modernised ? If it was up–graded, then this must surely have taken place in 1765, the date shown in the Table.

Up to this point the paper mills modernised within the central core of the Quelch empire have been examined, namely, Dartford Nos. 2 & 3; Basted and Gurney's; Poll and Upper Tovil mills; and those mills that might legitimately be considered as coming within its orbit of influence, namely, Hamptons, Chafford, Shoreham and Sundridge; and, near Dartford, Hawley, Eynsford, Cray Valley, (Foots Cray ?), St. Mary Cray and possibly Bromley; that is 14 mills and two queries.

Turning now to the Maidstone district it is not thought that the Quelch empire *per se* had any obvious influence on mills in this district other than those that had been occupied and modernised by them. If there were any links, they would have been far more tenuous than those in the West Kent Region. Changes in papermaking practices are more likely to have stemmed from either the elder Whatman's example (d.1759) or James Brooke (d.1750) and William Gill jnr. who, besides acting as Stationer to Whatman, would have looked after the interests of their own mills. Nevertheless, the Taylor family clearly had close links with the Russells e.g. John (possibly a s.o. Edward at Forstal or a descendant of the surviving John from Shoreham).[200] There is also another instance where Clement Taylor jnr. might have played a part in shaping Lewis Munn snr.'s future career in papermaking during the latter's residence in Hollingbourne, 1774–6.[201]

Before leaving the subject of the Quelch Empire mention may be made here of further extensions of Taylor influence in the Maidstone district other than that concerned with modernisation, e.g. after Clement jnr.'s bankruptcy in 1797 Upper Tovil mill was taken over temporarily by his cousins, Edward and Clement Taylor Russel; and further he entered into other partnerships on the eve of his demise, at Gurney's mill with William Edmeads (from Wrotham);[202] and James Smyth at Padsole.[203]

[199] After the Demezas West mill passed into the hands of the Wickwar family (1789); later they occupied Bagnor mills, Berkshire, and the 1816 EGL shows Wickwars at both Bagnor and Colthrop mill, Berkshire, having left West mills. The Wickwars produced White countermarked paper at both West and Bagnor mills (Gravell, T.L. Bib.68 No.773 "T Wickwar" and Nos. 771/2 "J Wickwar"). "D" countermarks have been recorded for this period, but these almost certainly represent Durham at Postlip mills, Gloucestershire.
[200] See this chapter pp.311/314.
[201] See App.I p.19 and App.II p.89.
[202] See this Chap. n.254.
[203] See this Chap. p.326.

PART VII

MAINLY THE MILLS OF THE MAIDSTONE AREA

The most convenient method of arriving at the dates proposed for the modernisation of the remaining mills in this district, and to determine whether the influence for this can be traced back to the elder Whatman, is to divide them into a number of separate groups (see Map 5).

GROUP I

Millhall Mill, Ditton
(East Malling Stream)
Whatman/Thomas Harris

> As before in the majority of cases there is no positive evidence of an installation or of direct influence. However, William Harris jnr., Richard's eldest brother,[204] must have known about the investment at Old Mill in 1733 and followed its development through to Turkey mill. He had moved to Ditton in 1724, so it would be reasonable to assume that this mill still used the Old Technology for making paper. By the time his brother's experiments were about to bear fruit, in fact as Whatman was taking over Turkey mill, Richard was dead (1739) and William followed him in 1741, leaving Thomas under age and unable to take over Millhall mill himself until 1744. It is unlikely then, especially during this period of crisis and lacking Whatman's finances to back him, that any attempt would have been made to up-date the mill before 1744. At the same time Thomas must have appreciated the advantages that would accrue from using the New Technology and would not have delayed its introduction any longer than was necessary. Hence the proposal made in Table XI for the up-grading of this mill at some point between 1745–55. It has been suggested earlier that Millhall mill was not engaged in making the top qualities of White paper, but rather Printing papers and perhaps Whited–Browns, product lines that would not have demanded an installation generating the maximum energy needed for processing strong rags. The system would thus have been suited to the very low position this mill occupied in the Medway flood plain. There is no evidence that this mill ever produced countermarked paper.

> An account of the Harris connection with this mill will be found in Appendix II.[205] By 1776 the mill had passed into the hands of the Golding family (Thomas Golding marrying a Mary Harris in 1768) and remaining under their control until ca.1832. Thereafter it was occupied by Robert Tassell (who had interests in all three of the East Malling mills at this time, see below) until it ceased work in 1847.

The East Malling Paper Mills
(East Malling Stream)

> The up-grading of these mills, where this was applicable, most probably stemmed from events at Millhall mill (2 miles further downstream), as opposed to influence from the Basted centre (7.5 miles to the West) and are, therefore, best considered as part of Group I.

> By 1780 there were three paper mills in the village.[206] Lower Mill (Excise No.313) was a Brown mill and started operating in 1780, by which date it would almost by definition have employed elements of the New Technology. Upper mill (Excise No.314) was the only true

---

[204] See App.II TABLE XXI.
[205] See App.II (under Harris).
[206] See App.IV (under "The Succession at the East Malling Paper mills, Kent").

Map 5

SKETCH–MAP: ILLUSTRATING THE LOCATION OF THE MILLS
OF THE MAIDSTONE DISTRICT CONSIDERED IN THE TEXT

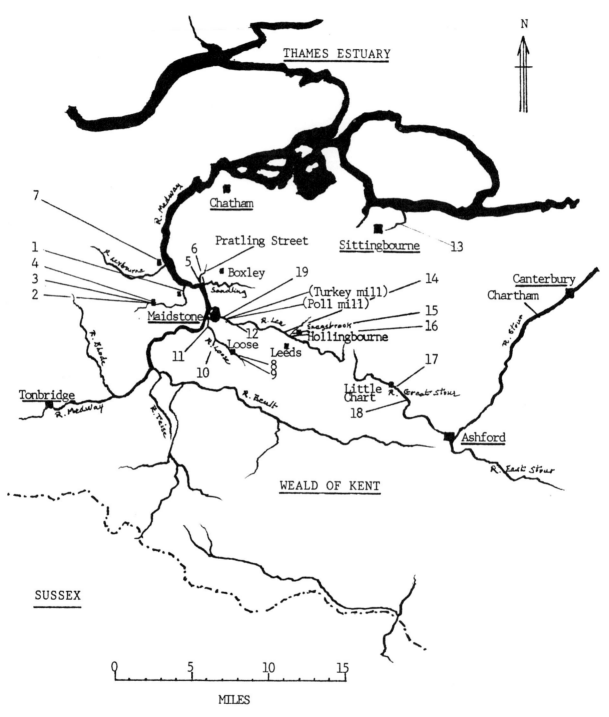

GROUP I

1. Millhall mill, Ditton.
2. Upper mill, East Malling.
3. Middle mill, East Malling.
4. Lower mill, East Malling.

5. Forstal mill, Boxley.
6. Cobtree mill, Boxley.
7. Snodland mill.

GROUP II

8. Upper mill, Loose.
9. Leg o' Mutton mill, Loose.

GROUP III

10. Great Ivy mill, Loose.
11. Lower Tovil mill, Tovil.
12. Otham paper mill.
13. Sittingbourne mill (North Kent).

GROUP IV

14. Old mill, Hollingbourne.
15. Eyehorne mill, Hollingbourne.
16. Park mill, Hollingbourne.
17. Ford mill, Little Chart.
18. Conyer mill, Hothfield.

White mill amongst the three. The first documentary evidence of its existence is in 1763, though it could have been operating earlier. On balance it is felt that in 1763 it may have been engaged in making second quality White paper raising its standards after the arrival of John Larking in 1780, the latter producing countermarked paper there in the 1790's. Finally, there is Middle mill (No.315), a mill that dated back to the 17th C. There is no positive evidence that it ever produced White paper, but possibly after the introduction of bleaching it may have ventured into this field though as late as 1832 George Blunden (jnr.) was described as a manufacturer of Brown paper there. So only Upper mill is considered here for modernisation. The ratable values, as with other properties, were doubled in 1757 for Middle and what is thought to have been Upper mill, so it cannot be regarded in this case as a change in status. It is much more likely that the advent of James Brooks and his insurance of Upper Mill in 1763 heralded either its conversion to the manufacture of White paper and the commissioning of a modernised facility or, perhaps less likely, the founding of a new paper mill altogether which by that date would automatically have employed the New Technology. Middle mill would probably have followed suit soon after. The Succession at these three mills will be found in Appendix IV. Both Larking (a prominent papermaking figure) and later, Tassell made countermarked paper at Upper mill. Lower mill closed ca.1848; Middle and Upper Mills continued operating under the name of Busbridge up till 1932.

Sandling Mills
Whatman/Gill
Snodland Mill

Forstal, Cobtree and Snodland paper mills can also be covered conveniently in the first Group. Geographically they were close neighbours to the paper mills on the East Malling stream; and both Forstal and Snodland mills were sited like Millhall mill within the Medway flood plain with the Cobtree site only minimally more elevated.[207] Undoubtedly as modernisation spread during the 18th C. these mills would have become progressively disadvantaged in the manufacture of White paper so long as they depended on water power, in spite of up-grading their equipment. As evidence of this deterioration Hasted made somewhat unfavourable comments (ca.1780) on their papers saying that they made "an inferior kind of merchandize"; but after this they must have raised their standards[208] because in 1832 George Fowle was described as "a maker of White Paper at Forestall Mill, Aylesford" while Smith and Allnutt may also have made some of their superior handmade coloured papers for Artists at Cobtree as late as the 1830's. Both these mills had ceased working by 1840.[209] Snodland eventually became a papermachine mill, probably in the 1830/40's, having three large papermachines by 1876 and surviving as a paper mill to the present day. Its survival was no doubt due in part to the fact that it was accessible by river for importing the various pulps and fuel needed for its production.

The reason for making these remarks on the later history of these three mills is merely to demonstrate that, in spite of the limitations imposed on them by the low level of their sites, they managed to survive beyond the 18th C. and it would be quite inconceivable, therefore, to imagine them continuing to use the Old Technology beyond a certain point within this century. One can only conclude that modernisation of the process under William Gill jnr.'s guidance took place when many other mills in the neighbourhood were engaged in the same operation, albeit with the Sandling mills it cannot be said that this necessarily led to an up-grading of their products, just a more efficient and economic process that helped them to survive.

---

[207] Both Forstal and Millhall mills were well below the 25 ft. contour; Cobtree only slightly below it.
[208] An "HR" countermark in a 1786 document may represent Hillier Russell at Forstal. For discussion see App.III under Forstal mill countermarks.
[209] See App.III for Synopses of the histories of these mills.

William Gill jnr. insured Forstal mill as his property in 1754[210] and on the death of James Brooke (1750) the lease of Cobtree mill (almost certainly it was this mill rather than Upper mill, Loose) also passed jointly into his hands and Thomas Wright's, his brother–in–law. At some later undetermined point both these mills became the property of another branch of the Gill family.[211] Since William jnr. must have been familiar with the developments at Turkey mill after his father's demise there and clearly succeeded Brooke as Whatman's Stationer, one can see him as the agent for bringing about the modernisation of these mills. That he maintained an interest in papermaking at Maidstone is demonstrated by the fact that he and his partner became interested (or renewed their interest) in Upper mill, and its neighbour, in Loose in 1770 and quite possibly earlier than this. In 1755 there were general adjustments to the Poor Rates in both Boxley and East Farleigh and whereas not all the rates were raised there were significant rises in the assessments for both the Sandling mills and Upper mill and its neighbour. This may have been purely fortuitous, but in the case of the Sandling mills this fact does tie in with William Gill jnr.'s reappearance on the papermaking scene. On this basis it seems reasonable to propose that these two mills were up–dated, perhaps in a restricted way only, ca.1755, the date shown in Table XI.[212]

Nothing is known about the early history of Snodland paper mill. Although there may have been a paper mill there, like Millhall and Forstal, dating back into the 17th C., the first documentary evidence of its existence is Jasper Crothall's insurance policy of 1755.[213] Snodland appears to have been a Brown or low grade paper mill (at least during the 18th C.) and in the absence of other evidence e.g. whether it was an old or a new–built mill, 1755 is a reasonable date for it to have acquired up–to–date beating equipment in line with its neighbours.

---

[210] SFIP 142250 (13:Aug:1754). For further details see App.IV under William Gill snr. and jnr.; and Chap.IV p.164.

[211] James Brooke held Forstal mill until his death (1750) in trust for William jnr. who insured it (three days after his father died) in 1754, probably a strong indication of up–dating. Likewise Brooke also left the leasehold of another mill jointly to William and his partner and brother–in–law, Thomas Wright (see App.IV p.172).

[212] See App.III Extracts from the Boxley Poor Ratebooks for this period.

[213] Mr. M.J. Fuller is currently working on the mills of the Leybourne stream of which Snodland was one. So far he has not come across any evidence that this mill was a paper mill before Crothall's Insurance Policy of 27:Aug:1755 (SFIP 148270) cited by Shorter, A. Bib.12 184. This does not mean that there was not a paper mill there before Crothall's appearance but no documents to confirm this and no Church Accounts have survived before 1769.

GROUP II

Upper Mill, Loose
Leg o' Mutton Mill
(Loose)
Quelch, Gill (Whatman)

The origin of these mills has been referred to earlier in Chapter IV.[214] Nothing certain is known about the manufacturing status of either of them or the nature of their equipment before the younger Whatman acquired Upper mill in 1774 and virtually rebuilt it as an up-to-date White mill in 1775. Upper mill had been operating as a paper mill from ca.1728; the first indication of operations at the other mill is in 1746,[215] when John Farley, already the occupant of Upper mill (from 1741), began working the property. Shorter shows that in 1770 Thomas Wright and William Gill jnr., the Stationers to Whatman, insured "their house in East Farleigh in the tenure of John Farley, paper maker; and the Old Paper Mill and the New Mill near".[216] Spain identifies one of these mills as Upper and by a process of elimination the other as Leg o' Mutton but was unable to decide which mill was the "New" and which the "Old".[217] Judging from the order in which they are named in the Policy (and in the Church accounts) Upper Mill must have been the Old mill, double the ratable value of the other, and Leg o' Mutton, converted at a later date, the New.[218]

As both of these mills lay only just over 200 yards from Gurney's mill which, it has been suggested, may have been modernised by William Quelch in 1741-2, it seems reasonable to assume that the conversion of Leg o' Mutton between 1741-1746 embodied some form of Engine in its reconstruction, in which one must see yet another extension of Quelch influence, if this was so. There was, however, only a marginal increase in the ratable value when it became operational in 1746. At the same time one has to take into account that it was known as the "New Mill". Shorter has demonstrated that it was a paper mill in 1770 and Spain's investigations show that its status changed in the 1740's and that it was in John Farley's hands up to 1775, followed by William Farley up to 1778; Michael Golden to 1792 and Thomas Golding (who might have been the Thomas at Millhall mill q.v. or connected with him) until ca. 1804, when it appears to have ceased working. There is no evidence that the younger Whatman, who acquired Upper mill in 1774, ever had any interest in this mill; Wright and Gill certainly had had an interest in it but it is not known how far back this extended.

It is not thought that Leg o' Mutton was ever a White mill in the fullest sense. It was too small to have had a proper sizing house for example; its paper could have been sized at Upper mill. The East Farleigh Parish Rates were raised in 1755 and this rise applied to both paper mills. The assessments were raised once again for both mills in Loose as well as East Farleigh in 1773, but the second increase would have been too late to indicate the stage of modernisation with which we are concerned here.[219] On this basis it is proposed that some

---

[214] See Chap.IV notes 1 and 2; and p.154.

[215] Both the East Farleigh Churchwardens' Accounts (KAO P 142 5/2) and the Loose Overseers' Accounts (KAO P233 12/5/2) show that the first assessments made against Farley for this mill were in 1746. Spain, R.J. (Bib.10 47) claims that Farley was undertaking the conversion of this mill from fulling to papermaking between 1742-5.

[216] Shorter, A. Bib.12 194 citing SFIP 292237 of 19:Dec:1770.

[217] Spain, R.J. Bib.10 49.

[218] East Farleigh RB. KAO P 142 5/2 and Loose Overseer's a/cs. P 233 12/5/2 & 12/6. Leg o' Mutton lay entirely in Loose; Upper mill and Gurney's mill half in Loose half in E. Farleigh. All the same Leg o' Mutton was assessed in both parish records, certainly up to 1774 when the East Farleigh entries cease.

[219] The Loose a/cs. show no change in the ratable value of either mill between 1746-1773. In E. Farleigh rates rose generally in 1755 and Upper mill's from £20-£30; Leg o' Mutton £8-£13 and in 1773 to £35 and £17 respectively. It may be noted that the identification of these mills as given by Balston, T. Bib.1 39 is incorrect as is Shorter's nomenclature in Bib.12 Mill Nos.27/29.

degree of up-dating took place during conversion (1742-6) from fulling. Hence a queried 1745 in TABLE XI where it has not been included under White mills.

In the case of Upper mill there is no evidence to show whether this mill had been up-dated prior to Whatman's rebuilding it in 1774/75. This seems to be altogether too late a date for it to have had nothing done to it when other mills in the vicinity had already been up-graded by one degree or another. Moreover, even though it was still known as Old Mill, it seems unlikely that Wright and Gill would have been interested in it, if it still employed the Old Technology as late as 1770. If nothing had been done to this mill before this date, they would surely have taken steps to modernise it then. But, if this had been the case, is it likely that Whatman would have rebuilt this mill completely within five years of their taking this step? The subject of the Gill family having had a possible interest in this mill as far back as its conversion in 1728 has been discussed previously, as also the further possibility that when William jnr. reappeared on the papermaking scene in 1754 he may have taken action (see the Sandling mills above) to up-date Upper mill in Loose ca.1755. Whatman's action is regarded here as a second stage improvement (particularly after his experiment with a new Engine at Hollingbourne in 1771) and, consequently, Table XI shows the first as probably having taken place at some point between 1755-1770. In the case of both Leg o' Mutton and Upper mills the ratable values do not appear to be a useful indicator of any changes in the mills' status after 1741 and do not reflect Whatman's rebuilding of Upper Mill at all.[220] Before Wright and Gill's and Whatman's time i.e. before 1770 a date for which there is any certainty, it is thought that Upper mill may have made Printings or other second class Whites, otherwise one wonders whether there was any potential in this mill that would have attracted their attention, a potential which Whatman was in actual fact to maximise after 1775 when it was employed in manufacturing the topmost classes of White paper.

Upper mill, which was a 1-vat mill, passed to Hollingworth and Balston with the sale of Turkey and Poll mills in 1794, Hollingworth retaining it until 1850 after which it was converted to corn.

Before leaving the subject of Upper mill the question may well be asked, what induced Whatman to acquire this mill when he already had Hollingbourne Old Mill at his disposal? Whatman's business, needing more production capacity, had obviously outgrown the water power available at the Turkey mill site. (He did not acquire Poll mill, even if he had wanted it, until 1787). Although he reoccupied Hollingbourne Old Mill in 1770, one can only surmise that he found some inadequacy there for his purpose, possibly something to do with the quality of the water; or, alternatively, it may have been too remote for him: or that he preferred to own a mill rather than lease one. The answer to this question is not known; but the fact is that he let it to Clement Taylor jnr. and acquired Upper Mill, Loose, himself, incorporating the results of his experiments with the new Engine at Old Mill. Upper mill had a pond fed entirely by an underground source and in the days before the chemical era clean water was of vital importance to the manufacture of the top qualities of White paper. Water may, therefore, have been the deciding factor in this case.[221]

[220] Upper mill's ratable value remained constant at £35 (E. Farleigh) and £26 (Loose) between 1773 until 1780 at least.
[221] See Chap.III Map 3; and more especially, Chap.VI n.96.

GROUP III

(a)   *The papermaking activities of the Pine family at Great Ivy, Lower Tovil and Otham mills.*

(b)   *Robert Wilson, Stationer of London, and Otham and Sittingbourne (North Kent Region) paper mills.* (Possibly remote influence from Quelch Dartford centre ?)

These four paper mills have been grouped together partly because the Pine family controlled three of them for most of the 18th C. (see Table XII), though in the case of Otham, a Pine mill, and Sittingbourne, nothing to do with the Pine family, Robert Wilson, the London Stationer, who has appeared previously as mortgagee for Josias Johannot's Cray Valley mill in 1742 (q.v.), may have been the catalyst in the up–dating of Otham and Sittingbourne mills in both of which he had interests; and partly because the Pines' three mills, although not White until relatively late in the 18th C., form an integral part of the Maidstone industry, cementing together its more important members and providing a platform for extending White paper manufacture towards the end of that century.

It is not known precisely why Wilson became interested in Otham paper mill. The effects of War had undoubtedly led to shortages of certain classes of paper and Stationers would, understandably, have been on the look–out for suitable sources of supply. By the time Wilson insured Otham, 1744, it seems certain that it had been a "dirty" mill for some years prior to this date;[222] one can only surmise then that Wilson was an opportunist and had seen the possibility of making, say, cartridge paper here using the same new beating Engine that Johannot was about to use at Cray Valley; or, less likely, it may have been a class of White paper that he wanted, remembering that Otham mill was not far from Turkey mill, downstream, and Hollingbourne Old Mill, upstream. These may not have been the mills that inspired Wilson's action directly since he had undoubtedly heard of the New Technology from fellow stationers such as Brooke; or Johannot via the Quelchs at Dartford; but they may nevertheless have focused his attention on this area. The fact is that Wilson and a paper maker called Alexander Mathison,[223] perhaps an undertenant of Thomas Pine's, insured this mill in 1744 (see Table XII). When Mathison moved to Sittingbourne in 1752,[224] Wilson followed him there shortly after. It is clear that so far as these two mills are concerned there was some underlying factor that permits us to group them together here. But before considering this subject further, the general set–up of the Pine family as paper makers in the Maidstone area needs unravelling.

The branch of the Pine family with whom we are dealing here[225] had been fullers at Tovil,

---

[222]   Before Thomas Pine snr. took it over the paper maker there had been a William Hills, whom Shorter believed had been an apprentice at Great Ivy mill under Burnham (Bib.12 189); and Great Ivy was definitely a Brown mill by the time Thomas Pine snr. took it over.

[223]   It is not known where Alexander Mathison came from. Was he a local paper maker, possibly from the Whatman or Quelch stable ? or was he a protégé of Robert Wilson's and perhaps familiar with Josias Johannot's venture at St. Paul's Cray ? Was he related to Richard Mathison who succeeded Josias Johannot 11 years later at Deptford mill ? (For comment on this Stationer/Paper Maker association see this chapter pp.279 & n.176).

[224]   Shorter, A. Bib.12 184.

[225]   The name is spelt variously, Pyend, Pien, Piene, Pine and Peene. Since their main concentration seems to have been in the Loose River valley one might assume that they were related to Richard, Tanner of Loose (d.1684) and his daughter,

(continued...)

TABLE XII

Papermaking Pine family & other makers at Great Ivy, Lower Tovil and Otham paper mills (17th–20th Cs.)
(Sources of information mainly SHORTER (Bib.12 & 7); also SPAIN (Bib.8, 10 & 11); and the Author's searches).

GREAT IVY MILL			LOWER TOVIL MILL			OTHAM	
1685 Richard Burnham 1696 (William Hills apprenticed)	£16		1686 Peter Musgrove	£20			17th C.
1703 Thomas Manktellow 1715 Thomas Pine snr.[1]	£16 £16		1702 Peter Musgrove jnr. 1722 William Gill snr. 1728 Thomas Pine snr.[2] 1731 (Mill destroyed by explosion; rebuilt immediately)	£25 £25 £25		1715 William Keble (d.1726 described as a "miller"). 1727 William Hills (see Great Ivy 1696).	18th C.
1741 Thomas Pine jnr. 1745 Simon Pine 1747 (No Maidstone RB for 15 yr.).	£16 £15		1741 Thomas Pine snr. 1745 Thomas Pine jnr.[6] 1750 Simon Pine took apprentices[7]			1742 Thomas Pine snr.[3] 1742 Alexander Mathison[4] 1744 Mathison (Robert Wilson)[5] 1756 Mathison last entry[8] 1757 Thomas, John & Simon Pine insured their untensils and stock.[9] (It is not clear though who insured the mill).	
1762 (Maidstone RB resumes) 1763 Thomas Pine jnr.[10] 1766) 1777) Simon Pine 1778) 1781) John Pine 1781 Thomas Pine insured the mill[11] 1785 Robert Edmeads name appears 1788 Robert Edmeads & Thomas Pine insured mill.[12]	£40 £40 £40		1763 Simon Pine 1780 Simon Pine 1781 John Pine 1795 John Pine & Co.[13]	£30 £30 £50		1779 Paper Mill for sale. 1782 Edward Pine, described as a paper maker, may have been here. 1792 Edw. & Thos. Pine insure paper and corn mill[14] 1796 Thomas Pine & Co.[15]	18th C.
1805 Pine & Edmeads mill & land. 1810 John Pine & Co. 1813 Pine, Smith & Allnutt 1816 Smith & Allnutt (EGL) 1835) 1882) Henry Allnutt: machine 1870's	£33 £65		1810 John Pine & William Thomas[17] 1814 Mill destroyed by fire.[20] 1816 John Pine (EGL) 1821 Papermachine installed 1824 Pine connection ends 1850 Henry Allnutt snr. & jnr. 1872+ In hands of Green family			1800s Pines partnered by Edmeads up to ca.1809.[16] 1810 Russell & Co.[18] 1812 Charles Brenchley[19] 1816 Charles Brenchley (EGL) 1819 Brenchley & Wise 1822 Thomas Pine & Edward Davis 1825 John Green snr. & jnr.[21] 1830s Papermachine installed 1859 Machine transferred to Turkey mill 1890s Disused.	19th C. 19th C.
1924 Closed			1956 Still working under name of Allnutt; closed later				20th C.

1. Thomas Pine snr. (1675–1757) Maidstone Grocer and son of Simon Pine (1634–1681), fuller of Tovil. Between 1719–23 the occupation of this mill alternated between Thomas snr. and Thomas Gilford. In 1716 Thomas snr. had taken Thomas jnr. and Arthur Pine as apprentices. (Shorter, A. Bib.12 192). Taken with the note below it is estimated that Thomas jnr. was born ca. 1706.

2. Shorter records (Bib.12 190) that 2 paper maker Thomas Pines took an apprentice in 1728.

3. SFIP 91037 29:Apr:1742.   4. SFIP 92874 18:Oct:1742.

5. Mill insured by Robert Wilson, Stationer, SFIP 100250 2:Oct:1744.

6. SFIP 103461 30:Sept:1745.   7. One of these was Thomas Stroud snr., father of Thomas jnr., see App.II Thomas Stroud.

8. This coincides with the announcement of a sale of the late Mathison's tools etc. at Sittingbourne, where he had insured the mill there in his own occupation in 1742, a paper maker of Otham, SFIP 129657 (18:Mar:1752). Shorter, A. Bib.12 184.

9. SFIP 156615 22:Mar:1757. Thomas Pine snr. died this year. Shorter believed that all 3 had an interest in this mill up till 1779.

10. Shorter's view was that Thomas jnr. was the Master Paper Maker here for the next 19 years. Since he had to run his grocer's business, he obviously had to delegate the papermaking to (i) Simon and (ii) John.

11. SFIP 443774 10:May:1781

12. SFIP 541482 27:Feb:1788. The names alternate in the Ratebook, sometimes as Pine & Co. The countermark is always "E & P" or full names.

13. The "Company" may have included Thomas No.3.

14. There had always been two Otham mills, the corn mill dating from 1086; the fulling mill from 1545, the latter converted to paper in 1715. (Spain, R.J. Bib. 8, 72).

15. This must have been Thomas No.3.

16. "EDMEADS & Co.1809" Gravell, T.L Bib.68 227. This could refer equally, or more probably, to Little Ivy mill (see this Chapter, note 234)

17. William Thomas had been paper maker at Cobtree (Boxley) between 1782–1808 (see App.III under Cobtree and Boxley RB. extracts). "PINE & THOMAS 1810, 1812" countermarks found (Shorter, A. Bib.7 July 58: Gravell, T.L Bib.68 564). Shorter (loc.cit.) lists several other countermarks for this period, "I PINE 1802"; "J & T PINE 1809"; "LOWER TOVIL 1806" and variants. "J PINE" is also found in the Sutton Valence 1793 Land Tax Return (KAO Q/RPI/374).

18. "RUSSELL & Co. 1810" countermark is believed to emanate from here (Shorter, A. Bib.7 May 54). Earlier Russell & Co. countermarks in 1797, 1799 probably came from Upper Tovil mill. (The "Russell" here might have been Clement Taylor Russell, see App.III, p.116 note 1).

19. See App.III under Pratling Street paper mill.

20. After this fire John Pine appears briefly at Forstal mill, Boxley (see App.III under Forstal mill), but more probably due to the installation of his papermachine than to the actual fire causing a disruption to production at Lower Tovil mill.

21. Also of Hayle mill, Tovil.

Maidstone, from at least Edward VI's reign before becoming paper makers in the 18th C.[226] Simon Pine (1634–81), the last of the family associated with Bridge mill in Tovil, was also an important early member of the Baptist movement.[227] His eldest son, John, is reputed to have been a paper mouldmaker,[228] which may account for his brother Thomas (1675–1757) becoming interested in papermaking, though the decline in the woollen cloth industry together with the family's long experience of working watermills may have been more important factors in this decision to change their business.[229] In actual fact both Thomas snr.'s and jnr.'s principal business during the 18th C. was as grocers in Maidstone, carried on at least until 1782, if not later.[230]

The Pines entered the field of papermaking on the crest of the second wave of Maidstone's expanding paper industry at Great Ivy mill, Loose, in 1715 following (as Table XII indicates) Thomas Manktellow and, earlier, Richard Burnham.[231] Great Ivy mill, though possibly once intended as a White mill, had undoubtedly become a Brown one by the time the Pines occupied it; it is known from an inventory of 1732 that they made Press papers, presumably for such of the woollen trade as remained in Kent, and Shop papers, a product one might expect them to make for their grocery business.[232]

In 1728 they occupied another paper mill, Lower Tovil, following William Gill snr., the occupant from 1722–27.[233] Somewhat ironically this mill was destroyed by an explosion in 1731 in the mill next door, Bridge mill, a mill which their family had worked for over 100 years as a fulling mill before being converted to gunpowder manufacture. The paper mill was rebuilt and in action again in a very short space of time. This event can be seen as the one opportunity when it might have had an early form of Hollander installed in it, which, as has been suggested, may have been the case at Gurney's mill, further upstream, in 1728 when under William Quelch. There was, however, no change in the ratable value, as at Gurney's, and as their product line seems to have been inferior papers, as at Ivy mill, made from rotten rags and old ropes, there was no compelling reason for them to change their process from the Old Technology.

One might conclude that, in view of the unfavourable conditions prevailing then in the market for White paper, the 1730's, there was no obvious incentive for the Pines to modernise either of these mills. Indeed their assessments remained unaltered until much later, Great Ivy's rising

---

[225](...continued)

Mary Peene, first wife of the James Whatman from Brenchley who later inherited and occupied the Peene tan yards in Loose. James, in his Will, left a considerable sum to "his servant and kinsman, Robert Peene". The elder paper maker Whatman started his life in these tan yards, so it is quite on the cards that he knew the papermaking Pines personally, though there were differences in their religious outlook that might have estranged the two families.

[226] For an account of Bridge mill, Tovil, see Spain, R.J. Bib.11 184–6. This mill passed out of the Pine family's hands in 1684 and was converted to a Powder mill between 1698–1704.

[227] After the Declaration of Indulgence (1672) Simon Pine provided land for a Baptist burial ground in Tovil, still extant, his headstone being the oldest there. (Russell, J.M. Bib.41 152/3).

[228] Russell, J.M. Bib.41 415.

[229] Equally important Thomas Manktellow, the previous occupant to Thomas Pine snr. at Great Ivy mill, had married Hannah Pine in 1699.

[230] Spain, R.J. Bib.8 75.

[231] See Chap.II Map 2.

[232] See Chap.V n.104.

[233] See Chap.IV p.152.

from £15 to £40 between 1747–63 (no Maidstone ratebook between 1747–62); and Lower Tovil's from £25 to £30 in the same period, the latter going up to £50 in 1781. Are there any other indicators of a change in status or of modernisation taking place in these two mills ?

Working backwards Table XII gives one the impression that John Pine snr. was an important agent in bringing about a new phase in the family's papermaking history. He appears, for instance, at Great Ivy mill in 1778 and at Lower Tovil in 1781, when the ratable value shot up. In both cases partnerships with other paper makers were formed within the next decade and a half, although it was probably the third Thomas who was involved in the Pine and Edmeads partnership at Great Ivy in the 1780's where Edmeads appears to have been the dominant partner (the countermarks are always "EDMEADS & PINE"),[234] but this may have been because Thomas' main preoccupation was still with the grocery business. John Pine snr. and jnr. were the presiding paper makers at Lower Tovil, working it from 1781–1824 and were obviously forward looking, installing a papermachine there in 1821–2, the third in Kent. Although in both of these cases one is concerned with the manufacture of White countermarked paper, it is felt that modernisation in terms of an improved stuff preparation system must have taken place much earlier and that the determining influence came from the activities of Robert Wilson and Mathison at Otham in the 1740's.

Mathison was running both Otham and Sittingbourne paper mills by the early 1750's, though not necessarily making White paper at either initially, but whatever he made he would have used the Hollander. He died in 1756; Thomas Pine snr. meanwhile regained the Otham tenancy (insuring the mill in the occupation of Henry Bishop). Thomas snr. died a year later and his three sons immediately insured their utensils and stock jointly maintaining an interest in the mill until 1779 (see Table XII), when it was up for sale. In occupying Otham all three would have become familiar with the New Technology and its benefits, applying the results of their experience to other Maidstone mills. This would coincide with the rises in the ratable values noted above.

What sort of construction can be placed on all these events ? It is clear that Thomas Pine snr. could not run three paper mills and a grocery business on his own. Great Ivy by itself was manageable and as soon as his son, Thomas jnr., was made free, he placed him in charge of Lower Tovil mill in 1728; and by 1745 both Thomas jnr. and Simon were taking part, the latter at Great Ivy and Thomas jnr. still at Lower Tovil. By that time Thomas snr. would have been aged 70. It is not surprising then that after adding Otham mill to his papermaking business he should have agreed to another paper maker running it for him, Alexander Mathison (or Matthewson). Mathison's origin is unknown but it seems highly improbable in 1742, the year he started work, that any of these three paper makers had *sufficient, if any, experience of the New (more advanced) Technology* to have enabled them to modernise their mills as early as this, certainly in the case of the Pines. This leaves Robert Wilson as the

---

[234] Little Ivy mill (upstream of Great Ivy) was converted to papermaking by William Edmeads & Co. in 1808/9 (Spain, R.J. Bib.10 67). Gravell, T.L. Bib.68 No.227 cites an "EDMEADS & CO 1809" mark. No EDMEADS & PINE marks have been noted for Great Ivy after 1808 and there is evidence pointing to Edmeads having left Great Ivy after 1808 leaving John Pine there on his own. Edmeads were bankrupted in 1813, Henry Allnutt taking over Little Ivy and at the same time he partnered John Pine at Great Ivy e.g. the mark "PINE, SMITH & ALLNUTT 1813". Between 1809–13 several "IVY MILL" countermarks have been noted and whereas these could refer to either mill, it seems more likely that John Pine used these marks to distinguish paper made at Great Ivy from that made at his other mills. This fits in with his use of "LOWER TOVIL etc." (q.v.) at this time.

initiator with the distinct possibility that he might have secured Mathison as a paper maker with previous experience of working an Engine, possibly from one of the New Technology mills on either side (Old Mill, for instance, was in very unsatisfactory hands in 1744/5 q.v.). As with Cray Valley, the proposal is made that the mill may have been only partially up-dated in the late 1740's with a further stage taking place when it became a fully fledged White mill with improved sizing and finishing facilities. This may not have taken place until the 1790's, although Shorter has suggested a rather earlier date, a date which seems to conflict with other aspects of the Pines' occupation of these mills.[235] Otham mill, however, is seen here as the key to the modernisation of the other two mills with Great Ivy following sometime between 1747-62 and Lower Tovil probably a little later in the 1760's, but with no major alteration until 1780 when the ratable value rose significantly.

To complete this group there remains Sittingbourne mill in the North Kent Region,[236] included because Mathison was paper maker at both Otham and the Sittingbourne mill for nearly four years. Mathison died in 1756 and within a very short space of time Robert Wilson, the Stationer of Lombard Street, insured Sittingbourne in the tenure of Samuel Lay (Ley).[237] The fact that Wilson appears so promptly on the Sittingbourne scene confirms the view that there must have been a more permanent connection either with the paper mills or the paper makers than would appear to be the case if judged solely on the somewhat random occurrence of his paper mill insurance policies. There is no doubt that at Sittingbourne both Wilson's and Lay's interest lay in the manufacture of White paper; Lay started making White countermarked papers almost as soon as he arrived.[238] The question that this poses is whether Lay modernised the mill for White paper manufacture when he took it over ? or had Mathison (perhaps helped by Wilson) done this prior to his arrival ?

Robert Archer's inventory[239] coupled with Peter jnr.'s move in 1732 (possibly indicating insufficient water power there) indicates that the beatermen in this mill must have had some experience of operating an Engine. Robert's successors, the millwright William Stevens and Laws, both of whom were bankrupted,[240] may not have had the means or the knowledge to up-grade the mill. It is much more likely that Mathison, the next occupant, with the help of Wilson undertook at least the preliminary stages of up-grading this mill and this is reflected in the dates (1756-6) shown in Table XI; Lay may have completed the task and without too much trouble.

Samuel Lay continued to occupy this mill (as well as St. Mary Cray from the mid-1770's) until his death in 1803/4. The 1816 Excise General List shows Edward Smith there; while

[235] Shorter, A. Bib.12 264 cites an "SP" countermark in a document of the 1770's which he attributes to Simon Pine at Otham (?). Whereas he claims that Thomas jnr., John and Simon all maintained an interest in Otham between 1757-1779, the indications are that Simon Pine was more positively associated with Lower Tovil between 1750-1780, more especially during the 1770's. If "SP" was a Simon Pine mark, then it points to the Pines making White paper at least a decade earlier than one might have expected.

[236] Previous references to Sittingbourne mill may be found in Chap.II n.25, 29; and Chap.IV pp.142/3.

[237] SFIP 151323 (12:Mar:1756).

[238] See earlier under St. Mary Cray this Chap. n.195. It is probable that Sittingbourne (as in the case of Peter Archer jnr.) may not have been the ideal mill for White paper manufacture and because of Wilson's knowledge of the area and, perhaps, intelligence of Sims' incapacity, Lay evidently seized the opportunity to move some of his operations to St. Mary Cray early in the 1770's.

[239] See Chap.IV n.25.

[240] Shorter, A. Bib.12 184.

Martha Lay continued at St. Mary Cray (q.v.). To follow the later history of this mill to Edward Lloyd's expansion of this site from a mill with one machine to one with eight between 1878–1898 leading to Bowater's giant complex there in the 20th C. is a subject in itself and really totally unrelated to this work. The geography of the site was undoubtedly an important factor for its survival and subsequent development.

GROUP IV

The Hollingbourne Paper Mills and Ford Mill, Little Chart

Apart from Padsole mill, which will be dealt with separately, this Group completes the Maidstone district and, although it lies outside it, Ford mill (with a mention of Conyer) has been included for reasons which will become clear. The synopses of the histories of these mills and their occupants will be found in Appendices I & II. This means that they can all be dealt with quite briefly here. Unlike the other groups we have been considering, the question of "modernisation" does not arise with any of the White mills in this Group; instead it is the influence that Old Mill exerted that is of interest here.

Old Mill
(Hollingbourne)
(As a paper mill 1733–1848)

Various periods in the history of this mill have been covered in different parts of this work, for example, its origins;[241] the practical aspects of installing an Engine there;[242] Harris' departure from it and move to Turkey mill;[243] John Terry's occupation of it between 1739–41;[244] the younger Whatman's temporary re–occupation of the mill in 1770 to carry out experiments with his new beater;[245] and Clement Taylor jnr.'s tenure from 1774–93.[246] All of these accounts demonstrate that, whilst the mill began its life as an experimental one–vat mill expanding later as some mills did to a five–vat mill towards the end of its life, historically it can be rated as one of the most important paper mills in Kent, if not in the United Kingdom. Not only did it provide a starting point for a revolution in the papermaking process as used by the majority of mills in Kent, but it also served as a kind of nursery for the growth of mills in its own area and as a training ground for paper makers who worked there as well as those who took their trade elsewhere, even as far off as the West Riding in Yorkshire,[247] events that are summarised in Table XIII.

There are two important periods in this mill's history that have not been considered yet; the first of these is the period between 1741, when John Terry left for Dartford, and the end of the Frenchs' tenancy in 1769, after which the younger Whatman re–occupied it briefly; and the second of these starts during Clement Taylor jnr.'s tenancy when it becomes obvious that with his increasing commitments he and his successors could no longer continue without the assistance of a mill manager, a new trend in the industry when people like the Salmons and Daniel Newman appear on the scene and, certainly in the case of Newman, undertook this task for him.[248]

Starting with the first period Terry was followed by a John Sanders who, one suspects, was unable to make the New Technology work; he disappeared from the scene after four years and was bankrupted shortly afterwards. It is possible that he may have been connected with the papermaking Edward and Samuel Sanders who were at Shoreham mill in the early 1720's[249] and, if trained there in the Old Technology, this might account for his failure at Old Mill. His demise forced the elder Whatman to assume responsibility for the mill again

---

[241] Chap.III p.112 ff.

[242] Chap.VI p.241 ff.

[243] Chap.IV pp.169 ff.; and this Chapter p.278.

[244] Chap.VII pp.280/1.

[245] Chap.VII pp.289,314; and App.V.

[246] Chap.VII p.289.

[247] See App.II (see the Salmons at Langcliffe mill).

[248] See App.I (see Synop. Old mill and Preamble to Park mill).

[249] Shorter, A. Bib.12 183 Samuel s.o. Edward Sanders, paper maker, was apprenticed at Shoreham in 1721.

TABLE XIII – THE INFLUENCE OF HOLLINGBOURNE OLD MILL AFTER 1741

OLD MILL, HOLLINGBOURNE[1]	DATE	LATER EVENTS ACTIVATED, DIRECTLY OR INDIRECTLY, BY THE EXAMPLE OR PRESENCE OF OLD MILL
Henry French tenancy starts	1749	
	1762	The building of *EYEHORNE MILL*, Hollingbourne,[2] the first purpose built paper mill in Kent since Old Mill itself.
The Henry French tenancy ends, but their papermaking continued at Gurney's mill.	1769	Proprietor James Austen : the first paper maker at Eyehorne was William Avery (1764–74).
The younger Whatman used the mill as a beating laboratory (see App.V).	1770–4	
Clement Taylor jnr.'s tenancy starts	1774	*Robert Williams*[3] successor to William Avery and paper maker at Eyehorne 1775–1803.
Lewis Munn snr.[4] in Hollingbourne. Munn may have undergone training in Old Mill under Taylor or at Eyehorne mill under Williams.	(1774–6)	Williams and Munn almost certainly met. For discussion of the significance of this see App.1.[5]
	1776	*FORD MILL*, Little Chart. It is not known whether Munn and Sweetlove converted an existing mill, added to one or built a new paper mill. The Little Chart Ratebook entries suggest building or conversion in progress.
A reasonable case can be made out for the training of *Henry* and *Thomas Salmon* at Old Mill during this period.[6] By 1784 Henry, the elder brother, might even have been acting as Clement Taylor's mill manager.	(1777–90)	
Again, a reasonable case can be made out for *Daniel Newman* taking over as mill manager at Old Mill in this year.[7]	1791	
During this period (1774–1793) it is thought, to judge from the Insurance Premiums, that the capacity of Old Mill may have been increased significantly by Clement Taylor.		
Clement Taylor jnr.'s tenancy ends.	1793	
The younger Whatman took over temporarily	1793–4	
	1794	*LANGCLIFFE MILL*, West Riding, Yorkshire[8] set up by Henry and Thomas Salmon from Hollingbourne with *John Crispe* of Sutton Valence, Kent, as Mortgagee.
Hollingworth and Balston take over Old Mill, although the signs are that *Daniel Newman* still acted as manager but was in the process of leasing it in partnership with (possibly) the same *John Crispe*[9] who was acting as mortgagee to the Salmons at Langcliffe.	1794–95	
	1800	*PARK MILL*, Hollingbourne,[10] a new pupose built paper mill initially under the direction of Crispe and Newman.
The evidence suggests that from ca.1795 to ca.1810 Old Mlll was sub-let to *Crispe* and *Newman* until ca.1802 and thereafter to *Stroud* and *Newman*. Certainly, in 1805 William Balston occupied Eyehorne mill and was followed there by one of the Hollingworths from 1806–8 indicating that they had no access to their own mill because it was already let. (See Eyehorne mill).	1802	The partnership at Park mill changed to Stroud and Newman
	1809	*Richard Barnard* snr. from Sutton Valence took over the running of Eyehorne mill (where he had been proprietor since ca.1781/2).
Ca. 1810–12 Hollingworths resumed control of Old Mill[11] and kept it going till 1848 when it ceased working as a paper milll.	1812	The partnership between Stroud and Newman came to an end. Thomas Stroud moved to *PRATLING STREET MILL*, Aylesford.[12] Daniel Newman continued at Park mill until 1818 after which it was taken over by Richard Barnard snr. & jnr.

FOOTNOTES
1. Synopsis of history see App.I. For details of occupants see App.II.
2. Synopsis of history see App.I.
3. See App.II (Robert Williams)
4. See App.II (Munn)
5. See App.I (Robert Williams)
6. See App.II (Salmon. Also App.I Table Leeds RB & LT Extracts Block I "Outdwellers" for details).
7. See App.II (Daniel Newman)
8. See App.II (Salmon)
9. See App.II (Crispe)
10. See App.I (Synopsis Park Mill)
11. See App.I (Synopsis Old Mill)
12. See App.II (Stroud); App. III (Pratling Street).

in 1746, quite possibly with a reduced output. In 1749 Henry French snr. and his family appeared on the scene and rented the mill for the next 19 years. It is not known where they came from,[250] but the intriguing fact is that they got the mill to work successfully using the New Technology and were producing White countermarked papers by 1760, if not earlier. It looks as if, having had the mill on his hands again, Whatman had selected and installed Henry French there. In the event the Frenchs did so well that Henry snr. expanded his business taking over Gurney's mill, Loose, (the old Harris and Quelch mill) in 1760,[251] leaving Henry jnr. to run Old Mill until the lease expired and putting his other son, Thomas, in charge of Gurney's ca.1771. The question as to whether Henry snr. modernised this mill or not in 1760 has been raised earlier,[252] where it was also noted that the ratable value of the property in Loose was raised by 50% in 1773 which may have signified some improvement or enlargement taking place under Thomas' direction.[253] Thomas remained at Gurney's until he died in 1795, succeeded there for one year by his widow.[254] Meanwhile Henry jnr. continued to run Old Mill until 1769; he died and was buried in Hollingbourne, still a relatively young man, six years later. If nothing else, the Frenchs' tenancy of 19 years demonstrates that Old Mill, probably little altered since its creation in 1733, could be operated satisfactorily for the manufacture of White countermarked paper.

The events and the influence arising from Old Mill in the second period are best summarised diagrammatically and are illustrated in the Table XIII opposite. It is only necessary to add one or two miscellaneous comments on the events illustrated there.

The first of these, which took place while the Frenchs still occupied Old Mill, was the erection of an entirely new mill in Hollingbourne, almost certainly inspired by the example of Old Mill. Why James Austen from Chatham came to build a mill there is not known, but the subject is aired in the section on Eyehorne mill below. The second point of interest is the arrival of Lewis Munn snr. in the village in 1774 aged 25 and within two years of this he set up his own mill in partnership with Thomas Sweetlove (of Leeds village) at Little Chart about 8.5 miles to the south-east of Old Mill and situated on the Great Stour. Nothing is known about Munn's training in papermaking; but clearly his stay in Hollingbourne provided him with the experience he needed to set up a mill of his own, quite possibly acquired from Clement Taylor jnr. who must have been enlarging Old Mill at this time.[255] Munn is also of interest in another connection, an event of the future that might have stemmed from a friendship with Robert Williams of Hollingbourne. This was the appearance of Lewis Munn jnr. at Mill End mill, Hertfordshire, between 1796–99, a mill that had earlier been occupied by Robert Williams, a paper maker of Rickmansworth who, in theory, could have been the Hollingbourne Robert Williams' father. (The subject is not relevant here; it is examined in detail in the Appendices).[256]

Table XIII also illustrates how Old Mill served as a training ground for paper makers like the Salmon brothers and Daniel Newman each of whom in turn founded new paper mills, and the interesting point about these is that they appear to have been funded by a new class of

---

[250] See App.II (French).

[251] See this Chapter p.286.

[252] See this Chapter p.281.

[253] Could this rise be ascribed to the installation of a new Engine of the same kind that the younger Whatman was experimenting with at Old Mill ? That there may have been a closer relationship than a casual one between Thomas and Whatman has been discussed in App.V p.287 regarding the question of "F" countermarks. Moreover, in the following year Whatman rebuilt Upper Mill right next door to Gurney's.

[254] The Frenchs were followed at Gurney's by the abortive partnership between Clement Taylor jnr. and William Edmeads ending with the former's bankruptcy in 1797. Thereafter it was Russell & Edmeads until ca.1803/4; Edmeads & Co. with William and John bankrupted in 1813. From 1814–50 the mill was part of the Hollingworth empire, continuing as a millboard mill under Gurney till it closed ca.1909.

[255] The references given in Footnote 4 TABLE XIII cover the whole question of Munn's origins, training (possibly under John Terry) and his arrival in Hollingbourne.

[256] See App.I p.19; and App.II Robert Williams.

person, either as mortgagee or partner, who as far as is known had no former connection with the paper industry or training as a paper maker. Other examples of this include the Elgars at Chafford, bankers; and John Larking at East Malling, banker and timber merchant. In this case one has Richard Barnard (Tanner) and John Crispe (Yeoman), both from Sutton Valence and far removed from a paper mill, the former becoming the proprietor of Eyehorne mill as early as 1781/2 and the latter acting as mortgagee to the Salmons and, less easily determined, partner to Daniel Newman at Old Mill and, later, at Park mill.[257] References to the details of their respective interests have been given in the notes to Table XIII.

One is seeing here the early phases of a more complex structure within the industry, the appointment of mill managers by mill owners who were at the same time Master Paper Makers, the managers becoming Master Paper Makers themselves, the subletting of mills, new financial arrangements involving non–paper makers etc. The stage had not yet been reached, however, where the control of these enterprises was remote and spread across the country. All the people concerned in these cases came from the locality and connections between them can still be found. Moreover, within this rapidly expanding paper industry one still finds the Master Paper Maker who was both a Master of his trade and an innovator. For the period under consideration, 1740–1800, Old Mill can be seen as a very important source of these new trends.

Eyehorne Mill (Hollingbourne)

The details of the history of this mill and its occupants are to be found in Appendices I & II. It was the first purpose–built White paper mill to appear in Kent after Hollingbourne Old Mill was built in 1733.[258] The question has been asked, why did James Austen of Chatham decide to build a mill of this kind in Hollingbourne ? The short answer to this question is that we do not know. The name is not uncommon and is found in many papermaking parishes of the 18th C. For all that is known about him, he might have been a relation of a paper maker in the Maidstone district or a friend or relation of, say, the Frenchs or the Barnard family (Richard being the next proprietor). He does not appear to have made paper himself, although one cannot be certain of this since there is a gap of 18 months between the time he first insured the mill and the appearance of William Avery, his paper maker. Mr. Austin died in 1768 and Mrs. Austen became the proprietress for the 11 years following and insuring the mill from a Maidstone address.

The significance of this undertaking lies in the fact that it is the first *new* paper mill for 29 years built on a *new* site (on the Snagsbrook, a tributary of the River Len) and designed and equipped specifically to manufacture White paper using the New Technology. Situated as it was in Hollingbourne, one cannot see this mill as coming from either the Quelch or the Chartham stables; *it must have been modelled on Old Mill.* Finding millwrights capable of constructing a mill of this kind in 1762 was clearly less of a problem than it had been in 1733. Nevertheless one is forced to conclude that Austen coming from a totally different district must have had some close contact with someone familiar with Old Mill and the geography of Hollingbourne and the factors that persuaded him to invest there may have been that it was a suitable centre for recruiting skilled craftsmen and close to mills with a high reputation for the manufacture of White paper, such as Whatman's, as well as being a place with an as yet unused mill site. The fact that it was a site suitable for the manufacture of White paper is proved by the paper makers who followed, including William Balston[259] and Hollingworth.

---

[257]   The proprietorship of Park mill is an unsolved mystery. It may have come under the Tax umbrella of Leeds Castle (see App.I Preamble to Park mill).

[258]   Upper mill, East Malling, is not considered to be in the same category. For one thing it appears to have been a watermill as far back as 1706; and it might possibly have made paper before 1763 but not insured for this purpose until then. (For details see App.IV The Succession at the East Malling Paper Mills, Kent).

[259]   William Balston occupied Eyehorne mill and *not* Old Mill as described by Balston, T. Bib.1 131.

Park Mill
(Hollingbourne)

There is nothing to add to what has been said above about this mill and the full particulars of its history will be found in Appendix I with notes on some of its occupants in Appendix II. It was a brand new purpose–built mill that was used for making White paper and what is so remarkable is the fact that whoever built it managed to cram it in to what vacant space remained on the Snagsbrook.

Ford Mill
(Little Chart)
(MR TQ 942460)

As noted in Table XIII it is not known whether Munn and Sweetlove erected a new mill on an old site or converted or added to a working mill of one sort or another. In 1779 Lewis Munn snr. insured a paper mill and a corn mill in Little Chart, but since there was a large corn mill further upstream, Swallow mill, the wording of the policy is not helpful.[260] The Ratebook for Little Chart shows a new entry in the second assessment for 1776 (Thomas Sweetlove £32).[261] In the first assessment for 1777 Sweetlove was assessed for £50 and in the second it was Munn's turn at £50. Henry Darrell, the owner, apart from a personal assessment against him for £75 was also assessed for "The Ford and mill land" at £5–10. Undoubtedly, there had been a mill of some sort on that site at an earlier date but, as in the case of Conyer mill (half in Little Chart and half in Hothfield) it may once have been a fulling mill that had fallen into disuse. There certainly had not been a paper mill there before Munn's arrival; the initial rise in the ratable value of the new paper mill, quoted above, indicates that building was in progress. It is of interest to note that the name Munn occurs in the parish registers in the 1720's, but it had disappeared by 1740. Munn was a name quite commonly found in Kent so that its appearance here has little significance beyond the remote possibility that these Munns might have been related in the past to the ones in North Kent and thus been a contributory reason for Lewis' choice of Little Chart.

Further details of Lewis Munn snr. and his family and connection with Lewis jnr. in Hertfordshire will be found in Appendix II. The mill after Lewis snr.'s death (1804) remained in the hands of the Munn family until ca.1814 when it passed into the hands of Edward Paine (see Conyer Mill below), the Munns transferring their papermaking activities to Hertfordshire and Norfolk. During the 19th C. the fortunes of the mill evidently declined until during the 1870's the mill was taken over by Joseph Batchelor, who described the place as being practically nothing more than farm buildings. Batchelor and Sons restored the mill so that it survived as an up–to–date mill into the 20th C. Although no longer in the hands of the Batchelors, the mill continued working until very recently (closed 1987) in a very highly specialised field of papermaking, manufacturing flong.[262]

Conyer Mill
(Little Chart/Hothfield)
(MR TQ 958460)

Only a brief mention will be made of this mill because it was a Brown mill during the 18th C. and therefore lies outside the scope of this work. The mill, long since disappeared, lay about a mile to the east and downstream of Ford mill on the Great Stour. In the 17th C. (1635) it had been a fulling mill belonging to Sir Anthony Dering at a time when Hothfield

---

[260]   Shorter, A. Bib.12 196 citing SFIP 411778 (26:Mar:1779). Munn was on his own by then and described as a paper maker and miller.

[261]   KAO P 82 12/1 and 12/2. The new entry appears between two quite substantial assessments, James Akehurst £18 and the Westwell meadows above and David Jenkins £16 below. These remain unaltered between 1774–79; Jenkins' assessment rose from 9/– to £16 in 1771.

[262]   The author had the privilege of visiting this immaculately clean and interesting mill in 1982.

was involved in the Broadcloth industry.[263] The mill lay on the parish boundary between Little Chart and Hothfield. Unfortunately, no church accounts have survived for the latter, so one has to rely on Little Chart's.

Thomas West snr. and jnr. are the only 18th C. Conyer paper makers that can be identified with certainty. The former was first assessed for the mill in 1740; it was also his first appearance in Little Chart (no Wests in Hothfield).[264] In the ratebook Thomas West's first assessment (£6 in 1740) is preceded by a similar assessment made against Mical Greatnail. From this it is not absolutely certain then that West was the first paper maker there; the fact that he took an apprentice and was described as a paper maker in 1743 confirms that he was a trained paper maker when he arrived in Little Chart.[265] But the uncertainty about Greatnail's trade raises the question as to whether one is witnessing another Goudhurst mill here, albeit a Brown mill in this case; or whether West arrived in Little Chart and converted an ailing fulling mill.

As always there is the problem, where did West come from ? and where did he receive his training ? He was having a family in Little Chart during the 1740's and there is no sign of a Thomas West burial up to the 1760's which suggests that he was a young man when he arrived there. It is a not uncommon name but it is perhaps worth mentioning that James West of Millhall mill[266] had a son Thomas (2) baptised in Aylesford in 1683, too old to have been the paper maker in Conyer; though it is possible that the latter may have been a grandson.

Finally, there are questions as to when or whether the mill was modernised and was it ever a White mill ? It continued as a paper mill into the 19th C., so one would expect some degree of modernisation to have taken place at an earlier date. This may have occurred in the 1770's, inspired by the example of Ford Mill. But whether it was ever a White mill is also uncertain. Two countermarks, "EDWARD PAINE LITTLE CHART 1810" and "EP 1811", have both been attributed to Paine at Ford and Conyer mills.[267] Paine is believed to have taken over Conyer mill ca.1809 and part of the mill certainly lay in Little Chart. But it is fairly certain (see App.II) that the Munn family retained control of Ford mill until ca.1814 and although Paine took this over eventually, it looks on the face of it as if Paine may have converted Conyer into a White mill ca.1809.

Padsole Mill
(Maidstone)

This mill has been included purely for the sake of completing the White paper mills built during the 18th C. in Kent and those in the Maidstone district in particular. It has nothing to do with the influence of the elder Whatman or with modernisation. In the rush to build paper mills towards the end of the 18th C. to meet the rapidly increasing demand for White paper, a very ancient mill (dating back at least to Richard II), formerly a fulling mill and later a corn mill, was converted from a very dilapidated state by one James Smyth into a paper mill in 1795/6.[268] Hollingworth initially had a share in this venture, but Smyth parted with his via Thomas Robert to Clement Taylor jnr. in 1798 just after he was made bankrupt.

[263] KAO P 195 28/3 "Antiquarian Notes" The Rev. H. Russell (1902). By 1780 Joseph Ashby appears to have been the proprietor, although Thomas West snr. still occupied property owned by Sir Edward Dering.
[264] Little Chart PRs. KAO P 82 1/1–6 : Hothfield PRs. KAO P 195 1/1–5.
[265] Shorter, A. Bib.12 196.
[266] See App.IV Millhall Mill.
[267] Shorter, A. Illustrates the 2 countermarks (Paper Maker and Brit Paper Trade Jo. 1959 Mar. 41/42)
[268] Spain, R.J. Bib.8 90/91. Gravell, T.L. Bib.68 Nos.639, 641 illustrates 2 "J SMYTH 1795 (1796)" countermarks.

In 1799 John Wise and John Hayes bought the mill from the Hollingworths. In 1805 it was Mr. Wise only; in 1810 Stacey Wise;[269] and in 1824 Wise and Brenchley. According to Spain in 1840 the mill was employed in an unsuccessful attempt to use a new papermaking fibre. In 1871 the mill was demolished, but later rebuilt as a flour mill; it had ceased making paper in 1846 (Excise General Letter). It is only noteworthy for its countermarks which include "H & W 1798"; "Hayes & Wise 1800"; "John Wise 1804"; "S Wise & Patch"; "S & C Wise"; and "Stacey Wise".

This completes the examination of the Maidstone mills, in which it can be seen that, indirectly, either through a Harris or William Gill jnr. connection the elder Whatman probably influenced the developments in the East Malling and Sandling areas and possibly at Upper Mill, Loose. Old Mill, Hollingbourne, the elder Whatman's memorial, can be seen as a very important centre for the training of White paper makers for the Kent industry and its expansion.

The modernisation of the Pine family's mills and that of Sittingbourne is a separate issue. Although it could be said to have been remotely connected with Quelch influence particularly in the later stages, the catalyst for change initially came in this case via the indirect course, described earlier, of the impact that Whatman's and Harris' innovations had on Stationers.

---

[269] In 1808 there was a brief partnership between Stacey Wise and Christopher Patch (see countermark). Shorter, A. Bib.7 (Apr.) 63. Christopher Patch jnr. was probably the son of Christopher snr. who had been MPM at Carshalton Lower mill (Surrey) d.1792 and was replaced there by Charles Ansell (the originator of the famous "C ANSELL" countermark auctioned in the first decade of the 20th C.). Patch jnr. formed a brief partnership with Stacey Wise in 1808 only to be dissolved in 1810. "C PATCH 1800" is found in Ightham Overseers' a/cs. KAO P 202 13/4.

PART VIII

MAINLY THE MILLS IN THE EAST KENT REGION AND THOSE REMAINING

Parts V–VII of this chapter have covered the paper mills in the North and West of Kent, Maidstone and Chafford in the South together with Ford and Conyer in the Eastern Region. This leaves eight mills in the East Kent Region and two in the South to consider. In the context of the theme of this book none of these mills, with the exception of Chartham mill, can be considered of much importance in this period. Several of these mills appeared at a late date in the 18th C. and it is more or less self–evident that they must have started their lives using the New Technology. This rather presupposes that they had some example in the district on which to model themselves. Others, although much longer established like Barton mill, Canterbury (17th C.); Buckland No.1 (Upper) mill (16th C.) and River No.1 mill (17th C.) both in the Dover area, were probably for most of their lives, if not entirely, Brown mills and thus only of secondary interest. All the same at some stage in their history they must have changed over to improved methods of stuff preparation and indirectly may provide clues as to the agencies that led to these changes. Did they, for example, relate in any way to those that had taken place earlier in other parts of Kent ? And by what means did these changes reach this Region ?

In considering these questions one has to take into account the geography and communications of this Region. From prehistoric times communications in Kent had been aligned along a roughly East/West axis and certainly from Roman times along Watling Street which from a general catchment area in Canterbury, arising from routes from the coast, passed through Sittingbourne and Dartford on its way to London. Curiously, though it must have been used by countless travellers to the Continent, part of the road between Canterbury and Dover was not turnpiked until after 1750 and the rest not until after 1780. In this sense then much of the East Kent Region must be seen as isolated, so far as land routes were concerned, from the papermaking activities in the rest of the County. Although by the 1790's paper makers like Edward Paine (Chartham), William Phipps (River), Austen Stace snr. and jnr. (Horn Street mill, Cheriton) and William Blackwell (South Kent) were attending meetings of paper makers in Maidstone (and later were corresponding with William Balston there),[270] there is no obvious sign of direct communication between the East Kent mills and the Maidstone district earlier than this and, at a guess, none at all in the 1740/50's. But they clearly knew of one another's existence.[271] Most of the early East Kent mills sent their paper to London by sea; and, if the paper makers themselves used a land route, their most direct road would have been along Watling Street. One would expect to find, therefore, that, if an effective form of the new Technology had not reached East Kent from other sources,

---

[270] A printed document recording Resolutions passed at a meeting of the Kent & Surrey paper makers at the Star Inn, Maidstone, 25:Feb:1796 with Nathaniel Davies as Clerk. William Balston took the Chair from ca.1798 onwards. The correspondence with William Balston is in the Master Paper Makers' Correspondence Collection (PSM).

[271] Possible examples of interregional movement in the early 18th C. have been mentioned in the cases of John Walter (m. to an Elizabeth Archer) and Thomas Radford of River No.1 Paper mill (See App.IV). Another more complex movement may be seen in the case of Peter Archer jnr. born in Boxley and ultimately converting Chartham mill (App.IV n.64). Others Willard/Wellard (App.IV Genealogy n.6); and Blunden (App.IV n.116).

information about it could have been picked up from the 1740's onwards at places along this route. Indeed, as events showed, this route was undoubtedly an important, if not the main, source of news that led to progress in the papermaking of this Region. One has to bear in mind though that initially the influence from the West would have been felt first by Chartham mill, which had been modernised to a degree by Peter Archer jnr. in 1732/3, and thence after a long interval by the mills along the coast; but, much later, as communications improved one can see the coastal mills making progress through more direct contact with centres like Dartford.[272]

As previously noted it is not known how effective Peter Archer's installation of two Engines in Chartham mill was compared to Whatman's and Harris' at Old Mill, Hollingbourne.[273] His early death may have brought this development to a near standstill and it will be seen in the pages that follow that it was to be another 30 years before White countermarked paper was produced at this mill. As it was, the mill had a rather chequered financial history from its starting point until the latter part of the 19th C. and with one noteworthy exception the occupants from Archer's day in the 1730's to William Howard in 1874 were either bankrupted or lived from mortgage to mortgage; and, in addition, they cannot be seen as having the same sort of driving force influencing the Region as some of the occupants of mills at Maidstone or in West Kent. The one exception, and even he only survived for most of his papermaking career with financial support from outside, was Leeds Paine. To judge from the Paine family's activities they seem to have been the most influential paper makers of this Region, very probably instrumental in bringing the mills in the Dover area up-to-date and, as seen earlier in this chapter, maybe converting Conyer mill for a short period from Brown to White Paper manufacture.

The paper mills of this Region will be considered in the following order; first, Barton mill, Canterbury, geographically at the centre and though possibly a nursery for many of its paper makers, as a production facility it was one of the least progressive; second, Chartham mill was undoubtedly the most important; third, the coastal mills in the Dover and Folkestone

---

[272] As discussed later in this chapter the Watling Street axis clearly influenced the succession at Chartham mill after Archer's death, at first just a trend difficult to focus precisely; but at the beginning of the 19th C. the influence of this axis on the whole Region becomes progressively more pronounced. In 1818 Chartham mill was acquired by William Weatherley and John Lane; Weatherley had a paper mill at Darenth and John Lane, his partner, was described as an "inn-holder" of Dartford. The latter would have been in a good position to pick up information of interest from passing travellers. Quite apart from the above, Dartford at the turn of the century had become and was to progress as an important centre for the future developments of the paper industry.

John Hall (son of William Hall, who had been a millwright there since 1755 but spending some of this time at Laverstoke, Hampshire) had established his blacksmith's shop in Dartford in 1785; Bryan Donkin F.R.S. who later developed the first viable model of the Fourdrinier papermachine had been apprenticed to him (and in fact was his brother-in-law through their wives). Hall was a man of many parts founding an engineering works at Dartford, had a paper mill at Horton Kirby (just south of Darenth), a gunpowder mill at Faversham and other interests (see Clapperton, R.H. Bib.75 App.V); he was responsible for the first papermachine reelers and paper guillotines. Another Dartford man was John Marshall, an important mould-maker and, later, a manufacturer of Dandy Rolls for the papermachine. All in all it was a nerve centre of the early 19th C. paper industry.

It is not surprising then to find John Phipps of the papermaking family at River one of the first paper makers in the country to install a new papermachine (1807) in his mill; and later John and Christopher Phipps inventing the Dandy Roll (1825) which Marshall, later, made for them. It is obvious that the Phipps were influenced by the activities at Dartford and one can easily visualize this kind of influence extending along this Watling Street axis back into the last decades of the 18th C. and to the paper industry in East Kent.

[273] This Chap. p.333.

districts; and, finally, the two mills in South Kent where information about their origin and history is very sparse.

Barton Mill
(Canterbury)

The early history of this mill has been discussed briefly in Chapter II and, again, when discussing the hand felt and Celia Fiennes' visit to the mill in 1697 in Chapter V[274]. It was assumed from the latter account, albeit a somewhat ambiguous reference to it, that White paper was made at this mill at times (though the City itself would almost certainly have made use of imported White paper for its principal records). The general impression one gains from the mill's later history is that it must have been a Brown mill for most of this period and a mill in decline. As the City of Canterbury increased in size, so pollution and other demands on the paper mill's water supplies would also have increased, making it difficult to compete with its rural neighbour Chartham. Additionally, its waterpower may also have decreased as appears to have been the case with other watermills along the lower reaches of the Great Stour. Whatever the determining factors were the paper side of this mixed mill ceased to function sometime between 1803–16; it had probably never been more than a secondary activity. Even as late as 1736 the paper mill was insured by a miller, John Deane,[275] and this was at a time when William Cooke was Master Paper Maker. In these circumstances it is difficult to discover to what extent the people named combined milling with papermaking. For instance, William Blunden "took over the mill" in 1754[276] but there is no indication in this announcement of his trade. Some Freemen Paper Makers had been apprenticed to William Cooke and a Ralph Blunden (decd.) *before* 1753; and by 1761 Ralph jnr., John and Mary Blunden were definitely in control of the paper mill.

There is nothing to suggest, as in the case of the Pine family's mills at Maidstone, that Barton mill played a similar role in the development of the Eastern Region's industry. It is true that at least 30 apprentices are listed among the Freemen Paper Makers of Canterbury between Gilmore (1664/5) and Stephen Steddy (1789). All of them were bound to paper makers at the mill with the exception of Gilmore and Wellard snr. who purchased their freedom indicating, perhaps, that they had come from outside.[277] A lot of them, whether made free by apprenticeship or patrimony, came from papermaking districts like the Dover area (mainly from River) and Milton (Sittingbourne); but whether they all returned to these districts has not been discovered.[278] Only three families emerge positively as being connected with the management of the paper mill for much of its history, the Wellards, Cookes and Blundens, the last taking over in 1754.[279] In 1781 Alan Greble, paper maker, insured *his* paper mill;[280] and in 1796, when the paper mill was advertised for sale as a Brown mill, the occupant was Thomas Kingsford, still there in 1803 but gone before 1816.[281]

[274] Chap.II p.54 and Chap.V pp.207/8.

[275] SFIP 70494 5:June:1736. See also PLATE 8 (Chap.IV) which demonstrates a further close link between Barton and Chartham.

[276] Kentish Post and Canterbury News Letter 13:Nov:1754.

[277] At this time there would have been only 2 papermaking centres in Kent along the Watling Street axis, at Dartford and in the Dover area. The name Richard Willard is to be found in both of these (though not necessarily associated with papermaking); see App.IV, Willard/Wellard genealogy n.6.

[278] List of apprentices supplied by Miss A.M. Oakley, Archivist, Cathedral, City & Diocesan R.O. (letter 3:July:1987). Shorter (Bib.12 198) mentions others which, if correct, would add to this total. Among them there was a Thomas White, freed 1761 by patrimony, who might have become the MPM. at Hay mills, Herefordshire ca.1764 or ditto at Rye mill, Buckinghamshire in 1788 ?

[279] App.IV n.116.

[280] SFIP 444178 16:June:1781.

[281] Present at the meeting of the Master Paper Makers held on 13:June:1803 (PSM). The genealogy of the Kingsfords has not been examined but it was noted that a Thomas was baptised in Buckland in 1779 s.o. William & Mary Kingsford; too young, however, for the Canterbury paper maker. Many Kingsfords were living in Canterbury at this time and it

(continued...)

Was this mill ever modernised ? As a Brown mill (it was advertised as such in 1754 and 1796) would it have needed new equipment for the kind of materials used in this class of paper ? It would be prudent to allow for a certain degree of modernising partly because of Celia Fiennes' reference to White (and where else could White have been made in East Kent in 1697 ? Dartford was the nearest White mill) and partly because an advertisement of 1793 stated that one of the Vats was used for making printings (normally classed as White).[282] Accepting this would the improvements have been early or late ?

In view of the proximity of Chartham paper mill (less than 5 miles away) the paper makers at Barton would undoubtedly have had opportunities of learning about the Engines that had been installed there either directly as a result of the Archer/Deane connection (John Deane, the miller at Barton was Peter Archer's contemporary and brother-in-law) or indirectly through movements in the workforce. As John Deane, whose father had been a millwright, would have known all about the conversion and installation at Chartham, it is perfectly reasonable to suggest that he might have introduced some form of Engine at Barton when he insured it in 1736; its task would not have been very demanding. On the other hand he was a miller and the paper makers (William Cooke et al.) may have been more hesitant particularly if they had delayed taking any action until after Peter jnr.'s death and seen his successors fail to make effective use of the new methods. No pointers to any improvement at Barton have come to light and the 1754 announcement only informs us that Brown and Ravel paper were for sale as usual (the latter may have been something like ravel bread incorporating coarse material like shive and chaff ?). TABLE XI reflects this uncertain situation. To judge from the mill's product range it seems unlikely that any more than a limited step towards modernisation in the full sense was ever undertaken, possibly modest improvements after the 1760's when Chartham began to use its equipment more gainfully. In other words one sees the paper makers at Chartham as being instrumental in bringing about any change at Barton rather than through any direct influence from some other source in Kent. The reason for this will become clear when Chartham's development is considered below.

Though an ancient mill Barton cannot be seen as contributing positively in any way to the progress of the paper industry. The best that can be said for it is that it appears to have provided training facilities for a lot of apprentices during its lifetime, though no paper makers of distinction.

---

[281](...continued)
seems fairly certain that the two lots were connected. Shorter refers to a letter written by Phipps (River mill) mentioning Thomas, 13:Apr:1796 (PSM).

[282] Shorter, A. Bib.12 393 citing notice in Kentish Gazette 1:Nov:1793, a two-vat mill with one Printing and the other in the Brown and Hand line.

The Table below has been compiled from extracts out of (1) the Dean and Chapter of Canterbury's Lease Books (1739–1832) [Lessees]; and (ii) the Overseers' Ratebooks U3/154 11/1–4 and the Church-wardens' Ratebooks U3/154 4/1,2 (1737–1818) [Occupants] held in the Cathedral, City and Diocesan Record office. The information was very kindly supplied by Miss A.M. Oakley, Archivist (10:June:1987)[1]

DATE	LESSEE	RATABLE VALUE	DATE	OCCUPANT	COUNTERMARK
1732–37	Peter Archer jnr.[2]	£10 (1737)	1732–37	Peter Archer jnr.[2]	
1738	(lease for sale)		1738–41	Mr. Short[3]	
1739–46	Alexander Nedriff (d.1746)[4] (London Rag Merchant)		1742–44	Daniel Jenkinson[5]	
		£14 (1745)	1745–49	Mr. Wackett[6]	
1746–53	Elizabeth Short (widow) of Deptford[7]		1750–57	Mr. William Herbert[8]	
1753–64	**WILLIAM PEARSON**[9] (Paper Maker, Horton mill Buckinghamshire)	£40 (1754)			
			1757–58	William Herbert & Edward Slater[10]	
		£80 (1762)[11]	1759–63	Edward Slater	
(1764)	Insured mill in tenure of... (SFIP 208349 9:Apr:1764)			Edward Slater & Co.	
			1763–77	Edward Slater &	
1765–74	Sarah Pearson of Windsor insured[12] mill (SFIP 214648 1:Jan:1765)			**LEEDS PAINE**[13]	"S & P" d.o.d.1767 (RIBA Drawing colln. L9 22/4).
1774	Francis Daniel (by assignment)				
1775–92	David Ogilvy of Datchet,[14] Buckinghamshire		1778–89	**LEEDS PAINE** (d.1790)	"L PAINE" d.o.d. 1784 (Gravell, T.L. Bib.68 552/3)
1792	Edward Paine (acquired lease from Ogilvy)		1790–95	Heirs of Leeds Paine[15]	"PAINE & SONS 1794" Letter Wm. Phipps to Wm. Balston 1796 (PSM); and Gravell, T.L. Bib. 68 554.
1795/6–99	George & Dean Raynor Pike & Edward Paine (partners)[16]		1796–98	The Pikes & Edw. Paine	"PIKES & PAINE 1796" (letter from Sir John Fagg to Wm. Balston on Whatman's death. PSM).
(1799)	(Paine sold his share)	£70 (1799)			
1799	Geo. & Dean Pike sold half [17] leasehold to Samuel Durrant Esq.		1799–1817	George Pike[18]	"G PIKE 1801" (MPM correspondence PSM)
1799–1806	George Pike acquired his brother's share				
1806	George Pike mortgaged his share to Durrant				
			1816 EGL	George Pike	
1817	George Pike sold his share to Durrant				
1818	Durrant sold leasehold to William Weatherley & John Lane[19]		1818	Weatherley & Lane	"WEATHERLEY & CO 1818" Gravell, T.L. Bib.68 744.
1822	William Weatherley		1822	William Weatherley	

1. The Dean & Chapter's Lease Book shows John Branch as Occupant (or late Occupant) up till Slater's time (1765); it is thought that he worked a fulling mill there from 1729 but for some unexplained reason he is shown as occupant during Nedriff, Short and Pearson's leases.
2. See Chap.II Table IV first mention of mill: Chap.IV p.133 phase III, Plate 8 & pp.140 ff. conversion of mill and early death; App.II Whatmans at Ospringe, Boughton–under–Blean and Chartham: App.IV (q.v.) the Archer Family, Peter Archer jnr.
3. Origin not traced, but IGI shows that it was a common name from Deptford (see widow's domicile) to East Kent; possibly Deptford?
4. Origin not traced, but IGI shows a Rebecca Nedriff at Deptford. Shorter, A. Bib.12 83 Notes 63–5 notes prevalence of rag dealers with premises along the Thames at Rotherhithe, Deptford etc. See also discussion in the text on William Pearson.
5. Origin not traced, but name common in Dartford, Canterbury and Sandwich.
6. Origin not traced, but possibly of immigrant descent? e.g. a Philipe Wacquet had daughters bapt. Canterbury 1629, 1634.
7. See Note 3 above; the Shorts and Nedriff may have been connected?
8. Origin not traced. Herberts noted in River; for others see Index, Paper Makers.
9. The reason for the Pearson family's long interest in Chartham paper mill is not known. For further details and discussion see text.
10. Herbert & Slater were bankrupted in Nov.1757, but Slater's certificate was allowed and he continued to work the mill until 1777.
11. All the assessments in Chartham were doubled in this year; the revaluation of the mill was not the result of a single enlargement.
12. Sarah Pearson also insured Coltnett mills, Wraysbury, Buckinghamshire (SFIP 237510 29:Sept:1766 : see also discussion in text).
13. Slater & Paine insured their utensils etc. (SFIP 209424 2:June:1764). For LEEDS PAINE see discussion in text.
14. Variously described as baker, gentleman and father-in-law to James (s.o. William) Pearson; see text for discussion.
15. The heirs were Elizabeth (widow), Edward and George (sons).
16. The Pikes may have had a Dartford origin (Shorter, A. Bib.12 180). Coleman, D.C. Bib.15 248 describes them as paper makers of Chartham.
17. Samuel & Mercer Durrant were also proprietors of Ockley mill nr. Hawkhurst (q.v.) Hawkhurst Land Tax KAO Q/RPI/167 Great Barnfield Ward.
18. The 1816 EGL shows Edward Paine at Ford & Conyer mills, Little Chart, this chapter pp.325/6; George Paine at Horn Street mill, Cheriton, Folkestone, see this chapter pp.346/7.   19.   For Weatherley and later history of mill and its financing see Coleman, D.C. Bib.15 248 ff.

CHARTHAM PAPER MILL

The history of this mill as a paper mill is regarded here as the key to understanding the modernising influence that affected the other paper mills in the Eastern region, this being distinct from modernisation resulting from a random evolutionary process that was no doubt the case with many mills in other parts of the British Isles. (Earlier references in this book to Chartham mill and its conversion by Peter Archer jnr. in 1732 are indicated in footnote 2 of Table XIV).

It has been assumed hitherto in this book that when Peter Archer jnr. converted this mill he installed two improved models of the Engine there. The installation took place only marginally before Whatman built his Hollingbourne mill where it is virtually certain an improved model had been installed and its operation mastered. Exactly what form these "improvements" took is not known; it might have been a heavier model; better control over the roll; a more effective ratio between energy demand and supply; any number of different factors could have formed the basis for an improved performance which in time matured at Turkey mill. The subsequent accomplishment of this at the latter, and at Old Mill under the Frenchs, proves this point.

In the case of Archer's installation there is an alternative interpretation for his move to Chartham. It will be recalled that he married Margaret Deane of Canterbury in 1708 and that his father-in-law, Robert, was a millwright there and that his mother-in-law came from Boughton-under-Blean, not far from Chartham. Clearly Robert Deane was familiar with many different watermills in that area, their condition and any prospects of a lease. The unknown quantity in this situation is Robert Archer also found at Sittingbourne. There are a number of different solutions to the question as to how he might have been related to Peter. Taking all the evidence that is available into consideration, it seems probable that he was Peter's elder brother and had precedence over him at Sittingbourne; and, as a consequence, when a lease became available, Peter decided to move and set up on his own. This could have been for family reasons, but the fact is that for one reason or another he made the move and could easily have installed two Engines in his converted mill that were merely repetitions of the one he had known at Sittingbourne with the result that effective up-dating of this mill was something that lay in the future. That there is some support for this suggestion can be seen in the slow progress that Chartham mill made after Peter's death in 1737.

On the other hand Peter Archer would almost certainly have had more water power at his disposal in his new mill than at Sittingbourne (and more spring water too); in addition considerable experience of operating Engines before he made the move; the fact that he installed two instead of one; and the conversion of this mill at such an unpropitious time are all considerations that support the notion that he was embarking on a technological advance which his successors do not appear to have been able to exploit to advantage for another 20 years.

In the event Peter died within four years of the mill being commissioned, leaving no heir to carry on his work. The fact that the lease of the mill was advertised for sale by his widow

TABLE XV – A COLLECTION OF MISCELLANEOUS INFORMATION & NOTES ON THE PEARSON FAMILY

At present all that is known with any certainty is that the Pearsons were paper makers at 2 mills in Buckinghamshire (1732–ca.1768), were lessees of Chartham paper mill (1753–92) and had other interests at times during this period.

The origin of William Pearson, the first member of the family recorded in this context, has not been discovered. His baptism does not appear in either the Wraysbury or Horton PRs.; no suitable candidates have been found in either the Buckinghamshire or Surrey IG Index. The only likely baptism found to date is:–

William s.o. William & Elizabeth Pearson of DARTFORD 1706

William & Elizabeth had had a previous son, William bapt.1702 who obviously had not survived. Further, from the information given in the Table below, it appears that William died 1764/5 and that Sarah must have been his widow.

DATE	COLTNETT MILL, WRAYSBURY	HORTON MILL	CHARTHAM MILL	MISCELLANEOUS
1732	John Crowder & William Pearson insured mill (SFIP 59511)[1]			
1737	Wm. Pearson took an apprentice, William Gill[1]			
(1745)	"CROWDER" Countermark[2]			
1753–64		(at Horton mill?) see under Chartham	Wm. Pearson paper maker of Horton lessee	
1758		In tenure of William Pearson, "the same who held the Wraysbury mills in 1760"[3]		
1762	Mary & John Crowder of Wraysbury and Wm. Pearson of Horton, paper makers insured their paper mill and corn mill			
1763		Thomas & James Pearson insured utensils & stock in the paper mill (SFIP 204962)		
1764				William Pearson, paper maker insured property (unspecified SFIP 207842) : must have died shortly after.
1765		Thomas Pearson insured "goods" (SFIP 216796).[4]	Sarah Pearson now lessee 1765–1774; insured house & mill (1:Jan:1765 SFIP 214648) described as "of Windsor".	
1766	John & Thomas Crowder of Wraysbury and Sarah Pearson of Windsor, millers and paper makers insured paper & corn mill under one roof (SFIP 237510. (Gone by 1769).			
1767		James Pearson probably working the mill; insured tenements in tenure of other paper makers		James Pearson insured his stock at Bull Wharf, Thames Street, (SFIP 243706 20:Mar:1767)[5]
1768		James Pearson bankrupted		
1770–73				A "Thomas Pearson" was at Wolvercote mill,
1775–92			David Ogilvy, father-in-law to James Pearson lessee.	Oxfordshire : countermark "T PEARSON" d.o.d.1773.[6]

1. Shorter, A. Bib.12 147. All other SFIP Policies listed in this Table are to be found in Bib.12.
2. Churchill, W.A. Bib.3 49. Gives no indication of provenance; assumed here to belong to Coltnett mill?
3. Gyll, G.W.J. "History of the parish of Wraysbury etc. and of Horton etc." (Bohn, London, 1862. 199).
4. Coleman, D.C. Bib.15 163 refers to Thomas & James Pearson carrying on in partnership at Horton "several trades and businesses of Paper Maker, Miller, Mealman and Farmer". (Messrs. Wiggins Teape were unable to help the author trace the MSS & Deeds referred to here).
5. Shorter, A. Bib.12 83 note 65.
6. It is not known whether the Wolvercote and the Horton Thomas Pearsons were one and the same person or not?

proves that there was no obvious continuity in the succession there.[283] Nothing positive is known about Mr. and Mrs. Short who took the mill over. He might have been a former employee there or related in some way to the Archers. The fact that Mrs. Short became lessee after Nedriff, a London Rag Merchant, certainly points to a more than passing interest in the establishment. All of them could have had a Deptford origin quite unconnected with the Archers, beyond the possibility that they may have supplied Peter and Robert with raw materials in the past (Deptford was an important centre for these) and thus seen opportunities for themselves in taking over his mill.

Table XIV illustrates (i) the lessees who succeeded Archer; and (ii) the occupants, the records also suggesting that there might still have been a fulling mill associated with the paper mill for a time (see Table XIV note 1). It will be seen that during the next 15 years (1738–53) there were no fewer than two lessees and four different occupants. Whether Short was a former employee or not, he must have died or retired by 1741 so that with such a rapid sequence of occupants it is not surprising to find that this new–built mill, allegedly modernised in 1732/3, left no mark. As indicated not a single origin of these early lessees and occupants has been traced with any certainty although the signs are that they may well have come from places lying on or near the Watling Street axis, Deptford, Rotherhithe, Dartford, and this indeed may be the key to understanding the next phase in the history of this mill. The view emphasised in earlier chapters that the Archers all belonged to the same family strengthens the notion that there was a more than casual link between Dartford No.2 with Richard as Master there and Peter jnr. at Chartham; and that this relationship persisted after their deaths, influencing events that were to shape the future of Chartham such as the arrival there of paper makers like Slater, Paine, the Pikes and Weatherley, all of whom are believed to have come from the Dartford area or close to the Watling Street axis.

Before discussing these paper makers, in whose hands obviously lay the potential to improve and maintain the reputation of this mill, an explanation must be put forward to account for the presence of the Pearson family who clearly had financial interests in the operation at Chartham, insured the premises for nearly 40 years and in whose power it was to maximise this potential.There was nothing particularly unusual in this situation[284] beyond the fact that this is one of the few examples among the mills in Kent where for the period between Archer and Edward Paine the paper maker at the mill may have been subservient to the requirements of the lessee; and, in the case of the Pearsons, the only mill that depended on another paper maker from another region altogether, namely to the West of London.[285]

The reason for the Pearsons' interest in Chartham has not been discovered; provisionally, a solution to this question that fits the known facts is proposed here. Table XV and Notes show that a William Pearson was born at Dartford in 1706. If he was brought up and trained there as a paper maker, then he would have known Richard Archer and quite possibly Peter jnr. at

---

[283] Neither Peter, nor his widow Margaret, appear to have made Wills. For Sale advertisement see Plate 8.

[284] Coleman, D.C. Bib.15 161–9 discusses the 18th C. financing of the paper industry.

[285] Other examples of Kent mills where some external control might have been practised are (i) those under the proprietorship of the Stationers, William Gill jnr. and Thomas Wright e.g. Forstal, Cobtree and Upper mill; (ii) those where Robert Wilson, another London Stationer, may have initially influenced the course of events e.g. Otham and Sittingbourne mills (q.v.); he also acted as mortgagee to begin with in Josias Johannot's venture at Cray valley mill, but probably acted more as a partner there than directing operations. It may be noted in this last context that parallel activities were taking place at Deptford paper mill in 1751 (this Chap. n.176.).

Sittingbourne. Pearson's first known appearance as a paper maker is at Coltnett mill, Buckinghamshire, in December 1732, for all intents and purposes simultaneous with Archer's move to Chartham. Although Churchill records a "CROWDER" countermark (see Table XV) from which one might infer that Coltnett mill was a White mill (not shown as such in Table X), Pearson's interests were evidently quite diverse and not confined exclusively to papermaking. Unlike Peter Archer he may not have been interested at that time in developing and applying, or indeed been aware of, the New Technology, despite the fact that he might have brought with him experience gained from using a primitive form of Engine at Dartford (assuming he worked there). Neither the history of Coltnett nor that of Horton mill suggest anything progressive taking place there during this period.[286]

If Pearson had been in close touch with Peter Archer and his new venture, then one might have expected him to have stepped in and taken over the lease of Chartham in 1738. However, he had left Kent before Phase III had got under way; but, because of a Kentish origin, one can envisage him at a later stage being interested in news from there, which he could have picked up when buying or collecting his rags from the Thames Street/Rotherhithe area; and, in particular, news that the Chartham lease was about to come up for sale. No doubt there are alternative hypotheses to this, e.g. the Pearsons and the Shorts may have been related etc. All the same it helps explain the rather surprising appearance of Pearson from Buckinghamshire as the lessee of Chartham mill in 1753.

The next question is, did Pearson make improvements to the mill ? Just after his arrival there the ratable value leapt from £14 to £40 suggesting that he did; for instance, he might have been responsible for up-dating the mill there with a new sizehouse or building, say, a capacious ragstore.[287] He had inherited William Herbert as an occupant and no doubt soon discovered that he was unsatisfactory, bankrupted three years later.

By 1753 the application and advantages of the New Technology must have become increasingly more widely known and Pearson, as a paper maker and with an allegedly modernised mill on his hands, no doubt wished to develop Chartham's potential. It has not proved possible to date to enlarge on Edward Slater (Herbert's successor) who made his appearance at this time. The only likely candidate discovered is an Edward baptised at Hoo in Kent in 1709,[288] a place close to the Watling Street axis and about mid-way between Dartford and Sittingbourne where, by this time, the paper mills had been modernised. There is no record of his apprenticeship but one might assume that he had received his training at one of these centres. Slater was to remain at Chartham for a further 20 years and was the senior tenant for this period. It was during his tenure that the first specimen of White countermarked paper to be identified from this source was made. From this one might deduce

---

[286] If one is to accept Shorter's account of these two mills (Bib.12 146/7) Coltnett mill, certainly at one stage in its history, was "a paper mill and a corn mill under one roof" and ceased papermaking between 1772–1844 and may, therefore, never have been modernised; and Horton, though a very ancient mill, does not suggest any up-dating before 1786 (see this Chap. Table X). In addition the Pearsons appear to have had interests not only in papermaking, but milling and farming in general, James' father-in-law being a baker as well.

[287] Shorter, A. Bib.12 85 note 96 quotes a reference saying that Chartham mill had "an extensive collection of country rags attached to the premises" (General Evening Post 27– 29:Nov.1798). It may also be noted that as from 1753, when Pearson first leased the mill, the Occupant entry in the Lease Book for what is thought may have been an associated fulling mill became "late John Branch".

[288] Eduardus f. Thomae & Mariae Slater bapt. 3:Apr:1709 at St. Werburgh, Hoo, Kent (MR TQ 783718).

that Slater had at least got the mill on to its feet again; but the successful manufacture of the countermarked paper is more likely to have originated from his partner, Leeds Paine, who joined him in 1763. This conclusion is based on what we know about Paine and his family.

Leeds Paine (1740–90) was born at Tenterden in Kent[289] and later apprenticed to John Terry of Dartford in 1756.[290] One can see at once that he could scarcely have had a better papermaking pedigree; in short yet another extension of the Quelch Empire. But it is not only from this that one sees the improving hand at Chartham but in his own and his family's later achievements. He was to become the sole occupant of Chartham in 1778 producing his own countermarked paper; he was without doubt responsible for the conversion of Henry Pain's corn mill at Buckland (near Dover) into Buckland No.2 paper mill ca.1770 (q.v.), that is while Slater was still active at Chartham; and his heirs continued to run Chartham for a further nine years after 1790, latterly in partnership with the Pikes, who also may have had a Dartford origin (Table XIV note 16). Finally, his sons, Edward and George, continued their papermaking careers well into the 19th C. at Little Chart[291] and Horn Street mill, Cheriton (near Folkestone) respectively. There is no need to continue with Chartham's history beyond this point except to note that the mill is still active to-day, albeit rebuilt, under the management of Messrs. Wiggins Teape.

To conclude, after a promising start under Peter Archer jnr. the mill went through a disappointing phase (1738–53). Pearson's obvious financial interest in this mill led to an improvement in its status culminating in the production of countermarked paper in the 1760's most probably due to Leeds Paine's influence[292] with Pearson's contribution seen as a directing role rather than technological. Table XI shows modernisation as parallel to Whatman's Old Mill, though it might be more accurate to represent it with a dotted line up to the 1760's.

THE COASTAL MILLS OF EAST KENT

It was a disappointment to discover after a disproportionately large effort had been devoted to unearthing the details of these mills that none of them are of much relevance to the subject of this book. Initially one could not be certain of this and the work was undertaken because it soon began to emerge that Shorter's account of these mills was inadequate on several counts and further investigations were considered necessary. This task was made more difficult due to the very patchy nature of the surviving parish records.[293] Mainly through the good offices

---

[289] Leeds s.o. Thomas & Margaret Pain 24:Oct:1740 at Tenterden, Kent. That this was the Leeds Paine in question is confirmed by the fact that the Kentish Gazette for 23–27:Apr:1790 reported that he died "on Sunday at Chartham in the 50th year of his age, Mr. Leeds Pain, papermaker".

[290] Apprentices of Great Britain (Soc.Genealogists) Book 20 fo.194.

[291] It is just possible that Leeds Paine and Lewis Munn (later of Little Chart q.v.) may have met at Dartford as young men in the early 1760's.

[292] One of the reasons suggested for Archer's move to Chartham was to obtain greater water power for his Engines. Among other reasons, one that was certainly important for the mill's later history, was the plentiful supply of spring water, said to be superior to any in the County (General Evening Post 27–29:Nov:1798).

[293] Conventional sources of information e.g. Poor Ratebooks are either non-existent or, as in the case of Buckland, fragmentary and unfortunately missing for the most important periods. In the case of the Stace family, the name of the first paper maker identified at Horn Street mill, Cheriton, the majority if not all of them were Baptists. Though records

(continued...)

of the East Kent Mills Group a number of valuable sources of new information on the mills concerned came to light, though with one or two exceptions the facts tended to be isolated and needed co–ordinating.[294]

During the 18th C. there were six paper mills that come within this group, a further two appearing in the 19th C. though the existence of one of these, River No.2, has been questioned:

Buckland No.1[295]	before 1600–present day	almost certainly a BROWN mill to ca.1820.
Buckland No.2	ca.1770–1846	WHITE
River No.1	ca.1689–1918	Blue and BROWN up to 19th C.; printings by 1852; later real cartridge paper.
Crabble mill	1791–1895	BROWN and Logwood
Bushey Ruff	ca.1791 brown ca.1794 white – ca.1850	mixed BROWN and low grade WHITE
Horn Street Cheriton	ca.1771–1868	WHITE from the 1780's.

Two points emerge from this list (i) that there were only two truly WHITE mills among them producing countermarked papers and neither of them produced these before the 1770/80's; and (ii) it is virtually certain that the first mill to be up–dated was Buckland No.2, built on the site of an old corn mill in 1770, that is 30 years after modernisation had taken place in mills at Maidstone and in the Basted and Dartford centres. This confirms the impression that although there were two mills with a long history in this group[296] taken as a whole this area was little more than a backwater compared to the paper industry in other parts of Kent during the 18th C. In fact a painting of Buckland No.1 paper mill made in 1770[297] shows it to have been little more than an average sized domestic house with a waterwheel attached, in Mr. Welby's words showing that "the Horn family's papermaking business was still a cottage industry" as indeed River mill must have been at this time also.

[293](...continued)
of their marriages have survived between 1726–1837 (Folkestone Publ. Libr.) they do not appear to throw any light on their papermaking activities.

[294] The main sources of information were (i) Lambeth Palace Library for early history of Buckland No.1 mill (search carried out on author's behalf by Mr. Simeon Clarke A.G. & R.A.); (ii) Overseers' Accounts, St. Andrews, Buckland, and Thomas Horn's Will (1750) inf. Mr. Michael Heenan, Genealogist; (iii) Inf. Buckland No.2 mill from the late Mr. C.P. Davies; (iv) The River, Crabble and Bushey Ruff mills inf. from Mr. Douglas Welby (author of "The Kentish Village of River" Crabwell Publications, 1977) together with other 19th C. inf. on all the mills in the Dover area; the Phipps Deeds of River (1689–1827) KAO U 47/28 T1; (v) Shorter, A. Bib.12 199/200; and the author's own searches. Much general information on the mills in the area was also provided by the late Mr. C.P. Davies of Cheriton.

[295] This mill collapsed in 1664 and was rebuilt in 1676 (Lambeth Palace Library Records); "suffered a fire" ca.1790 and was rebuilt and enlarged; burnt down in 1810, rebuilt and considerably enlarged; and in 1887 a fire destroyed much of the mill; acquired by Wiggins Teape in 1890 and extensive additions made in 1893 (inf. Welby). These facts are given merely to illustrate that during the four centuries of its existence as a paper mill the premises were clearly altered beyond recognition.

[296] Welby believes that River No.1 may have been a paper mill long before 1789, the first documented reference to it, and being worked as such by the Hatton family in the 1660's. He has also pointed out that Thomas Chapman usually associated with Buckland No.1 mill in 1638 (Chap.II n.17) is found living in River a year later, but this last could have been due to the fact that his wife came from there.

[297] A painting by T. Forrest "Buckland Paper Mill from the Churchyard" (1770) kindly brought to the author's attention by Mr. Welby.

In spite of the late development of papermaking technology in this area (and in some respects it made up for this in the early decades of the 19th C.)[298] and the generally low grades of paper produced there, a brief account of these mills is given below more for the sake of completeness than any technological significance in their papermaking operations.

Buckland No.1 Paper Mill
(River Dour)
(MR TR 304427)

As mentioned in Chapter II this was one of the oldest paper mills in Kent, founded sometime before 1600, though there is no evidence that it produced any White paper before 1820 at the earliest. Coleman believes that the abundance of cordage and sails in the nearby port may have led to the founding of a Brown mill in the Dover area; his port book evidence of paper being shipped from here in the 1660's probably refers to paper produced at this mill (but there is the remote possibility that River No.1 mill may also have been operating by then).

The 18th C. Records for this mill are far from complete. Using a combination of leases[299] and fragmentary Overseers' Accounts[300] it can be shown that the mill was leased to the Hatton family from 1720–43 and that sometime before 1750 (the next lease) Thomas Horn, a millwright of Dover, became the occupant, the Accounts suggest the year 1749.[301] Nothing is known about the paper makers. Shorter mentions a John King, paper maker, who was married there in 1705 and two entries in the Overseers' Accounts confirm his presence in the area in 1706, otherwise no mention of him between 1696–1713.

Thomas Horn died in 1750[302] and the lease of the paper mill passed to his son, Ingram (d.1783), and thence to a grandson Thomas, who bought the mill from the Archbishop of Canterbury in 1799 and continued to run it until he auctioned it in 1820. The Horn family, therefore, held it for a considerable period in its history and very probably the youngest Thomas modernised it after the fire in 1790 when it was rebuilt and enlarged. The 18th C. valuations tend to support this assumption as also the previous comments made on the 1770 painting of the mill referred to above.[303] Accordingly the up–datings shown in Table XI reflect this proposal, 1790 + .

Of its later history it is perhaps worth mentioning two of the occupants. In 1822 the mill was in the hands of the reckless George Dickinson[304] who installed a paper machine (an advertisement of 1838 claimed that by that date it had three machines); Dickinson was bankrupted in 1837, the mill being occupied for a time by the Devisees of Thomas Horn. It is also of interest to note that between 1846–9 the mill was occupied by a Mr. Weatherley, brother of William at Chartham.

[298] This recovery was mainly due to the activities of the Phipps family at River. John Phipps was one of the first Kent paper makers to install the new Fourdrinier papermachine (Clapperton places him two years earlier than Buttanshaw at West Peckham; but Coleman, D.C. Bib.15 Table XV opp.p.196 indicates that both were licensed in 1807). This installation seems to have set the pace for this group of mills, George Payne (s.o. Leeds Paine) installing a machine at Cheriton in 1822; Christopher Phipps at River No.1 by 1825 (as shown by a plan of the mill); and George Dickinson at Buckland No.1 ca.1824 etc.

[299] Lambeth Palace Library TA 560/2–13.

[300] Canterbury Cathedral, City and Diocesan R.O. Buckland Overseers' Accounts 1682–1763.

[301] First assessment in the Overseers' Accounts made against Thomas Horn, 1711 for £2, shows that he had some interest or property in Buckland at that time. But it is not till 1749 that the assessment rose to £9 (the same year that Henry Pain, see Buckland No.2 mill, first appears in the book assessed at £8 + £2).

[302] Canterbury Consistory Court 63/262 proved in 1750. In this Thomas left the leaseholds of Buckland to his son Ingram and Charlton corn mill to Thomas. The two properties belonged to the Archbishops of Canterbury.

[303] Lambeth Palace Library TC 7, 10. These show that in 1641 the value of the paper mill was £14 (Charlton Corn mill £16); in 1682 the values were respectively £20 and £12; in 1785 the two combined were valued at only £38.

[304] Younger brother of John Dickinson of Apsley, Nash and Batchworth mills in Hertfordshire; for further details of George's career see Dr. Joan Evans' "The Endless Web" (Cape 1955 25/26).

(It was stated earlier that two further paper mills made their appearance in this area during the 19th C., one of these, River No.2, will be discussed later; the other, known as Spring Gardens, was set up by George Dickinson in the 1830's and operated for a short time in Dover, see Note 304 ref. to "The Endless Web").

Buckland No.2 Paper Mill
also known as Lower Mill
(River Dour)
(MR TR 308425)

Among this coastal group this mill is the most interesting in the context of *modernisation in the 18th C.* It was noted in the account of Buckland No.1 mill (this Chap. n.301) that Henry Paine, the owner of this mill, made his first appearance in the Overseers' Accounts (£8 + £2) in 1749. In 1747 he had married the widow of the previous owner, William Kennet. Henry was a miller; his origin has not been traced, but could have been local.[305] It seems certain that he was related in some way to Leeds Paine (b.Tenterden).

The first documentary evidence of the paper mill is an Insurance Policy, Henry Pain, miller, insured a paper mill in the tenure of Leeds Pain, paper maker, in 1770, the latter insuring his stock and utensils later in the same year.[306] A Deed of 1775 confirms that the paper mill was "lately erected" and that it had been built on the foundations of a very old corn mill adjacent to a fairly old established corn mill (evidently the one Pain had inherited from Kennet) both using the same mill pond.[307]

The fact that there were two mills there is borne out by Henry Pain's next Policy, taken out in 1783, when as a miller he insured a corn mill and a paper mill at Buckland, the tenant of the latter not being named.[308] As Leeds Paine had been in sole charge of Chartham mill since 1777, the occupant of the Buckland mill must have been an unknown paper maker appointed by him (no ratebook to supply the information).[309]

Leeds Paine died in 1790 and the next news of this mill is an advertisement for its sale in 1794.[310] Henry Pain died ca.1795 and in the same year William Kingsford must have taken over the paper mill; a countermark "K DOVOR 1795" bears this surmise out.[311] It is quite possible that William Kingsford had been the paper maker at Buckland before this date as the Parish Registers show that a William and Mary Kingsford were having a family in Buckland as early as 1779. Kingsford was at a meeting of the Master Paper Makers in 1803 (PSM)[312] and the 1816 EGL also records him as being at the Buckland mill. The history of this mill has not been pursued further than this point except to note that it was offered for sale together with adjoining properties in 1846 and closed down that year.

---

[305] With a name as commonly found as this one might search endlessly, but it has been noted that Henry Pain baptisms are recorded in the Ringwould PRs (just over 5 miles NE of Dover) for 1711, 1715 and 1724, all of which would fit in with the Buckland Henry.

[306] Shorter, A. Bib.12 199 citing SFIP 281986 (5:Mar:1770) and 288710 (6:Sept:1770).

[307] Inf. late Mr. C.P. Davies.

[308] SFIP 482993 (26:Sept:1783).

[309] In 1774, although still the owner, Henry Pain had given up working the corn mill to run a baking business in Dover (Davies).

[310] Kentish Gazette 18:Nov:1794. The mill was described then as "in the occupation of Henry Pain", but clearly not as a paper maker.

[311] Shorter, A. Bib.12 263 No.96.

[312] Gravell, T.L. Bib.68 Nos.462/3 illustrates a "WILLIAM KINGSFORD 1803" countermark in an American document; a capital "N" is incorporated with the Fleur de Lys of the watermark.

The points to note about this account are:-

(i)   It was clearly built as a paper mill in 1770 and this must have been carried out by Leeds Paine who would have had some 14 years experience of the New Technology by that date. One can assume, therefore, that the paper mill was equipped for this when it was built; and, moreover, almost certainly the first example in this area. Table XI shows this.

(ii)   Although no countermarks can be associated with this mill before Kingsford's of 1795, it is clear that the mill was built with the object of making White paper.

(iii)   The question might be asked, why did not Leeds Paine's heirs carry on working this mill after their father's death ? For one thing the mill belonged to Henry Pain and was not theirs; in addition the site was never a very satisfactory one. At a much later date it is known that the mill had problems in obtaining access to a source of water power. This might have taken place when Henry Pain's property was sold in 1795. The 1846 sale advertisement makes it clear that the "Freehold Paper Mills" would be sold without any right of water power; indeed it had already been driving some of its machinery by means of a longshaft running through an adjacent brewery.[313]

Alternatively, if Henry Pain had installed Kingsford (in place of Leeds Paine) in the 1770's, Edward and George Paine may have had no other option but to look elsewhere for their future,[314] moving to Cheriton; and, after Edward had transferred his interests from Chartham, to Little Chart. In fact at Horn Street the Paine family remained there until the mill was closed in 1868 (q.v.).

---

[313]   Letter from the late C.P. Davies (1:Nov:87). A waterwheel acquired from Bushey Ruff mill (q.v.) was connected to the paper mill by a shaft that passed through Harding's Wellington Brewery.

[314]   It may be noted that according to Welby, D. "The Kentish Village of River" (Crabwell Publications, 1977. 126) both William Phipps and his brother, John (1759–1835 : note no children), "had connections with Lower Buckland Paper mill", the former ca.1792, clearly only for a short time since he was back again at River No.1 mill in 1792 (q.v.); but the latter, John, may have been at Buckland No.2 mill before 1790 since he took out a Patent in that year for making lined Writing paper, which he would not have been able to make at the River mill. This, however, does not obviate the notion that Kingsford may have been a or *the* (Master) Paper Maker at Lower Buckland mill.

River No.1 Paper Mill
(River Dour)
(MR TR 291436)

Similar to Buckland No.1 paper mill River No.1 was another ancient Kent paper mill; almost certainly up to the 1790's it could be described as a cottage industry making brown and blue paper; and probably only up–dated during the 1790's. As a result it has little claim on our interest, but a brief summary of its history is given below mainly for the sake of providing a focal point for references to various paper makers mentioned in this book. The most complete history of the mill can be found in Mr. Welby's book "The Kentish Village of River".[315]

1609	Described as a fulling mill.
1689	Sale document describes it as "now used for a paper mill".
ca.1690	In the hands of the Hatton family.
1704	Passed into the hands of the Sturgis family.
[1714]	Thomas Bannister, paper maker of River, was made free by apprenticeship at Canterbury. The only evidence that suggests that he might have returned there is in Reads Weekly Journal or British Gazetteer 26:May:1733 which mentions him as a
[1733]	paper maker of River.
1717	John Walters (sic) is recorded as a paper maker at River. In Katherine Sturgis' Will of that year she left him (as tenant of the paper mill) £5, the inference from this being that he had perhaps been there for some time. The question as to whether he came from Aylesford and had married Elizabeth Archer is discussed in App.IV The Walters and Elizabeth Archer p.143. Certainly his first wife was Elizabeth buried at River ca.1737/40.
1719	John Walters took an apprentice Thomas Langley.
[1735]	Thomas Radford m. Sarah Lamber at River. The question as to whether he might have been the grandson of Thomas and Jane, who had a daughter baptised in Boxley, 1683, and who Shorter suggested[316] might have been a paper maker there, is also discussed in App.IV (The Radfords) as also the fact that he might have followed Walter to River.
1742	Documentary evidence that the paper mill was leased to Thomas Radford by Isaac Hammond.
1756	Radford's lease renewed by Proprietors Simmons and Groombridge. In the same year the paper mill was sold to Thomas Radford and his wife, Sarah.
1760	Thomas Radford died aged 50 i.e. born "somewhere" in 1710 and, if connected with the Boxley Radford, can only have been a grandson.
1764–74	A bad time for the mills; Sarah Radford took out two mortgages on the property (unlikely that this was connected with any modernisation of the mill).
1780	William Phipps, journeyman paper maker, became Sarah's tenant,[317]
[1765]	William having married Sarah's daughter, Sarah (1745–77), in 1765.

---

[315] Crabwell Publications, 1977, 125 ff. (also private communication 22:Aug: and 7:Dec:1987); and in the Phipps Title Deed KAO U 47/28 T1.

[316] Shorter, A. Bib.12 57.

[317] No relationship has been discovered between William Phipps (Kent) and Christopher Phipps who insured Sarratt paper mill, Hertfordshire, 1742-1759. William Phipps of River had a brother Christopher (1749–1831) not in papermaking and a son, Christopher; these facts suggest that there may have been some connection.

ca.1780	The mill was sold to William Phipps and John Aldridge.
1782	Phipps and Aldridge were bankrupted; property bought by Israel Claringbould.
1784	Mill leased to a Mr. Low. In the meantime Phipps' fortunes improved; he was connected in some way with Lower Buckland mill (still under Henry Pain) and must have gained some experience of the New Technology there. In addition Phipps had established Crabble mill (see below) as a paper mill.
1792	Phipps once more the occupant of River No.1 paper mill.
1800	Phipps acquired River No.1 from Claringbould. Early in the 19th C. John Phipps (b.1782) had become a forward looking paper maker and acquired one of the first Fourdrinier machines installing it in Crabble mill (see below). Also in the first decade Phipps countermarks start appearing in White paper (for discussion see River No.2 below).
1816	The Excise General List records William Phipps & Sons at three mills, two at River and one called "Crabhole".
1819	William Phipps snr. died leaving his business to Christopher (b.1790) and John.
ca.1825	Christopher Phipps installed a papermachine at River.[318]
1918	Final closure of mill. For remaining history see Welby (op.cit.). The mill remained in the hands of the Phipps family up until ca.1894.

As mentioned, during his brief connection with Buckland No.2 mill between 1784–92 William Phipps obviously became familiar with the New Technology and when he returned to River No.1 he up–dated it, the period indicated in Table XI. The evidence points, however, to it being a Blue and Brown mill well into the 19th C. Shorter cites a letter of 1796[319] stating that William Phipps had been a paper maker "in the blue and brown line" for over 16 years.

The industry was experiencing problems in labour relations and between 1789–96 Phipps reported that journeymen had consistently refused to work in mills where Irish and Scottish paper makers were employed on account of the lower wages paid to them compared to those in force in Kent.[320]

River No.2 Paper Mill
(19th C. only ?)

> The existence of this mill has been questioned by Welby who has not found any documents that might confirm this claim. But the inescapable fact is that the Excise Records list two Phipps mills (Nos.30, 31) at River in 1816 quite distinct from their paper mill at Crabble (No.29). It is possible that this mill only had a short history; that it was a 19th C. extension

---

[318] As mentioned in note 272 John and Christopher Phipps invented the Dandy roll, a light wire–covered de–watering roll used near the end of the Fourdrinier papermachine wire, imparting to the wet web look–through characteristics required in the finished sheet, in 1825. (John & Christopher were sons of William snr. by his second marriage, to Ann Claringbould in 1781: William jnr. by his first).

[319] Shorter, A. Bib.12 401. The letter is in the PSM.

[320] See this Chap. p.262 & Coleman, D.C. Bib.15 263.

of their business; and that it had ceased to function sometime before 1832 when the contemporary Excise letter refers only to No.31 at River.

It is suggested here that it may have been annexed to River No.1 mill.[321] The reason for suggesting this is that No.1 mill was clearly a "dirty" mill which had been making, and probably continued to make in the 19th C., blue and brown papers thus rendering the mill unsuitable for the manufacture of White. The existence of a White mill (No.2) would explain the occurrence of White papers bearing Phipps countermarks without having to recourse to the notion that William Phipps had these made for him at another mill.

The countermarks themselves suggest that the papers were the result of a separate operation, that is if one assumes that after John Phipps had come of age (1803) he was responsible for running Crabble mill and installing the papermachine there in 1807. The Phipps countermarks bear the title "PHIPPS & SON" (son in the singular)[322] implying that William and Christopher ran the River mill(s).

One might speculate further that the original River Paper mill had managed to get by using primitive pulping equipment since the materials it used were in a rotten state. Crabble mill had obviously been modernised from the time it was built (1791); but the River mill may have been modernised only in stages. The introduction of an up-to-date Engine there would have given them the ability to process the much stronger materials (rags) used in White paper, but not required for their blue and brown products. So one might envisage temporarily a small White mill adjacent to the Brown (outlined in Note 321 below). Table XI does not distinguish between River No.1 and 2 mills, but suggests that the mill there had perhaps incorporated a modern Engine by the end of the 18th C.

Crabble Paper Mill
(MR TR 299430)

The history of this mill does not really concern us, but to place it in context with the others the Universal British Directory of ca.1791 refers to it as "lately erected" and it was insured by Phipps in 1792.[323] It was in this mill that John Phipps installed his papermachine in 1807. Apparently (Welby op.cit.) the Brown (logwood) paper made on this machine, though reeled, was always cut into sheets by hand and loft dried. After it had shut down in 1895, the mill was rebuilt and used as a rag preparation plant by Messrs. Wiggins Teape. After World War II war damage was made good and the premises since used as a storage depot.

One might say almost by definition this mill was "modernised" when it was built.

---

[321] In "The Kentish Village of River" Welby illustrates (p.127) a plan of River mill in 1825. A Survey of 1821 described the property as a two-vat mill with a drying loft over, with an Engine room next door to it. The 1825 plan shows that by that time a papermachine had been installed alongside vats with a drying loft over and on the other side of the river a store room and salle with another drying loft over; in addition the premises included a sizing room (more usual for White paper manufacture) and two raghouses. One can easily imagine that the 1821 survey represented the mill in a stage of transition and that the two vats had originally been where the storeroom is shown in the 1825 plan and that the White mill, with the Engine adjacent, had lost its vat-room in readiness to receive the papermachine together with the vats resited. On this basis the White mill must have gone *before 1821*.

[322] Springfield collection (PSM) Other Makers pack "PHIPPS & SON 1807 and 1808" (Laid); Pack 8 "PHIPPS & SON 1810"; Gravell, T.L. Bib.68 No.558 "PHIPPS & SON 1808". Among the Master Paper Makers' Correspondence (PSM) there are two letters from William Phipps; the first dated 1796 bearing the stereotype "GR"; the second of 1799 is countermarked "PAINE & SONS 1794"; but in the Springfield Collection (PSM) Pack 8 there is a letter to William Balston from a Richard Cowper of London marked "WP 1804" which might represent William Phipps on his own as Christopher (b.1790) would only have been 14 then.

[323] A stone inscribed TLJ 1788 found recently in one of the more modern buildings of this mill is thought to have come from the neighbouring Crabble Farm owned then by Thomas Lamb and thus does not indicate that the paper mill was built in 1788.

Bushey Ruff Paper Mill
(River Dour)
(MR TR 283436)

This paper mill was sited further upstream than River mill on the Dour. Shorter has recorded[324] that a Richard C. Wakefield insured it as his paper mill in 1795. Welby[325] refers to written evidence recorded in the Dover Telegraph of 1856, arising out of a contemporary dispute over the ownership of nearby land, in which two locals (one of them formerly an apprentice at Bushey Ruff mill) state that a Brown mill was built first, ca.1791, to which a White mill was added ca.1794. It also appears that the first mill was driven by a centrifugal wheel but later replaced with an overshot wheel ca.1794/5 as the former had proved unsatisfactory. It was not a noteworthy mill as an Insurance Survey of 1815 cited by Welby described it as a "miserable place". A plan of 1825 shows that the mill was carefully divided into White and Brown departments; and other surveys indicate three vats making Brown and what can only have been low grade White.

It is assumed here that the mill was erected in the first place by Wakefield who was still there in 1796 but moved soon after to Folkestone.[326] He was replaced before the end of the century by William Knocker, there by 1803, still there in 1816 (EGL) but gone by 1823. For a very short period this mill (and Horn Street mill, Cheriton q.v.) was occupied by Cooper, Packham & Co. who were bankrupted in 1824. They were succeeded there by George Dickinson until he was bankrupted in 1837. The mill closed down ca.1850.[327] On the basis of the above it might be said that the mill was not effectively modernised until the overshot waterwheel had been installed i.e. 1794/5.

Horn Street Mill
(Cheriton, Nr. Folkestone; on the Seabrook Stream)

A White mill, probably the more important of the two coastal mills, but its origins are not known though the history of the locality points to a mid to late 18th C. one. Unlike Dover the port at Folkestone did not make a real contribution to the prosperity of the town until the latter part of the 18th C. It had been an important centre ever since Roman times and, in fact, had later been one of the Cinque ports. In spite of this, due to the encroaching sea its port facilities had declined until steps were taken in the 17th C. to remedy this state of affairs. Even so shipping and fishing made little impact on the place until the latter part of the 18th C., a situation unlikely to have stimulated the early founding of a paper mill there.

The first documentary evidence for the existence of the paper mill is a 1781 settlement examination concerning a paper maker, John Millbourne, of South Stoneham (Hampshire) who, it was claimed, had been apprenticed to John Stace in the parish of "Sharington" (Kent) ca.1771,[328] the inference being that John Stace had been a paper maker in Cheriton at that date and that he, in turn, must have been trained somewhere as a paper maker before 1771. The Stace family were well established in the district[329] and it is, therefore, not

---

[324] Richard C. Wakefield, described as a paper maker, insured his mill SFIP 638170 (6:Feb:1795). He appeared at a Master Paper Makers' meeting on the 25:Feb:1796 (PSM).
[325] Private communication from Douglas Welby (letter 29:Jan:88).
[326] Richard Castlerow Wakefield was married in Folkestone in 1796, settled and had a family there.
[327] Inf. D. Welby op.cit.
[328] Shorter, A. Bib.12 200.
[329] Davies, C.P. (letter 20:Oct.87) pointed out that 31 Stace marriages between 1726–1837 appear in the printed Canterbury Marriage Licences. There is also a Stace family history in the Folkestone Public Library including photostats of the Mill Bay Chapel Registers (in part); the Staces were mainly Baptists. There is no indication there as to where they learnt papermaking.

unreasonable to assume that John Stace might have learnt his papermaking in the Dover area as a maker of Brown paper.[330] The increased activity in the port must have led to a corresponding increase in the supply of cordage and canvas and prompted the Staces, who were millers, to exploit this situation.

It is clear from other records that the Staces had a paper mill in Cheriton during the 1770's;[331] taken together these facts point to John and Austen Stace being brothers who had a joint interest in the paper mill. For instance, the Land Tax Returns for 1780–82 record John Stace as proprietor and occupant[332] and an insurance policy of 1781 was taken out by Austen Stace for his corn mill and paper mill.[333] This dual interest is reflected in later records as well.[334] By 1796 Austen Stace snr. and jnr. were the paper makers in control.[335] A countermark in the Hothfield Land Tax Return for 1804 shows that they were still there;[336] but by 1806 a John Norwood, a paper maker from River, had bought the mill. He was bankrupted in 1811 and sometime between then and 1816, as shown by the Excise List, George Paine from Chartham had taken over (for a summary of the later history see below).

Though Horn Street may have started as a Brown mill, it had turned over to White during the 1780's (see note 332) when the increasing prosperity of Folkestone would have created a local market. "A STACE [date]" countermarks in the 1790's are not uncommon[337] and despite the absence of a contemporary Ratebook for Cheriton to confirm any change in assessments, it is thought that the first effective use of the New Technology would not have been before the 1780's (Table XI).

There is one other technical point that is of interest. Shorter[338] refers to Hasted's comment in 1790 that the paper and corn mills at Cheriton were worked at times both by wind and water. Davies[339] on the other hand could see no good reason for believing that the paper mill had any need for windpower. The Seabrook stream powered three mills.[340] He suggested instead that if the water had been "worked down" at Horn Street (presumably referring to well water), then the paper makers may have resorted to "working it down" at Seabrook windmill about a quarter of a mile distant. There is no doubt that the Staces worked a corn and a paper mill, but there is nothing to suggest in the insurance policies that these were under the same roof. The Cheriton Land Tax Returns on the other hand show only one entry (per annum) for Stace property.

---

[330] The IGI records that a John Stace underwent "Adult Baptism" at St. Mary the Virgin, Dover, in 1746.

[331] Inf. Davies. Austen Stace was married to Hannah Hill at St. John's, Southwark in 1775. He was described as living at Cheriton and had a paper mill there (Davies was at pains to point out that this did not prove that he was making paper at Horn Street). His son, Austen jnr. was born in 1778.

[332] Cheriton Land Tax Returns KAO Q/RP1/79. The Returns for 1790 and 1793 show that Austen was not only the proprietor/occupant and Assessor but that they also bear "AS" within the surround of Britannia watermarks.

[333] SFIP 446113 (19:July:1781).

[334] After 1786 the Cheriton L.T. shows Austen Stace (propr.)/himself (occ.); whereas Shorter (Bib.12 200) cites the Universal British Directory for ca.1791 stating that John Stace was the paper maker at the mill.

[335] Master Paper Makers of Kent & Surrey meeting on 25:Feb:1796 (PSM).

[336] Hothfield Land Tax KAO Q/RP1/187 for 1804 "A STACE"; also a printed notice of MPM Resolutions for 13:June:1803 lists Austin (sic) Stace.

[337] Apart from "AS" marks (note 332) several "A STACE" marks are found in the PSM or mentioned by Shorter and Gravell. The latter (Bib.68 no.31) also illustrates an "AS" mark (d.o.d.1796) which in the author's view is dubious. The "A" has a depressed cross-bar usually characteristic of German marks; the Crown is also unusual.

[338] Shorter, A. Bib.12 62 note 8 citing Hasted (1790) III.391.

[339] Letter 6:Aug:1987.

[340] Davies' words "a significant source of power"; see further comment in text on the new waterwheel installed there in 1822(?).

Summarising the information presented above:–

ca.1771	Horn Street paper mill active probably making Brown paper under John Stace.
1775	Austen Stace m. in Southwark; domicile Cheriton with a paper mill there.
1781	Austen Stace, miller and paper maker insured his corn mill and paper mill.
1780–82	John Stace/himself Cheriton L.T. (tax £15–3).
1783–85	John Stace/Austen Stace.
1786 +	Austen Stace/himself (tax £15–3) Austen Stace the Assessor.
1790	Austen Stace took an apprentice Wm. Hendon Harlestone (Davies).
1790's	First "AS" countermarks.
1791	UBD states John Stace paper maker at Horn Street.
1796–1803	Printed notices mentioning Austen Stace.
1806	John Norwood, paper maker of River, bought Horn Street mill (Davies citing WPTR. 20:0ct:1948 Thos. Ash b.River 1740 and worked at the mill, his dtr. Martha m. John Norwood b.1767 who also worked at River & Buckland mills and then bought Horn Street).
1811	Norwood bankrupt.
1816	George Paine (from Chartham) occupant.
1822	George Paine installed a Fourdrinier paper machine in his two–vat mill. Davies has suggested that a breast wheel 32 ft. high and 5 ft. wide may have been installed then (this wheel survived up till 1961, when it was destroyed).
1822	An unexplained invasion by Henry Cooper & Packham & Co., Paper Makers of Bushey Rough. Bankrupt in same year. Contents of Horn Street advt. in Kentish Gazette 30:Nov:1824.
1826	George Paine listed there again.
1838/39	George Paine, Directories show him as owner of paper mill and flour mill. At some point he formed a partnership with Justinian Quare, the latter may have been a sleeping partner.
1845	Paine & Quare partnership which included paper manufacture and Oil crushing dissolved (London Gazette 22:July:1845).
1850 +	Directories sometimes refer to George and sometimes to John Paine.
1851	Census lists number of employed there.
1852	The mill described as having 2 beating engines.
1868	Mill ceased making paper.

This concludes the section on the Coastal mills of East Kent.

THE REMAINING MILLS OF SOUTH KENT

There are only two known mills to consider here (i) Ockley mill, Hawkhurst; and (ii) Hinksdon mill, Benenden,[341] and very little information can be added here to that found in Shorter.

Ockley Mill

The first evidence of its existence is an insurance policy of 1755[342] in which the mill was insured by Edward Blackwell, paper maker. No meaningful Poor Rate Records have survived, only isolated documents that are not applicable. The first records that have survived are Land Tax Returns[343] for Great Barnfield Ward, Hawkhurst, and these show Mercer and Samuel Durrant as Proprietors (see also under Chartham mill (Table XIV) for the year 1806) and Edward Blackwell as the occupant (tax £53). There is absolutely no indication on present evidence of the mill's origin or the nature of its products. As no Blackwell countermarks

---

[341] Shorter, A. Bib.12 197.
[342] SFIP 145836 (3:Apr:1755).
[343] Hawkhurst Land Tax KAO Q/RP1/167.

(originating from this mill)[344] have ever come to light elsewhere or in local documents, the assumption has been made that for much, if not all, of the 18th C. it made Brown paper.

As to the origin of this mill, like Goudhurst mill (ca.5 miles away), it had perhaps been founded early in the 17th C. as a Press paper mill occupying the premises of a redundant Furnace mill (MR TQ 775314), but no evidence for this has yet come to light. Failure to detect any paper makers who may have migrated from there could be due to the fact that they might have gone south to one of the early 18th C. Sussex paper mills rather than north into Kent. Are there any other aspects of this situation that lend support to the surmises made above or which throw any light on the function and survival of a mill like this into the 19th C. (cf. Goudhurst) ? First, one is dealing with a mill in a remote area. Second, unlike many of the other mills in Kent there were no shipping facilities in the immediate vicinity by means of which it could export its products. Up to the 17th C. the River Rother had been navigable as far as Newenden (Kent) and Bodiam (Sussex), a minimum of 5 miles distant from the paper mill. This might have led to a marginally wider market so long as this facility continued; but, as Hasted has described so graphically, the local roads were deplorable. Third, the fact that the mill continued to operate as a paper mill for as long as it did shows clearly that it met the needs of the locality. Fourth, if one adds to this the fact that the mill is not described as new-built in the insurance policy nor as a mixed mill, one senses that the act of insuring does not necessarily signify that this was the date when it began operating but rather that because it had served an increasingly important function for that area, Edward Blackwell now deemed it necessary to insure it.

Edward Blackwell re-insured "his" mill again in 1785,[345] though the Land Tax Records show that the proprietors were Mercer and Samuel Durrant.[346] By 1787 this situation had altered. William and Henry Blackwell appeared on the scene and now insured "their" paper mills, one at Ockley and the other at Hinksdon.[347] William was a co-partner of Edward's, but the partnership was dissolved in 1796. Although Edward was still named as a paper maker of Ockley and continued to appear as one, for instance at the meeting of the Master Paper Makers in 1803,[348] William[349] and Henry had taken over the mills by 1800. One senses that the really active member of the family at this time was William who had already represented the mills in 1796 at a meeting of the Master Paper Makers of Kent and Surrey at Maidstone.[350] The 1816 Excise General List shows John Blackwell at Ockley and Thomas and Ann at Hinksdon (Sussex Collection). No later information on Ockley is known to the author; but to judge from the Excise Letters of the next few years it must have continued to function as a paper mill for some time more.

1787 seems to have been a turning point in the history of papermaking in this area. The Ockley mill must have been a sufficiently prosperous business for the Blackwell family for them to have set up another paper mill further downstream on the Hexden and since Ockley continued to function for at least another 30-40 years, one might safely assume that it had been modernised at about this time in line with the new mill at Hinksdon. Word must have been getting through to them of the changes that had taken place in other mills; the most direct source for this would have been Maidstone (the roads between Maidstone and Hawkhurst had been turnpiked during the second half of the 18th C.). The 1780's is, therefore, the period indicated in Table XI for its up-dating. Despite the fact that there is nothing to indicate that in its early history it made White paper, one can easily imagine that

---

[344] Not to be confused with the Blackwell countermarks originating from Nash mill Hertfordshire (see Gravell, T.L. Bib.68 Nos.99–104).

[345] SFIP 503632 (16:Apr:1785).

[346] KAO Q/RP1/167 Great Barnfield Ward.

[347] SFIP 534545 (25:Aug:1787)

[348] Listed among Master Paper Makers at a General Meeting held on 13:June:1803 (PSM).

[349] This may have been William (aged 26) of Hawkhurst, Kent, referred to in a marriage licence of 1760 (Canterbury), bride Martha Hood (inf. Mrs J. Stirk).

[350] Attended a Meeting of Master Paper Makers of Kent & Surrey at the Star Inn, Maidstone 20:Feb:1796 (PSM).

in serving the needs of such an isolated market it could have supplied inferior grades of printing etc. for the locality. Hence the fact that the Table shows the products of these mills as "mixed".

Hinksdon Paper Mill
(Benenden)
(MR TQ 786309)

As indicated above the first evidence to be found for the existence of a paper mill here (sometimes known as the Lower Paper Mill) is the insurance policy of 1787, when it was jointly insured with Ockley. Had it had an earlier existence one would have expected the Blackwells to have insured it as they had done for Ockley, but there is nothing to show that a mill of any kind had been sited here before. Although the policy does not describe it as a new–built mill it is assumed that it must have been and hence "modernised" from the time it came into being, a date reflected in Table XI. No parish rate assessments have survived for Benenden, only disbursements,[351] so no help in that direction.

William Blackwell appears to have been the paper maker in charge of the mills at the turn of the century, but was replaced at Hinksdon by Thomas and Ann Blackwell in or before 1816 (EGL). The last news to emerge for this mill is, first, a Sale of Lower Paper Mill by widow Blackwell and Thomas in 1826;[352] among the contents there was a proportion of White paper in the paper stock. And, second, Bagshaw's Directory for 1847 names Richard Blackwell as a paper manufacturer of "Inkstand" mill and mentions the fact that they made mainly Brown paper there but with some White.[353]

These two mills initially served the needs of a local market outside the mainstream of papermaking in Kent. Ockley may have had an early origin and could have supplied limited quantities of the lower qualities of White paper from time to time. But, clearly, they imported paper from outside for their more important records as shown, for example, by the papers used for the early Hawkhurst and Sandhurst Land Tax Returns[354] which bear countermarks of "J TAYLOR" and "R WILLIAMS". But perhaps of more interest are the returns for the Cuthole Ward of Hawkhurst where the papers appear to have been Dutch in origin[355] implying that the area was still a backwater albeit by then in a state of transition.

---

[351] KAO P 20 5/2 (1743–1803) No assessments. The Land Tax KAO Q/RP1/325 is divided between Hawkhurst and Sandhurst. A search of the card index did not reveal any Deeds or other possible references to paper mills in Hawkhurst or Benenden.

[352] Inf. late C.P. Davies. Extracts from Kentish Gazette 17:Oct:1823.

[353] Inf. late C.P. Davies.

[354] KAO Q/RP1/167 and Q/RP1/325. No Blackwell countermarks.

[355] KAO Q/RP1/168 Land Tax for Hawkhurst Cuthole Ward Returns for 1780/83 bear the countermark "HR" together with a cypher in the centre of the sheet similar to those illustrated in Gravell, T.L. Bib.68 Nos.346–8 spanning documents dated 1738–1790. It seems unlikely that these marks represent either Hillier Russell or Henry Revell (Eghams Green, Buckinghamshire), but more probably Hendrik Raket in view of the date span of Gravell's marks. The 1784 return bears the mark "SI" or just conceivably "SL" (Samuel Lay); 1787 "MF" unidentified; 1788 "T FRENCH" (Gurney's mill, Maidstone). No Blackwell countermarks.

SUMMARY

Besides being a long chapter this may well have been a difficult one also for some readers to take in. It would be helpful, perhaps, to restate briefly the main points covered in it.

[Pt.I] Earlier in this book a background has been provided, where formerly it was lacking, for the elder Whatman's official début as a paper maker in August 1740. In addition some account of the New Technology has been given and the technical problems it would have created for paper makers proposing to introduce it into their mills. In this present chapter attention is focused summarily on Whatman's achievements during the 19 years of his papermaking career, the successful mastery of the New Technology; the invention and development of Wove paper; the gaining of a pre-eminent position for himself in a highly competitive market and a distinguished reputation for the quality of his paper; and, above all, his creation of a highly prosperous business and, so it has been claimed, the largest paper mill in the country at that time. He thus provided a very secure foundation for his famous son's future career during the second half of the 18th C. The question that follows from this is whether there is any evidence to show that he influenced other paper makers in Kent thereby contributing to the general advance of the industry in the county.

[Pt.II] Before the second subject could be considered it was necessary to disentangle from one another the different economic factors that were either impeding, protecting or advancing the industry as a whole in one way or another in the period that followed Whatman's emergence, namely, the effects of foreign competition, embargoes, war, protective Customs duties and restrictive Excise impositions, fluctuating costs of materials and labour etc. in order to determine the significance and impact of the New Technology on the ever-changing situation which the paper makers in the White paper industry had to face. The conclusion was reached that all but one of these influences affected in varying degrees of severity the fortunes of the industry adversely; the increasingly protective nature of the Duties merely kept the foreigners out of the market place but did nothing to advance the industry or place it on a more competitive footing: they merely prevented its extinction. The one and only positive component in this equation was the New Technology. Only through this could the industry lift itself out of the quagmire that encased it. In other words, if the elder Whatman made any contribution at all to resolving this impasse, it can only have been through his example of and expertise in the New Technology.

[Pt.III] The year 1740 has generally been regarded as an important landmark in the history of the English White paper industry largely, it has been claimed, due to the stimulus given to it by war. Be that as it may, if there had been no other factor, the industry would have merely expanded but not bettered itself. 1740, certainly in the case of Kent, is also seen as a watershed in the technology of the domestic industry. Consideration is given to the question, how did the industry respond to innovation in the period that followed ? To try to answer this further questions have to be asked such as, from what basis does one compile a list of White mills ? How does one group them ? Having established the two most important papermaking regions for this period, what sort of expansion took place in these, Kent versus the West of London, between 1740-1800 ? And, in the almost total absence of documentary evidence, can one determine when White mills in these regions adopted the New Technology?

Inadequate as they may be Tables have been compiled from the limited data available in an attempt to illustrate these aspects purely for comparative purposes and to indicate the order of magnitude of change in the two regions *in very general terms*. Furthermore it was recognized that any advances arising from Whatman's work were not likely to have extended much beyond the boundaries of Kent. Nevertheless, in spite of these shortcomings, it is clear that percentage–wise both the expansion and the modernisation of White mills in Kent was much more rapid than to the West of London; in actual numbers the difference is not so marked, but one has to take into account that one is comparing the progress in one county as against 9 in the other region. All in all by 1800 it might be said that Kent had a significantly larger share of the top end of the White paper market than elsewhere, so that technological progress there could be regarded as a useful sample of the changes that were taking place within the British industry as a whole. The difficulties encountered in creating a credible picture of progress within the Kent industry made it quite impractical to undertake a similar exercise for the West of London Region,[356] so one has to accept for the present that a comparison in like terms of the two regions is not feasible. However, earlier in this book it was shown that the *basis* for the New Technology had been introduced into this country at the end of the 17th C., but, despite spasmodic adoption, during the ensuing years no noticeable improvement in the economic performance of the industry had manifested itself. Normal evolutionary forces would in time have made it increasingly more effective, so that Whatman or no Whatman, it would *ultimately* have achieved the same end. However, Whatman did exist and, what is more, despite the unfavourable conditions that prevailed, attained a distinguished and successful position in this industry. One returns then to the question, did he accelerate the evolutionary process ? For the time being the only place where we have any hope of measuring this is in his own county.

[Pt.IV] Confining the investigation to Kent and accepting that Whatman and Harris had made significant advances in the New Technology the next point to be considered was the question as to how these innovations were transmitted. Since no records have survived of the elder Whatman having had any contact with local paper makers, the evidence has to be sought in a mill by mill examination of occupants of other mills, their relationships and movements.

[Pt.V] The key to this was the occupation of Hollingbourne Old mill by John Terry at the end of 1739 and his relationship to the Quelchs. Initially, developments arising out of this were confined to the Quelch family and ramifications of this, termed broadly here as the Quelch empire and its satellites.

---

[356] This must remain at present a task for other investigators and in these times could prove to be an expensive exercise. In Dr. Shorter's day there still appear to have been a number of beneficent incumbents who no doubt had time to spare to study their records and supply him with information. Most of these records have now been deposited in Archive Offices or Libraries and thus have to be searched by the investigator himself or undertaken by a person in the locality qualified to do this. In either case, if it is out of his area, the costs of achieving his or her end are quite considerable. Even during the preparation of this work the cost of examining parish registers where they were still held by the incumbent had risen in the early 1980's from a small contribution to the offertory box to a charge of £3.00 an hour and are even more now. Professional charges are considerably more than this (the going rate in 1990 appears to be ca.£25 per hour) which renders the task of obtaining detailed information on paper makers and mills in more distant regions quite impracticable. As mentioned already it is hoped that members of the recently formed British Association of Paper Historians may rectify this situation and build up a corpus of useful information for future works on the history of the industry.

[Pt.VI] The paper mills comprised within this sphere of influence cover limited interests in the Maidstone district but much more extensive ones in the case of the mills in the West Kent Region and, probably, one in the South, Chafford, all the latter being grouped under the headings of the Basted and Dartford centres. Later, some members of this empire, the Clement Taylors, reversed this trend and returned to convert or occupy mills in the Maidstone area. A brief account of each mill and its occupants is given in an attempt to interpret sparse information and establish a date for the introduction of the New Technology there.

[Pt.VII]   Attention was then directed to the remaining mills in the Maidstone area and to some that were obviously linked to it such as Sittingbourne mill in North Kent and Ford mill at Little Chart. For convenience these mills have been subdivided into 4 groups where it was thought that influence spread through other contacts of Whatman's such as William Gill jnr.; Thomas Harris; a combination, perhaps, of both Quelch and/or Gill jnr.; the Pine family's venture into papermaking; and, finally, probably the most important of all, a return is made to the very considerable influence of Old Mill in the Hollingbourne district and extensions of it to the paper mills at Little Chart in the Eastern Region and Langcliffe mill in the West Riding. A similar procedure as used above was employed here for estimating the date of conversion where this was applicable.

[Pt.VIII] Lastly one comes to the Eastern Region of Kent and certain isolated mills in South Kent to consider whether Whatman's influence had extended as far as this. These mills present us with a rather different situation because for geographical reasons and the restraints these placed on communication, the mills in this part of Kent lay outside the mainstream of papermaking activity in the County. This constraint, as events showed, impeded the developments that had led to the technological advances made in the other districts. It is conceivable that, if Peter Archer jnr. had lived longer than he did, the picture might have been rather different. As it was, Chartham, the first mill to be modernised in any sense at all in this part of Kent, had to wait another 30 years before the paper makers there mastered the New Technology. It has been suggested that links had been established at an earlier date between Richard Archer at Dartford and Peter at Chartham and that these eventually were to bear fruit when Leeds Paine moved to Chartham after completing his apprenticeship under John Terry at Dartford No.2 mill in 1763. From this date onwards the Region started developing; after Chartham, Paine's experience of the New Technology led him to build Buckland No.2 mill in the Dover area and one can see this influence spreading to the other coastal mills. It was altogether a much later development than that which had taken place at Maidstone and in the West of Kent some 30 years previously and thus long after the elder Whatman's death (1759). Nevertheless, Leeds Paine who can be seen as the architect behind this extension of the New Technology there had been apprenticed to John Terry who, earlier, had been instrumental in disseminating Whatman's and Harris' achievements at Hollingbourne Old Mill in the first place. So, indirectly, a tenuous link can be identified here that may have accelerated the modernising of this Region ahead of what would eventually come about as a result of normal evolutionary processes.

Apart from one or two isolated instances such as Cray Valley, Poll mill, Chartham and Sittingbourne, no documentary references to the installation of Engines have been discovered in any of the other 42 Kent mills, although it is quite evident that many of them were equipped with them by the end of the 1760's when in 1771 the younger Whatman installed a remarkably modern version of one at Hollingbourne Old Mill, at a time when he compared its performance with those used by other paper makers (see App.V pp.225–244). It has therefore been necessary to examine the history of the remaining Kent mills for any clues, however remote, that might indicate the New Technology being adopted there; the gathering together of a lot of detail for this purpose was, as a consequence, unavoidable. The fact that a mill was making *White countermarked paper* by, say, the 1770's, provided one with good grounds for believing that a given mill had been up–dated by then, if not before; at least 13 Kent mills had achieved this state (11 certain, 3 probable).[357] In other cases one has to seek evidence elsewhere e.g. as in the case of Dartford No.2 and Buckland No.2 mills, deducing this from the paper makers who moved there, John Terry and Leeds Paine; or from the proximity of one mill, status unknown but which survived into the future, to another which had clearly been modernised and which would have set an example to the other. Some of the conclusions reached may attract criticism but, by and large, a good case has been made out for the achievements of Harris and Whatman in the 1730's accelerating the advances made in papermaking methods used in most, if not all, of the other Kent mills.

It was demonstrated in the preamble to Part VIII (East Kent Mills) of this chapter how their development had depended on the flow of information and paper makers along the "Watling Street Axis" on which much later were situated progressive mills such as Sittingbourne and, more important, the Dartford ones. Earlier chapters in this book have been concerned with the origins of papermaking in the Maidstone district and, later, the dominating position it maintained during the 18th C. But by the close of the century one is beginning to see, already foreshadowed in the influence of the Watling Street axis, a shift in the importance of Maidstone as a centre to Dartford. It was not a sudden transition and Maidstone, as a manufacturing centre of the top qualities of White paper, held its position well into the 19th C. But Dartford was in reality the cradle of the next phase in the development of papermaking, that of the emerging papermachine, though as the 19th C. progressed and the scale of operations increased so the number of centres multiplied and became dispersed throughout the United Kingdom.[358]

---

[357] Countermarks from Turkey mill (1740), Sittingbourne (1750's), Old Mill (by 1760), Chartham (1760's); Eyehorne, Basted, Hamptons, Poll mill, St. Mary Cray, Ford mill, Sundridge (1770's); Cray Valley, Foots Cray and Dartford No.3 (by 1780). One has to remember also that increasingly the countermark in addition to its alleged benefit in claiming drawback of Duty on paper exported became a status symbol. The Master Paper Makers' Memorial presented to the Commissioners of Excise on 2:Dec:1764 (for full text see Balston, T. Bib.1 App.III 149) included the following "The almost certainty of the Manufacture being brought to a still greater degree of Perfection by the emulation between the Makers when their Names are in their Paper" (150).

[358] For an account of the growth and dispersion of the paper industry in the 19th C. and after see Shorter, A. Bib.9 Chaps.IV–VI.

Chapter VIII

CONCLUSIONS

There are many occasions in Life where one has to make an appreciation of a situation. It may be a case of dealing with a question set by an examiner or the preparation of a report or working out tactical orders for battle. In every case one is instructed to follow very sound precepts for marshalling one's thoughts preparatory to taking some action or other. But, first, one must be absolutely clear what *the object* of the exercise is. The information is then gathered, examined, arranged and related; conclusions drawn and perhaps recommendations made as the case may be, all very neat. But, as Disraeli once said, "What we anticipate seldom occurs, what we least expect generally happens".

In Chapter III a number of reasons were given for undertaking a study of the elder James Whatman and in the course of preparing material for it frequent references have been made to another work by the author concerning the Development of Wove paper (Bib.76) described as "in preparation". The draft for the latter was in fact prepared before the present book was ever considered (1980). The stumbling block to its completion had been the almost total absence of information which could be used for a chapter relating the development of this new kind of paper to the author of the project, the elder Whatman. The objective, therefore, became one of "find out more about the elder Whatman and his background". But, just as in the case of the study of Wove paper and its development where it had become immediately apparent that the issues were quite different to those which had hitherto been imagined, so as more and more information was unearthed on Whatman and his background it became progressively obvious that a retrogressive investigation was unlikely to end neatly at some preconceived point such as his baptism, for example; or, more pertinently, to the source of his knowledge of papermaking. One could have terminated the exercise there; but it would have been a case of perpetuating a fault that manifests itself in many accounts of the history of English papermaking, particularly those in which Whatman is concerned; in short treating him as an isolated figure unrelated to the industry that surrounded him.

Whereas one might say that the objective was still to "find out more about the elder Whatman and his background", as the investigation proceeded it can be seen from the previous chapters in this book that the emphasis has shifted more and more from Whatman himself to the changing conditions of his background. Whatman still remains the centrepiece but it was no longer his character or family life or wealth that mattered but his potential for bringing about change in the fortunes of the paper industry that emerged and began to take precedence. At that stage one was not quite sure what this involved, but it gradually became apparent that his influence was much more extensive and significant for the future prosperity of the industry than that generally attributed to him.

No useful purpose would be served by going through all the deflections that have taken place in the course of pursuing the original objective. Sufficient be it to say that it has been a long, hazardous and speculative journey to reach this point; long because it became necessary to traverse some three centuries of papermaking in England; hazardous because in the absence of much vital information one had to take chances on many issues; and speculative because the paucity of documentary evidence, a characteristic and unremitting feature of the early history of this industry due partly to its remote setting and partly, one suspects, to illiteracy, constantly forced one into conjectural conclusions where, if one only had only known the full facts, one might easily have found the truth proving to be the reverse of the case proposed.[1] The point of this preamble is to make it quite clear that since the objective has turned out to be anything but straightforward and because examination has repeatedly exposed new facets of the subject the conclusions reached will be diverse and in some instances, perhaps, debatable.

In retrospect one can see that the Hollingbourne project, the building of Old Mill, is really the keystone in the sequence of events that span the ground covered in this work. The question as to why Whatman, a tanner, should undertake an investment of this magnitude led inevitably to a host of other matters where one had to determine whether these were related to this or not, and only by probing further has it proved possible to provide a coherent picture of events before and after this undertaking. As anyone who has embarked on work of this kind will know, Disraeli's aphorism could hardly have been more applicable than to unravelling the motives that led to this episode. In attempting to create some order out of chaos the investigation has followed the stages summarised below. These are not in any particular date order, nor was the position reached by any straight path through reasoning. Instead it was more a case of constantly encountering the unexpected and dealing with this.

1. The close relationship between the Whatman and Harris families was noted, especially between James and Richard.
    The proximity of their business premises explained how James had gained his knowledge of papermaking. The interwoven nature of their trades, the tanner providing the paper makers with sizing materials, would have given James an insight into the state of the local paper industry and, perhaps, beyond this.
    And what sort of state was this in ?

2. Further investigation revealed that 20–30 years before James was born only the rudiments of a paper industry existed in the Maidstone district. Kent could scarcely be considered a papermaking county at that time. Bearing the maxim in mind that paper makers do not appear out of thin air, the next questions to be answered were where from and why did paper makers converge on Maidstone and almost all of them simultaneously ?

    What were their aspirations ? The circumstances prevailing suggested that the manufacture of White paper was their aim arising out of the current embargo on French goods, but that with one or two exceptions this aim was not realised for a number of different reasons. For the first wave of paper makers the main reason for this was the monopoly granted to the powerful Joint Stock COMPANY for this manufacture (see below). Later, increased protective Duties encouraged a second wave of papermaking activity in the district; but in spite of this assistance this movement stagnated.
    Arising from this situation it became clear that two factors were to influence the direction of the path

---

[1] In situations where absolutely no data has survived, frequently the case where the Poor Rate Books have been lost, or where the purpose of a project, such as building Hollingbourne Old Mill, has never been set down on paper anywhere, the method used here for reaching any sort of conclusion may be likened to the way in which one might tackle a jig–saw puzzle, namely to provide a framework using the straight–edged pieces, in this case the known facts, to enclose the unknown territory and thus reduce the unknown areas to more manageable proportions. Then by making various assumptions and projecting them into this void one can often see whether the proposals are in any way justifiable and consistent with the general picture of events; and, indeed, consider whether any alternative is even feasible. In its finished form the result may appear to be straightforward and simple; but initially, confronted with a near void, it was not easy to know in which direction to turn. Only a handful of the jig–saw lay scattered about and most of that hidden from view.

subsequently followed by the young James and Richard, the stimulus of the "Challenge" and current advances in papermaking technology that led to more productive processes and better quality products, the New Technology.

3.   The formation of the new papermaking industry at Maidstone in the last quarter of the 17th C. brought to the fore the Master Paper Maker operating in his own right and no longer subservient to the entrepreneur and exemplified in particular by the Ancient Paper Makers. But in spite of the demise of the COMPANY at the end of this century, the crippling effects of their monopoly and the depressed state of the trade temporarily discouraged further expansion until the New Duties stimulated another extension of the local industry. Even so the greater part remained in a state of stagnation.

The "Challenge" originated from this conflict with the COMPANY. Their history revealed that through the practical application of many contemporary Patents which they had appropriated, as well as through imported expertise, they had introduced important elements of the New Technology, but they never succeeded in making its principal component effective. The weaponry was there for the asking but with no-one able to make successful use of it.

The secret of Harris' and Whatman's success lay in surmounting the unsolved problems connected with the New Technology with its first *successful* application in Kent, if not in the whole of the United Kingdom, at Old Mill Hollingbourne.

4.   Possible sources from which these two had acquired knowledge and experience of these innovations were investigated. It became clear that some of these derived from practices introduced and employed in the West Kent Region by the COMPANY and the immigrant Johannots and transferred to Whatman's doorstep by the Quelch family while the former was still a tanner. But *the whole conception and timing of the investment in a brand new paper mill by Whatman* four years later, choice of site etc. suggested that these influences can only be regarded as straws in the wind. The new mill must have incorporated exceptional and novel features wanting in previous enterprises which one either has to attribute to the inventiveness of Harris and Whatman; or, in the absence of any other known source, Harris training in Holland, the only country at that time possessing necessary expertise in the use of the powerful new Engine and for which a period of training was absolutely mandatory. This notion is further supported by a longstanding legend that Whatman had learnt his papermaking there.

The Hollingbourne venture is regarded as an experimental operation, Harris subsequently transferring his papermaking operation to Turkey mill. The events that led to this, its conversion to the New Technology, the role of James Brooke and the legacy of the Gill family have all been investigated and interpreted.

5.   Having identified the broader aspects of the New Technology, its main element, the new Engine, its design and operation in preparing stuff for the vat, has been compared with the Old process with special emphasis on the complexity of the new equipment and the difficulties it would have presented to the English paper maker. The economic advantages of these innovations have been demonstrated and shown to be the one positive feature that led the British paper industry into a competitive position *vis-à-vis* its continental counterparts.

6.   Harris died (1739) before the conversion of Turkey mill had been completed. Whatman had overlooked the whole undertaking from its inception and took over the reins officially in August 1740. His achievements during the remaining nineteen years of his life are reviewed summarily. These illustrate that his contribution to papermaking was a great deal more than merely putting up money to finance an enterprise executed by another.

Subsequent achievements apart, did the successful application of the New Technology at Old Mill and Turkey mill influence other paper makers in Kent and the future course of the industry there ?

A rough comparison has been made between the expansion of and the progress made by the White paper industry in Kent versus the nine counties (Middlesex excepted) lying immediately to the West of London for the period 1740-1800.

The conclusion was reached that more rapid progress was made in Kent and that by 1800 it had the largest share of the top echelons of the White paper market.

Progress in the application of the New Technology in the Kent paper mills was examined. Certain streams of influence were identified, the first and most noteworthy being via the Quelch family and paper makers associated with them, principally in West Kent.

Influence in the Maidstone area was also identified, particularly the example of Old Mill itself.
Finally, though later in time, a connection can be reasonably demonstrated between the earlier streams and
the *effective* adoption of the new methods in East Kent.

These six aspects of the subject may be likened to the various views one might have of a
landscape seen from the windows of a house facing in different directions. All these facets
required the exploration of entirely different disciplines embraced within the history of
papermaking. Although it has been said here that the elder Whatman is the centrepiece and
the Old Mill project the Keystone in this scene, the first conclusion to be drawn from this
study is that the *primum mobile* for all this activity was the Engine itself and that when
properly utilized it made the most important contribution to the advancement of the British
paper industry in the 18th C. So it is worth considering why this should have been so and
how this came about.

Although protected from foreign competition by high rates of Duty and its expansion
encouraged by a number of other factors, the improvement in the fortunes of the domestic
White paper industry in the 18th C. turned on the ability to apply a greatly increased quantum
of mechanical energy than had formerly been practicable to the linen fibre in preparing it for
the sheetmaking process. The importance of this may be compared to the successful
application of thermal energy to the papermaking process early in the 19th C., the
introduction of which consummated the potential of the newly invented papermachine,
enabling it to manufacture dry paper as fast as it was mechanically possible to make it in the
wet state;[2] but, like the introduction of the Engine, this too had its attendant problems.[3]

---

[2] As a brief reminder of this situation Nicholas Louis Robert had developed a working model of the papermaking machine
in France by 1798 (patented here in 1799). The drawings and samples of the web were brought to England in 1801. The
first English version of it was erected at Frogmore Mill (Herts.) in 1803 and redesigned there by Bryan Donkin (later
F.R.S.) in 1804. The latter built a larger and improved machine and erected it at Two Waters mill nearby in 1805. This
served as a production model which was licensed for sale in 1807. (For John Gamble's account of this invention in full
see Pilkington, A. Bib.77 97–101; and for its development and other types of papermachines see Clapperton, R.H. Bib.75
and Hills, R.L. Bib.78). Other types of papermaking machine e.g. mould machines were being developed in parallel. None
of these machines was able to produce dried paper. Instead the wet paper was wound onto a drum, cut into lengths on
a table and these strips hung to dry in loops. It was not until 1817 that Didot noted "that it was expedient to dry the paper
as fast as it was made" and provision was made in his design for a hollow cylinder for the paper web to pass over through
which steam could be blown. At the same time John Dickinson, a mould machine enthusiast, was experimenting with
a drying cylinder, using it to dry the paper partially prior to sizing it in the moist state. But it was not until 1820 that
Thomas Bonsor Crompton of Farnworth, Lancashire, obtained a patent covering his invention of heated drying cylinders
for use with the Fourdrinier papermachine, inventing in addition the "dry" felt (linen warp/woollen weft) that carried the
web through the cylinder stack. By the mid–20th C. papermachines were capable of carrying webs of paper 20–30 feet
(7–10m) in width through banks of drying cylinders at rates of 3000–4000 feet (900–1200m) per minute to be reeled at
the other end dry. Though at narrower widths even faster speeds than these are achieved today e.g. over a mile of paper
a minute.

[3] The effects of the intercellulose hydrogen bonding on the end properties of the paper resulting from the *extension* and
contraction that take place in drying the web on a papermachine are extremely complicated and much will depend on
the wetness of the stuff, the furnish and the effects of overdrying on bond formation.

The length of the web as it passes through the machine is increased. In contrast, the width, at first temporarily increased
in the press section, then contracts on entering the driers (ca.1:1 cellulose/water ratio), except when not restrained by the
dry felt, to a web width less than when it was formed. The anisotropic properties of this sheet are quite distinct from the
air–dried handmade papers considered in this book. This state of affairs is aggravated by a tendency to over–dry machine
made paper, which increases the number of strong and more permanent bonds, making it even more difficult to relax
strains built into a distorted web (see App.V).

Before examining this critical level of mechanical energy in the beating process it may be helpful to restate here the features that made the introduction of the Engine such an important innovation in 18th C. British papermaking, though by no means the only positive one in the armoury of the New Technology. The advantages of the Engine were:–

(a)   Scale of production in time and unit volumes increased many times over compared to the older process. This accomplishment was an essential prerequisite for the success of the next major change, the mechanization of the process, albeit not envisaged then.

(b)   The abandonment of the rag fermentation process was beneficial both in terms of reducing chemical damage to the fibre; greater cleanliness; and releasing space within the mill for expansion.

(c)   A more compact process releasing further space.

(d)   Greater efficiency in rag–washing.

(e)   The improvement in productivity arising made a dramatic contribution towards lowering production costs when other costs were escalating rapidly and led eventually to a competitive product *vis–à–vis* imported papers.

(f)   Although initially accompanied by problems with quality, experience overcame these, leading to much higher standards in the top classes of paper.

The New Technology taken as a whole was in reality a much more complicated innovation than the statements made above suggest and one that affected the whole infra–structure of the industry. Moreover, in attempting to adapt the new machinery to the local water supply, the increased demands for power may also have influenced the rate and direction of the industry's growth in different localities.

There can surely be no doubt about the first conclusion to be drawn from this work, namely, the overriding importance of the Hollander beating engine for the British paper industry in its struggle to liberate itself during the 18th C. from the restraints that had hampered its progress and success in the past.

Turning to the energy requirement, for most of the 18th C. the White paper industry relied on linen rags for its raw material, and the strongest of these and, in the absence of any method of bleaching,[4] the whitest, would have been used for this class of paper. At some point earlier in the history of papermaking it had been discovered that the fibres that made up these rags were for the most part too resistant to respond satisfactorily to the limited energy generated by the stampers; it had been necessary to employ a fermentation process prior to beating to achieve a properly dispersed pulp. It was only by trial and error that paper makers in those times were able to realise their aims. But, to–day, it can be seen that the purpose of this treatment was to loosen the fibre bundles in the linen yarn, where this was as yet incomplete, using biochemical means somewhat similar to the retting process employed in extracting the flax from the plant stem in the first place; and, further, we also know now that the same end could be achieved by another route, namely, by directing greater and more concentrated mechanical energy than formerly was possible to the yarn itself to separate it into its ultimate fibres.

The process of fermenting rags may have suggested itself initially to paper makers as a result of the experience of flax producers; this seems to be a likely source; but its discontinuance was probably accidental rather than intentional. As explained in Chapter VI the origins and ancestral form of the Engine are not known beyond the fact that it was invented and developed in Holland, in the Zaanland province where the paper makers had never made use

[4]   See App.V pp.200–203.

of a rag fermentation process. It is thought that an archetype of this appliance had been used initially to reduce rotten rags and other weak materials used in Brown paper and that with time, experience and improvements it was discovered that much stronger materials, such as those used in White papers, could be treated satisfactorily in the same kind of Engine. The point to note in this case is that the Paper makers of the Zaanland had adequate windpower at their disposal to drive their much more powerful Engines and make the transition from weak to strong rags without this question of a critical quantity of energy needed to break down the intractable elements of the linen yarn ever raising its head. Indeed, unlike us to-day, would they have realised that a certain minimum in-put of energy was necessary for this conversion ? And would they have had any means of determining the necessary criteria had they suspected it ? One can only conclude that this advance just happened.

The English paper makers, however, did not have this practical experience nor the windpower which, fortuitously, had given the Dutch their ability to treat strong rags in this way. This brings us to the next, and perhaps more debatable, conclusion which concerns the first *effective* application of the new Engine in Britain, claimed here to have been at Old Mill. There is no evidence that it had been applied so advantageously anywhere else in Kent prior to the Old and Turkey mill projects and, so far as is known, the same assertion holds good for the rest of the country.[5] Although much of the evidence is circumstantial the claim is based on factors discussed previously such as the choice of a site with great reserves of water power in preference to converting existing mills available at that time and moreover a project undertaken when the industry was in a parlous state (numerous bankruptcies) and, even more significant, when there was no shortage of imported paper. Collectively all these factors point to an investment of a most unusual character. One cannot imagine an alternative, but for what purpose ?

On the face of it the prime motive for this investment would appear to have been a requirement for greater water power than was available elsewhere in that area. This certainly would accord with what has been said above regarding the energy factor in treating strong rags by the new method. But instruction in a Dutch mill for this alone may not have been an essential feature in attempting to explain the success of this venture since by this time English paper makers must have known about the Dutch wind-powered paper mills and would also have known from their own windmills that these generated more power than the waterwheel. Nevertheless the notion that Harris had trained abroad not only takes care of the "legend" and likewise explains his absence[6] but, as things turned out, the fact that later he was able to transfer his operations successfully to Turkey mill, a more conventional mill albeit still with above average water power, indicates that Harris had over-estimated his energy requirements; and the inference from this is that the technical progress achieved in the Whatman/Harris enterprise must have owed its success to something over and above the application of greater

[5]   Previous references in this work to early Engines may be found in Chap.V pp.189/190, discussion of Bladen's Patent (1682) and Lady Theodosia's acquisition of this; Chap.V p.176, the first application in practice referred to in Dupin's 1690 inventory of equipment in his Dublin mill; Chap.IV n.107 gives references to other early installations following discussion in the text; and additional installations are suggested by the author at Dartford No.2 Chap.IV n.36 and Basted and Gurney's mill in Chap.IV p.153; and the Archers at Sittingbourne and Chartham Chap.IV pp.140/143.
[6]   There are no entries against Richard Harris in the Loose Churchwarden's a/cs. (KAO P233 5/2) for the years 1726–33. This is no proof, of course, of his absence. He might have been domiciled with Whatman at Brook House, for example. There is also a house shown as "William Harris, *Outdweller*"; entries for this cease in 1733 (reappear later in the a/cs. and probably refer to William and Frances Harris).

energy to the fibre. What these unidentified factors were may never be known. The plain fact is that although the Engine had been in use in this country for over 40 years it had made little, if any, impact on the viability of the domestic White industry. In some cases this failure might have been due to insufficient power; or to poor transmission of this; and in others the causes may have lain in faulty design in the Engine itself leading to imperfect circulation, inadequate fibrages, a roll rotating too slowly or a combination of any of the other elements described in Chapter VI needed for an effective beating operation.

Having identified the Engine and the Old Mill venture as major features in transforming the deadlocked state of the industry into a progressive one, we can revert to the original objective and centrepiece of this work, the elder James Whatman and his background; to this we might add "and his legacy". In other words the findings indicate that he was not only a centrepiece in a figurative sense but his achievements can also be seen as marking the most important technological watershed of the 18th C., certainly in the history of papermaking in Kent and possibly for the whole of the United Kingdom as well. It brought together in a more fruitful way than formerly other important elements of the New Technology, a combination of the Exchange process and improved hand–felts to produce paper surfaces that rivalled imported products; and the application of the "loom" not only for accelerating mould construction but enabling the fabrication of moulds of exceptional quality, leading ultimately to the invention and development of Wove paper.

At no time should one forget the very important role played by Richard Harris in initiating this achievement. All the same, vital though this may have been to the success of this enterprise and even though Whatman was not a paper maker at the time, he not only put up the money, put up the mill, but continued to oversee the project, negotiated the acquisition of Turkey mill and acted as a Trustee in this conveyance. Moreover, his subsequent achievements in papermaking make it quite clear that even though he started life as a tanner, he became a more than competent paper maker later. There is also a hint that he may have been something rather more than this, perhaps with some special gift for mathematics, mechanics and practical engineering in general[7] that helped in the design and construction of Old Mill and the later conversion of Turkey mill.

Standing back from this picture one can see that it embraces on the one hand the developments that led up to the watershed and the flow of events that followed once it had been crossed. During the ascent to this point the slow beginnings of the White paper industry, blowing hot one minute and cold the next, were disclosed, culminating in the stand made by the Ancient Paper Makers of whom George Gill was the most distinguished and whose mill and activities undoubtedly dominated the Maidstone papermaking scene and whose example must have exerted an important influence on the young Harris and Whatman who were, later, to be drawn into the mixed fortunes of his son and his protector and Stationer, James Brooke.

From this watershed one might discern three streams emerging; first, Whatman, confident in his own abilities and the quality of his papers, providing both a very large and well equipped

---

[7] See Chap.IV, note 103, with references to advances in mould construction and involvement in the design of an equation clock.

manufacturing base and an established position in the market place for his son to carry on with, going from strength to strength; second, the influence he exerted on other Kent paper makers through John Terry and the Quelch empire together with the example of his original mill at Hollingbourne; and, third, the lessons that the Stationers must have learnt from this undertaking passed on through Brooke to his contemporaries and successors. The conclusion reached from this was that the father was in reality more enterprising than "his more famous son". One sees the son's achievements more as a refinement of his father's work rather than in major innovations of his own making, albeit what he did do he did well, becoming in time the figurehead and principal spokesman of the British paper industry in the 18th C. Through all the trials and tribulations of that age, in contrast to the bankruptcies common to this industry, both father and son maintained a steady and prosperous course and a notable reputation for the quality of their products. In short much is owed to both of them, but in retrospect it is the elder James Whatman, an historical figure, who deserves to be better known.